D1212820

TRANSIENT AND STEADY-STATE ANALYSIS OF ELECTRIC NETWORKS

Edited by
HERBERT J. REICH
Dunham Laboratory, Yale School of Engineering

SHEINGOLD, ABRAHAM — Fundamentals of Radio Communications

KING, DONALD D. — Measurements at Centimeter Wavelength

REICH, H. J., ORDUNG, P. F., KRAUSS, H. L., SKALNIK, J. G. — Microwave Theory and Techniques

REICH, H. J., SKALNIK, J. G., ORDUNG, P. F., KRAUSS, H. L. — Microwave Principles

MURPHY, GORDON J. — Basic Automatic Control Theory

MURPHY, GORDON J. — Control Engineering

HUTTER, RUDOLF G. E. — Beam and Wave Electronics in Microwave Tubes

FITCHEN, FRANKLIN C. — Transistor Circuit Analysis and Design

MOON, PARRY, and SPENCER, DOMINA E. — Foundations of Electrodynamics

MOON, PARRY, and SPENCER, DOMINA E. — Field Theory for Engineers

GÄRTNER, WOLFGANG W. — Transistors: Principles, Design, and Applications

REICH, H. J. — Functional Circuits and Oscillators

KU, Y. H. — Transient Circuit Analysis

PESKIN, EDWARD — Transient and Steady-State Analysis of Electric Networks

A series of text and reference books in electronics and communications. Additional titles will be listed and announced as published.

TRANSIENT AND STEADY-STATE ANALYSIS OF ELECTRIC NETWORKS

by

EDWARD PESKIN, D.E.E.
Associate Professor of Electrical Engineering
Stevens Institute of Technology
Hoboken, New Jersey

D. VAN NOSTRAND COMPANY, INC.

PRINCETON, NEW JERSEY

TORONTO LONDON

NEW YORK

D. VAN NOSTRAND COMPANY, INC.
120 Alexander St., Princeton, New Jersey (*Principal office*)
24 West 40 Street, New York 18, New York

D. VAN NOSTRAND COMPANY, LTD.
358, Kensington High Street, London, W.14, England

D. VAN NOSTRAND COMPANY (Canada), LTD.
25 Hollinger Road, Toronto 16, Canada

Published simultaneously in Canada by
D. VAN NOSTRAND COMPANY (Canada), LTD.

PRINTED IN THE UNITED STATES OF AMERICA

TO
MARION AND CHARLIE

PREFACE

This book has as its purpose the presentation of the theory and techniques of network analysis in a unified form, applicable both to problems involving transients and to problems limited to the sinusoidal steady state. Linear, lumped, finite circuits of both passive and active types are dealt with throughout. The presentation is at the first-year graduate or advanced undergraduate level.

The basis of analysis is the Laplace transformation, which leads to equations identical in form with those of alternating-current circuit analysis. This formal correspondence between the Laplace-transform equations and the alternating-current circuit equations appears immediately in problems involving circuits which are initially at rest. In other cases, the same formal correspondence is achieved when the transforms representing initial currents and voltages are regarded as representing sources applied to the circuit, along with sources of generated e.m.f. or current; the general form of the network equations is then unchanged.

The power of alternating-current circuit analysis stems from the fact that its complex voltages and currents satisfy Kirchhoff's laws. These laws also relate the Laplace transforms of currents and voltages. Since the deductions made from Kirchhoff's laws constitute the whole body of circuit analysis, the various methods and techniques of circuit analysis may be presented in terms of current and voltage transforms.

The mathematical background for the application of the Laplace transformation is not brief. This material, however, is itself of interest to electrical engineers. Chapter 1 contains a general statement of the circuit problem, circuit laws and definitions, circuit equations and a discussion of initial conditions, and a brief review of the classical and Heaviside-Carson methods of attack on the circuit problem. Chapter 2 is largely devoted to Fourier analysis and some of its applications. The Laplace transformation is derived from the Fourier integral theorem, and a number of theorems or properties of the Laplace transform are also presented. Chapter 3 is concerned with complex variable theory and the residue method of evaluation of the inversion integral, or inverse Laplace transform. The partial fraction expansion is also obtained in a general manner with the aid of the Laurent series. With this chapter we can establish the tie between the complex plane and circuit response, which appears throughout all network theory.

With the Laplace transform as background, a statement of Kirchhoff's laws for the transforms of voltage and current is given in Chapter 4, where simple problems in transients are then solved in order to show the technique of the Laplace transformation and the role of initial conditions. In Chapter 5, the methods of loop and node analysis are developed in terms of the Laplace transform. The question of determining an independent set of equations is discussed with the aid of network topology. The observations made in the illustrative problems of Chapters 4 and 5 lead to a classification of network response in accordance with the location and order of the poles of the transform of that response. Tabulation of this information is an aid in the study of the distribution, in the complex plane, of the poles and zeros of network functions. The relation of these poles and zeros to sinusoidal response is considered, the pole-zero distributions of specific circuits are studied, and the relation between the real and imaginary parts of impedance is established.

Network theorems are derived in Chapter 6, with special attention to their application to both transient and sinusoidal steady-state problems. Chapter 7 treats the theory of two-port networks and develops the requisite matrix algebra. Chapter 8 is devoted chiefly to the development and applications of the Mason signal flow graph, and also presents the Coates flow graph, with its application to determinant evaluation.

In a number of illustrative problems, circuit equations are first set up in general form. Special attention is then given to the means of obtaining the response of the circuit to a suddenly applied voltage or current (e.g., a step voltage) and the steady response to a sinusoidal wave. The former response is obtained through evaluation of the inverse Laplace transform, while the latter response is obtained through simple redefinition of the symbols in the transform equations. In the discussion of each technique of network analysis, particular attention is given to the problems of linear active as well as passive circuits.

Many influences affect the writing of a book. Foremost among these is the influence of the author's teachers. In particular, I gratefully acknowledge Professor Ernst Weber's invaluable courses and research guidance when I was a graduate student and research associate at the Polytechnic Institute of Brooklyn.

W. van Roosbroeck of Bell Telephone Laboratories and L. Staschover of North Hills Electronics Company have both read early phases of the manuscript and offered constructive suggestions and encouragement.

Professor W. L. Sullivan of Stevens Institute of Technology has stressed the importance of the Fourier integral and its applications when presenting the development leading to the Laplace transformation: this viewpoint has been accepted in the present text. I am happy, also, to acknowledge the contribution of informal discussions, chiefly on transients, with my colleagues at Stevens, particularly Professors A. C. Gilmore, H. W. Phair, and J. C. Shouri.

Again, informal discussions with my neighbor, F. J. Braga, of Bell Telephone Laboratories, have proved most valuable.

Marion Peskin has made a major contribution in examining paragraphs for smoothness of writing and sentences for logical structure. She has verified bibliography, written the index, and typed large portions of the manuscript.

Charles Peskin tested signal flow graphs on his high school algebra problems, and his comments and questions were most stimulating.

Secretaries of the Electrical Engineering Department at Stevens, and also Mrs. Grace Sullivan, have been very helpful in connection with preparation of the manuscript, and thanks are also due to D. Backus for drawing some of the graphs.

Morristown, New Jersey EDWARD PESKIN
July 1961

CONTENTS

Chapter 1

THE CIRCUIT PROBLEM

In a vast number of physical problems, we are concerned with calculating the response of a system to a known excitation. When, for example, the system is mechanical, the excitation can be an applied force and the response a resulting motion. Electric networks give rise to many important problems of this type. The circuit is the system, the excitation is applied voltage or current, and the response is a current or voltage measured anywhere in the circuit. The function stating the time variation of the applied voltage or current may be termed a *driving function*.

The driving function, whether periodic or consisting of isolated pulses, may assume a wide variety of forms. The sinusoid, saw-tooth, and square wave are typical illustrations. One phase of electric network analysis, then, requires a uniform, compact method for obtaining the response of circuits to many forms of applied voltage or current. This is of major importance even when the circuit is simple.

The system or circuit may also take on various forms. Its geometric configuration may vary from the extremely simple to the highly complex. The nature of the circuit may be *passive* or *active*. A *passive circuit* is defined(21) as one containing no sources of energy. An *active circuit* is defined(21) as one containing energy sources. Clearly a circuit devoid of energy is devoid of interest, save for the study of network geometry. The study of passive circuits, however, concerns problems in which sources of voltage and current are *applied to* circuits which of themselves are passive. Such circuits may contain resistances, capacitances, self- and mutual inductances, ideal transformers, and gyrators. Vacuum-tube and transistor circuits contain internal sources which augment the energy of applied sources (or signals); such circuits are, therefore, active. Thus electric circuits vary both as to their geometric form and as to the nature of their components. Another phase of the electric network problem, then, is the analysis of the circuit for its simplest mathematical representation.

Both phases of the problem (treatment of driving function and analysis of the circuit itself) are equally important. We shall find, on developing the method of the Laplace transformation, that these two aspects of electric circuit analysis become subject to a single uniform treatment.

1-1 Kirchhoff's Circuit Laws

Kirchhoff's laws form the basis of all electric network analysis. While they are obtainable from more general laws of field theory, we may regard them here as axiomatic. These laws are:

(1) The sum of the voltage-increases (or voltage-decreases) in a specified direction around any closed path is zero at any instant.
(2) The sum of the currents entering any point in a network is zero at any instant.

For a sum to be zero, its terms cannot all be of like sign (unless all the terms are individually zero). Therefore, unless every voltage in a closed path is zero, one or more, but not all, will be negative, i.e., directed opposite to the specified direction around the closed path. Similarly if the currents entering a point are not all zero, one or more, but not all, will be negative, i.e., directed away from the point.

The closed path referred to in the voltage law is drawn through a sequence of two-terminal circuit elements. Such a path is termed a *mesh* or *loop** provided that when one of these elements is removed the remaining ones do not form a closed path. The point referred to in the current law is chosen at the meeting of two or more such circuit elements and is termed a *node*. It is often convenient to refer to several two-terminal circuit elements in series as a single *branch*, and to define *nodes* as the points at which two or more branches meet.[22] A *two-terminal circuit element* is the simplest possible electrical device, such as a resistance, inductance, capacitance, or pure source of e.m.f. or of current. In this connection it is well to point out that some authors restrict the meaning of *circuit element* to a two-terminal device,[12] while others allow more general use of the term so that it might include, for example, a vacuum triode.[22]

1-2 Symbols and Sign Conventions

Kirchhoff's two laws yield the equations from which the voltage or current variations in a network may be determined. The circuit diagram,

* This statement is equivalent to the definition by the IRE Standards Committee.[22]

with appropriate sign conventions, is essential to the writing of the Kirchhoff's-law equations for an electric network. Since the diagram and equations state the same information, the symbols in the two must be given in a consistent manner. Current is indicated on a circuit diagram by an arrow with the letter i or I alongside it. Voltage, i.e., potential difference, is designated in this text by an arrow with the letter v or V alongside it. (When a voltage arrow indicates the potential difference maintained by an e.m.f. source, the letter e or E may be used. The letters e and E are also used for vacuum-tube voltages.)

Current Arrow

The current arrow specifies a current reference direction. The number or expression giving the value of the current i has a positive value at every instant when current flows in the arrow or reference direction. When current flow is oppositely directed, i is negative. In a problem containing unknown currents, the signs in the equations are written, and the solutions are interpreted, in a manner consistent with assigned reference directions. The current arrow is used in a similar manner whether we deal with direct currents, currents of arbitrary time variation, or sinusoidal currents.

A direct current, i.e., a current constant in time, is simply given by a number of amperes, as 5 amperes. The number is positive when the current flow is directed as the current arrow. The same current oppositely directed is -5 amperes.

When current varies in time, its values are given by an expression in t, as $i = a+b\cos(\omega t+\phi)$. The constants of the expression must be such that, at every instant when current flows in the arrow direction, i is a positive number. At other times, i must be negative or zero.

In problems involving the sinusoidal steady state, complex numbers are used to represent current. The current reference direction retains essentially the same meaning. To see this clearly, consider a complex current, as $I = 5\underline{/60^\circ}$. This represents the current $i = \sqrt{2}\, 5\cos(\omega t+60^\circ)$.* The phase angle is commonly written in degrees, with the understanding that it must be converted to radians before it can be added to ωt, or, of

* Two points should be kept in mind here. First, while sine or cosine may equally well be chosen to represent a sinusoid, a consistent terminology should be used; i.e. either the cosine or sine basis should be taken throughout. Second, the instant $t = 0$ is arbitrarily chosen in a problem involving the sinusoidal steady state. However, one particular voltage (or current) is a phase reference, i.e., described as $v = v_{\max}\cos\omega t$ (or $i = i_{\max}\cos\omega t$). Then the instant $t = 0$ is defined as the time this voltage (or current) goes through a positive peak, and all other phase angles are evaluated relative to this. (Here we have used the cosine basis.)

course, ωt can be replaced by an equivalent number of degrees for evaluation of the cosine. The complex current $-I$, which equals $-5\underline{/60°}$ or $5\underline{/240°}$, represents the current $-\sqrt{2}\,5\cos(\omega t+60°)$ which equals $\sqrt{2}\,5\cos(\omega t+240°)$. We see then that the sign and angle of the complex current determine the sign of the instantaneous current. The values of the instantaneous current must be positive during the portions of a cycle when its flow is in the arrow direction. In order to determine the signs of the complex currents, however, it is not necessary to write instantaneous expressions. The complex currents and voltages of steady-state a-c analysis obey Kirchhoff's laws. The circuit equations are, therefore, directly written in a manner consistent with the arrow directions of the circuit diagram.

*Voltage Arrow**

The voltage arrow alongside a circuit element specifies a voltage reference direction. The number or expression giving the value of the voltage, v, is so written as to be consistent with this reference direction. At every instant when the node point nearest the arrowhead is at a higher potential than the node point at the tail end of the arrow, the quantity v has a positive value. In a problem containing unknown voltages, the signs in the equations are written and the solutions are interpreted in a manner consistent with assigned reference directions.

A voltage may be constant and specified by a number, it may have an arbitrary time variation and be given by an instantaneous expression in t, or it may have a steady sinusoidal variation specified by a complex number. As with current, the expression for the voltage must in every case lead to instantaneous values which are consistent with the choice of arrow direction.

1-3 Nature of Circuit Equations

Kirchhoff's two laws in combination with the voltage–current relations for the elements of a network yield the equations from which the voltage or current variations in the network may be determined. The voltage–current characteristic (or law) for the individual circuit elements may be extremely simple, as Ohm's law

$$v = Ri \tag{1-1}$$

for a resistance. On the other hand we may have a complicated characteristic requiring more than one equation for its statement. Thus for a

* While this is not the only possible convention, it is adopted in this book as it is one of the unambiguous voltage conventions.

vacuum diode, the plate current i is related to the plate voltage e_b approximately as follows:

$$i = 0 \qquad \text{when} \quad e_b < 0 \tag{1-2}$$

$$i = k(e_b)^{3/2} \qquad \text{when} \quad e_b > 0 \tag{1-3}$$

provided that current flow is space-charge limited.

From these illustrations it is evident that voltage–current relationships may vary widely with the type of circuit element. This means that Kirchhoff's laws yield all sorts of equations, some easy of solution, others amenable only to graphical or numerical methods.

1-4 Linear Electric Circuits

This text is limited to the very large and important class of circuits termed *linear*. A system is linear if its response may be obtained as the solution of linear differential equations. An ordinary linear differential equation in its most general form[4] is

$$f(t) = \alpha_0(t)\frac{d^ny}{dt^n} + \alpha_1(t)\frac{d^{n-1}y}{dt^{n-1}} + \cdots + \alpha_{n-1}(t)\frac{dy}{dt} + \alpha_n(t)y \tag{1-4}$$

The function $f(t)$ is a known function of time. It may be the driving function or a combination of terms involving the driving function and its derivatives. The coefficients in this equation, $\alpha_0, \alpha_1, \ldots, \alpha_n$, are functions of time only, i.e., independent of the response y.

The electric circuits which we shall study will be described by linear equations of a far less general form than (1–4). In fact any circuit we shall treat in this text may be described by a set of equations such as the following:

$$\begin{aligned} f_1(t) &= l_{11}y_1 + l_{12}y_2 + \cdots + l_{1n}y_n \\ f_2(t) &= l_{21}y_1 + l_{22}y_2 + \cdots + l_{2n}y_n \\ &\vdots \\ f_n(t) &= l_{n1}y_1 + l_{n2}y_2 + \cdots + l_{nn}y_n \end{aligned} \tag{1-5}$$

In this list of equations the y's may be current response and the f's applied voltage, or the y's may be voltage response and the f's applied current. In either case, each l represents a linear operator, the typical one being

$$l_{rs} = a_{rs}\frac{d}{dt} + b_{rs} + c_{rs}\int_0^t [\quad] d\tau \tag{1-6}$$

with a_{rs}, b_{rs}, and c_{rs} *each a constant.* The meaning of the symbolic equation (1–6) becomes clear if we write

$$l_{rs}y_s = a_{rs}\frac{dy_s}{dt} + b_{rs}y_s + c_{rs}\int_0^t y_s(\tau)\,d\tau \tag{1–7}$$

The integral in the third term on the right-hand side of (1–7) requires comment and will be discussed in detail in Chapter 2. At this point it is sufficient to note that the variable of integration, τ, varies from zero to an arbitrary time, t. The derivative of this integral is the integrand y_s evaluated at the instant t, since, here, y_s can be expressed as a function of τ only, i.e., as $y_s(\tau)$ and not as $y_s(t, \tau)$. The presence of these integrals in (1–5) gives rise to the term *integro-differential* equations. However, the integrals may be removed by differentiating each of the equations (1–5) once with respect to time. Since such a step could not alter the solution, we still regard each equation of the set (1–5) as a special case of the general linear differential equation (1–4)—special because in place of the coefficients $\alpha(t)$ we have constants, and because the derivatives are not of an arbitrary order n.

Let us consider any circuit for which the application of Kirchhoff's laws leads to a set of equations such as (1–5) with the definition (1–6). This circuit is termed *linear*, since these equations are linear. The circuit is said to be *lumped* (or to consist of *lumped elements*), since in these equations time is the only independent variable, i.e., voltage or current variation with space coordinates has not entered the problem.* The circuit is also *finite*, since the finite number of equations, each with a finite number of terms, implies a finite number of circuit elements. Finally, since a_{rs}, b_{rs}, and c_{rs} are independent of time, the circuit is said to have *constant parameters*. The present text, then, is limited to a study of *linear, lumped, finite* networks with constant parameters.

The reader will recognize, and we shall demonstrate shortly, that the terms on the right-hand side of (1–7) can represent the voltage across an inductance, resistance, or capacitance when y_s is current. If y_s is voltage, these terms can respectively represent current through a capacitance, resistance, and inductance. However, it is not our purpose at this point to justify these equations from circuit laws. We merely assert that only circuits whose laws lead to such equations are to be considered. Their properties will be revealed by the characteristics of the linear equations (1–5).

* A "non-lumped" system is termed *distributed*. A transmission line is an example of a distributed system. We note that the voltage and current along a transmission line are each a solution of partial differential equations with the two independent variables: distance along the line, and time.

In equations (1–5) we observe that:

(1) Each $f(t)$ is independent of every y.

(2) Each y, each derivative of a y, and each integral of a y is simply multiplied by a coefficient and the terms are added.

(3) The coefficients a, b, c which enter each l are constants.

Linear Sources of E.M.F. and Current

The first statement listed immediately above requires that each driving function must be independent of response. Superficially, this might seem to eliminate circuits having imperfect regulation or having feedback. Such, however, is not the case when physical generators can be represented properly. To this end, we first define pure or ideal e.m.f. and current sources:

> An *ideal e.m.f. source* creates a potential difference between two points that is entirely independent of the current flowing through those points.
>
> An *ideal current source* drives a current through two points that is entirely independent of the potential across those points.

When a physical generator is represented as an ideal source with constant circuit elements in series or shunt, the ideal source becomes the excitation and the circuit elements form part of the network. We have, then, a driving function $e(t)$ or $i(t)$ which is independent of load, satisfying the first requirement of linearity.

There is, however, another type of source: In any problem involving transients, we seek the voltage or current which follows a switching operation. The instant the switch moves is designated as $t = 0$. We may have a voltage across a capacitance, or a current in an inductance, at this instant. This initial voltage or current is one of the excitations or sources applied to the circuit. When a circuit is analyzed in terms of the voltages around loops (loop analysis), an initial voltage across a capacitance appears in equations (1–5) as a direct voltage suddenly applied to the circuit. When a circuit is analyzed in terms of currents at nodes (node analysis), initial current in an inductance appears in (1–5) as a direct current suddenly applied to the circuit. Equations (1–5) will not explicitly contain both these sources; the one not explicitly present enters as a condition for the determination of integration constants. However, when circuit equations are later set up in terms of Laplace transforms (Chapters 4 and 5), all initial conditions will appear as sources or driving functions applied to the circuit.

We may define as *linear sources* those sources whose time variation can appear as $f_1(t), f_2(t) \ldots$ in the linear equations (1–5); these are:

(a) an ideal e.m.f. source
(b) an ideal current source
(c) an initial voltage across a capacitance
(d) an initial current in an inductance.

A physical generator, when it can be represented as an ideal e.m.f. or current source with constant circuit elements in series or shunt, contributes a linear source to the circuit.

Passive Bilateral Linear Circuit Elements[6]

Having considered sources, we now turn to the circuit itself. The nature of the circuit components determines the nature of the equations which result from the application of Kirchhoff's laws. The laws of the basic circuit elements *inductance, resistance,* and *capacitance* are now to be considered. These two-terminal elements are completely symmetrical with respect to their terminals, and are, therefore, called *bilateral.* We shall express the law of each in two forms, one expressing voltage in terms of current, the other expressing current in terms of voltage.

INDUCTANCE. The voltage across an inductance is related to the current through it by

$$v = L\frac{di}{dt} \tag{1–8}$$

where L represents *self-inductance.*

In this equation it is to be understood that the voltage reference direction is taken opposite to the current reference direction. In order to visualize this, we may picture the ideal coil as horizontal, and define current flow to the right as positive. Then at any instant when the derivative di/dt is a positive number, the left-hand coil terminal is at a higher potential than the right-hand one. (The derivative di/dt can, of course, be positive at a certain instant, even though i itself is negative at that time.)

In order to obtain the current in terms of the voltage across the coil, both sides of (1–8) are integrated between zero and an arbitary instant of time. We obtain

$$\int_0^{t'} \frac{di}{dt}dt = \int_0^{t'} \frac{v}{L}dt \tag{1–9}$$

The left-hand side of (1–9) yields $i - i_0$, where i is the current at the instant t' and i_0 is the current at the instant $t = 0$. Now t' is any instant of time, so that we may call it t and use some other letter τ, say, as the variable of integration on the right-hand side of (1–9). Hence we find

$$i = \frac{1}{L}\int_0^t v\,d\tau + i_0 \tag{1–10}$$

RESISTANCE. The voltage–current relation for a resistance can be written as either

$$v = Ri \tag{1–11}$$

or

$$i = \frac{1}{R}v \tag{1–12}$$

Here again the voltage reference direction is understood to be opposite to the current reference direction. In order to visualize this, we picture the resistor as horizontal. Then at any instant when current flows to the right, the left-hand terminal will be at a higher potential than the right-hand one.

CAPACITANCE. The voltage across a capacitance C is proportional to its charge q in accordance with the relation

$$v = \frac{1}{C}q \tag{1–13}$$

Differentiating both sides of (1–13) with respect to time, we find

$$i = C\frac{dv}{dt} \tag{1–14}$$

In this equation it is, again, to be understood that the voltage and current reference directions are opposite to each other. If the capacitance be pictured as horizontal, let v be the potential of the left-hand terminal relative to the right-hand terminal. Then the current i to the right will be positive at any instant when dv/dt is a positive number.

Comparing equation (1–14) with (1–8), we see that they are identical in form. The current i replaces v, the capacitance C replaces L, and the voltage v replaces i. Hence if we interchange i and v and also C and L in (1–10), which is the solution of (1–8), we have the solution of (1–14) for v in terms of i, namely

$$v = \frac{1}{C}\int_0^t i\,d\tau + v_0 \tag{1–15}$$

The first term on the right-hand side of equation (1–15) represents the voltage caused by the charge added to the capacitance after the instant $t = 0$.

We observe that the right-hand sides of (1–8, 10, 11, 12, 14, and 15) are all linear. Any one of these might appear as a term in the linear equations (1–5). When either i_0 or v_0 appears, it must be included as part of an $f(t)$. A simple illustration will prove helpful:

Let a sinusoidal voltage be applied to the series RLC circuit of Fig. 1–1. The switch S closes at an instant when the sinusoidal source is at the peak of its positive half-cycle. We designate this instant as $t = 0$. Suppose

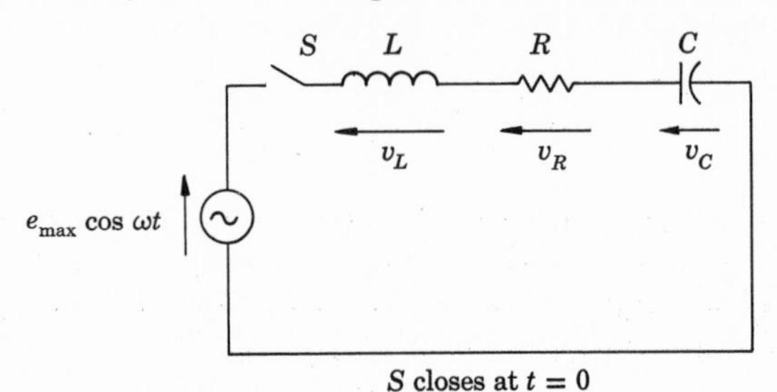

Fig. 1–1.

further that there is a voltage v_0 across the capacitance at this instant (which occurs if the capacitance is charged before the switch closes). Kirchhoff's voltage law yields (for $t > 0$)

$$e_{max} \cos \omega t = v_L + v_R + v_C \tag{1–16}$$

where v_L, v_R, and v_C represent the voltages across the inductance, resistance, and capacitance, respectively. From Kirchhoff's current law we know the currents to be identical for all three elements in series. We therefore apply the voltage–current relation for each element as given in (1–8, 11, 15) to obtain

$$e_{max} \cos \omega t = L\frac{di}{dt} + Ri + \frac{1}{C}\int_0^t i\,d\tau + v_0 \tag{1–17}$$

Here we may consider the driving function to be $f(t) = e_{max}(\cos \omega t) - v_0$, and write (1–17) in the concise form

$$f(t) = li \tag{1–18}$$

where l is the linear operator

$$l = L\frac{d}{dt} + R + \frac{1}{C}\int_0^t [\,]\,d\tau \tag{1–19}$$

Comparison with (1–5) and (1–6) shows that we have a special case of that set of linear equations. The number of equations is reduced to one, i replaces y, and L, R, $1/C$ are the constants a, b, c of (1–6).

If an initial current were present in the inductance, it would not appear explicitly in (1–17), but would be a condition determining integration constants. As was mentioned earlier, however, when the Laplace transform method is introduced, all initial conditions will be represented as applied sources.

Mutual Inductance. The effect of mutual inductance is simply to add to or subtract from the voltage across a coil which is magnetically coupled to another coil. Thus for the circuit of Fig. 1–2 we have

$$v_1 = L_1\frac{di_1}{dt} \pm M\frac{di_2}{dt} \tag{1–20}$$

$$v_2 = \pm M\frac{di_1}{dt} + L_2\frac{di_2}{dt} \tag{1–20a}$$

The choice of sign preceding M will be considered in the following subsection. Since mutual inductance is given by the relation $M = k\sqrt{L_1L_2}$

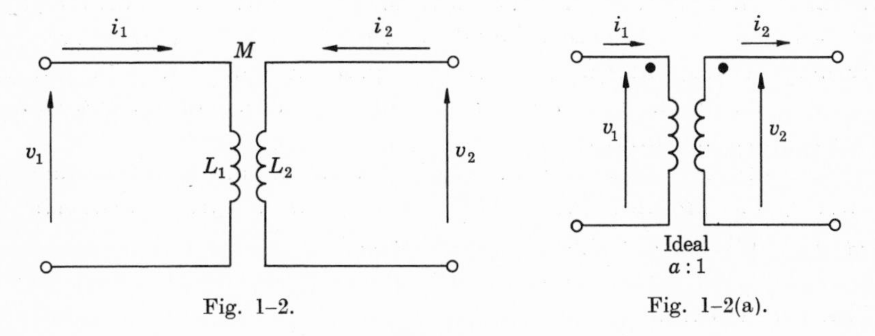

Fig. 1–2. Fig. 1–2(a).

with $0 \leqq k \leqq 1$, it evidently cannot be present in the absence of self-inductance. Since mutual inductance cannot exist alone, we refer to it, not as a circuit element, but simply as a property of coils linked by common magnetic flux.

Sign of Voltage Caused by Mutual Magnetic Flux(12)

When two coils are coupled by a mutual magnetic flux, the voltage across each is given by a sum of terms; e.g., $L_1(di_1/dt) \pm M(di_2/dt)$ is the voltage across the first coil. Now let it be understood that the voltage reference direction is opposite to the current reference for each of the two coils. The changing flux created by the varying current i_1 of the first coil induces the voltage $L_1(di_1/dt)$. The changing flux created by the varying current i_2 of the second coil induces the further contribution, $\pm M(di_2/dt)$, to the voltage of the first coil. This latter contribution depends upon the degree of flux linkage, which determines the value of M, and upon the flux directions. When the fluxes caused by i_1 and i_2 are in the same direction at any instant when each of these currents is positive, the positive sign precedes $M(di_2/dt)$, for then a positive di_2/dt adds to the effect of a positive di_1/dt. When the fluxes caused by i_1 and i_2 oppose at any instant when each of these currents is positive, the negative sign precedes $M(di_2/dt)$ since increasing i_2 will oppose the effect of increasing i_1. Complete circuit data, then, must include information on relative flux directions.

To show relative flux directions on a circuit diagram, a dot is placed at one end of each coil of a pair of magnetically coupled coils.* The positions of these dots indicate that when current enters each coil at the end marked by a dot the fluxes will be additive. Hence if currents are drawn as entering the dot end of each coil, $M(di_2/dt)$ adds to $L_1 di_1/dt$, for an increasing i_2 adds to the effect of increasing i_1. If one current is drawn entering its coil at the dot end, while the other current enters its coil at the terminal far from the dot, $M(di_2/dt)$ subtracts from $L_1 di_1/dt$, for an increasing i_2 opposes the effect of increasing i_1. When several coils are magnetically interlinked, each coil pair must have its own dot pair, e.g., dots *aa* for the first and second coils, *bb* for the second and third, *cc* for the third and first, etc.

Examples of the use of the dot convention, along with other sign conventions, are illustrated and discussed in a later subsection (see Fig. 1–3 and the accompanying discussion).

Ideal Transformer

The *ideal transformer* of Fig. 1–2(a) can be defined as a new circuit element having an input terminal pair and an output terminal pair. Its properties can be stated in a number of ways leading to the relations $v_1 = av_2$, $i_1 = (1/a)i_2$, where the factor a is a constant independent of the time variation of v_1 and i_1. At reasonable sinusoidal frequencies, this leads to a realistic first approximation to physical transformer action.

Another viewpoint can be adopted, however.(5,19) Rather than treat the ideal transformer as a new type of circuit element, we can simply regard it as a limiting case of coils coupled by mutual magnetic flux. We therefore begin as if the transformer of Fig. 1–2(a) were not ideal. With i_2 drawn to the right and with the winding sense indicated by the

* Another convention lets M itself take an appropriate sign.

dots in Fig. 1–2(a) assumed, and, further, with $M = \sqrt{L_1L_2}$ (i.e., flux linkage at a maximum), equations (1–20 and 20a) become:

$$v_1 = L_1\frac{di_1}{dt} - \sqrt{L_1L_2}\frac{di_2}{dt} \tag{1–20b}$$

$$-v_2 = -\sqrt{L_1L_2}\frac{di_1}{dt} + L_2\frac{di_2}{dt} \tag{1–20c}$$

We find on solving for di_1/dt and di_2/dt that the determinant of these equations is zero. Hence if di_1/dt and di_2/dt are each finite, the numerator determinants are also zero.

Thus:

$$\begin{vmatrix} v_1 & -\sqrt{L_1L_2} \\ -v_2 & L_2 \end{vmatrix} = 0 \tag{1–20d}$$

and

$$\begin{vmatrix} L_1 & v_1 \\ -\sqrt{L_1L_2} & -v_2 \end{vmatrix} = 0 \tag{1–20e}$$

Either of these equations yields $v_1/v_2 = \sqrt{L_1/L_2}$. If we take $\sqrt{L_1/L_2}$ as the constant a (and it can also be shown to equal the turns ratio of the coils) we have *the first ideal transformer relationship*

$$\frac{v_1}{v_2} = a \tag{1–20f}$$

Now rewriting equation (1–20b) and introducing the constant a, we find

$$\frac{v_1}{L_1} = \frac{di_1}{dt} - \frac{1}{a}\frac{di_2}{dt} \tag{1–20g}$$

If the ratio $\sqrt{L_1/L_2}$ is maintained constant, and L_1 allowed to increase without limit, (1–20g) becomes

$$0 = \frac{di_1}{dt} - \frac{1}{a}\frac{di_2}{dt} \tag{1–20h}$$

Taking $t = 0$ as an instant at which both currents are equal to zero, and integrating (1–20h) with respect to time (assuming finite derivatives), we find

$$i_1 = \frac{1}{a}i_2 \tag{1–20i}$$

which is the *second ideal transformer relationship.*

Sign Conventions and Linear Circuit Laws Illustrated in Fig. 1–3

Fig. 1–3 illustrates the sign conventions for coils coupled by mutual flux and for the elements L, R, and C. Current reference directions are arbitrary. The solved equations will yield solutions for the currents consistent with these assumed reference directions. Potential across a

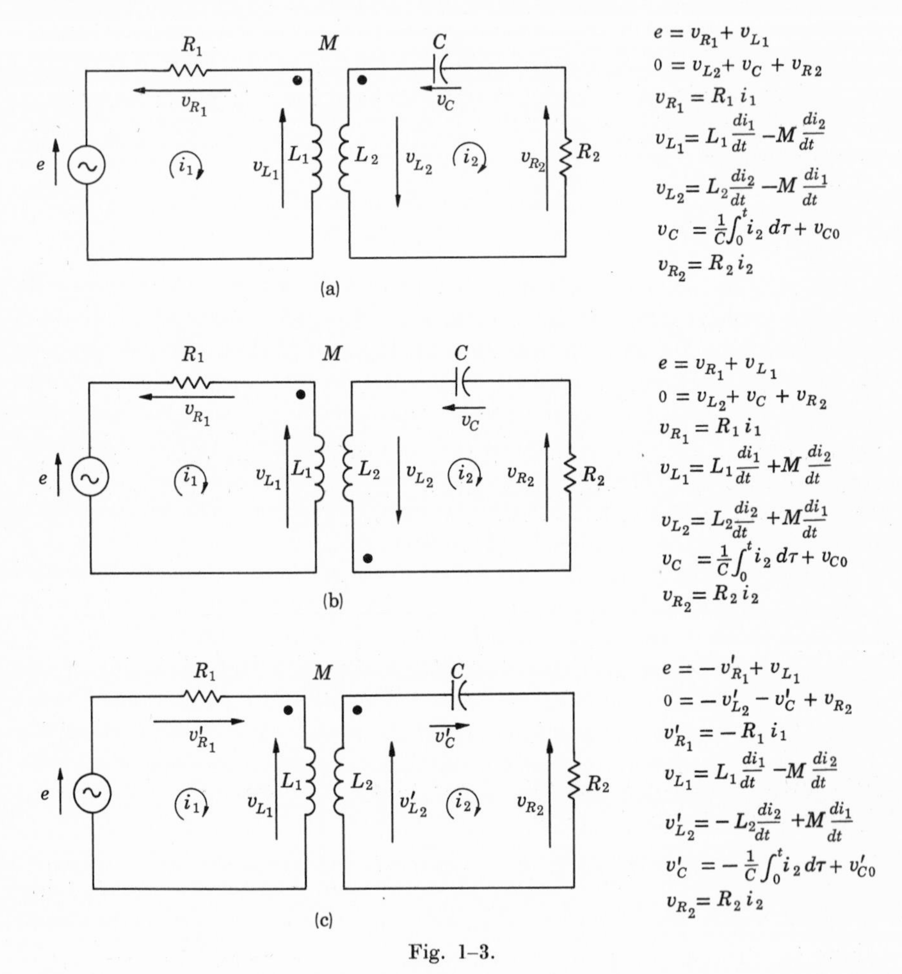

Fig. 1–3.

resistance, self-inductance, or capacitance will be positive in a direction opposite to that of the current arrow at an instant when Ri, $L(di/dt)$, and

$$(1/C)\int_0^t i \, d\tau + v_{C0}$$

are positive quantities. Hence it is generally convenient to draw voltage arrows in a direction opposite to that of the current arrows.

Fig. 1–3(a) illustrates a circuit with voltage and current arrows and the corresponding Kirchhoff's-law equations. Fig. 1–3(b) differs from Fig. 1–3(a) in that the winding sense of one of the coils has been reversed. Fig. 1–3(c) has been added to show that we may draw voltage arrows in a different way and still obtain correct equations. On noting that

$$v_{CO}' = -v_{CO}$$

we see that the equations of Fig. 1–3(c) agree with those of Fig. 1–3(a).

The Duality Principle

The voltage–current relations for passive bilateral circuit elements reveal a general property of electric networks: the principle of duality. If we consider the pair of equations (1–10) and (1–15), we find them to be identical mathematical forms: one equation can be obtained from the other simply by interchange of the variables v and i, and the constants L and C. If two such equations referred to different physical systems, they would be termed *analogs*. Since both refer to circuits, they are called *duals*. Duality will also be seen in two other pairs of equations: (1–8) and (1–14), as well as (1–11) and (1–12).

In general, two networks are called *duals* if their equations have the following relationship: interchange of voltage and current, of inductance and capacitance, and of resistance and conductance, turns the equations of the first network into those of the second, and the equations of the second network into those of the first. We shall find duality when comparing loop and node analysis, we shall see it as a relation between voltage and current sources, and we shall see it again as a relation between series impedances and parallel admittances.

Linear Devices with Active Response

The vacuum tube and the transistor may, under appropriate conditions, be termed linear devices with active response. In each case an applied signal causes or controls an output which may have more energy than the signal—the additional energy coming from d-c power supplies. The conditions for linear operation require a small signal. At least two equivalent circuits, valid over a limited frequency range, may be derived for each device.[13–18]. For each device, the equivalent circuit contains an ideal e.m.f. or current source (or both) in combination with passive elements. For the tube, the source voltage or current in the equivalent circuit is proportional to a voltage (e_g). In the case of the transistor, the source voltage or current is proportional to a current (i_e).* This proportionality leads to two conclusions: First, the relationships arising from the equivalent circuits will fit into the form of the linear equations (1–5), i.e., these equivalent circuits are linear. Second, the proportionality means that the voltage or current source in the equivalent circuit is dependent upon the applied signal and, when feedback is present, upon the output as well. We have in the equivalent-circuit generators, then, not independent sources but active responses to the applied (independent) sources of e.m.f. or current. These generators in the equivalent circuit may also be referred to as *dependent* or *controlled* sources of e.m.f. or current.

We see then that the general methods of linear network theory can apply to vacuum-tube and transistor equivalent circuits. These circuits, however, because of their active response, have properties distinct from those of passive circuits.

There will be some limitations on the vacuum-tube and transistor circuits treated in this text. For vacuum tubes, negative total instantaneous grid potential will be assumed and lead-inductance and transit-time effects neglected. Interelectrode capacitance is included in some problems although not in others. The vacuum tubes to be considered are triodes. The theory will apply to pentodes when screen and suppressor grids are to be regarded, for the equivalent circuit, as effectively at cathode potential. Analysis of transistor circuits will be confined to the low-frequency sinusoidal steady state.

1-5 Initial Conditions

An electric circuit problem is not completely specified by the values of the circuit parameters and the geometric arrangement of the circuit elements. The initial state of the system must also be known, for without this information the circuit differential equations would yield a solution containing undetermined constants. With the application of sufficient information concerning the initial values of current, voltage, and their derivatives, the solution becomes unique.

In the following discussion (and throughout this text) idealized circuit elements are assumed, except where the opposite is stated. An *ideal inductance*, an *ideal resistance*, and an *ideal capacitance* are defined as elements which are entirely characterized by the laws $v = L\,di/dt$,

* Some transistor equivalent circuits include more than one controlled source (see Section 5–2). For a vacuum-tube equivalent circuit with more than one controlled source, see reference 7 at the end of Chapter 7.

$v = Ri$, and $i = C dv/dt$, respectively. An *ideal switch* S between two points a and b is a device which can be in only one of two states:

(1) *closed*—that is, with zero potential difference between a and b, or
(2) *open*—that is, with zero current flow from a to b.

Since this definition allows no other state, S closes or opens in zero time, i.e., instantaneously.

Initial Current in Inductance

Let us suppose that we seek the response of a network subsequent to a certain switching process. We shall require the initial current in each inductance in the circuit. By *initial current*, i_0, is meant the value of the current immediately after switching, that is

$$\lim_{t \to 0} i,$$

with t positive during the limiting process or $i(0+)$.* The initial value is defined in this way because the circuit differential equations and their solutions apply to the range of time $0 < t$.

Since the condition of the circuit prior to switching is ordinarily known, the problem of finding the initial current in an inductance reduces to that of relating the current in the inductance immediately after switching to that immediately before switching. Since the voltage across an inductance is $L(di/dt)$, a discontinuity in current implies an infinite voltage across the inductance. In most problems one can immediately reject this possibility as violating at least one of Kirchhoff's laws. Such will clearly be the case in the circuit of Fig. 1-4(a) when S closes, and in the circuit of Fig. 1–4(b) when S either closes or opens. Hence a usual assumption in the solution of problems in transient analysis is the continuity of inductive current, i.e., it is assumed that the current in an inductance is the same immediately before and after switching.

In some circuits, however, we find that the assumption of current continuity in inductance, along with the assumption of an idealized circuit, leads to a result which contradicts Kirchhoff's current law. In Fig. 1–4(c), if S opens, these assumptions require a finite current in series

* In general,

$$f(0+) = \lim_{t \to 0} f(t) \quad \text{where } t > 0 \text{ during the limit process}$$

$$f(0-) = \lim_{t \to 0} f(t) \quad \text{where } t < 0 \text{ during the limit process}$$

If $f(t)$ is continuous at the instant $t = 0$, then $f(0+) = f(0-)$.

with an open switch. Again in Fig. 1–4(d) these assumptions lead to unequal currents in L_1 and L_2 immediately after S opens. But L_1 and L_2 are then in series! We recognize at once that these circuits are not ideal, that the voltage across each inductance is not infinite but very large, that a large voltage also appears across each switch, and that arcing occurs. One might, on the grounds that an arc is a nonlinear phenomenon, omit these problems from a treatment of linear circuits. A different approach can be adopted, however,(10,12) provided that the arc is of extremely

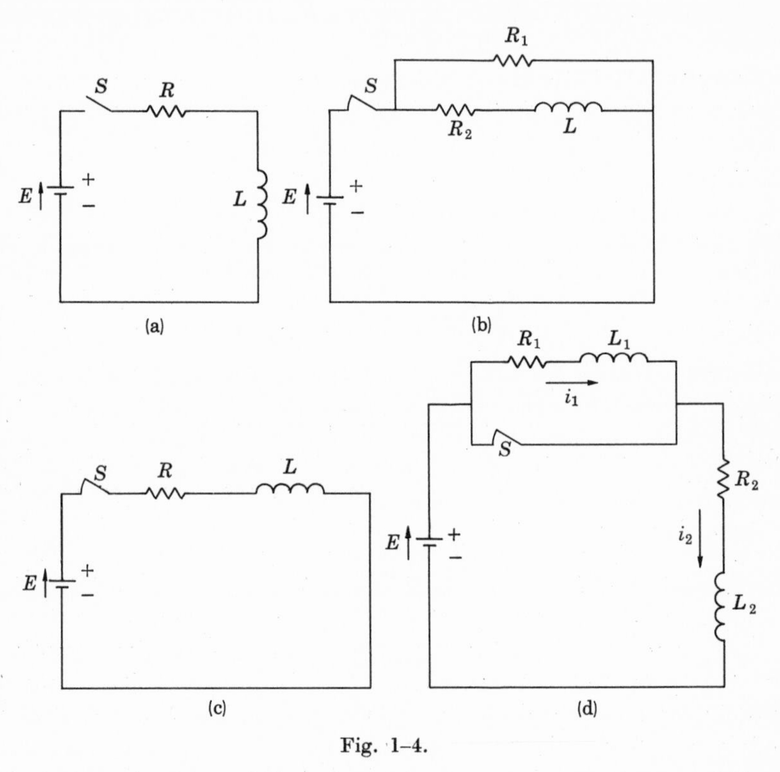

Fig. 1–4.

short duration. One assumes first that the current change takes place in a finite but short time ϵ. When ϵ reduces to zero, the circuit is again idealized, and a discontinuity in current can be evaluated. To see how this is done, consider the circuit of Fig. 1–4(d). Suppose the d-c steady state to be established prior to the instant $t = 0$ at which the switch S opens. The equation valid for $t > 0$ is:

$$E = R_1 i_1 + L_1 \frac{di_1}{dt} + R_2 i_2 + L_2 \frac{di_2}{dt} \tag{1–21}$$

and at $t \geqq \epsilon$ (when the arc is extinguished)

$$0 = i_1 - i_2 \tag{1-22}$$

where i_1 is the current in R_1L_1, and i_2 the current in R_2L_2. These currents are clearly equal after S is open, i.e., after the arc is extinguished, but unequal before this instant. Now integrate both sides of (1–21) with respect to time between the limits 0 and ϵ. Then

$$\int_0^\epsilon E\,dt = R_1 \int_0^\epsilon i_1\,dt + L_1 \int_0^\epsilon \frac{di_1}{dt}dt + R_2 \int_0^\epsilon i_2\,dt + L_2 \int_0^\epsilon \frac{di_2}{dt}dt \tag{1-23}$$

If ϵ be taken arbitrarily small, the integrals

$$\int_0^\epsilon E\,dt, \quad \int_0^\epsilon i_1\,dt, \quad \text{and} \quad \int_0^\epsilon i_2\,dt$$

can be neglected. We assume, of course, that their integrands are finite, so that these three integrals approach zero as ϵ approaches zero.

Evaluating the remaining two integrals, we find

$$0 = L_1[i_1(\epsilon) - i_1(0)] + L_2[i_2(\epsilon) - i_2(0)] \tag{1-24}$$

Directly from the circuit and as stated in equation (1–22), $i_1(\epsilon)$ and $i_2(\epsilon)$ are equal. Since the current values have been tentatively assumed to require a finite (although small) time to change, the currents at zero time $i_1(0)$ and $i_2(0)$ are equal respectively to zero and E/R_2, i.e., their values prior to opening of S. Hence,

$$0 = (L_1 + L_2)i_1(\epsilon) - L_2\frac{E}{R_2} \tag{1-25}$$

or

$$i_1(\epsilon) = \frac{E}{R_2}\,\frac{L_2}{L_1 + L_2} \tag{1-25a}$$

Now if ϵ be approximated as zero, the circuit is idealized and the changes in current from 0 to $i_1(\epsilon)$ in L_1, and from E/R_2 to $i_1(\epsilon)$ in L_2, may be regarded as current discontinuities in the inductances, each accompanied by an instantaneously infinite voltage. It is also of interest to note that the flux linkage after switching is the same as that prior to switching. This *conservation of flux linkage*(12) can be seen from the identity

$$\frac{E}{R_2}L_2 \equiv \left(\frac{E}{R_2}\,\frac{L_2}{L_1 + L_2}\right)L_1 + \left(\frac{E}{R_2}\,\frac{L_2}{L_1 + L_2}\right)L_2 \tag{1-26}$$

The circuit of Fig. 1–4(c) can be regarded as a limiting case of the more general circuit Fig. 1–4(d). If R_1 (Fig. 1–4(d)) is assumed to be infinite, equation (1–25a) cannot be used, since that equation was based on the assumption

$$\lim_{\epsilon \to 0} R_1 \int_0^{\epsilon} i_1 \, dt = 0$$

However, equation (1–21) yields $i_1(\epsilon) = 0$ for $R_1 = \infty$ and $\epsilon > 0$. If L_1 is assumed to be infinite, either (1–24) or (1–25a) yields $i_1(\epsilon) = 0$.

When idealization of a circuit requires an infinite voltage, $L\,di/dt$, at the instant of switching, this voltage is termed an *impulse voltage* and is represented by an *impulse function*. The impulse function will be defined precisely through a limit process in Chapter 2. For the present, it is sufficient to say that when a physical quantity varies as an impulse function, it is instantaneously infinite and has a finite effect. Thus an instantaneously infinite voltage produces a finite current change in an inductance. In mechanics, a sudden blow, described as an instantaneously infinite force (or impulse force), produces a finite change in momentum.

We have then two types of problem involving initial current in inductance. The first, and far more common, is that in which continuity of coil current must be assumed in order not to violate Kirchhoff's circuit laws. Then the initial current in an inductance will equal the value of current in the inductance just prior to switching. The second type of problem occurs with circuits in which the usual assumptions of an ideal circuit and of continuity of inductive current violate Kirchhoff's current law. In such a case, the current discontinuity results in an instantaneously infinite voltage, or impulse voltage. (In a physical circuit, high voltage and arcing occur.) A very simple approach(10,11) to this second case can be obtained through use of Laplace transforms and the impulse function (see Chapter 4).

Initial Voltage Across Capacitance

When seeking the response of a network subsequent to a switching process, we shall also require the initial voltage across each capacitance in the circuit. The *initial voltage* v_0 *across a capacitance* is defined as the value of the voltage across the capacitance immediately after switching, i.e.,

$$\lim_{t \to 0} v$$

with t positive during the limiting process, or $v(0+)$. It is, therefore, necessary to relate the voltage across each capacitance just after switching to its value immediately before switching. Since the voltage–current relation for a capacitance, equation (1–14), is dual to the voltage-current relation for an inductance, we expect a duality in the criteria for obtaining initial conditions. That is, we expect the treatment of capacitive voltage to follow the same lines as the preceding discussion of inductive current.

We first observe that since $i = C\,dv/dt$, an instantaneous finite change in the voltage across a capacitance implies an infinite current to the capacitance. In many circuits the assumption of an infinite current to the capacitance will contradict at least one of Kirchhoff's laws.

The circuit of Fig. 1–5 affords a simple illustration. Let the switch S close at $t = 0$, prior to which the capacitance C is uncharged. If we were erroneously to assume an initial value v_{C0} other than zero for the voltage across C, we would find the currents, at this instant, to be $i_1 = (E - v_{C0})/R_1$, $i_2 = v_{C0}/R_2$, and $i_3 = (E/R_1) - v_{C0}(R_1 + R_2)/R_1R_2$. This last result contradicts the requirement that i_3 be infinite if v_C jumps from zero to a non-zero value of v_{C0}. Thus only the assumption of continuity of capacitive voltage is consistent with Kirchhoff's current law in this circuit. Such circuits in which a discontinuity of capacitive voltage is impossible are by far the most common in the analysis of transient phenomena.

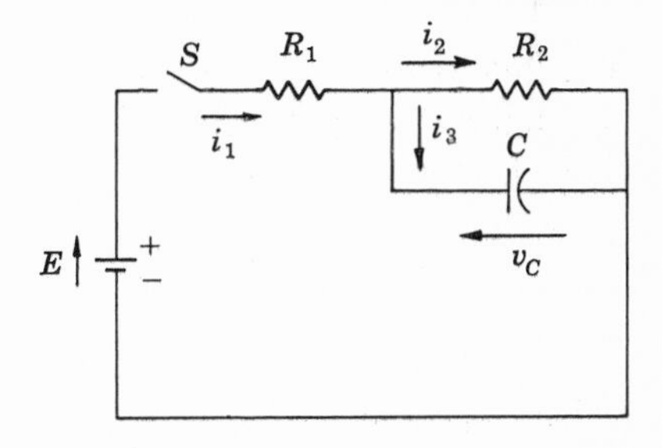

Fig. 1–5.

In certain instances, the assumption of an ideal circuit, together with the assumption of continuity of voltage across capacitance, lead to a conclusion which contradicts Kirchhoff's voltage law. Thus when S closes in the circuit of Fig. 1–6(a), continuity of capacitive voltage would yield $v_C \neq E$ if v_C were unequal to E prior to switching. Again, in the circuit of Fig. 1–6(b), if S closes when the voltages across C_2 and C_1 are unequal, continuity of capacitive voltage would lead to unequal voltages across parallel branches. We therefore recognize that these circuits cannot be ideal, and that, as a result of lead and switch resistance, the circuits cannot be represented as drawn until a finite time, ϵ, after switching.

Let us first consider Fig. 1–6(a). We suppose first that during the interval $0 < t < \epsilon$, we cannot neglect the voltages across the leads and the switch, because of the large current. Then for $t > \epsilon$, we have

$$E = v_C \tag{1–27}$$

where v_C is the voltage across the capacitance. Clearly if we suppose ϵ

equal to zero, we assume an ideal circuit in which the voltage across C jumps instantaneously from zero to E.

Fig. 1–6(b) affords another circuit in which idealization requires a discontinuity in voltage across capacitance. The circuit also illustrates the duality principle when its equation is compared with that corresponding to the circuit of Fig. 1–4(d). We suppose that before S closes, the current source I establishes a d-c steady state, the capacitance C_1 being uncharged. Then at a certain instant, designated as $t = 0$, S closes. Clearly, if we assume no sudden change in the voltage across either capacitance, we shall violate Kirchhoff's voltage law.

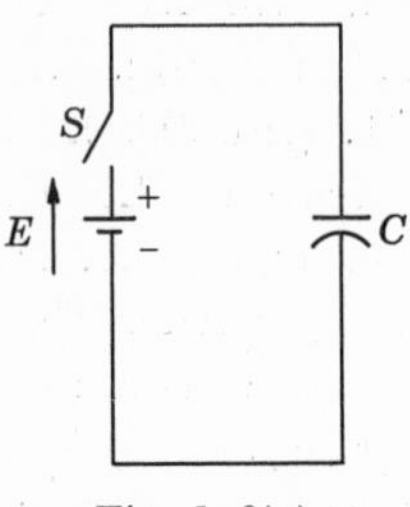

Fig. 1–6(a).

We now assume that, for a short time ϵ, after the instant $t = 0$, the current through the switch S and to the capacitance C_1 is so large that the voltage across S and the voltages across the leads of C_1 cannot be neglected. During and after this interval, i.e., for all $t > 0$, Kirchhoff's current law yields

$$I = G_1 v_1 + C_1 \frac{dv_1}{dt} + G_2 v_2 + C_2 \frac{dv_2}{dt} \tag{1–28}$$

where v_1 is the voltage across G_1C_1 and v_2 is the voltage across G_2C_2.

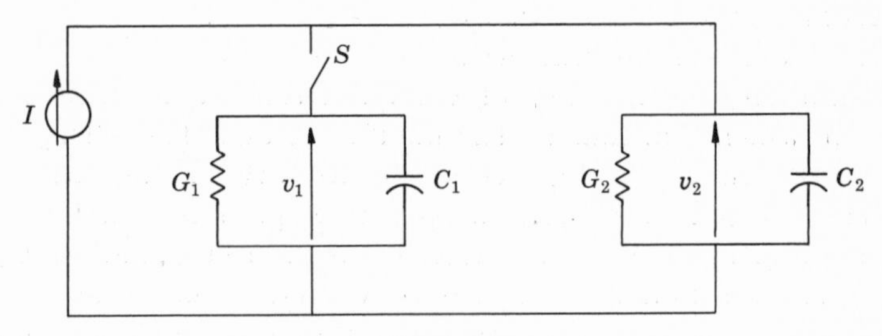

Fig. 1–6(b)

From time $t = \epsilon$ onward, we neglect the voltages across the leads and the switch, and write

$$0 = v_1 - v_2 \quad \text{for } t > \epsilon \tag{1–29}$$

Now if we allow ϵ to reduce to zero, the circuit is idealized, and a discontinuity of capacitive voltage appears. A number of steps may now be saved if we observe the duality existing between the circuits of Figs. 1–4(d) and 1–6(b). The equation pair (1–21, 22) and the equation pair

(1–28, 29) are mathematically identical save for interchange of letters E and I, R and G, L and C, and finally i and v. Hence rather than repeat the argument subsequent to (1–21 and 22), we shall obtain a correct result from (1–25a) simply by interchanging letters:

$$v_1(\epsilon) = \frac{I}{G_2} \frac{C_2}{(C_1 + C_2)} \tag{1–30}$$

We observe that the discontinuity in voltage across the first capacitance is an increase from 0 to $v_1(\epsilon)$, while that across the second capacitance is an instantaneous decrease from I/G_2 to $v_1(\epsilon)$. The total charge on C_1 and C_2 does not change as we cross the instant of switching, for

$$\frac{I}{G_2} C_2 = \frac{I}{G_2} \frac{C_2}{(C_1 + C_2)} C_1 + \frac{I}{G_2} \frac{C_2}{(C_1 + C_2)} C_2 \tag{1–31}$$

is an identity. The result (1–30) is, therefore, consistent with charge conservation.

The instantaneously infinite current associated with a discontinuity in the voltage across a capacitance is termed an *impulse current.* Instantaneously infinite, it effects a finite change in the charge on the capacitance.

We have with the capacitance, as with the inductance, two types of problem. The first and far more common is that in which continuity of voltage across capacitance must be assumed in order not to violate Kirchhoff's laws. Then the initial voltage across a capacitance will equal the value of this voltage just prior to switching. The second case is that in which the assumption of continuity of voltage across capacitance will violate Kirchhoff's voltage law. In such a case (occurring only in an idealized circuit), the voltage discontinuity results in an instantaneously infinite or impulse current. We may add that in Chapter 4, a simpler approach to the second case will be presented.[10,11]

Other Initial Quantities

When using the classical method of solution of linear differential equations we may require the initial values of various derivatives of current or voltage. When the initial values of derivatives are desired, they can be obtained from the fact that each differential equation of the circuit must be valid at the instant $t = 0$ (approached from $t > 0$).* An illustration of this technique will be carried out in Section 1–7 where the value of $L(di/dt)|_{t=0}$ will be an initial datum of the problem.

* In some cases the equations may require further differentiation.

1-6 Steady-State and Transient Response

Certain terms used to characterize the response of electric circuits require definition. A voltage or current is termed *periodic* if its values repeat over equal time intervals, the length of one such interval being called the *period.*

A constant or periodic voltage or current is in the *steady state.**

A voltage or current not in the steady state is in the *transient state.**

The solution of an electric circuit problem often contains several terms. Those which are constant or repeat form the steady-state response of the network. The transient response of a circuit usually decreases to zero. When increasing transients do occur, as in an unstable feedback circuit, the circuit elements must become altered by high currents or voltages, so that linearity no longer applies.

While there are many important forms of steady-state response (Chapter 2), the steady sinusoid is most prominent both in application and in analysis.

1-7 The Classical Method

The problem of circuit analysis is essentially one of solving the linear differential equations which yield the response of electric networks. A number of works on differential equations describe the classical method of solution.[4,8,9] When a circuit requires several simultaneous differential equations, we first eliminate all but one unknown current (or voltage) in order to obtain a single equation having the general form (1–4) but with constant coefficients. The problem is then reduced to that of solving a single equation. An effective technique for carrying this out is given by Ince.[8,9]

As a review of the classical method of solving a linear differential equation with constant coefficients, we shall obtain the instantaneous current in the circuit of Fig. 1–1. Our solution of this relatively simple transient problem will reveal the need for the more effective methods of solution to be presented in later chapters. A comparison with the a-c circuit procedure for obtaining the steady-state part of the solution will indicate the direction in which we must move to find more effective tools

* This definition of *steady state* and, by implication, of *transient state* will be convenient for our later development (see also Gardner and Barnes[6]). Some authors, however, identify the term *steady-state solution* with the particular integral obtained in the solution of linear differential equations with constant coefficients (see Section 1–7). The latter definition and the one preferred in this text become consistent when a constant or sinusoidal source is applied to the circuit.

for solving the entire (transient and steady-state) problem, as well as problems with other than sinusoidal applied voltages.

Solution of a Single-Loop Circuit Problem by the Classical Method

Applying Kirchhoff's voltage law to the circuit of Fig. 1–1, we have the equation

$$e_{\max} \cos \omega t = L\frac{di}{dt} + Ri + \frac{1}{C}q \tag{1–32}$$

Differentiating both sides yields

$$-\omega e_{\max} \sin \omega t = L\frac{d^2i}{dt^2} + R\frac{di}{dt} + \frac{1}{C}i \tag{1–33}$$

where (dq/dt) has been replaced by i.

From theorems of linear differential equations, we know that the solution of (1–33) consists of the sum of two functions of time. The first of these, which we shall call i_T, is the solution of

$$0 = L\frac{d^2i}{dt^2} + R\frac{di}{dt} + \frac{1}{C}i \tag{1–34}$$

The second, which we shall term i_s, is any function satisfying (1–33) identically. The function i_s is called the *particular integral* in the solution. If $i_s + i_T$ is substituted for i in (1–33) we find that the sum $i_s + i_T$ is also a solution of that equation. This follows from the fact that the terms involving i_T add to zero when the substitution is carried out. It may be demonstrated[4] that the sum $i_s + i_T$ is also the general solution of (1–33).

The function i_T may be obtained with the aid of the theory of the classical method as

$$i_T = A\,e^{k_1t} + B\,e^{k_2t} \tag{1–35}$$

where A and B are constants to be determined by initial conditions, and where k_1 and k_2 are the roots of the auxiliary algebraic equation

$$Lx^2 + Rx + \frac{1}{C} = 0 \tag{1–36}$$

obtained from (1–34) by replacing each derivative by a power of x equal to the order of that derivative. Then

$$k_1 = -\frac{R}{2L} + \sqrt{\left(\frac{R}{2L}\right)^2 - \frac{1}{LC}} \tag{1–37}$$

$$k_2 = -\frac{R}{2L} - \sqrt{\left(\frac{R}{2L}\right)^2 - \frac{1}{LC}} \tag{1–38}$$

The variation of i_T will depend on the nature of these roots. When the roots are real and unequal, i_T will decay exponentially. When the unequal roots are complex, i_T will oscillate as it falls off exponentially. When $k_1 = k_2$, the exponential decay of i_T will be modified by a factor t.*

Our present purpose, however, is not to study RLC circuit response in detail but rather to review the broad outline of the classical method of solution. We turn, therefore, to a means of finding i_s.

The fact that sin ωt appears on the left side of (1–33) suggests that we try the form

$$i_s = a \cos \omega t + b \sin \omega t \tag{1–39}$$

This function i_s will be a solution of (1–33) provided that a and b can be so determined that i_s reduces (1–33) to an identity in t. Substituting the expression for i_s into (1–33), we obtain

$$\begin{aligned} -\omega e_{\max} \sin \omega t = & -\omega^2 La \cos \omega t - \omega^2 Lb \sin \omega t \\ & -\omega Ra \sin \omega t + \omega Rb \cos \omega t \\ & + \frac{1}{C} a \cos \omega t + \frac{1}{C} b \sin \omega t \end{aligned} \tag{1–40}$$

In order that this equation be valid for all values of time, we must equate the coefficients of cos ωt on both sides of the equation and also the coefficients of sin ωt. (The coefficient of cos ωt on the left side of 1–40 is zero.) We therefore obtain two equations determining a and b:

$$e_{\max} = Ra + \left(\omega L - \frac{1}{\omega C}\right) b \tag{1–41}$$

and

$$0 = \left(\omega L - \frac{1}{\omega C}\right) a - Rb \tag{1–42}$$

Solving for a and b, we find

$$a = \frac{e_{\max} R}{|Z|^2} \tag{1–43}$$

* The case $k_1 = k_2$ is generally obtained independently.(4) If we seek to find it as a limit of the more general solution, allowing $(k_1 - k_2)$ to approach zero, we must *first* evaluate the constants A and B as these will depend on k_1 and k_2.

and

$$b = \frac{e_{\max}\left(\omega L - \dfrac{1}{\omega C}\right)}{|Z|^2} \tag{1-44}$$

where

$$|Z|^2 = R^2 + [\omega L - (1/\omega C)]^2.$$

Now defining the angle ϕ by $\cos\phi = R/|Z|$ and

$$\sin\phi = [\omega L - (1/\omega C)]/|Z|,$$

we find

$$i_s = \frac{e_{\max}}{|Z|}\cos(\omega t - \phi) \tag{1-45}$$

Hence the current in the circuit of Fig. 1–1 is

$$i = \frac{e_{\max}}{|Z|}\cos(\omega t - \phi) + Ae^{k_1 t} + Be^{k_2 t} \tag{1-46}$$

where

$$|Z| = \sqrt{R^2 + [\omega L - (1/\omega C)]^2}$$

and

$$\phi = \tan^{-1}[\omega L - (1/\omega C)]/R.$$

The quantity $|Z|$ and the angle ϕ are, of course, the magnitude and angle of the complex impedance Z of alternating-current circuit analysis (equation 1–52).

The constants A and B will now be determined for the case in which the capacitance was uncharged prior to switching. The available data are that the current in the inductance and the voltage across the capacitance are both zero before switching. A sudden current change in the inductance would result in instantaneously infinite voltage across the inductance, contradicting Kirchhoff's voltage law for the loop. A sudden change in voltage across the capacitance would result in instantaneously infinite current, contradicting Kirchhoff's current law at the junction of the capacitance and the adjoining series element. Hence we have continuity of inductive current and capacitive voltage, whence

$$i_0 = 0 \tag{1-47}$$

and

$$v_{C0} = 0 \tag{1-48}$$

Further, applying Kirchhoff's law to the circuit at this instant, we find that

$$e_{\max} = L\frac{di}{dt}\bigg|_{t=0}$$

(This is equation 1–32 at $t = 0$.) Hence the constants A and B are determined by the conditions

$$i_0 = 0 \tag{1–47}$$

$$\frac{di}{dt}\bigg|_{t=0} = \frac{e_{\max}}{L} \tag{1–49}$$

Applying (1–47) and (1–49) to (1–46), we find

$$A = \frac{-\dfrac{k_2}{|Z|}\cos\phi - \dfrac{1}{L} + \dfrac{\omega}{|Z|}\sin\phi}{k_2 - k_1}e_{\max} \tag{1–50}$$

$$B = \frac{\dfrac{k_1}{|Z|}\cos\phi + \dfrac{1}{L} - \dfrac{\omega}{|Z|}\sin\phi}{k_2 - k_1}e_{\max} \tag{1–51}$$

Equations (1–50) and (1–51), together with (1–46) and the values of k_1 and k_2 in (1–37) and (1–38) complete the solution. When one considers that the circuit of Fig. 1–1 contains but one loop, the desirability of briefer methods of attack becomes very evident.

The Steady-State Solution by Alternating-Current Circuit Calculation

We shall now obtain the steady-state solution to the previous problem by the method normally used in alternating-current circuit analysis. This method, familiar to the reader, is presented as the first step toward the simplification of the solution of circuit problems.

The impedance of the circuit in Fig. 1–1 is the complex number

$$Z = R + j\left(\omega L - \frac{1}{\omega C}\right) \tag{1–52}$$

In terms of the complex applied voltage, the complex current is

$$I = \frac{E}{Z} \tag{1–53}$$

whence

$$|I| = \frac{|E|}{|Z|} \tag{1-54}$$

and

$$\underline{/I} = \underline{/E} - \underline{/Z} \tag{1-55}$$

Now if the applied voltage is taken as phase reference, the instantaneous expression for the steady-state current is directly obtained as

$$i = e_{\max} \cos(\omega t - \phi) \tag{1-56}$$

where

$$\phi = \underline{/Z} = \tan^{-1} \frac{\omega L - \dfrac{1}{\omega C}}{R}$$

and

$$e_{\max} = \sqrt{2}|E|$$

The method of alternating-current circuit analysis has many attractive aspects. It leads to an answer in a simple, direct manner. Once the method of complex algebra and the impedance concept have been established, the circuit differential equations need hardly be considered. The instantaneous expression for the steady-state response is taken directly from the complex-number solution. We shall find that the formal procedures of this method may be extended so as to apply to transient as well as to steady-state problems.

1-8 The Operational Method

The Heaviside operational calculus extends the impedance concept to problems of transient analysis. In addition it reduces the circuit differential equations to algebraic ones. On the other hand, it is of limited applicability, and its justification is difficult. For these reasons, we shall merely survey the Heaviside method as an important step in the development of more modern methods.* The student, therefore, whose sole interest is to gain familiarity with the most efficient means of problem solving, may omit the sections on the Heaviside calculus proper. The sections introductory to these—on indicial response and the superposition integral—are important in themselves, however.

* A complete exposition of the Heaviside method is given by Weber[20].

The significance of the Heaviside method for the development in this text lies in its historical importance, in that it demonstrated the possibility of replacing circuit differential equations by algebraic equations similar to those of a-c analysis. As will be seen in succeeding chapters, this end and more are attained through the development and application of the Laplace transformation.

Indicial Response

Heaviside's operational calculus deals chiefly with the response of circuits to suddenly applied direct voltage. A circuit in which each current in an inductance and each voltage across a capacitance are initially zero is termed a circuit *initially at rest.* When a unit direct voltage is applied at $t = 0$ (i.e., when a *unit-step voltage* is applied) to a circuit initially at rest, the current as a function of time, $A(t)$, is termed the *indicial response.*[12] (*Indicial admittance* was an earlier term for the response $A(t)$[3].) Clearly $A(t)$ is zero for all negative values of t, since effect cannot precede cause. If a unit direct voltage be applied at, say, $t = T$, the response is $A(t-T)$ where $A(t-T)$ is zero when the argument $(t-T)$ is negative.

Superposition Integral

The importance of the Heaviside calculus is enhanced by a theorem of basic significance in circuit theory. The superposition integral theorem (equation 1–58) demonstrates that when the circuit response to a suddenly applied direct voltage is known, the response to other applied voltage can be obtained. We shall derive this theorem for a circuit initially at rest.

Let t be the value of time at which we seek the current $i(t)$. Define the variable, τ, as time during the interval $0 < \tau < t$. Let the voltage during this interval be given by the continuous function $e(\tau)$ with continuous first derivative $e'(\tau)$. A discontinuity at zero time may be assumed, i.e., $e(0)$ need not be zero, although $e = 0$ for all negative values of time. As an approximation, this voltage is regarded as a succession of steps applied at equal intervals $\Delta\tau$ apart (see Fig. 1–7). The step voltage applied at $\tau = 0$ produces a current whose value at the later instant t is $e(0)A(t)$. The step voltage $\Delta_k e$ applied at the time $\tau = \tau_k$ produces a current whose value at the instant t is $\Delta_k e\, A(t-\tau_k)$. Now

$$\Delta_k e = e(\tau_k) - e(\tau_{k-1}) = e'(\tau_{k-1})\Delta\tau$$

provided that the intervals $\Delta\tau$ are small. The total current at the instant

t is then

$$i(t) = e(0)A(t) + \sum_{k=1}^{n} e'(\tau_{k-1})A(t-\tau_k)\Delta\tau \tag{1-57}$$

As the intervals $\Delta\tau$ approach zero (and their number becomes infinite), $e'(\tau_{k-1})$ approaches $e'(\tau_k)$, and we have the *superposition integral theorem*:

$$i(t) = e(0)A(t) + \int_0^t e'(\tau)A(t-\tau)\,d\tau \tag{1-58}$$

Several other forms of the superposition integral theorem can be derived.[1,3] The form (1–58) has been derived under the assumption

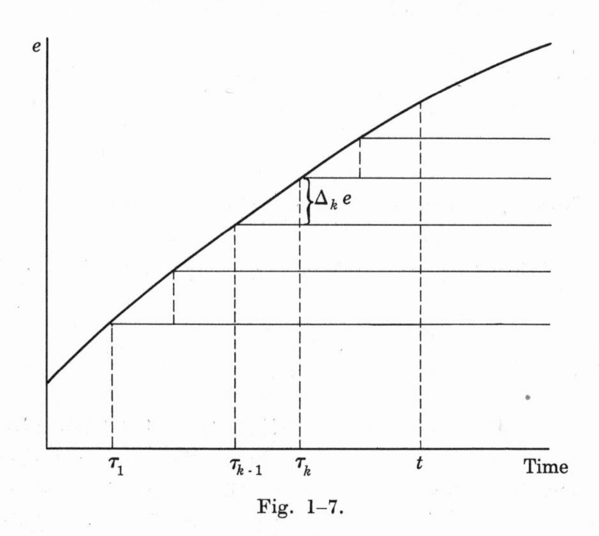

Fig. 1–7.

that e and its first derivative are continuous. When discontinuities occur, we divide the interval into ranges in each of which e and e' are continuous. Each discontinuity in e will then require an additional term in (1–58), so that the resultant contribution to the current will be included.[7] The term $e(0)A(t)$ is, in fact, an illustration of such a term. Bush[1] further modifies the theorem to take into account the effect of impulse currents when e appears across capacitance with resistanceless leads.

In order to illustrate the superposition integral theorem, let us apply the voltage in Fig. 1–8 to the RL circuit of Fig. 1–9. This voltage has a discontinuity at T_2 and its derivative is discontinuous at T_1. Analytically the applied voltage is given by the following four equations:

$$e(\tau) = 0 \qquad \tau < 0 \tag{1-59}$$

$$e(\tau) = \frac{V}{T_1}\tau \qquad 0 < \tau < T_1 \tag{1-60}$$

$$e(\tau) = V \qquad T_1 < \tau < T_2 \tag{1-61}$$

and

$$e(\tau) = 0 \qquad T_2 < \tau < t \tag{1-62}$$

where t is a fixed value of time (greater than T_2) at which we seek the current $i(t)$.

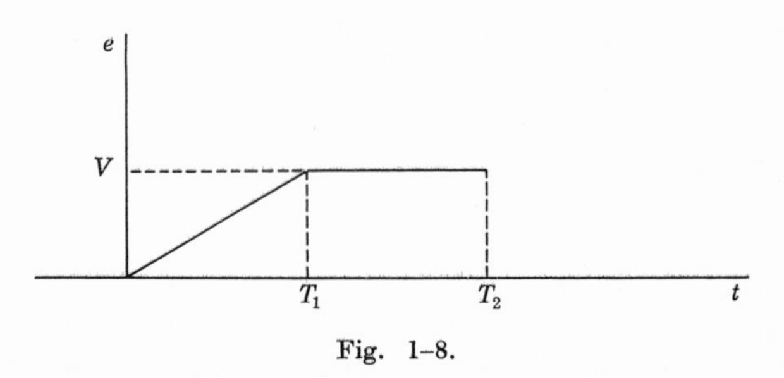

Fig. 1–8.

In view of the discontinuities, (1–58) takes the form

$$i(t) = e(0)A(t) + \int_0^{T_1} e'(\tau)A(t-\tau)\,d\tau + \int_{T_1}^{T_2} e'(\tau)A(t-\tau)\,d\tau$$

$$+(-V)A(t-T_2) + \int_{T_2}^{t} e'(\tau)A(t-\tau)\,d\tau \tag{1-63}$$

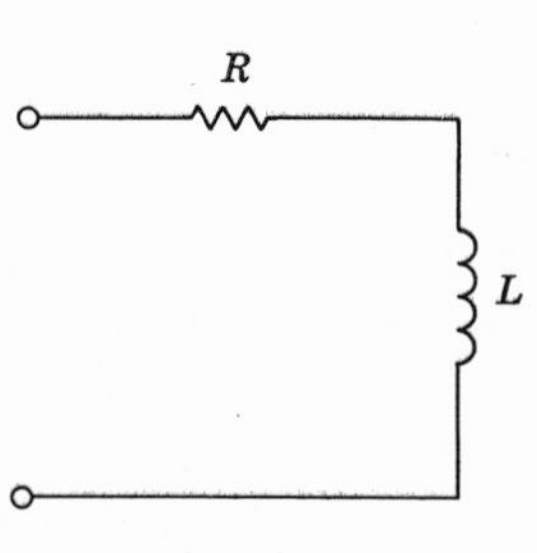

Fig. 1-9.

Equation (1–63) simplifies at once, since $e(0) = 0$, and $e'(\tau) = 0$ both in the range $T_1 < \tau < T_2$ and in the range $T_2 < \tau < t$. In the range $0 < \tau < T_1$, $e'(\tau) = V/T_1$. Now the RL circuit with unit direct voltage applied at $t = 0$ is easily solved by the classical method, so that

$$A(t) = (1/R)(1 - e^{-(R/L)t})$$

Hence equation (1–63) becomes

$$i(t) = \int_0^{T_1} \frac{V}{T_1 R}[1 - e^{-(R/L)(t-\tau)}]\,d\tau - V\frac{1}{R}[1 - e^{-(R/L)(t-T_2)}] \tag{1-64}$$

where $t > T_2$.

In carrying out the integration it is important to bear in mind that t is a constant and τ the variable. We find, then, that with $t > T_2$,

$$i(t) = \frac{V}{R}\left[1 - \frac{L}{T_1 R}(e^{-(R/L)(t-T_1)} - e^{-(R/L)t})\right] - \frac{V}{R}(1 - e^{-(R/L)(t-T_2)}) \tag{1-65}$$

Clearly, the constant terms V/R cancel, so that the current falls toward zero for large t.

Now if we seek $i(t)$ at an instant t in the range $T_1 < t < T_2$, we recall that $A(t-T_2) = 0$ when $t < T_2$, and find

$$i(t) = \frac{V}{R}\left[1 - \frac{L}{T_1 R}(e^{-(R/L)(t-T_1)} - e^{-(R/L)t})\right] \tag{1-66}$$

with $T_1 < t < T_2$.

If we seek the current $i(t)$ at an instant in the range of time $0 < t < T_1$, $A(t-T_2)$ is again zero and the first integral in (1-63) and the integral in (1-64) must have t rather than T_1 as upper limit. (The second integral of equation (1-63) happens to be zero in this problem since $e'(\tau) = 0$ during the interval $T_1 < \tau < T_2$; however, it should be borne in mind that, even if $e'(\tau)$ had a value during this interval, the second integral would still be eliminated for $t < T_1$, since $A(t-\tau) = 0$ when $\tau > T_1 > t$.) We therefore find

$$i(t) = \frac{V}{R}\left[\frac{t}{T_1} - \frac{L}{T_1 R}(1 - e^{-(R/L)t})\right] \tag{1-67}$$

with $0 < t < T_1$.

Carson's Integral Theorem

Carson's integral theorem offers a means of testing certain of the rules of Heaviside's operational calculus. The derivation of the integral theorem involves a study of the solution of the circuit equations with e^{pt} as driving function and all initial values equal to zero. The factor p in the exponent is real and positive or, more generally, complex with positive real part.* From our review of the classical method it is evident that the solution of the circuit equations consists of two terms. One

* In later chapters, the letter s is used to represent a complex variable. Here, the letter p is used to facilitate comparison with Heaviside notation. In general if $p = \alpha + j\omega$, the real numbers α and ω, designated respectively as $\mathscr{Re}\, p$ and $\mathscr{Im}\, p$, are called the *real* and *imaginary parts* of p; see *International Dictionary of Mathematics* (Reference 20 of Chapter 7). The term *component* may be used in place of *part*; *imaginary component* is preferred by some authors to *imaginary part* for the coefficient of j; see Churchill (Reference 2 of Chapter 3).

term is the solution when the driving function is replaced by zero (compare i_T in Section 1–7). The other term of the solution is proportional to $1/Z(p)$ where $Z(p)$ is identical in form with the impedance used in sinusoidal steady-state analysis—the letter p replacing $j\omega$. In order to see how this comes about, we shall consider a single loop, initially at rest, containing inductance, resistance, and capacitance in series. The loop voltage equation is

$$e^{pt} = L\frac{di}{dt} + Ri + \frac{1}{C}\int_0^t i\,d\tau \qquad (1\text{–}68)^*$$

Differentiating once in order to have an equation free of the integral, we find

$$pe^{pt} = L\frac{d^2i}{dt^2} + R\frac{di}{dt} + \frac{1}{C}i \qquad (1\text{–}69)$$

The function Ke^{pt} is a solution of (1–69), provided that the constant K equals $1/Z(p)$ with

$$Z(p) = Lp+R+\frac{1}{Cp} \qquad (1\text{–}70)$$

That $i = [1/Z(p)]e^{pt}$ is a solution of (1–69) is easily verified by substitution. Carson(3) in his general development obtains the form $(1/Z)e^{pt}$ starting with a circuit consisting of n loops, with the driving function e^{pt} used as e.m.f. applied in one loop.

The general solution of (1–68) or (1–69) is, then,

$$i = \frac{1}{Z(p)}e^{pt}+i_T(t) \qquad (1\text{–}71)$$

where $i_T(t)$ is the solution of the equation obtained upon replacing pe^{pt} in (1–69) by zero. In a passive dissipative circuit, $i_T(t)$ will approach zero as time increases without limit. (We assume no purely reactive path.)

The solution for the current, $i(t)$, can also be obtained from the superposition integral theorem. This theorem can be expressed in several forms in addition to the form (1–58) (see Bush(1) and Carson(3)). One of these forms is

$$i(t) = \frac{d}{dt}\int_0^t e(t-\tau)A(\tau)\,d\tau \qquad (1\text{–}72)$$

$A(t)$ or $A(\tau)$ is the current response to a unit – step voltage, i.e., the indicial

* The dimensionless number e^{pt} is assumed to be multiplied by 1 volt in this equation and in the remainder of the derivation.

response. Here the derivative of the integral is *not* the integrand, since t appears in the integrand as well as in the limit. However, upon substituting the specific form $e^{p(t-\tau)}$ for $e(t-\tau)$, and realizing that t is a constant during the integration, we find

$$i(t) = \frac{d}{dt}\left[e^{pt}\int_0^t e^{-p\tau}A(\tau)\,d\tau\right] \tag{1–73}$$

in which the integrand does not contain t. Hence differentiating the product of e^{pt} and the integral yields

$$i(t) = \left[pe^{pt}\int_0^t e^{-p\tau}A(\tau)\,d\tau\right] + e^{pt}A(t)e^{-pt} \tag{1–74}$$

Equating this expression for $i(t)$ with that in (1–71) yields

$$\frac{1}{Z(p)}e^{pt} + i_T(t) = pe^{pt}\int_0^t e^{-p\tau}A(\tau)\,d\tau + A(t) \tag{1–75}$$

Multiplying both sides of (1–75) by e^{-pt} and then letting t increase without limit, we find

$$\frac{1}{Z(p)} = p\int_0^\infty e^{-p\tau}A(\tau)\,d\tau \tag{1–76}$$

Let us accept equation (1–71) as the form of solution for Carson's case of a circuit consisting of n loops. We obtain (1–76) provided that we assume (certainly correctly for passive circuits) that $i_T(t)e^{-pt}$ and $A(t)e^{-pt}$ each vanish when t increases without limit. The integral in (1–76) will have the same value regardless of the particular letter used for variable of integration, so that Carson's integral theorem is written

$$\frac{1}{p}\,\frac{1}{Z(p)} = \int_0^\infty e^{-pt}A(t)\,dt \tag{1–77}$$

Carson's integral theorem relates the indicial admittance to the circuit impedance $Z(p)$. If two functions $A(t)$ satisfy (1–77) for a given $Z(p)$, the two functions $A(t)$ can differ only at isolated points (see Lerch's theorem[(2)]).

Clearly it will be extremely difficult to find $A(t)$ from Carson's integral equation, for to find an integrand, given the integral, is not a simple task. However, if an $A(t)$ can be arrived at by any method (even guesswork or intuition), its validity can be checked by substitution into Carson's integral theorem. One such use of Carson's integral theorem has been in connection with the Heaviside operational calculus.

*Heaviside's Operational Methods**

Let us consider the RL circuit of Fig. 1–9 and the RC circuit of Fig. 1–10. If we use (following Heaviside) the symbol $\mathit{1}$ to represent a unit direct voltage applied at the instant $t = 0$, or unit-step voltage, the differential-integral equations for the current in these circuits are

$$\mathit{1} = L\frac{di}{dt} + Ri \tag{1–78}$$

and

$$\mathit{1} = Ri + \frac{1}{C}\int_0^t i\,d\tau \tag{1–79}$$

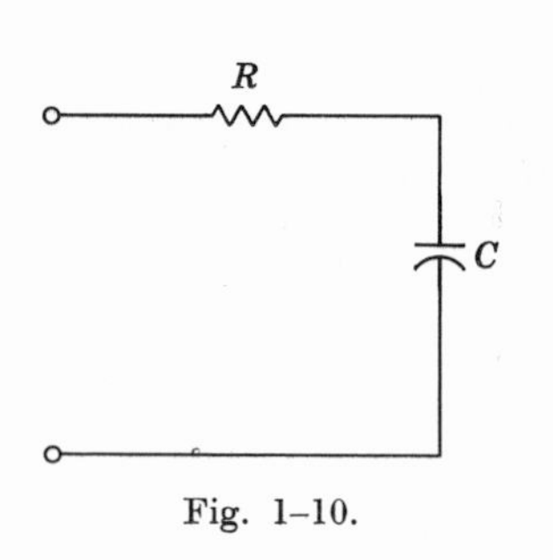

Fig. 1–10.

In each case we assume the circuit initially at rest. We now introduce the notation p for (d/dt) and $1/p$ for

$$\int_0^t [\quad]\,d\tau$$

Zero is taken as the lower limit of integration, since the circuits are initially at rest. With this notation our equations take the form

$$\mathit{1} = Lpi + Ri \tag{1–80}$$

and

$$\mathit{1} = Ri + \frac{1}{Cp}i \tag{1–81}$$

Now, in each case we solve for i *as if* p were an algebraic quantity. This yields

$$i = \frac{\mathit{1}}{L[p + (R/L)]} \tag{1–82}$$

$$i = \frac{p\mathit{1}}{R[p + (1/RC)]} \tag{1–83}$$

Equations (1–82) and (1–83) are termed the *operational forms* of the respective solutions. One wonders, at this point, whether a result so obtained can have any meaning. However, each operational form is obtained from a differential equation by a step-by-step procedure following

* We consider here only non-impulsive response and circuits initially at rest.

the unambiguous rules of algebra. Hence to each differential equation there corresponds a certain operational form.* Since to each differential equation there is also a time-function as solution,* we anticipate that there must be a correspondence between time-functions and operational forms. The Heaviside calculus consists of the rules for obtaining these correspondences. In simple cases the correspondence is known. For example, the solutions to (1–78) and (1–79) are easily determined by the classical method as

$$i = \frac{1}{R}(1 - e^{-(R/L)t}) \tag{1–84}$$

and

$$i = \frac{1}{R}e^{-(t/RC)} \tag{1–85}$$

Hence we have the correspondence of two operational forms to time-functions, namely

$$\frac{1}{L[p+(R/L)]}1 \to \frac{1}{R}(1 - e^{-(R/L)t}) \tag{1–86}$$

and

$$\frac{p}{R[p+(1/RC)]}1 \to \frac{1}{R}e^{-(t/RC)} \tag{1–87}$$

The arrow, representing correspondence, means that the operational form on the left represents the differential equation whose solution appears on the right. This representation will be useful, however, only if we find a means of obtaining a time-function from an operational form without separately solving the differential equation.

With this in view, two facts are observed: First, the operational forms (1–86 and 87) are identical with the a-c circuit impedance, provided that p is written in place of $j\omega$. Since the right-hand side of each of these equations is the indicial admittance, (1–86) and (1–87) illustrate the general relationship

$$\frac{1}{Z(p)}1 \to A(t) \tag{1–88}$$

Secondly, $Z(p)$ in Carson's integral theorem is also the a-c circuit impedance with p in place of $j\omega$. Now the definition of p in the Carson integral theorem differs from its definition in the Heaviside calculus. In the integral theorem, p is a number, either real and positive or complex

* See footnote, page 36.

with positive real part. In the Heaviside calculus, p is an operator or symbol, treated as if it were an algebraic quantity. However, equation (1–88) and the integral theorem represent the same relationship, namely, that between the impedance expression $Z(p)$ and the indicial admittance $A(t)$. One might, therefore, think of (1–88) as a shorthand notation for the Carson integral theorem. Now $Z(p)$ in the Carson integral theorem is subject to the ordinary rules of algebra. Since $Z(p)$ in (1–88) is formally identical with $Z(p)$ in Carson's theorem, one surmises that $Z(p)$ in (1–88) will also be subject to ordinary algebraic rules. To surmise, of course, is not to prove, but with the integral theorem available one can test the validity of any conclusion obtained from (1–88), however arrived at.

As an illustration let us suppose that a certain $Z(p)$ can be expressed by the relationship

$$\frac{1}{Z(p)} = \frac{1}{Z_1(p)} + \frac{1}{Z_2(p)} \tag{1–89}$$

and let us say further that

$$\frac{1}{Z_1(p)}1 \rightarrow A_1(t) \tag{1–90}$$

$$\frac{1}{Z_2(p)}1 \rightarrow A_2(t) \tag{1–91}$$

are known results. It might be guessed then, that

$$\frac{1}{Z(p)}1 \rightarrow A_1(t) + A_2(t) \tag{1–92}$$

This guess, however, can easily be proven to be correct by use of (1–77); thus

$$\frac{1}{p}\,\frac{1}{Z_1(p)} = \int_0^\infty A_1(t)e^{-pt}\,dt \tag{1–93}$$

$$\frac{1}{p}\,\frac{1}{Z_2(p)} = \int_0^\infty A_2(t)e^{-pt}\,dt \tag{1–94}$$

Adding (1–93) and (1–94), we find

$$\frac{1}{p}\left(\frac{1}{Z_1(p)} + \frac{1}{Z_2(p)}\right) = \int_0^\infty [A_1(t) + A_2(t)]e^{-pt}\,dt \tag{1–95}$$

or

$$\frac{1}{p}\,\frac{1}{Z(p)} = \int_0^\infty [A_1(t) + A_2(t)]e^{-pt}\,dt \tag{1–96}$$

Hence, $A_1(t)+A_2(t)$ is the indicial admittance corresponding to the circuit whose impedance is $Z(p)$. This result was our guess in forming (1–92) and once demonstrated becomes an elementary theorem of the Heaviside calculus.

Another result easy to justify is the theorem

$$k\frac{1}{Z(p)}1 \rightarrow kA(t) \tag{1–97}$$

provided that

$$\frac{1}{Z(p)}1 \rightarrow A(t) \tag{1–98}$$

As an illustration of the Heaviside procedure, using these two theorems let us obtain the indicial admittance of the circuit of Fig. 1–1.

The differential equation follows from Kirchhoff's voltage law as

$$1 = L\frac{di}{dt} + Ri + \frac{1}{C}\int_0^t i\,d\tau \tag{1–99}$$

With the zero initial current in L, zero initial charge on C, and one volt applied e.m.f., the current i is the indicial admittance of the circuit. Replacing d/dt by p, and

$$\int_0^t [\quad]\,d\tau$$

by $1/p$ (keeping in mind that i is zero for $t < 0$), and solving as if p were an algebraic quantity, we find

$$i = \frac{1}{Lp+R+(1/Cp)}1 \tag{1–100}$$

The reader will note that $Lp+R+(1/Cp)$ is the circuit impedance $Z(p)$. Cognizant of the fact that the equals sign has little meaning here and that i is the indicial admittance usually written $A(t)$, we rewrite (1–100) as

$$\frac{p}{L[p^2+(R/L)p+(1/LC)]}1 \rightarrow A(t) \tag{1–101}$$

where the form of the fraction has also been altered. Now factoring the denominator on the left side of (1–101) in terms of its roots, k_1 and k_2, yields

$$\frac{p}{L(p-k_1)(p-k_2)}1 \rightarrow A(t) \tag{1–102}$$

The fraction on the left-hand side of (1–102) is of higher degree in the denominator than in the numerator. If $k_1 \neq k_2$, the following partial fraction expansion is possible

$$\frac{p}{L(p-k_1)(p-k_2)} = \frac{A}{p-k_1} + \frac{B}{p-k_2} \tag{1–103}$$

The equation (1–103) can then be expressed as

$$\frac{1}{L}p = (A+B)p - Ak_2 - Bk_1 \tag{1–104}$$

valid for all p (regarded as an algebraic quantity), provided that

$$A+B = \frac{1}{L} \tag{1–105}$$

$$-Ak_2 - Bk_1 = 0 \tag{1–106}$$

Solving for A and B, we find that (1–102) can be written

$$\left(\frac{k_1}{L(k_1-k_2)}\frac{1}{p-k_1} + \frac{k_2}{L(k_2-k_1)}\frac{1}{p-k_2}\right)1 \rightarrow A(t) \tag{1–107}$$

Now consider the operational form (1–86). From the theorem on multiplication by a constant (1–97, 98), it is evident that (1–86) can be written

$$\frac{1}{p+(R/L)}1 \rightarrow \frac{1}{R/L}(1-e^{-(R/L)t}) \tag{1–108}$$

Since R/L might be any constant a, (1–108) can be given the general form

$$\frac{1}{p+a}1 \rightarrow \frac{1}{a}(1-e^{-at}) \tag{1–109}$$

The ratio of circuit constants (R/L) is real, but (1–109) might have been obtained from a differential equation with more general constants yielding a complex a. Hence whether k_1 and k_2 be real or complex, the time-function corresponding to each term on the left side of (1–107) is found by comparison with (1–109). We try adding these time-functions as in (1–96), although (1–96) was based on Carson's theorem derived for real indicial response of a physical circuit. We then find

$$A(t) = \frac{k_1}{L(k_1-k_2)}\frac{1}{(-k_1)}(1-e^{k_1t}) + \frac{k_2}{L(k_2-k_1)}\frac{1}{(-k_2)}(1-e^{k_2t}) \tag{1–110}$$

This expression simplifies at once to

$$A(t) = \frac{1}{L(k_2 - k_1)}(e^{k_2 t} - e^{k_1 t}) \tag{1–111}$$

Clearly $A(0) = 0$, in agreement with the fact that initially $i = 0$. The initial voltage across the inductance, $L(dA/dt)|_{t=0}$, is equal to 1, as it must be, since there is no current in R and no charge on the capacitor at this instant. Since the real parts of k_1 and k_2 are each negative, $A(t)$ will subside to zero at $t = \infty$. If k_1 and k_2 are complex, oscillation occurs with exponential decay. If k_1 and k_2 are real, we have exponential decay without oscillation.* These solutions will be considered carefully in Section 5–5.

In view of the mathematically dubious nature of some of the operational procedures, let us check the result in the Carson integral theorem. We find

$$\int_0^\infty \frac{e^{k_2 t} - e^{k_1 t}}{L(k_2 - k_1)} e^{-pt}\,dt = \left[\frac{1}{L(k_2 - k_1)}\right]\left[\frac{e^{(k_2-p)t}}{k_2 - p} - \frac{e^{(k_1-p)t}}{k_1 - p}\right]\Bigg|_{t=0}^{t=\infty} \tag{1–112}$$

Now $\mathcal{Re}\, p > 0$, $\mathcal{Re}\, k_1 < 0$, and $\mathcal{Re}\, k_2 < 0$; therefore, both terms vanish at the upper limit. Hence

$$\int_0^\infty \frac{e^{k_2 t} - e^{k_1 t}}{L(k_2 - k_1)} e^{-pt}\,dt = \frac{1}{L}\,\frac{1}{(p - k_1)(p - k_2)} \tag{1–113}$$

Comparison of (1–113) and (1–102) shows that the right side of (1–113) equals $1/pZ(p)$, as it should.

Having found the response of an RLC circuit to a unit-step voltage, we can calculate the response to other applied voltage with the aid of the superposition integral theorem.

Further Discussion of the Heaviside Method

The preceding paragraphs have given an indication of the Heaviside procedure along with Carson's method for its justification. The effectiveness of the operational calculus is considerably enhanced by a number of rules or theorems, relating transformations of operational forms to corresponding transformations of the indicial admittance. The simplest

* Equation (1–103) is valid only when $k_1 \neq k_2$. The special case $k_1 = k_2$ may be arrived at independently, which would require additional operational forms, or it may be obtained as a limiting result from equation (1–111). In this connection compare with the footnote following equations (1–37) and (1–38) and note that in equation (1–111), the integration constant has already been evaluated.

of these operational theorems are the rules for addition and multiplication by a constant: these were essential in the preceding problem. The theorems of the Heaviside calculus need not be presented at this point, since equivalent theorems will be developed as properties of the Laplace transformation in Chapter 2. By way of illustration, however, let us state one of the theorems of the Heaviside calculus, namely:

If

$$\frac{1}{Z(p)}1 \rightarrow A(t) \tag{1–114}$$

then

$$\frac{1}{p}\frac{1}{Z(p)}1 \rightarrow \int_0^t A(\tau)\,d\tau \tag{1–115}$$

As a simple application of this theorem, write (1–87) in the form

$$\frac{p}{p+a}1 \rightarrow e^{-at} \tag{1–116}$$

Then the general relationship (1–115) leads to the conclusion

$$\frac{1}{p+a}1 \rightarrow \frac{1}{a}(1-e^{-at}) \tag{1–117}$$

The theorem (1–114, 115) makes it possible to derive the operational equation (1–117) from (1–116).

Theorems such as (1–115) have made possible the development of tables of operational forms and corresponding time-functions.(1) The partial-fraction technique of algebra proves useful in expressing new operational forms as sums of simpler ones listed in tables. Thus, tables and partial-fraction expansion become the means of attack on transient problems.

There are certain clear advantages as well as obvious weaknesses in the Heaviside method. The weakness is found in the difficult manner in which its procedures must be justified. Extension of the method to new situations is essentially one of guess or trial with later justification. The advantage of the method lies in the simplicity of its procedures when compared with those of classical mathematics. Through the introduction of the impedance concept, we deal with algebraic rather than differential equations. Since a correspondence of operational forms and indicial admittances is built up, the necessity of evaluating integration constants is eliminated. Thus as a means of *procedure*, the Heaviside calculus is a forward step from classical mathematics. As such a step, its main ideas have been reviewed.

1-9 Summary

This chapter first stated the circuit problem in extremely general terms as the problem of determining any voltage or current in any electric circuit, subject to an excitation varying in any way with time. Kirchhoff's voltage and current laws were stated, since these form the basis of all circuit analysis. The sign conventions and symbols to be used in conjunction with these laws were then formulated.

It was pointed out that in order to obtain specific circuit equations from Kirchhoff's laws, the voltage–current characteristics of individual circuit elements were required. At this point the scope of the text was limited to the subject of linear, lumped, finite circuits with constant parameters.

Sources of excitation were discussed, and the voltage–current laws of linear-circuit components were stated. The duality principle became evident here. With the information available for the formulation of circuit equations, the means of determining initial conditions were studied. These were required in order to have unique solutions to the circuit differential equations, i.e., to determine the values of the integration constants in the solution. Two cases were considered: the usual case in which current in inductance and voltage across capacitance are continuous, and the unusual case in which a discontinuity in one or both of these quantities occurs, resulting in an instantaneously infinite voltage or current.

When the formulation of the circuit differential equations and their corresponding initial conditions had been discussed, the question of method of solution was introduced. The terms *transient* and *steady state* were defined. The classical method of solution of linear differential equations with constant coefficients was reviewed with the aid of an example. Although the classical method could always be used, it was seen to be unwieldy. The relative ease of alternating-current calculation of the sinusoidal steady state was demonstrated in order to provide motivation for seeking a similar means of attack on the more general problem.

To this end, the Heaviside operational calculus was reviewed as an important contribution to the techniques of circuit analysis. As preliminaries to the consideration of Heaviside calculus, indicial response was defined, and the superposition integral theorem and Carson's integral theorem were presented. With the former theorem, the circuit responses to non-d-c excitation could be obtained from the indicial response. With the latter theorem, any expression for indicial response, however obtained, could be verified. The basic ideas of the Heaviside method for obtaining indicial response were then reviewed and illustrated with an example.

Cognizant of the power of Heaviside's method (as a means of obtaining answers), yet conscious of its weaknesses (from the viewpoint of mathematical rigor and generality), we shall turn to mathematically sounder methods of achieving similar techniques with wider applicability.

Problems

1-1. A section of a uniform transmission line, which is initially at rest, extends from a distance x to a distance $x+\Delta x$ from the input terminals of the

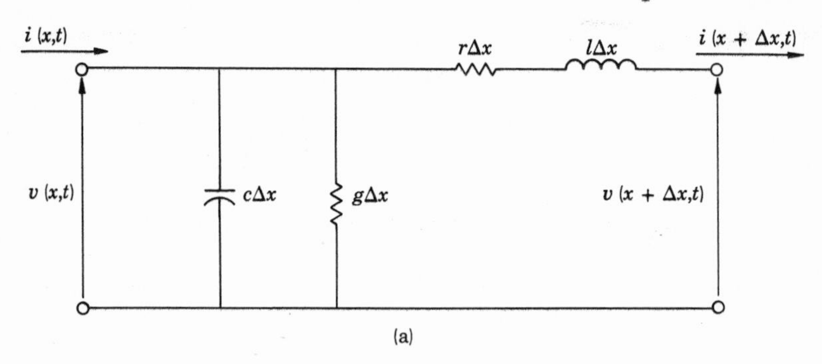

(a)

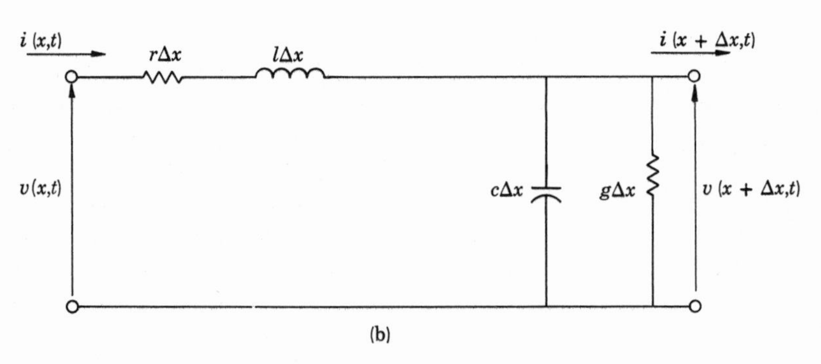

(b)

Problem 1-1.

line. This portion of the line is approximately represented by either of the circuits (a) or (b) in the figure.

(A) State the units and physical meaning of r, l, g, and c.

(B) Apply Kirchhoff's laws to circuit (a) and to circuit (b) in the figure.

(C) Permit Δx to approach zero and obtain the basic transmission line differential equations.

(D) State why the transmission line is not included in the class of linear, lumped, finite circuits with constant parameters.

(E) Which of the circuit characteristics listed in (D) are true for the transmission line?

1-2. A direct voltage E is applied to a series RL circuit at the instant $t = 0$. The circuit is initially at rest. The resistance R varies according to the equation $R = R_0 \sin \omega t + 2R_0$.

(A) Write the differential equation, valid for $t > 0$, for the current in this circuit.

(B) State why this circuit is not included in the class of linear, lumped, finite circuits with constant parameters.

(C) Which of the circuit characteristics listed in (B) are true for the circuit in this problem?

1-3. A direct voltage E is applied to a series RC circuit at the instant $t = 0$. The circuit is initially at rest. The resistance R is given by $R = R_0 + kR_0 i^p$.

(A) Write the integro-differential equation, valid for $t > 0$, for the current in this circuit.

(B) State why this circuit is not included in the class of linear, lumped, finite circuits with constant parameters.

(C) Which of the circuit characteristics listed in (B) are true for the circuit of this problem?

1-4. (A) Write the differential equations for i_1 and i_2 in the circuit (a) shown in the figure.

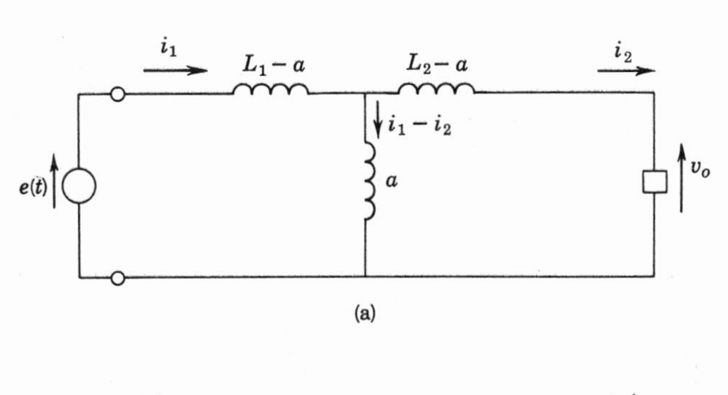

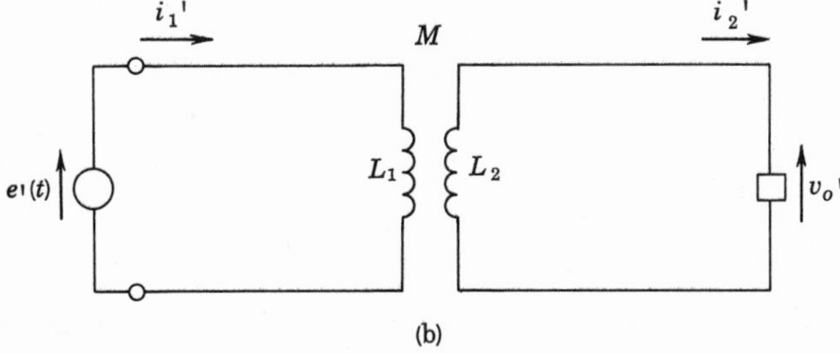

Problem 1–4.

(B) Write the differential equations for i_1' and i_2' in the circuit (b) in the figure. Do this for both possible winding senses.

(C) Now let $e'(t) = e(t)$ and find a value of the constant a for which the two circuits are equivalent.

(D) In this chapter we have defined *bilateral two-terminal circuit elements.* If it is known that a theorem is valid for any network of bilateral two-terminal elements, will such a theorem also hold when mutual inductance is present? Base your answer on part (C). (See reciprocity theorem of Chapter 6.)

(E) Answer part (D), assuming the presence of an ideal transformer in a network.

1-5. With the switch S open, a d-c steady state is established in the circuit shown in the figure. At the instant $t = 0$, S closes. Find the initial values of: (A) v_{R2}, (B) v_C, (C) v_L, (D) v_{R1}, (E) i_1, (F) i_2, (G) (di_1/dt).

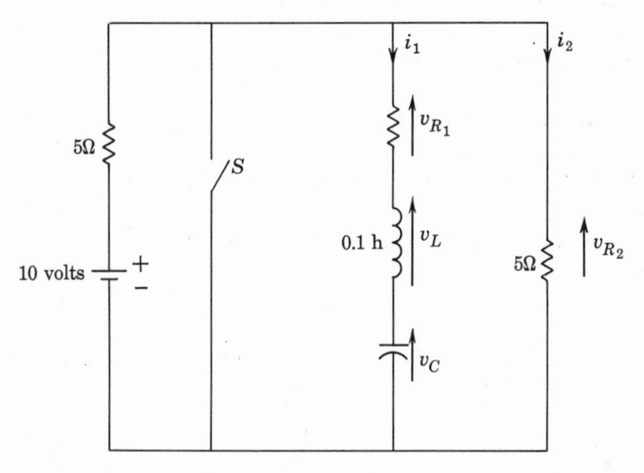

Problem 1–5.

1-6. The switches, S_1 and S_2 in the figure, have been closed for a sufficient

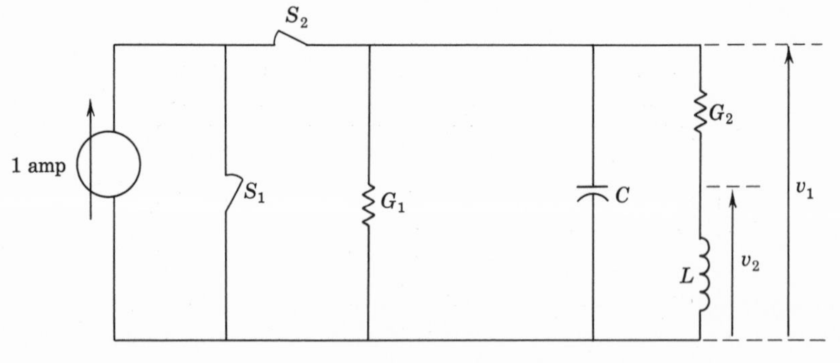

Problem 1–6.

time for a steady state to be established. The switch S_1 opens at $t = 0$. Obtain a differential equation valid for $t > 0$, with the potential v_1 as the only dependent variable. Express the initial values which will determine the constants in the solution.

1-7. The switch S_1, in the circuit of Problem 1–6, remains open until a steady state is established. At an instant $t' = 0$, S_1 closes and S_2 opens. Repeat Problem 1–6 for $t' > 0$. (Since the switches are assumed to be ideal, we assume that S_1 closes and S_2 opens instantaneously at $t' = 0$).

1-8. With the switch S open, the circuit in the figure is in a steady state. The current source supplies a direct current I. The switch closes at the instant $t = 0$. Evaluate:

(A) $v_{a1}(0-)$, $v_{a2}(0-)$, $i_3(0-)$, $v_b(0-)$.

(B) $v_{a1}(0+)$, $v_{a2}(0+)$, $i_3(0+)$, $v_b(0+)$. State all assumptions used.

(C) $i_{C1}(0+)$, $i_{C2}(0+)$. Should the instantaneously infinite currents enter these values?

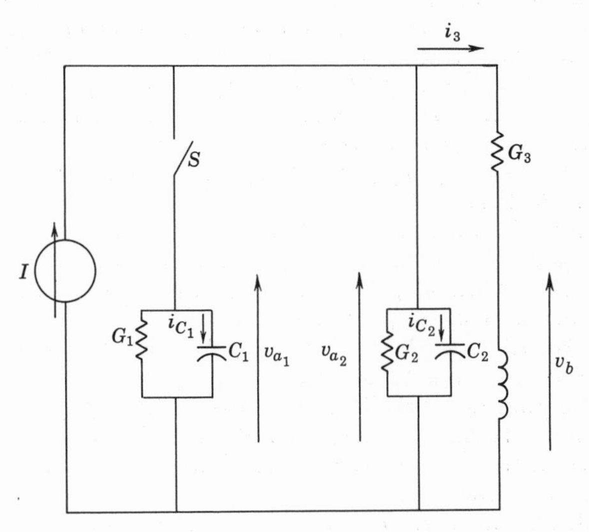

Problem 1–8.

1-9. A voltage v is applied to a series RC circuit initially at rest.

$$v = 0 \quad \text{when} \quad t < 0$$
$$v = 5\,(e^{1000t} - 1) \quad \text{when} \quad 0 < t < 10^{-3}$$
$$v = 0 \quad \text{when} \quad 10^{-3} < t$$

The product RC is 10^{-3} second.

(A) Find the indicial admittance of the circuit.

(B) Calculate $i(t)$ during the intervals $0 < t < 10^{-3}$ and $10^{-3} < t$ by means of the superposition integral.

1-10. Verify the solution to Problem 1–9(A) by means of the Carson integral theorem.

References for Chapter 1

1. Bush, V., *Operational Circuit Analysis*, John Wiley & Sons, Inc., New York, 1937.
2. Carslaw, H. S., and Jaeger, J. C., *Operational Methods in Applied Mathematics*, 2nd ed., Oxford University Press, London, 1949.
3. Carson, J. R., *Electric Circuit Theory and the Operational Calculus*, 1st ed., McGraw-Hill Book Co., Inc., New York, 1926; 2nd ed., Chelsea Publishing Co., New York, 1953.
4. Cohen, A., *An Elementary Treatise on Differential Equations*, D. C. Heath & Co., Boston, 1906; 2nd ed., 1933.
5. Crosby, D. R., "The Ideal Transformer," IRE *Trans. Circuit Theory*, Vol. CT-5, p. 145 (June, 1958).
6. Gardner, M. F., and Barnes, J. L., *Transients in Linear Systems Studied by the Laplace Transformation*, John Wiley & Sons, Inc., New York, 1942.
7. Goldman, S., *Transformation Calculus and Electrical Transients*, Prentice-Hall, Inc., New York, 1949.
8. Ince, E. L., *Integration of Ordinary Differential Equations*, Oliver and Boyd, Ltd., Edinburgh, 1939; 6th rev. ed., Interscience Publishers, Inc., New York, 1956, reprinted 1959.
9. Ince, E. L., *Ordinary Differential Equations*, Dover Publications, Inc., New York, 1944; 4th ed., 1953.
10. Jaeger, J. C., *An Introduction to the Laplace Transformation with Engineering Applications*, Methuen and Co., Ltd., London, 1949.
11. Jaeger, J. C., "Switching Problems and Instantaneous Impulses," *Phil. Mag.*, Ser. 7, Vol. 36, pp. 644–651 (1945).
12. LePage, W. R., and Seely, S., *General Network Analysis*, McGraw-Hill Book Co., Inc., New York, 1952.
13. Members of the Staff of the Dept. of Electrical Engineering, Massachusetts Institute of Technology. *Applied Electronics*, John Wiley & Sons, Inc., New York, 1943; Gray, T. S., *Applied Electronics*, 2nd ed., John Wiley & Sons, Inc., New York, 1954.
14. Ryder, J. D., *Electronic Fundamentals and Applications*, Prentice-Hall, Inc., New York, 1950; 2nd ed., 1959.
15. Ryder, R. M., and Kircher, R. J., "Some Circuit Aspects of the Transistor," *Bell Telephone System Monograph* 1726, pp. 33–66 (1949).
16. Seely, S., *Electron-Tube Circuits*, McGraw-Hill Book Co., Inc., New York, 1950; 2nd ed., 1958.
17. Shea, R. F., Editor, *Principles of Transistor Circuits*, John Wiley & Sons, Inc., 1953; *Transistor Circuit Engineering*, John Wiley & Sons, Inc., New York, 1957.
18. Shockley, W., *Electrons and Holes in Semiconductors with Applications to Transistor Electronics*, D. Van Nostrand Co., Inc., New York, 1950.
19. Tuttle, D. F., Jr., *Network Synthesis*, Vol. I, John Wiley & Sons, Inc., New York, 1958.

20. Weber, E., *Linear Transient Analysis*. Vol. I. *Lumped Parameter Two-Terminal Networks*, John Wiley & Sons, Inc., New York, 1954.
21. American Standards Association, *American Standard Definitions of Electrical Terms, Group* 65 *Communication, ASA C42.65 1957*, American Institute of Electrical Engineers, New York, 1957.
22. Institute of Radio Engineers, "Standards on Circuits: Definitions of Terms in Network Topology, 1950," *Proc.* IRE, Vol. 39, pp. 27–29 (1951).

Chapter 2

FOURIER ANALYSIS AND THE LAPLACE TRANSFORMATION

We have seen in Chapter 1 that the electrical engineer desires a general method of circuit analysis having the simplicity of alternating-current circuit analysis. The impedance concept of a-c circuit analysis, with p replacing $j\omega$, appears in Heaviside's solutions. This reappearance of an impedance of the same form is, of course, not an accident, but results from the nature of the circuit differential equations. One seeks, then, a broadening of the a-c concept to include non-sinusoidal variations and finds the necessary mathematics developed by Fourier in the early 1800's prior to the existence of electrical engineering.

Through Fourier analysis it is possible to treat non-sinusoidal waves in terms of alternating-current concepts and ideas. The Fourier series yield steady-state solutions to problems involving repeating waves. More important, these series lead to the Fourier integral theorem, through which it is possible to apply alternating-current thinking to non-repetitive waves. With the Fourier integral theorem, the response of a circuit to single pulses of voltage can be studied in terms of the sinusoidal steady-state characteristics of the network. Finally the Fourier integral theorem leads to the Laplace transformation, which can be taken as a basis for general circuit analysis.

2-1 Fourier Series

The Fourier series gives the communications engineer a direct means of analyzing repeating voltages and currents in terms of procedures used for the sinusoidal steady state. This fact becomes immediately evident when the series is written. Let us suppose that $g(t)$ is a repeating function of time representable as a Fourier series. Then

$$g(t) = A_0 + A_1 \cos \omega_1 t + A_2 \cos 2\omega_1 t + \cdots \\ + B_1 \sin \omega_1 t + B_2 \sin 2\omega_1 t + \cdots \quad (2\text{–}1)$$

where the constant $\omega_1 = 2\pi/T$, and T is the period of the wave. Since (2–1) expresses $g(t)$ in terms of sines and cosines (the constant term A_0 may be thought of as $A_0 \cos 0\omega_1 t$), the Fourier series is clearly the key to the application of alternating-current analysis to non-sinusoidal voltages and currents.

Dirichlet's Conditions

The broad application of Fourier analysis to electric circuit problems stems from the fact that these methods apply to an extremely general class of functions. A function satisfies Dirichlet's conditions in the interval $t_1 \leqq t \leqq t_2$, provided that

(a) the number of maxima and minima of $g(t)$ is finite,
(b) the number of discontinuities of $g(t)$ is finite,
(c) at no point in the interval does $g(t)$ approach infinity.*

If the function $g(t)$ satisfies Dirichlet's conditions, its value is given by the Fourier series at any point in the interval $t_1 < t < t_2$ at which $g(t)$ is continuous. At a point of finite discontinuity the series converges to an average value. For example, a Fourier series for the function illustrated in Fig. 2–1 would yield $g(t) = 0$ at the point of discontinuity $t = 0$. Now if the function $g(t)$ is periodic, we may write the series for a range of time equal to one cycle, i.e., we select $t_2 - t_1 = T$, the period of the wave. Examination of the terms of equation (2–1) shows that the series must then duplicate its values over successive cycles of length T. Hence if

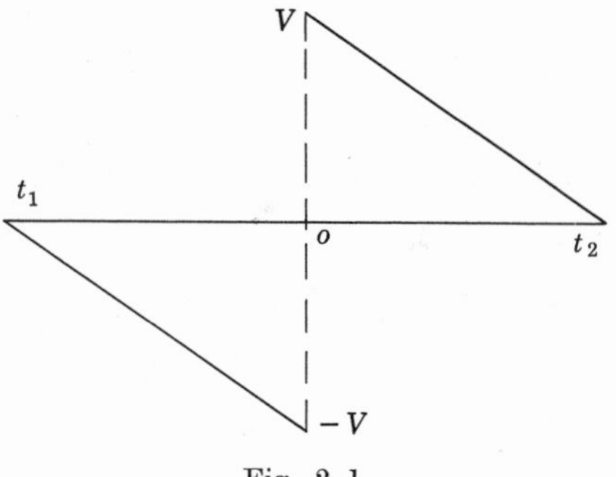

Fig. 2–1.

* Dirichlet's conditions can also be stated in a more general form omitting condition (c), but excluding points at which the function becomes infinite and requiring that

$$\int_{t_1}^{t_2} |g(t)|\, dt$$

be finite. See References 2, 11, and 20 in the list at the end of this chapter.

$g(t)$ is periodic and satisfies Dirichlet's conditions, it is represented for all time (i.e., $-\infty < t < \infty$) by a summation of sinusoidal terms, i.e., the Fourier series (2–1). If $g(t)$ is not periodic, the series can represent it only in a finite interval.

For our purpose, the chief conclusion to be drawn from Dirichlet's conditions is that repeating voltages and currents in communication circuits can always be represented by a Fourier series valid over the entire time range. Circuits will not, for example, have voltages or currents with an infinite number of discontinuities or an infinite number of maxima and minima in a finite interval of time. Voltages or currents in actual circuits do not rise toward infinity* at certain instants without consequences bringing them outside the field of linear circuit analysis. Square-wave and saw-tooth voltages are commonly used, but their discontinuities are finite in number during a cycle and their peak values are finite in height. Hence the Fourier series can be applied with confidence in communication circuit problems. In many cases we wish to represent an *unknown* repetitive current or voltage by a Fourier series and then determine the coefficients of the series. The assumption that this current or voltage can, indeed, be represented by the series is justified by the extremely general nature of the Dirichlet conditions.

Coefficients of the Fourier Series

The coefficients of the series may be found in simplest form if the change in variable $\theta = \omega_1 t$ is first introduced. The function $g(t)$ is then expressed as $f(\theta)$ with period 2π, and (2–1) becomes

$$\begin{aligned} f(\theta) = {} & A_0 + A_1 \cos\theta + A_2 \cos 2\theta + \cdots + A_n \cos n\theta + \cdots \\ & + B_1 \sin\theta + B_2 \sin 2\theta + \cdots + B_n \sin n\theta + \cdots \end{aligned} \tag{2–1a}$$

The expressions for the A's and B's are found after the following integrals are evaluated:

$$\int_{-\pi}^{\pi} f(\theta)\, d(\theta)$$

$$\int_{-\pi}^{\pi} f(\theta) \cos n\theta \, d\theta$$

* The limiting cases of an instantaneous change in the charge on a capacitance or current through an inductance, which lead respectively to infinite current to a capacitance and infinite voltage across an inductance, are considered elsewhere in this text, both in terms of classical solution of differential equations (Chapter 1, Section 1–5) and in terms of the Laplace transformation (Chapter 4).

and

$$\int_{-\pi}^{\pi} f(\theta)\sin n\theta\, d\theta$$

In each case the integral is evaluated by substituting the series (2–1a) for $f(\theta)$ and integrating term by term. The procedure is made easy by the fact that the integration yields zero for all but one term. This follows from the relationships

$$\int_{-\pi}^{\pi} \cos n\theta\, d\theta = \int_{-\pi}^{\pi} \sin n\theta\, d\theta = 0 \qquad \text{(2–2)}$$

$$\text{with} \quad n = 1, 2, \ldots$$

$$\int_{-\pi}^{\pi} \cos n\theta \cos m\theta\, d\theta = \int_{-}^{} \sin n\theta \sin m\theta\, d\theta = 0 \qquad \text{(2–2a)}$$

$$\text{when} \quad n = 1, 2, \ldots$$

$$\text{and} \quad m = 1, 2, \ldots$$

$$\text{provided } m \neq n$$

and

$$\int_{-\pi}^{\pi} \cos n\theta \sin m\theta\, d\theta = 0 \quad n = 1, 2, \ldots \quad m = 1, 2, \ldots \qquad \text{(2–2b)}$$

Carrying out the indicated integrations, with use of (2–2, 2a and 2b), leads to the result

$$A_0 = \frac{1}{2\pi}\int_{-\pi}^{\pi} f(\theta)\, d\theta \qquad \text{(2–3)}$$

$$A_n = \frac{1}{\pi}\int_{-\pi}^{\pi} f(\theta)\cos n\theta\, d\theta \quad n = 1, 2, \ldots \qquad \text{(2–3a)}$$

$$B_n = \frac{1}{\pi}\int_{-\pi}^{\pi} f(\theta)\sin n\theta\, d\theta \quad n = 1, 2, \ldots \qquad \text{(2–3b)}$$

The term A_0 is simply the average value of the function and is often referred to as the d-c component of the series. If the series represents a voltage or current, the term A_0 equals the reading on a direct-current instrument to which this voltage or current is applied. The physical significance of the coefficients A_n and B_n becomes more evident when we combine the nth cosine and sine terms into a single term. Writing the identity

$$A_n \cos n\theta + B_n \sin n\theta$$

$$= \sqrt{A_n{}^2 + B_n{}^2}\left(\frac{A_n}{\sqrt{A_n{}^2+B_n{}^2}} \cos n\theta + \frac{B_n}{\sqrt{A_n{}^2+B_n{}^2}} \sin n\theta\right) \tag{2-4}$$

and defining an angle ϕ_n as $\tan^{-1}(B_n/A_n)$ we find by comparison with the triangle in Fig. 2–2, that

$$A_n \cos n\theta + B_n \sin n\theta = \sqrt{A_n{}^2+B_n{}^2}(\cos\phi_n \cos n\theta + \sin\phi_n \sin n\theta) \tag{2-5}$$

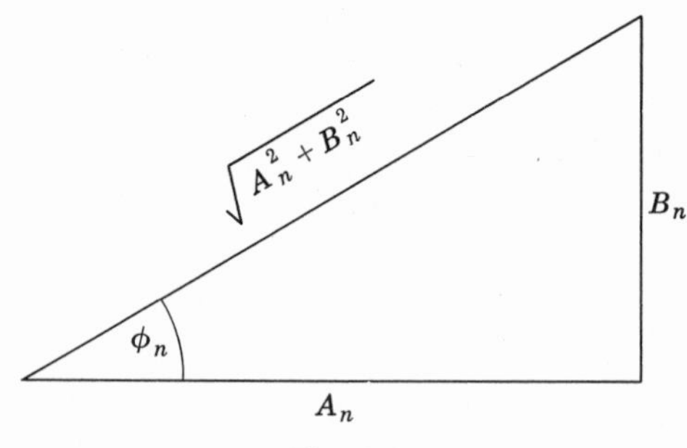

Fig. 2–2.

or more concisely

$$A_n \cos n\theta + B_n \sin n\theta = \sqrt{A_n{}^2+B_n{}^2} \cos(n\theta - \phi_n) \tag{2-6}$$

The expression (2–6) shows that the nth sine and cosine terms represent a single sinusoidal term of amplitude $\sqrt{A_n{}^2+B_n{}^2}$. The angle ϕ_n will differ for successive terms of the series. The series may now be expressed

$$f(\theta) = \gamma_0 + \gamma_1 \cos(\theta - \phi_1) + \gamma_2 \cos(2\theta - \phi_2) + \cdots + \gamma_n \cos(n\theta - \phi_n) + \cdots \tag{2-1b}$$

where

$$\gamma_n = \sqrt{A_n{}^2+B_n{}^2}, \quad \phi_n = \tan^{-1}(B_n/A_n),$$

A_n and B_n are obtained by (2–3a and 3b), and $\theta = \omega_1 t$ with $\omega_1 = 2\pi/T$.

Evaluation of the Coefficients when $f(\theta)$ is Even or Odd

An even function is one for which

$$f(\theta) = f(-\theta) \tag{2-7}$$

while for an odd function,

$$f(\theta) = -f(-\theta) \tag{2-8}$$

Examples of even and odd functions are illustrated in Figs. 2–3(a) and (b). In the case of the even function, replacement of θ by $-\theta$ leaves the value of the function unchanged. In the case of an odd function, we find the same magnitude but a reversal in sign on replacing $+\theta$ by $-\theta$. If a Fourier series represents $f(\theta)$ for all time, i.e. $-\infty < \theta < \infty$, we can select the origin $\theta = 0$ at will, since this point is an arbitrary reference. This fact leads to two very important special cases. We may be able to select the point $\theta = 0$ so that the wave to be represented by the series, $f(\theta)$, is an even function. Then $f(\theta) \cos n\theta$ is also even and

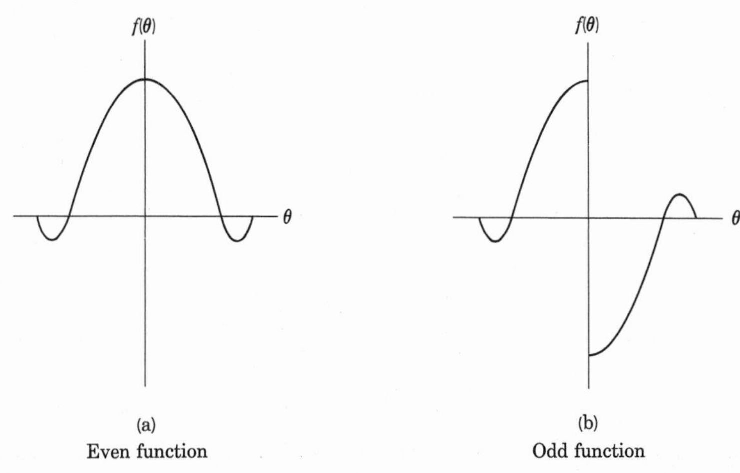

Fig. 2–3.

$f(\theta) \sin n\theta$ is odd. The integrals (2–3 and 3a) over a complete cycle now become twice their value over a half cycle, while the integral (2–3b) reduces to zero. Hence, if $f(\theta) = f(-\theta)$,

$$A_0 = \frac{1}{\pi} \int_0^{\pi} f(\theta)\, d\theta \tag{2-9}$$

$$A_n = \frac{2}{\pi} \int_0^{\pi} f(\theta) \cos n\theta\, d\theta, \quad n = 1, 2, \ldots \tag{2-9a}$$

and

$$B_n = 0 \quad n = 1, 2, \ldots \tag{2-9b}$$

The second case occurs when we can so select the origin $\theta = 0$ that $f(\theta)$

is an odd function. In this event $f(\theta)\cos n\theta$ is also odd, while $f(\theta)\sin n\theta$ is even. We then find,

$$\text{if}\quad f(\theta) = -f(-\theta)$$

$$A_n = 0 \quad n = 0, 1, 2, \ldots \tag{2–10}$$

$$B_n = \frac{2}{\pi}\int_0^{\pi} f(\theta)\sin n\theta\, d\theta \quad n = 1, 2, \ldots \tag{2–10a}$$

By way of illustration we shall apply these principles to a simple example. Consider the voltage illustrated in Fig. 2–4. The height of each pulse is V, the period of repetition in terms of time is T, and again

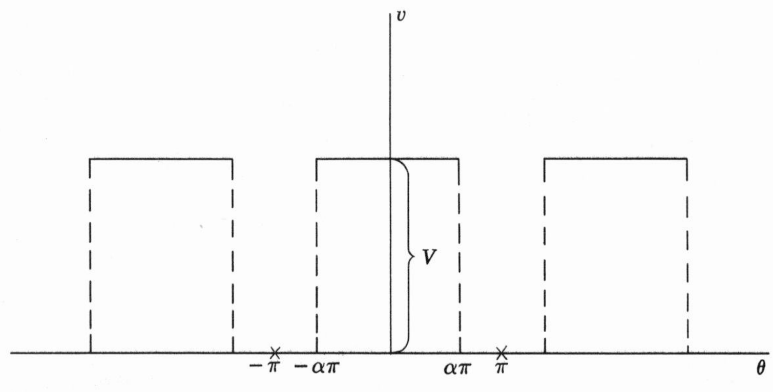

Fig. 2–4.

$\omega_1 = 2\pi/T$, and $\theta = \omega_1 t$. Analytically the voltage v may be described as a function of θ by

$$\left.\begin{aligned} v(\theta) &= 0 \quad \text{when} \quad -\pi < \theta < -\alpha\pi \\ v(\theta) &= V \quad \text{when} \quad -\alpha\pi < \theta < \alpha\pi \\ v(\theta) &= 0 \quad \text{when} \quad \alpha\pi < \theta < \pi \end{aligned}\right\} \tag{2–11}$$

and $0 < \alpha < 1$.

Now $v(\theta)$ is clearly an even function through the choice of the reference point $\theta = 0$, so that the coefficients of the series are evaluated by use of (2–9, 9a, 9b). A_0 is simply the average value of the function. Either by integration or inspection,

$$A_0 = \alpha V$$

Using (2–9a)

$$A_n = \frac{2}{\pi}\int_0^{\pi} v(\theta)\cos n\theta\, d\theta = \frac{2}{\pi}\int_0^{\alpha\pi} V\cos n\theta\, d\theta = \frac{2V}{n\pi}\sin n\alpha\pi$$

whence the series becomes

$$v(\theta) = V\left[\alpha + \sum_{n=1}^{\infty} \frac{2 \sin n\alpha\pi}{n\pi} \cos n\theta\right] \tag{2–12}$$

In the particular case $\alpha = \frac{1}{2}$, i.e., where each pulse length is half a cycle, only odd-numbered terms have non-zero coefficients and (2–12) reduces to

$$v(\theta) = \frac{2V}{\pi}\left[\frac{\pi}{4} + \cos\theta - \frac{1}{3}\cos 3\theta + \frac{1}{5}\cos 5\theta - \cdots\right] \tag{2–13}$$

Complex Form of the Fourier Series

The complex form of the Fourier series will have several advantages for our purpose. It expresses the series and its coefficients in an extremely compact manner, is convenient for further derivations, and, most important, can be used consistently with the complex impedance concept of alternating-current calculations. The following derivation will show it to be nothing more than another form of the series as stated in (2–1 or 1a).

With the exponential forms for $\cos n\theta$ and $\sin n\theta$, the nth term in the series becomes

$$A_n \cos n\theta + B_n \sin n\theta = \frac{A_n}{2}(e^{jn\theta} + e^{-jn\theta}) + \frac{B_n}{2j}(e^{jn\theta} - e^{-jn\theta}) \tag{2–14}$$

or

$$A_n \cos n\theta + B_n \sin n\theta = (A_n - jB_n)\tfrac{1}{2}e^{jn\theta} + (A_n + jB_n)\tfrac{1}{2}e^{-jn\theta} \tag{2–15}$$

Now substituting the expressions (2–3a) and (2–3b) for A_n and B_n, and using the relation $e^{jn\theta} = \cos n\theta + j \sin n\theta$, we find after a few steps that

$$\tfrac{1}{2}(A_n - jB_n) = \frac{1}{2\pi}\int_{-\pi}^{\pi} f(\theta)e^{-jn\theta}\, d\theta \tag{2–16}$$

and that

$$\tfrac{1}{2}(A_n + jB_n) = \frac{1}{2\pi}\int_{-\pi}^{\pi} f(\theta)e^{jn\theta}\, d\theta \tag{2–16a}$$

When (2–16) and (2–16a) are integrated, the limits π and $-\pi$ are substituted for θ, so that each integral is a function only of the parameter n or jn rather than θ. We therefore define

$$\alpha_n = \frac{1}{2\pi}\int_{-\pi}^{\pi} f(\theta)e^{-jn\theta}\, d\theta \tag{2–17}$$

whence

$$\alpha_{-n} = \frac{1}{2\pi} \int_{-\pi}^{\pi} f(\theta) e^{jn\theta} \, d\theta \tag{2–17a}$$

The definition of α_{-n} in (2–17a) is obtained by replacing n in (2–17) by $-n$. (One could, of course, define the integral (2–17) as α_{-n} and then call the integral in (2–17a) α_n, but this would not yield the standard *form* of the complex Fourier series.)

The general term in the Fourier series now becomes

$$A_n \cos n\theta + B_n \sin n\theta = \alpha_n e^{jn\theta} + \alpha_{-n} e^{-jn\theta} \tag{2–18}$$

Hence the complete series can be written as

$$f(\theta) = A_0 + \sum_{n=1}^{\infty} \alpha_n e^{jn\theta} + \sum_{n=1}^{\infty} \alpha_{-n} e^{-jn\theta} \tag{2–19}$$

No change is introduced in the second summation if n is replaced by $-n$ and the sum taken over negative values of n, i.e., $n = -1, -2, \ldots$. We also note that if n be given the value zero in (2–17), the expression for α_0 is precisely that given for A_0 in (2–3). Equation (2–19) for $f(\theta)$ can, therefore, be expressed compactly as

$$f(\theta) = \sum_{n=-\infty}^{\infty} \alpha_n e^{jn\theta} \tag{2–20}$$

with α_n defined in (2–17). The expression (2–20) is the *complex Fourier series.*

When using the complex Fourier series to represent a real function of time, it is important to know the mechanism by which pairs of terms combine to give real quantities. The definition of α_n (2–17) shows that α_{-n} must be its conjugate. This is evident from the fact that replacing n by $-n$, in (2–17), is equivalent to changing j to $-j$. Now let us consider two typical terms of the series, namely, $\alpha_n e^{jn\theta}$ and $\alpha_{-n} e^{-jn\theta}$. Each term involves j both in the exponential factor and in α, but wherever j occurs in the first term, $-j$ appears in the second. The term $\alpha_{-n} e^{-jn\theta}$ is then the conjugate of $\alpha_n e^{jn\theta}$ and we have at once

$$\alpha_n e^{jn\theta} + \alpha_{-n} e^{-jn\theta} = 2 \, \mathcal{R}e \; \alpha_n e^{jn\theta} \tag{2–21}$$

Now the real part of a complex number is most directly obtained as the product of its magnitude and the cosine of its angle, so that (2–21) becomes

$$\alpha_n e^{jn\theta} + \alpha_{-n} e^{-jn\theta} = 2|\alpha_n| \cos(n\theta + \phi_n) \tag{2–22}$$

where $\phi_n = \angle \alpha_n$, and the peak value of the wave is seen to be *twice the magnitude of* α_n.

2-2 The Superposition Principle

Perhaps the most important principle in the application of Fourier analysis to linear engineering problems is that of superposition. The electronics engineer, for example, dealing with non-sinusoidal but repetitive wave forms, treats these as a superposition of sinusoidal waves. Each pure sinusoid, obtained from the Fourier series of the original wave, is regarded as separately applied to the circuit of interest and the results are then superposed. We shall justify this principle in terms of an example, the nature of which will make clear the general applicability of the method.

Let us consider a typical electronic situation. The plate current of a tube is repetitive but non-sinusoidal and is applied to the parallel resonant circuit shown in Fig. 2-5, where the current i is the negative of the plate current. We seek the voltage across the capacitance, assuming the Fourier series for the current i to be known. The usual custom is to use the method of superposition. Our present purpose is to arrive at this principle through a more general approach to the problem. Hence we write the basic relations for the instantaneous voltage and current:

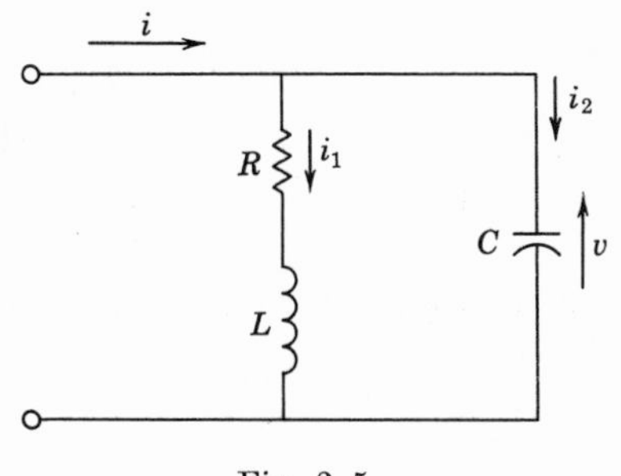

Fig. 2-5.

$$i_2 = C\frac{dv}{dt} \tag{2-23}$$

$$i_1 = i - i_2 \tag{2-24}$$

and

$$v = L\frac{di_1}{dt} + Ri_1 \tag{2-25}$$

Substituting (2-23) into (2-24) and the result, in turn, into (2-25), we obtain the differential equation relating instantaneous current i to the instantaneous voltage v across the tuned circuit, namely,

$$LC\frac{d^2v}{dt^2} + RC\frac{dv}{dt} + v = L\frac{di}{dt} + Ri \tag{2-26}$$

Now the repetitive current i is known and given by a Fourier series

$$i = \sum_{n=-\infty}^{\infty} \alpha_n e^{jn\omega_1 t} = \sum_{n=-\infty}^{\infty} \tfrac{1}{2} I_n e^{jn\omega_1 t} \tag{2-27}$$

where the magnitude of I_n is the peak value of the instantaneous current at frequency $n\omega_1/2\pi$ and the angle of I_n is ϕ_n which equals $\underline{/\alpha_n}$. The fact that the peak value is twice the magnitude of α_n was demonstrated in the preceding section.

Ignoring transient effects, we seek the steady-state voltage, which must repeat with the same period as the plate current. We assume, of course, that this voltage will satisfy Dirichlet's conditions. Hence we assume for this unknown voltage the Fourier series

$$v = \sum_{n=-\infty}^{\infty} \beta_n e^{jn\omega_1 t} = \sum_{n=-\infty}^{\infty} \tfrac{1}{2} V_n e^{jn\omega_1 t} \tag{2-28}$$

where the magnitude of V_n is the peak value of the sinusoidal wave at frequency $n\omega_1/2\pi$. The base angular frequency ω_1 is the same in (2–28) as in (2–27), because the period of the voltage and current waves will be equal. Now the solution of a differential equation must reduce it to an identity. We therefore substitute (2–27) and (2–28) into (2–26), finding

$$\sum_{n=-\infty}^{\infty} [-LC(n\omega_1)^2 + jn\omega_1 RC + 1]\frac{V_n}{2} e^{jn\omega_1 t} = \sum_{n=-\infty}^{\infty} [Ljn\omega_1 + R]\frac{I_n}{2} e^{jn\omega_1 t} \tag{2-29}$$

Since this equality holds for all values of $n\omega_1 t$, we must have for each value of n

$$[1 - (n\omega_1)^2 LC + jn\omega_1 RC]V_n = [R + jn\omega_1 L]I_n \tag{2-30}$$

or

$$V_n = \frac{R + jn\omega_1 L}{1 - (n\omega_1)^2 LC + jn\omega_1 RC} I_n \tag{2-30a}$$

The coefficient of I_n in (2–30a) is precisely the input impedance of the circuit in Fig. 2–5 at the frequency $f = n\omega_1/2\pi$. Hence we can write more succinctly

$$V_n = Z(n\omega_1)I_n \tag{2-31}$$

where $Z(n\omega_1)$ is the complex impedance of the circuit at the frequency $n\omega_1/2\pi$ c.p.s.

We now have the Fourier series for the output voltage,

$$v = \sum_{n=-\infty}^{\infty} \tfrac{1}{2} Z(n\omega_1) I_n e^{jn\omega_1 t} \tag{2-32}$$

where the coefficient $Z(n\omega_1)I_n$ is known if the current i is a known repetitive current. The final equation (2–32) illustrates the superposition principle, which enables us to obtain steady-state solutions without overt use of the differential equations of the circuit. We simply regard each term in the Fourier series for the applied voltage or current as separately applied to the circuit, and compute the corresponding sinusoidal response. The results of these individual calculations may then be superposed, yielding a summation of terms for the resultant current or voltage.

In many applications, adequate representation of the response can be obtained with a few terms or only one term. The circuit of Fig. 2–5 affords a well-known illustration. Let the circuit be tuned to resonance at the frequency $\omega_1/2\pi$, i.e., choose L and C such that $\omega_1^2 = 1/LC$.* Further, with Q for the ratio $\omega_1 L/R$, the impedance $Z(n\omega_1)$ can be expressed as

$$Z(n\omega_1) = \frac{R[1+jnQ]}{1-n^2+j(n/Q)} \tag{2–33}$$

Now, if, say, $Q = 25$, we find with the aid of easily justifiable approximations that

$$\frac{|Z(2\omega_1)|}{|Z(\omega_1)|} < 0.03 \tag{2–34}$$

so that for most purposes the a-c response is adequately given by the terms with $n = +1$ and $n = -1$ in the summation (2–32). Combining the terms for $n = 1$ and $n = -1$, in that summation, and using

$$Z(\omega_1) \cong 625R$$

as found with $Q = 25$ in (2–33), we obtain

$$v \cong 625R|I_1| \cos(\omega_1 t + \phi_1) \tag{2–35}$$

where ϕ_1 is given by $\underline{/I_1}$. (The voltage and current at this frequency are, of course, approximately in phase since $\underline{/Z(\omega_1)} \cong$ zero.)

2-3 Fourier Integral for Excitation and Response

Let us consider a network with input and output terminal-pairs as illustrated in Fig. 2–6. If a voltage v_1 is applied to the input terminals, a response v_2 will appear at the output end. If v_1 is a sinusoidal voltage and we are concerned only with the steady-state response, we shall find

$$V_2 = G(\omega)V_1 \tag{2–36}$$

* This adequately defines resonance when Q is large.

where V_1 and V_2 are complex input and output voltages and $G(\omega)$ is the complex gain. If the circuit is passive, $|G(\omega)|$ is apt to be fractional. In general $G(\omega)$ is determined both by the circuit within the box and the external load impedance connected to it. For our present purpose it is important to note that $G(\omega)$ is a complex function of frequency. We assume throughout the remainder of this section that v_1 is the only excitation applied to the circuit.

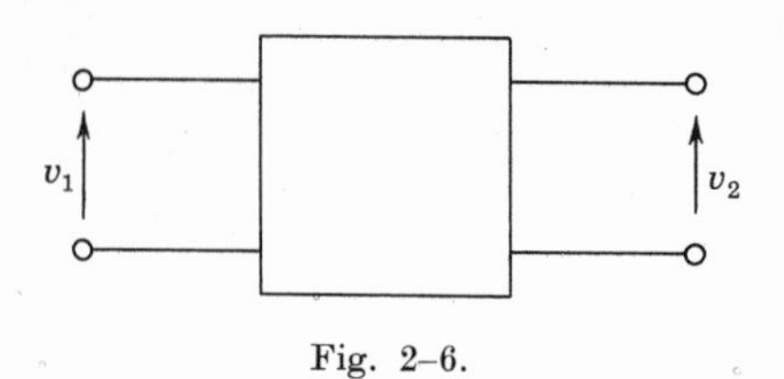

Fig. 2–6.

Suppose, now, that v_1 is a repetitive voltage represented by the Fourier series

$$v_1 = \sum_{n=-\infty}^{\infty} \tfrac{1}{2} V_n e^{jn\omega_1 t} \tag{2–37}$$

Using the principle of superposition we find

$$v_2 = \sum_{n=-\infty}^{\infty} G(n\omega_1)\frac{V_n}{2} e^{jn\omega_1 t} \tag{2–38}$$

In both (2–37) and (2–38)

$$\tfrac{1}{2} V_n = \frac{1}{T}\int_{-T/2}^{T/2} v_1(t)e^{-jn\omega_1 t}\,dt \tag{2–39}$$

where $\omega_1 = 2\pi/T$, T being the period of the wave. The magnitude of V_n is again the peak value of the sinusoidal wave of frequency $n\omega_1/2\pi$. The expression (2–39) is another form of (2–17) with θ replaced by $\omega_1 t$ and $(1/2)V_n$ in place of α_n.

Let us consider the problem, of general interest, in which the applied voltage v_1 is not repetitive; it may, for example, be a single pulse. Since v_1 is to be the only excitation, all capacitive voltage and inductive current must be zero prior to its application. A non-repetitive wave such as v_1 may be regarded as the limiting case of a repeating function of infinite period. This viewpoint provides a bridge between periodic and non-periodic functions and leads to the formulation of the Fourier integral theorem.

Let us select a fixed value of frequency such that $\omega = n\omega_1$. For large values of T, i.e., for a function whose base period is long, it is evident that ω_1, equal to $2\pi/T$, is small and that n is large. If we also observe that $(n+1)\omega_1 - n\omega_1 = \omega_1$, we see that ω_1 represents the spacing between successive harmonics in the Fourier series. Since ω_1 is, then, a small increment added to $n\omega_1$ (i.e., to ω), we shall call it $\Delta\omega$. With this notation in mind, equation (2–39) can be written for large values of T as

$$\tfrac{1}{2}V(\omega, T) = \frac{\Delta\omega}{2\pi}\int_{-T/2}^{T/2} v_1(t)e^{-j\omega t}\,dt \tag{2–40}$$

where V_n has been expressed as a function of the parameter ω and the large period T.

Substituting (2–40) into (2–37) and (2–38) leads to

$$v_1 = \sum_{n=-\infty}^{\infty} \frac{1}{2\pi}\left[\int_{-T/2}^{T/2} v_1(t)e^{-j\omega t}\,dt\right]e^{j\omega t}\Delta\omega \tag{2–41}$$

and

$$v_2 = \sum_{n=-\infty}^{\infty} G(\omega)\frac{1}{2\pi}\left[\int_{-T/2}^{T/2} v_1(t)e^{-j\omega t}\,dt\right]e^{j\omega t}\Delta\omega \tag{2–42}$$

as the expressions for the input and output voltages v_1 and v_2 when T is large. We now define:

$$g(\omega) = \int_{-\infty}^{\infty} v_1(t)e^{-j\omega t}\,dt \qquad (2–43)^*$$

where $g(\omega)$ represents the limit, as T becomes infinite, of the expression in square brackets in each of the preceding equations. The function $g(\omega)$ is known as the *Fourier integral* or *Fourier transform* of the input voltage v_1. The factor $1/2\pi$ or $1/\sqrt{2\pi}$ is often included in this definition. This, however, is not an essential matter and the definition chosen will prove convenient for our derivation of the Laplace transformation.

If we tentatively replace the square bracket in (2–41) and (2–42) by its limit for T infinite, we obtain

$$v_1 = \frac{1}{2\pi}\sum_{n=-\infty}^{\infty} g(\omega)e^{j\omega t}\Delta\omega \tag{2–44}$$

$$v_2 = \frac{1}{2\pi}\sum_{n=-\infty}^{\infty} G(\omega)g(\omega)e^{j\omega t}\Delta\omega \tag{2–45}$$

Now, in the absence of a pure mathematician, one quickly asserts that each of these sums is a definite integral since $\Delta\omega$ approaches zero as T

* The notation $V_1(j\omega)$ may also be used for the integral (2–43). That the integral can be regarded as a function of ω or $j\omega$ is clear. In certain problems, the actual expression for $g(\omega)$ or $V_1(j\omega)$ will not normally reveal $j\omega$ as a variable. It will be hidden in ω^2 equal to $-(j\omega)^2$ or in a function whose power series expansion contains even powers of ω (see (2–66)). For this reason our discussions read more easily if we express the integral as a function of ω alone. The letter g for the Fourier integral of a time-function will also be found in Reference 10.

goes to infinity. The conclusion is correct but the step is not rigorous. The definition of a definite integral requires a summation in terms of a given function of ω. The function in square brackets in (2–41) and (2–42) is not $g(\omega)$, but changes and becomes $g(\omega)$ only in the limit. Since one may also question the convergence of the Fourier series under these limiting processes, the reader is referred to References 2, 5, 7, and 14 in the list at the end of this chapter for complete proof of the Fourier integral theorem. Accepting the conclusion and replacing the sums (2–44 and 45) by the integrals they represent, we have at once the Fourier integral expressions for both input and output voltages, namely,

$$v_1 = \frac{1}{2\pi} \int_{-\infty}^{\infty} g(\omega)\, e^{j\omega t}\, d\omega \tag{2–46}$$

$$v_2 = \frac{1}{2\pi} \int_{-\infty}^{\infty} G(\omega) g(\omega)\, e^{j\omega t}\, d\omega \tag{2–47}$$

where

$$g(\omega) = \int_{-\infty}^{\infty} v_1(t)\, e^{-j\omega t}\, dt \tag{2–43}$$

and $G(\omega) = V_2/V_1$, the ratio of complex output voltage to complex input voltage at the frequency $\omega/2\pi$ c.p.s. Equations (2–43) and (2–46) constitute a statement of the Fourier integral theorem, while (2–47) is the Fourier integral expression for an output voltage and represents the basis of applications of the theorem. Equation (2–47) has a broader significance than is implied by $G(\omega)$ as a voltage ratio. It is a relation between response and excitation, applicable to many physical systems. In an electric circuit problem, the excitation applied to the network may be either a voltage or a current, and the response of interest may also be a voltage or current at either input or output terminals. Depending on the problem, therefore, $G(\omega)$ can represent not only the voltage ratio of the foregoing development, but *also a current ratio or an input or transfer impedance or admittance.* The equation (2–47), then, expresses the response when the Fourier integral of the applied voltage or current has been determined.

A Physical Interpretation of the Fourier Integral $g(\omega)$

In order to have a better understanding of the role of the function $g(\omega)$ in circuit analysis, we again consider the equation (2–40). Dividing both sides by $\Delta\omega$ yields

$$\frac{V_n}{\Delta\omega} = \frac{1}{\pi}\int_{-T/2}^{T/2} v_1(t)\, e^{-j\omega t}\, dt \tag{2-40a}$$

where $\Delta\omega$ is the separation between successive terms in the Fourier series, ω is equal to $n\Delta\omega$, and V_n is the complex voltage amplitude at the frequency $\omega/2\pi$ c.p.s., which was expressed as $V(\omega, T)$ in equation (2–40). (One pair of terms in the complex Fourier series, then combine to yield $|V_n| \cos(\omega t + \phi_n)$ with $\phi_n = \underline{/V_n}$.) The forms (2–40) and (2–40a) are written for T large so that $\Delta\omega$ is small. We now consider the ratio $V_n/\Delta\omega$. As T increases without limit, V_n and $\Delta\omega$ each decrease, approaching zero as a limit. However, from (2–40) and the definition of $g(\omega)$, (2–43), it is evident that

$$\lim_{\substack{\Delta\omega \to 0 \\ T \to \infty}} \frac{V_n}{\Delta\omega} = \frac{1}{\pi}\, g(\omega) \tag{2-40b}$$

The dimensions of either side of this equation are clearly voltage/frequency. We note that $(1/\pi)g(\omega)$ is the complex sinusoidal voltage amplitude per unit length of the ω axis. As a simple analogy let us consider a string of negligible cross section, but with the variable density λ kg/meter, along its length. The mass at any point along the string is zero. However, the mass of a length dx is clearly $\lambda\, dx$ kg. In the same way, if we seek words to describe equation (2–40b), we may say that the complex voltage amplitude V_n at a discrete point on the ω axis is zero, but that over a small range, $d\omega$, the complex voltage amplitude has a value $(1/\pi)g(\omega)\, d\omega$. Then from ordinary a-c circuit techniques we would expect that the corresponding complex output voltage amplitude would be $(1/\pi)G(\omega)g(\omega)\, d\omega$. The integral (2–47) confirms this expectation.

Since $g(\omega)$ is a representation of the applied voltage, in terms of a distribution of sinusoidal voltage along the frequency axis, $g(\omega)$ is often termed the *spectrum* or *Fourier spectrum* of the applied signal. The spectrum of the output voltage is then $G(\omega)g(\omega)$.

Functions to Which the Fourier Integral Theorem Is Applicable

Since the Fourier integral is obtained from the Fourier series, we expect that Dirichlet's conditions must again be satisfied. Since the basic period of the series has now been extended to include all time, these conditions should apply to the entire range of time $-\infty < t < \infty$. In addition, the limiting process must not lead to divergent integrals. When

the Fourier integral theorem in the form (2–43 and 46) is rigorously derived, it is found that the theorem is valid provided that:
(a) $f(t)$ satisfies Dirichlet's conditions for any finite interval[3] in the entire range of time $-\infty < t < \infty$ and

(b) $\int_{-\infty}^{\infty} |f(t)|\, dt$ is finite.*

It is interesting that the condition (b) rules out all periodic functions where the series applies. Figs. 2–7(a) and (b) illustrate two functions which violate condition (b). In both cases the area under the absolute magnitude of the function is not finite. The periodic function of Fig. 2–7(b), page 67, is, of course, representable by a Fourier series.

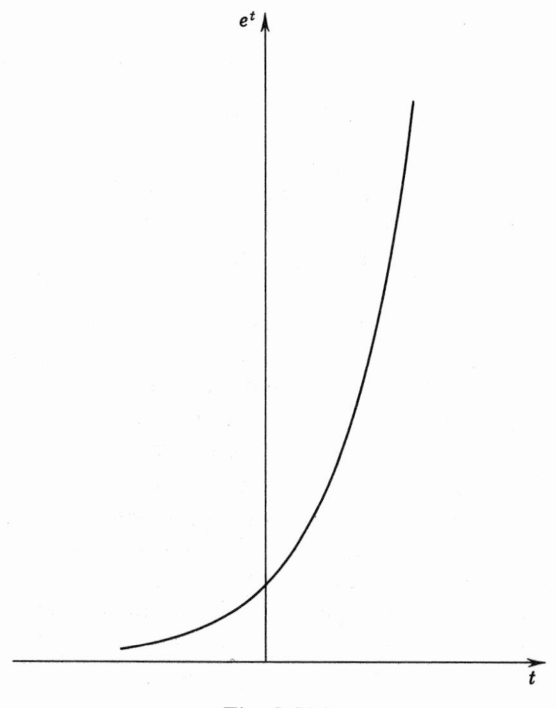

Fig. 2–7(a).

The single square pulse of voltage, Fig. 2–8, is a function for which the Fourier integral theorem is valid. It is continuous over the finite interval $-T/2 < t < T/2$, where its value is 1, as well as over the two

* The range of applicability of the Fourier integral may be extended with the introduction of a convergence factor; see the discussion preceding equation (2–102) on page 88 and also Reference 21.

infinite ranges $-\infty < t < -T/2$ and $T/2 < t < \infty$, where its value is 0. At the points of discontinuity $t = -T/2$ and $t = T/2$, the function is presumed to have the average value 1/2.

An interesting question occurs. How do we know, at the outset of a problem, that the circuit response which we seek satisfies the requirements of Fourier integration? In some cases this is known from the

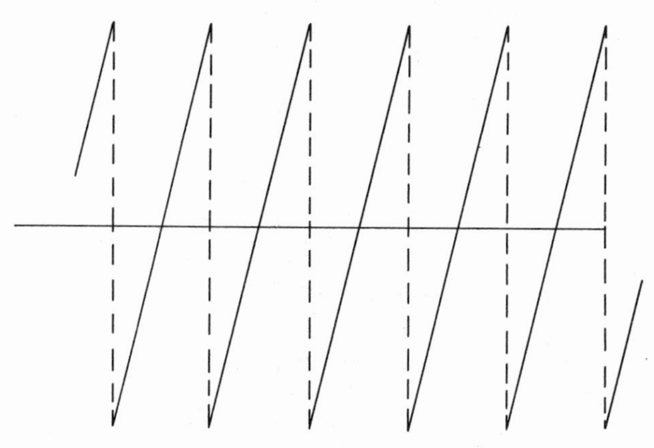

Fig. 2–7(b).

general characteristics of the circuit and of the applied signal, e.g., if v_1 in Fig. 2–6 is of finite duration, we may easily have enough information about the circuit within the box to be certain that v_2 consists of one or more terms which decay exponentially after v_1 reduces to zero. More generally, however, the solution for the circuit response may be verified by substituting it into the circuit differential equations and examining whether it satisfies these, and the initial data of the problem. If v_2 satisfies the requirements of the integral theorem, comparison of (2–47) with (2–46) shows that the Fourier integral of v_2 is $G(\omega)g(\omega)$. On further comparing with (2–43), we conclude that the Fourier integral of the output voltage is given by

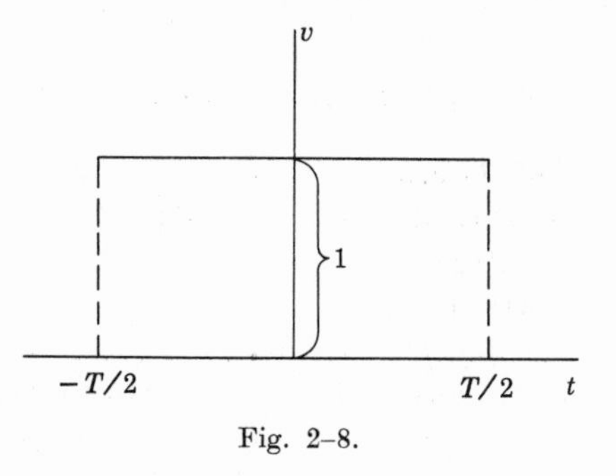

Fig. 2–8.

$$G(\omega)g(\omega) = \int_{-\infty}^{\infty} v_2(t)\, e^{-j\omega t}\, dt \qquad (2\text{–}48)$$

Equation (2–48) is implied in the derivation of (2–47). The Fourier coefficient for the output voltage at frequency $(n\omega_1/2\pi)$ is given by

$$(1/T)\int_{-T/2}^{T/2} v_2(t)e^{-jn\omega_1 t}\,dt$$

When T is large, we express $1/T$ as $(\Delta\omega/2\pi)$ and $n\omega_1$ as ω. We then find, on comparing the result with the right side of (2–42), that

$$\int_{-T/2}^{T/2} v_2(t)e^{-j\omega t}\,dt$$

is equal, for large T, to

$$G(\omega)\int_{-T/2}^{T/2} v_1(t)e^{-j\omega t}\,dt$$

When T becomes infinite, we have precisely (2–48).

One should note that comparison of (2–43), (2–46), and (2–47) to obtain (2–48) assumes uniqueness of these integrals, i.e., that the integral specifies the integrand. In the same way if (2–48) is obtained from the series, as indicated in the preceding paragraph, the uniqueness of the series is assumed, i.e., it is assumed that the sum specifies the coefficients uniquely.

Equations (2–43) and (2–46) constitute the Fourier integral theorem. Equations (2–47) and (2–48) add the concepts of superposition and gain (or transfer) function $G(\omega)$, in order that the theorem may be applied to physical systems.

2-4 Applications of the Fourier Integral Theorem*

The Fourier integral theorem will be used to relate the response of a system to its excitation in terms of the a-c frequency characteristics of the system. If a network is known, the response may be calculated. More important, if a certain response is desired, the appropriate or ideal frequency characteristic may be determined. The theorem will also be used to derive the Laplace transformation, which will prove particularly applicable to problems involving specific circuits and which will form the basis of our later circuit analysis.

The reader desirous of arriving directly at the Laplace transform analysis of electric circuits can omit the following applications of the Fourier integral theorem to communications, and go directly to its use in deriving the Laplace transformation (Sections 2–5 and following). The

* See also Guillemin(10) and Weber(21).

author believes, however, that the applications of the Fourier integral theorem will be of interest in themselves.

Ideal Transmission Characteristics

As a first example, let us find the frequency characteristic of a system which will transmit a signal entirely without distortion. The applied voltage in Fig. 2–6 is v_1. We require that the output voltage v_2 be an undistorted reproduction of v_1, i.e., it may be v_1 multiplied by a constant and delayed in time, but the shape must be otherwise undisturbed. We wish to determine $G(\omega)$ for the circuit in the box in Fig. 2–6. The Fourier integral of the output voltage has been stated as

$$G(\omega)g(\omega) = \int_{-\infty}^{\infty} v_2(t)e^{-j\omega t}\,dt \tag{2–48}$$

where $g(\omega)$ is the Fourier integral of the input voltage, i.e.,

$$g(\omega) = \int_{-\infty}^{\infty} v_1(t)e^{-j\omega t}dt \tag{2–43}$$

and $G(\omega)$ is the complex gain of the circuit which we seek. Now our requirement is that v_2 shall be related to v_1 by

$$v_2(t) = kv_1(t-t_d) \tag{2–49}$$

A plot of any simple function will show at once that if every t in its expression be replaced by $t-t_d$, the function is unchanged but shifted in time by the constant delay t_d. The constant k is a real number. Placing (2–49) in (2–48) yields

$$G(\omega)g(\omega) = k\int_{-\infty}^{\infty} v_1(t-t_d)e^{-j\omega t}\,dt \tag{2–50}$$

Now letting $\tau = t-t_d$, we find that (2–50) becomes

$$G(\omega)g(\omega) = ke^{-j\omega t_d}\int_{-\infty}^{\infty} v_1(\tau)e^{-j\omega\tau}\,d\tau \tag{2–50a}$$

where, being constant, $e^{-j\omega t_d}$ is placed outside the integral sign. Let us compare the integral in (2–50a) with that in (2–43). We observe that these must be identical quantities. One integral is expressed with the letter τ, the other with t, but the integrands are the same function, and the limits of integration are identical. Hence (2–50a) becomes

$$G(\omega)g(\omega) = ke^{-j\omega t_d}g(\omega) \tag{2–51}$$

or

$$G(\omega) = ke^{-j\omega t_d} \qquad (2\text{–}51a)$$

A little reflection shows that this solution is somewhat too restricted. In this solution, the exponent, in which ωt_d represents phase shift, is zero at $\omega = 0$. The right-hand side of (2–51a), however, may be multiplied by $e^{\pm jn\pi}$ with $n = 0$ or any other integer, and no basic change is introduced. If n is even, $e^{\pm jn\pi} = 1$, while if n is odd, $e^{\pm jn\pi} = -1$. Multiplication by -1 does not preclude attainment of distortionless transmission, since the sign of k is here unimportant. Hence our result may be expressed more generally by

$$G(\omega) = ke^{-j(\omega t_d \pm n\pi)} \quad n = 0 \text{ or any other integer} \qquad (2\text{–}52)^*$$

Now the phase shift through a network at a frequency $\omega/2\pi$ c.p.s. may be called $\beta = \underline{/V_1} - \underline{/V_2}$. Then $\beta = -\underline{/G(\omega)}$. Using this notation and equating magnitudes and angles in the complex equation (2–52), we have

$$|G(\omega)| = k \qquad (2\text{–}52a)$$

$$\beta = \omega t_d \pm n\pi \qquad (2\text{–}52b)$$

as the requirements for ideal or distortionless transmission. For ideal transmission, then, the gain must be a constant independent of frequency, while the phase shift should be a straight line passing through zero or a multiple of π at $\omega = 0$. The slope of this straight line, $d\beta/d\omega$, will be the time delay t_d. The distortion caused by a curved phase-shift characteristic is then interpreted by regarding the curved characteristic as made up of small straight-line segments, the slope of each representing a different time delay. (Another source of distortion is the fact that the intercept of the extension of each straight line segment at $\omega = 0$ is not zero or a multiple of π.)[10, 12]

Ideal Characteristic of a Band-Pass Filter

We now suppose that the voltage v_1 applied to the input terminals of the network in Fig. 2–6 consists of two signals: v_1' to be transmitted and v_1'' to be rejected. We shall further suppose that the frequency content

* The phase and amplitude characteristics obtained here are ideal, and are not intended to represent physically realizable networks. One property of physical networks may be introduced to make the idealized $G(\omega)$ in (2–52) more specific. The function G of a linear, lumped finite network can be expressed as a ratio of polynomials in the variable $j\omega$. Thus reversal of the sign of ω is equivalent to reversal of the sign preceding j. From this we deduce that reversal of the sign of ω replaces G by its conjugate, i.e., replaces $\underline{/G}$ by its negative. We conclude then that the sign of n in the angle $\omega t_d \pm n\pi$ should be reversed when ω changes from positive to negative.

of v_1' lies entirely in the range $\omega_1 < \omega < \omega_2$, while the frequency content of v_1'' is entirely outside this range. While this assumption is extreme, it can easily be approximated in practice. Our problem is to find the characteristics of the network in the box which will transmit v_1' without distortion and reject v_1'' entirely. This will be an ideal band-pass filter.

To put the problem in more precise terms we first observe that if

$$v_1 = v_1' + v_1'' \tag{2–53}$$

and

$$g(\omega) = \int_{-\infty}^{\infty} v_1 e^{-j\omega t}\, dt \tag{2–54}$$

we find by substitution of (2–53) into (2–54) that

$$g(\omega) = g'(\omega) + g''(\omega) \tag{2–55}$$

where

$$g'(\omega) = \int_{-\infty}^{\infty} v_1' e^{-j\omega t}\, dt$$

and

$$g''(\omega) = \int_{-\infty}^{\infty} v_1'' e^{-j\omega t}\, dt$$

Now we recall that in the complex Fourier series, from which the integral was obtained, the term at $+n\omega$ combined with that at $-n\omega$ to yield a real sinusoidal term at frequency $n\omega/2\pi$ c.p.s. In a similar way our statement that the entire frequency content of v_1' lies in the range $\omega_1 < \omega < \omega_2$ must be interpreted to mean that its Fourier transform $g'(\omega)$ is not 0 in the ranges $\omega_1 < \omega < \omega_2$ and $-\omega_2 < \omega < -\omega_1$. Outside these ranges $g'(\omega) = 0$. Now v_1'' was said to have a frequency content outside the range of v_1'; thus $g''(\omega) = 0$ for all values of ω at which $g'(\omega) \neq 0$.

The output voltage we seek can be expressed analytically as

$$v_2 = kv_1'(t - t_d) \tag{2–56}$$

i.e., v_1' may be amplified* or attenuated, and delayed in time, but must be otherwise undistorted. On the other hand, v_1'' must not affect the output voltage in any way. We may now find the required $G(\omega)$ for the network in the box which will meet these idealized demands.

* The word "filter" in this section is used for a frequency selective circuit, e.g., an amplifier in cascade with a passive filter, not merely the usual passive filter circuits.

Using, as in the preceding problem,

$$G(\omega)g(\omega) = \int_{-\infty}^{\infty} v_2(t)e^{-j\omega t}\,dt \tag{2–48}$$

and substituting (2–55 and 56) into this equation, we have

$$G(\omega)[g'(\omega)+g''(\omega)] = k\int_{-\infty}^{\infty} v_1'(t-t_d)e^{-j\omega t}\,dt \tag{2–57}$$

The substitution $\tau = t-t_d$ yields

$$G(\omega)[g'(\omega)+g''(\omega)] = ke^{-j\omega t_d}\int_{-\infty}^{\infty} v_1'(\tau)e^{-j\omega\tau}\,d\tau \tag{2–58}$$

The integral on the right is seen by the argument of the previous section to be identical with $g'(\omega)$ defined after (2–55). Hence

$$G(\omega)[g'(\omega)+g''(\omega)] = ke^{-j\omega t_d}g'(\omega) \tag{2–59}$$

Since this equation must hold for all frequencies, it must be valid for values of ω at which $g'(\omega) = 0$ as well as those for which $g''(\omega) = 0$. Now for $-\omega_2 < \omega < -\omega_1$ and $\omega_1 < \omega < \omega_2$, $g'' = 0$ and $g' \neq 0$, so that

$$G(\omega)g'(\omega) = ke^{-j\omega t_d}g'(\omega) \tag{2–60}$$

Outside the above ranges of ω, $g'(\omega) = 0$, $g''(\omega) \neq 0$, and (2–59) becomes

$$G(\omega)g''(\omega) = 0 \tag{2–61}$$

As on page 70, (2–60) is not altered (save possibly in sign) if we multiply by $e^{\pm jn\pi}$. Hence for an ideal band-pass filter we must have, from (2–60) and (2–61)

$$G(\omega) = ke^{-j(\omega t_d \pm n\pi)} \tag{2–60a)*$$

in the pass band, and

$$G(\omega) = 0 \tag{2–61a}$$

outside the pass band. If we let the phase shift β equal $-\underline{/G(\omega)}$, as before, these requirements become: In the pass band:

$$|G(\omega)| = k \tag{2–60b}$$

$$\beta = \omega t_d \pm n\pi \tag{2–60c}$$

* According to the footnote to equation (2–52), it is reasonable to assume that the sign of n in the range $-\omega_2 < \omega < -\omega_1$ is opposite to its sign in the range $\omega_1 < \omega < \omega_2$.

Outside the pass band: $|G(\omega)| = 0$ (2–61b)

Thus, for the ideal band-pass filter, we require a constant amplitude characteristic in the transmission band, and infinite attenuation outside this band. Phase shift must be a straight line in the pass band, the extrapolation of this line going through the origin or a multiple of π at $\omega = 0$. The slope of the phase shift versus frequency plot is the time delay of the desired signal.

Ideal Characteristic of a Low-Pass Filter

A low-pass filter is essentially a band-pass filter without a lower cutoff frequency. If we repeat the development of the preceding subsection with a pass-band in the range, say, from 0 to ω_c, the basic results will be unaltered. Hence for the low-pass filter we again will require, for ideal action, constant amplitude in the pass band and infinite attenuation outside this range. Phase shift must be a straight line in the pass band with intercept zero or a multiple of π at $\omega = 0$. The slope of this line again represents time delay.

Application of Sinusoidal Voltage Pulse to an Ideal Band-Pass Filter

We shall now determine the output of an ideal band-pass filter when a pulse of high-frequency sinusoidal voltage is applied to its input terminals. In the foregoing sections we dealt with a signal entirely confined to the filter pass band, and another entirely outside it. Here we shall apply an actual voltage pulse, a portion of whose spectrum falls within the filter pass band. The parameters will be chosen in such a manner that the response of a low-pass filter to a pulse of direct voltage can be obtained as a special case of the band-pass problem. The pulse of sinusoidal voltage to be applied to our ideal band-pass filter is described analytically as

$$
\begin{aligned}
v(t) &= 0 && \text{when } t < -\frac{T}{2} \\
v(t) &= V_m \cos \omega_a t && \text{when } -\frac{T}{2} < t < \frac{T}{2} \qquad (2\text{–}62) \\
v(t) &= 0 && \text{when } \frac{T}{2} < t
\end{aligned}
$$

Such a pulse is illustrated in Fig. 2–9.* The cutoffs of the ideal band-pass

* Naturally, the pulse may contain many more cycles than shown in the figure.

filter will be chosen such that ω_a in (2–62) is the average of the two cutoff frequencies.

We first seek the Fourier transform or spectrum of the applied voltage Substituting (2–62) into (2–43) yields

$$g(\omega) = \int_{-T/2}^{T/2} V_m \cos \omega_a t \, e^{-j\omega t} \, dt \tag{2–63}$$

or

$$g(\omega) = V_m\left(\int_{-T/2}^{T/2} \cos \omega_a t \cos \omega t \, dt - j \int_{-T/2}^{T/2} \cos \omega_a t \sin \omega t \, dt\right) \tag{2–64}$$

where we have expressed the exponential in (2–63) in trigonometric

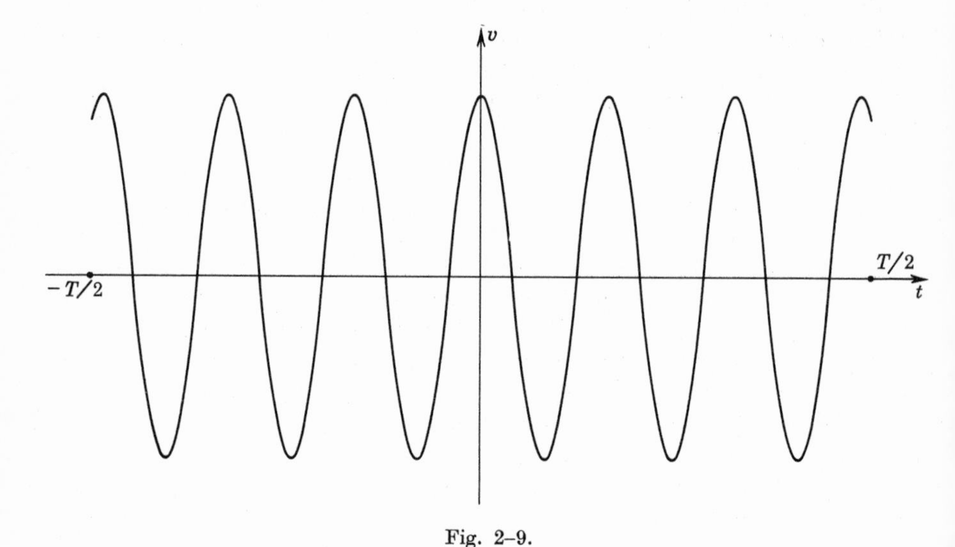

Fig. 2–9.

form. Now the integrand in the second term is an odd function of time, so that integration from $-T/2$ to $T/2$ must yield zero. The integrand in the first term is an even function of time, so that the integral from $-T/2$ to $T/2$ is twice the integral from zero to $T/2$. Hence

$$g(\omega) = 2V_m \int_0^{T/2} \cos \omega_a t \cos \omega t \, dt \tag{2–65}$$

With the trigonometric identity

$$\cos \omega_a t \cos \omega t = [\cos(\omega - \omega_a)t + \cos(\omega + \omega_a)t]/2$$

equation (2–65) becomes

$$g(\omega) = V_m \int_0^{T/2} [\cos(\omega - \omega_a)t + \cos(\omega + \omega_a)t]\,dt \qquad (2\text{–}65a)$$

Evaluating the integral, we obtain the result

$$g(\omega) = \frac{V_m T}{2}\left(\frac{\sin\theta}{\theta} + \frac{\sin\theta'}{\theta'}\right) \qquad (2\text{–}66)$$

where $\theta = (\omega - \omega_a)T/2$ and $\theta' = (\omega + \omega_a)T/2$. The term $(\sin\theta)/\theta$ is plotted in Fig. 2–10. Its maximum value is seen to occur at $\theta = 0$, i.e., $\omega = \omega_a$. It should also be noted that the major portion of the area under the curve $(\sin\theta)/\theta$ lies in the range $-\pi < \theta < \pi$. If $\omega_a T/2$ is large, $(\sin\theta')/\theta'$ will be much less than 1 in the range of frequency for which

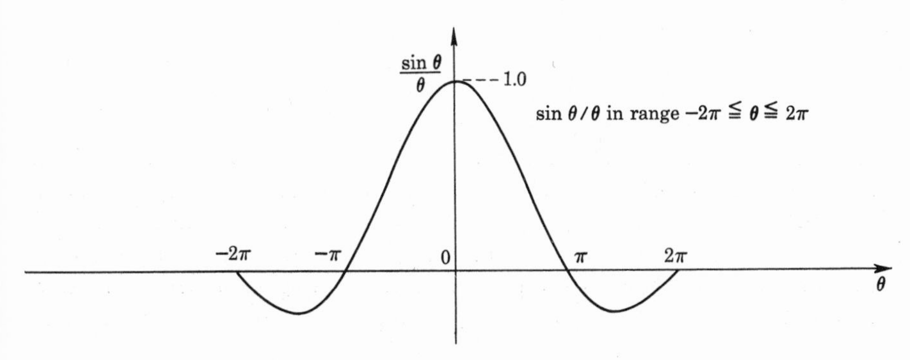

Fig. 2–10.

ω is close to ω_a, but not in the corresponding portion of the negative half of the frequency axis, i.e., ω close to $-\omega_a$.

We are now in a position to calculate the response of the ideal filter to the sinusoidal voltage pulse which we have studied. Let us first specify $G(\omega)$ for this filter in a general way.

$$G(\omega) = ke^{-j\omega t_d} \qquad (2\text{–}67a)$$

when $-\omega_2 < \omega < -\omega_1$ and $\omega_1 < \omega < \omega_2$, and

$$G(\omega) = 0 \qquad (2\text{–}67b)$$

for all other ω. In equation (2–67a) we may allow the sign of k to be plus or minus, thus including the constant phase angle $\pm n\pi$, which can be added to the exponent of the transmission characteristic of the ideal filter. Substituting (2–67a, b) into the general expression for the output voltage (2–47), we obtain

$$v_2 = \frac{1}{2\pi}\left[\int_{-\omega_2}^{-\omega_1} kg(\omega)e^{j\omega(t-t_d)}\,d\omega + \int_{\omega_1}^{\omega_2} kg(\omega)e^{j\omega(t-t_d)}\,d\omega\right] \tag{2–68}$$

Expressing the exponentials in trigonometric form

$$v_2 = \frac{k}{2\pi}\left[\int_{-\omega_2}^{-\omega_1} g(\omega)\cos\omega(t-t_d)\,d\omega + j\int_{-\omega_2}^{-\omega_1} g(\omega)\sin\omega(t-t_d)\,d\omega\right.$$
$$\left. + \int_{\omega_1}^{\omega_2} g(\omega)\cos\omega(t-t_d)\,d\omega + j\int_{\omega_1}^{\omega_2} g(\omega)\sin\omega(t-t_d)\,d\omega\right] \tag{2–69}$$

This lengthy expression shortens considerably if we see that $g(\omega)$ is an even function of ω. Considering the definitions of θ and θ' following equation (2–66), we note that $\theta(-\omega) = -\theta'$ and $\theta'(-\omega) = -\theta$. Using this in (2–66), we find

$$g(-\omega) = \frac{V_m T}{2}\left(\frac{\sin(-\theta')}{-\theta'} + \frac{\sin(-\theta)}{-\theta}\right) = g(\omega) \tag{2–70}$$

Comparison of the second and fourth integrals in (2–69) shows at once that they cancel, for their integrands are odd functions of ω, $g(\omega)$ being even and $\sin\omega(t-t_d)$ being odd. This cancellation is consistent with the fact that the instantaneous voltage v_2 is, in fact, real. The first and third integrals in (2–69) are equal since their integrands are even functions of ω, both $g(\omega)$ and $\cos\omega(t-t_d)$ being even. Hence (2–69) appears concisely as

$$v_2 = \frac{k}{\pi}\int_{\omega_1}^{\omega_2} g(\omega)\cos\omega(t-t_d)\,d\omega \tag{2–71}$$

The more specific data of our problem may now be introduced. The cutoffs ω_1 and ω_2 will be so chosen that $\omega_1 = \omega_a - (W/2)$, and $\omega_2 = \omega_a + (W/2)$, where $W = \omega_2 - \omega_1$. Thus the cutoffs are so chosen that the mid-band frequency of the filter pass-band equals the frequency of the applied sinusoidal pulse.* Further, let $\omega_a T/2 >> 1$ and let $W << \omega_a$; the first stipulation means that the applied pulse contains, within it, a large number of cycles, the second that the filter band-width is narrow in relation to its mid-band frequency. Under these assumptions, $(\sin\theta')/\theta'$ can be neglected when compared with $(\sin\theta)/\theta$ over the frequency range for which $\omega_1 < \omega < \omega_2$, as will be evident upon inspection

* The mid-band of a band-pass filter may be defined as the geometric mean of the cutoffs. However, because we shall assume that $W << \omega_a$, the average and the geometric mean of the cutoffs are approximately equal.

of the definitions of θ and θ' immediately following (2–66). (Clearly we shall have to revise the stipulation $\omega_a T/2 >> 1$ when we wish to apply a d-c pulse ($\omega_a = 0$) to a low-pass filter. Such a step, however, will be accomplished with little difficulty in the next subsection.) Now by use of $g(\omega)$ in the approximate form valid for $\omega_a T/2 >> 1$ and $W << \omega_a$, the expression for the output voltage becomes

$$v_2 = \frac{kV_m T}{2\pi} \int_{\omega_a-(W/2)}^{\omega_a+(W/2)} \frac{\sin\theta}{\theta} \cos\omega(t-t_d)\,d\omega \tag{2–72}$$

where $\theta = (\omega - \omega_a)T/2$. Changing the variable of integration from ω to θ, we find, with $\tau = t - t_d$,

$$v_2 = \frac{kV_m 2T}{\pi 2T} \int_{-WT/4}^{WT/4} \frac{\sin\theta}{\theta} \cos\left(\frac{2\tau}{T}\theta + \omega_a\tau\right) d\theta \tag{2–72a}$$

Expanding the cosine in the integrand as the cosine of the sum of two angles and noting that $\omega_a\tau$ is constant when we integrate with respect to θ, we find

$$v_2 = \frac{kV_m}{\pi}\left[\cos\omega_a\tau \int_{-WT/4}^{WT/4} \frac{\sin\theta}{\theta} \cos\frac{2\tau}{T}\theta\,d\theta - \sin\omega_a\tau \int_{-WT/4}^{WT/4} \frac{\sin\theta}{\theta} \sin\frac{2\tau}{T}\theta\,d\theta\right] \tag{2–73}$$

The integrands do not become infinite at $\theta = 0$, since

$$\lim_{\theta\to 0} [(\sin\theta)/\theta] = 1$$

The second integral vanishes since its integrand is an odd function of θ. Noting that the integrand in the first integral is an even function of θ, we have

$$v_2 = \frac{2kV_m}{\pi} \cos\omega_a\tau \int_0^{WT/4} \frac{\sin\theta}{\theta} \cos\frac{2\tau}{T}\theta\,d\theta \tag{2–74}$$

The factor $\cos\omega_a\tau$, equal to $\cos\omega_a(t-t_d)$, alone, would yield a sinusoidal voltage at the same frequency as that of the applied pulse, but delayed in time by t_d seconds. We expect that the output of the filter will be a sinusoidal pulse at this frequency, perhaps not rising or cutting off as sharply as the applied pulse. The integral in (2–74) should tell the remainder of the story. Using the trigonometric identity

$$\sin\theta\cos(2\tau/T)\theta = (\tfrac{1}{2})\sin\theta[1+(2\tau/T)] + (\tfrac{1}{2})\sin\theta[1-(2\tau/T)]$$

puts (2–74) in the form

$$v_2 = \frac{kV_m}{\pi} \cos \omega_a \tau \left\{ \int_0^{WT/4} \frac{\sin\{[1+(2\tau/T)]\theta\}}{\theta} d\theta + \int_0^{WT/4} \frac{\sin\{[1-(2\tau/T)]\theta\}}{\theta} d\theta \right\} \tag{2–75}$$

Letting

$$y = [1+(2\tau/T)]\theta \quad \text{and} \quad y' = [1-(2\tau/T)]\theta,$$

we find that (2–75) takes the form

$$v_2 = \frac{kV_m}{\pi} \cos \omega_a \tau \left[\int_0^{[(1/2)+(\tau/T)]WT/2} \frac{\sin y}{y} dy + \int_0^{[(1/2)-(\tau/T)]WT/2} \frac{\sin y'}{y'} dy' \right] \tag{2–76}$$

Each of the integrals in (2–76) is a function of the upper limit alone and is seen to be a sine integral function. The *sine integral function* is defined as

$$\mathrm{Si}(x) = \int_0^x \frac{\sin y}{y} dy \tag{2–77}$$

While not explicitly integrable, this function has been computed for values of x. Hence we write our final answer, valid for large ω_a and the approximations introduced in the derivation,

$$v_2 = \frac{kV_m}{\pi} \cos \omega_a \tau \left\{ \mathrm{Si}\left[\left(\frac{1}{2} + \frac{\tau}{T}\right)\frac{WT}{2}\right] + \mathrm{Si}\left[\left(\frac{1}{2} - \frac{\tau}{T}\right)\frac{WT}{2}\right] \right\} \tag{2–78}$$

Since $\mathrm{Si}(x) = -\mathrm{Si}(-x)$, (2–78) is equally well written as

$$v_2 = \frac{kV_m}{\pi} \cos \omega_a \tau \left\{ \mathrm{Si}\left[\left(\frac{\tau}{T} + \frac{1}{2}\right)\frac{WT}{2}\right] - \mathrm{Si}\left[\left(\frac{\tau}{T} - \frac{1}{2}\right)\frac{WT}{2}\right] \right\} \tag{2–78a}$$

The sine integral functions, which depend on the band-width of the ideal filter and the period of the applied pulse, determine the envelope of the response. The envelope of the voltage v_2 is plotted in normalized form in Fig. 2–11 (see also equation 2–82).

Several over-all properties of the output voltage are significant. The response consists of a cosine wave at frequency $\omega_a/2\pi$ c.p.s., limited by an envelope given by the expression in the outermost bracket in equation (2–78a). Let us first consider the sharpness in rise of the response envelope. Since the signal voltage pulse was suddenly applied, distortionless transmission would require an instantaneous rise for this envelope. Earlier, (pages 69–70), it was demonstrated that perfect response requires constant gain and linear phase shift over an infinite frequency band. In this problem, we have assumed perfect transmission characteristics over a finite band-width, the applied signal having but a portion of its energy in this frequency range. However, as can be seen in Fig. 2–10, the spectrum of the applied signal is largely concentrated about ω_a. Since the voltage over any frequency range far from the frequency $\omega_a/2\pi$ will be of negligible magnitude, it seems reasonable to define *a measure of* the effective signal band-width. This measure will be an inverse indication of the degree of bunching of the signal energy about ω_a. With this in view, let

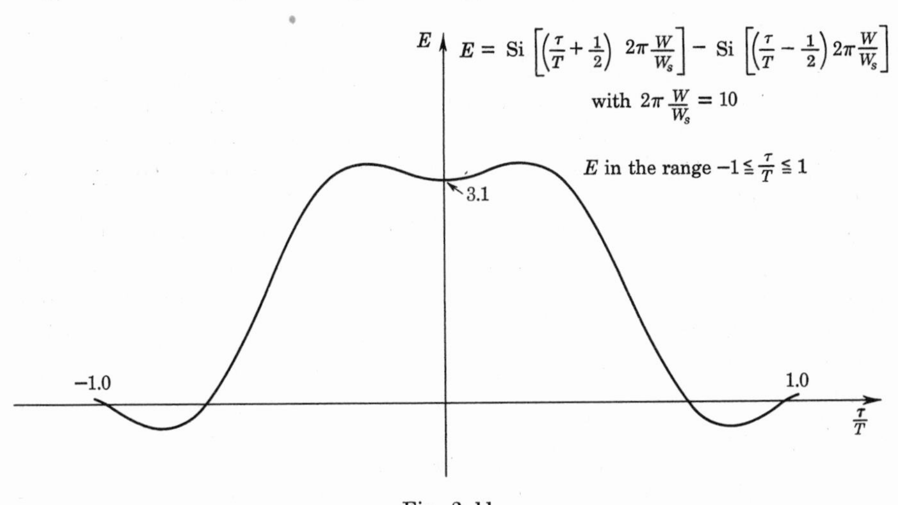

Fig. 2–11.

W_s be the range of ω for which $-\pi < \theta < \pi$ (see Fig. 2–10).* Then if ω' and ω'' are defined by

$$\pi = (\omega' - \omega_a)\frac{T}{2} \tag{2–79}$$

and

$$-\pi = (\omega'' - \omega_a)\frac{T}{2} \tag{2–79a}$$

$$W_s = \omega' - \omega'' \tag{2–80}$$

* The quantity W_s is not intended to be the effective signal band-width, but merely a parameter to be taken as a measure of this quantity. The effective signal band-width will be a factor times W_s, and will depend on the distortion which can be tolerated in a particular application.

or

$$W_s = \frac{4\pi}{T} \tag{2-81}$$

as is easily seen upon subtracting (2–79a) from (2–79). The expression for the response envelope as given by the outermost bracket in (2–78) can now be written

$$\frac{\pi}{kV_m} \times (\text{envelope}) = \text{Si}\left[\left(\frac{\tau}{T} + \frac{1}{2}\right)2\pi\frac{W}{W_s}\right] - \text{Si}\left[\left(\frac{\tau}{T} - \frac{1}{2}\right)2\pi\frac{W}{W_s}\right] \tag{2-82}$$

Clearly, the rate of change of the sine integral will depend on the ratio W/W_s.* The envelope will have both a steep rise and a sharp cutoff when W/W_s is large. We, therefore, conclude that distortion decreases as the pass band of the ideal filter increases in comparison to the effective signal band-width.†

The response of the ideal filter also shows distortion in the form of "overshoot," as can be seen in Fig. 2–11. A study of the sine integral function will show that increasing the band-width of the filter does not reduce the height of the peak response, but decreases the duration of the "overshoot."

* This can be demonstrated rigorously if we use the theorem, to be derived in a later section,

$$\frac{d}{dx}\int_0^x f(y)\,dy = f(x)$$

(see derivation of equation 2–119). Then

$$\frac{d}{dx}\text{Si}(x) = \frac{d}{dx}\int_0^x \frac{\sin y}{y}\,dy = \frac{\sin x}{x}$$

Further, if

$$x = \left(\frac{1}{2} + \frac{\tau}{T}\right)2\pi\frac{W}{W_s}$$

then

$$\frac{d}{d(\tau/T)}\text{Si}(x) = \frac{d}{dx}\text{Si}(x)\frac{dx}{d(\tau/T)}$$

so that

$$\frac{d}{d(\tau/T)}\text{Si}(x) = \frac{\sin x}{x}2\pi\frac{W}{W_s}$$

Hence the rate of change will always depend directly on W/W_s as well as on $(\sin x)/x$.

† The solution (2–78a) was derived for the conditions $\omega_a T/2 >> 1$ and $W << \omega_a$. The increase in band-width considered should, of course, be subject to the latter condition when a conclusion is drawn from (2–82).

In defining ideal transmission, time delay was accepted as a characteristic of an undistorted response. The required $G(\omega)$ of an ideal band-pass filter was arrived at on this basis. It is, therefore, not surprising that the response is a function of τ, i.e. of $t-t_d$ where t_d is the slope of the filter phase shift in the pass band. In the present problem, part of the signal energy lies outside the filter pass band, resulting in a distorted response. When the distortion is not extreme, however, the constant t_d will still represent time delay. This can be seen upon examination of the expression for the response envelope (2–82). The sine integral is an odd function having relatively small oscillations about the value $\pi/2$ for values of its argument greater than π, at which point the sine integral is a maximum. Hence the first term on the right-hand side of (2–82) rises from a negative to a positive peak when its argument, $[(\tau/T)+\frac{1}{2}]2\pi W/W_s$, moves through the interval from $-\pi$ to π. While the first term undergoes this increase in value, the second term simply adds approximately $\pi/2$ if $2\pi W/W_s$ is sufficiently large. The rise of the first term is half completed when the argument $[(\tau/T)+\frac{1}{2}]2\pi W/W_s$ is zero, i.e., when $\tau/T = -\frac{1}{2}$, or $t-t_d = -T/2$. Hence when $2\pi W/W_s$ is sufficiently large, the rise of the response envelope is approximately half complete t_d seconds after the initial application of the signal at $t = -T/2$.

It is also important to note that, according to the sine integral solution, there is some response even before $t = -T/2$. This response occurs prior to application of the signal, i.e., effect precedes cause. This small but paradoxical voltage appears in the solution because an ideal filter was assumed. Amplitude and phase characteristics were arbitrarily specified for all frequencies; specifically, linear phase shift and constant gain in the pass band and complete cutoff outside the pass band were assumed. While such specification is possible on paper, it is not physically realizable. However, in filter design one often strives to approximate the phase and amplitude characteristics of ideal filters.

Response of Ideal Low-Pass Filter to a D-C Pulse

We shall solve this problem by comparison with the preceding one. First we note that if ω_a of the last subsection be taken as zero, $\cos \omega_a t$ becomes 1 and the sinusoidal pulse will become the d-c pulse illustrated in Fig. 2–12.

The pass band of the ideal low-pass filter is the frequency range

$$0 < \omega < \omega_c.$$

Hence in the complex Fourier integral, $G(\omega)$ must be ideal in both the positive range $0 < \omega < \omega_c$ and the negative range $-\omega_c < \omega < 0$. Since $G(\omega)$ is zero outside these ranges,

$$v_2 = \frac{1}{2\pi}\int_{-\omega_c}^{\omega_c} kg(\omega)e^{j\omega(t-t_d)}\,d\omega \tag{2-83}$$

Now with ω_a replaced by zero, $g(\omega)$ as given in (2–66) reduces to

$$g(\omega) = V_m T\frac{\sin\theta}{\theta} \tag{2-84}$$

with $\theta = \theta' = \omega T/2$, as can be seen from the definitions of θ and θ' following (2–66). Clearly $g(\omega)$ is an even function of ω. If we expand $e^{j\omega(t-t_d)}$ into trigonometric form, the integrand of (2–83) will then be the sum of an even and an odd function. The integral of the odd function is zero. That of the even function becomes

$$v_2 = \frac{kV_mT}{\pi}\int_0^{\omega_c}\frac{\sin\theta}{\theta}\cos\omega(t-t_d)\,d\omega \tag{2-85}$$

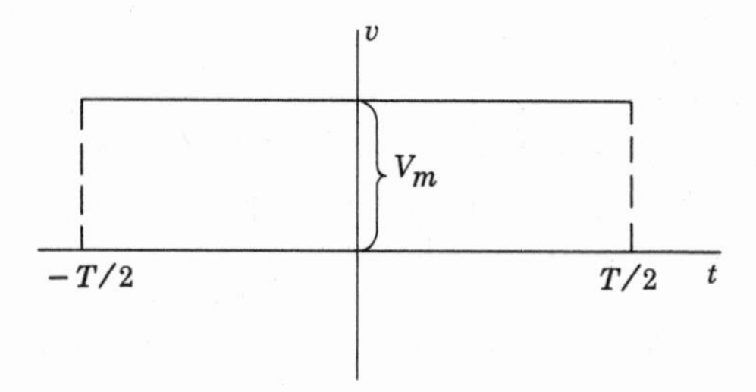

Fig. 2–12.

Equation (2–85) may be evaluated by comparison with (2–72). The parameters in (2–72), ω_a and $(W/2)$, are respectively replaced by zero and ω_c. Then θ in (2–72) is reduced to the θ in (2–85) and the integrands in these equations become identical. The limits in (2–72) become $-\omega_c$ and ω_c, making that integral precisely twice the integral in (2–85). Since the coefficient preceding the integral in (2–72) is half that in (2–85), the right-hand sides of (2–72) and (2–85) become identical. The expression for v_2 is, therefore, obtained directly from (2–78a) as

$$v_2 = \frac{kV_m}{\pi}\left\{\mathrm{Si}\left[\left(\frac{\tau}{T}+\frac{1}{2}\right)\omega_c T\right] - \mathrm{Si}\left[\left(\frac{\tau}{T}-\frac{1}{2}\right)\omega_c T\right]\right\} \tag{2-86}$$

where ω_a has been equated to zero and $W/2$ to ω_c in (2–78a) in order to obtain (2–86).

Comparison of Low- and High-Frequency Circuits

It is interesting to compare our results for low-pass and band-pass filters, since these illustrate a general principle. Let us compare the envelope of signal and response of the ideal band-pass filter with the instantaneous signal and response of the ideal low-pass filter. The signal applied to the band-pass filter was a cosine wave during the interval $-T/2 < t < T/2$, and zero for all other time. The envelope of this signal was a square pulse identical with the signal applied to the low-pass filter. As seen in equations (2–78a) and (2–86), the envelope of the response of the band-pass filter and the actual response of the low-pass filter were also identical. These results were arrived at under certain simplifying assumptions: ideal filters, relatively narrow bandwidth and high mid-band frequency* for the band-pass filter, and an applied signal which was a symmetrical sinusoidal pulse (Fig. 2–9) whose frequency coincided with the mid-point of the filter pass-band.

Despite these limiting assumptions, however, our results illustrate a general principle.[4,18,19] A condition can be stated, relating two networks, which results in an identity between the response envelope of the one and the actual response of the other, provided that their signals are related in the same way. For convenience we refer to these circuits as L and H, since the former is designed for a low-frequency application, while the latter is designed for a corresponding high-frequency application. For the network L, let $m_i(t)$ be the signal applied to its input terminals and $m_o(t)$ be the response appearing at its output terminals. Then $G_L(\omega)$ is the ratio of the Fourier integral of $m_o(t)$ to the Fourier integral of $m_i(t)$. Now we seek a network H for which the response at the output terminals will be $m_o(t) \cos \omega_0 t$, provided that the signal applied to its input terminals is $m_i(t) \cos \omega_0 t$. Thus, with $m_i(t)$, $m_o(t)$, $G_L(\omega)$, and ω_0 given, we seek $G_H(\omega)$, i.e., the ratio of the Fourier integral of $m_o(t) \cos \omega_0 t$ to the Fourier integral of $m_i(t) \cos \omega_0 t$. We assume, of course, that the Fourier integrals of the time-functions exist and that the network L, characterized by $G_L(\omega)$, is a linear network consisting of a finite number of lumped, constant elements. Whether or not $G_H(\omega)$, also, can be realized physically by such a network remains to be seen.

The following analysis parallels that in Reference 18, except that here the Fourier integral, rather than the Laplace transform, is used as a basis.

For the network L we have

$$G_L(\omega)g(\omega) = \int_{-\infty}^{\infty} m_o(t)e^{-j\omega t}\, dt \tag{2–87}$$

* See discussion preceding equation (2–72) and footnote to that discussion.

where

$$g(\omega) = \int_{-\infty}^{\infty} m_i(t)e^{-j\omega t}\,dt \tag{2-88}$$

The Fourier integral of the signal applied to the network H can be written

$$\int_{-\infty}^{\infty} \frac{m_i(t)}{2}[e^{-j(\omega-\omega_0)t} + e^{-j(\omega+\omega_0)t}]\,dt = \tfrac{1}{2}[g(\omega-\omega_0)+g(\omega+\omega_0)] \tag{2-89}$$

The left-hand side of (2–89) is easily obtained by introducing the form $(\frac{1}{2})(e^{j\omega_0 t} + e^{-j\omega_0 t})$ for $\cos\omega_0 t$. The right-hand side of (2–89) can be obtained directly: We note that the left-hand side of this equation can be written as the sum of two integrals each multiplied by $\frac{1}{2}$. The first of these integrals is identical with the integral in (2–88) except that $\omega - \omega_0$ replaces ω. The second of these integrals is also identical with the integral in (2–88) except that $\omega + \omega_0$ replaces ω. Since the integral (2–88) is a function of ω alone, we obtain the right-hand side of (2–89).

We now require that $G_H(\omega)$ satisfy

$$G_H(\omega)\tfrac{1}{2}[g(\omega-\omega_0)+g(\omega+\omega_0)] = \int_{-\infty}^{\infty} \frac{m_o(t)}{2}[e^{-j(\omega-\omega_0)t}+e^{-j(\omega+\omega_0)t}]\,dt \tag{2-90}$$

where the right-hand side of (2–90) is the Fourier integral of the required output $m_o(t)\cos\omega_0 t$. Comparing each integral on the right-hand side of (2–90) with the integral in (2–87), we see that the right-hand side of (2–90) is equal to

$$\tfrac{1}{2}[G_L(\omega-\omega_0)g(\omega-\omega_0) + G_L(\omega+\omega_0)g(\omega+\omega_0)],$$

so that:

$$G_H(\omega) = \frac{G_L(\omega-\omega_0)g(\omega-\omega_0) + G_L(\omega+\omega_0)g(\omega+\omega_0)}{g(\omega-\omega_0)+g(\omega+\omega_0)} \tag{2-91}$$

Since $G_H(\omega)$ depends on the Fourier integral g of the signal $m_i(t)$, it is evident that no linear network can be characterized by $G_H(\omega)$. However, if $m_i(t)$ is such that $g(\omega) \cong 0$ for $\omega > \omega_0$ and for $\omega < -\omega_0$, we may neglect $g(\omega+\omega_0)$ when ω is positive, and also $g(\omega-\omega_0)$ when ω is negative. With this approximation, we find

$$G_H(\omega) = G_L(\omega-\omega_0) \quad \text{when } \omega > 0 \tag{2-92}$$

$$G_H(\omega) = G_L(\omega+\omega_0) \quad \text{when } \omega < 0 \tag{2-93}$$

Thus by limiting the signals $m_i(t)$ to those with frequency content in the range $|\omega| < \omega_0$, we obtain a function $G_H(\omega)$ independent of $g(\omega)$.

Another difficulty occurs, however. The function $G_L(\omega)$ will, in general, be a ratio of polynomials of finite degree with $j\omega$ as variable; for example,

$$G_L(\omega) = \frac{a_0(j\omega)^2 + a_1(j\omega) + a_2}{b_0(j\omega)^2 + b_1(j\omega) + b_2} \tag{2-94}$$

might occur. Now a_0, a_1, a_2, b_0, b_1, b_2 are real constants, since j appears only as a coefficient of ω when the network equations are written. Now if ω is replaced by $\omega - \omega_0$ or by $\omega + \omega_0$, we shall find at once that we have a ratio of polynomials containing coefficients which are *not* real. Thus $G_H(\omega)$ cannot characterize a circuit of physical elements.

Despite the foregoing, $G_H(\omega)$ can be *approximated* by the $G(\omega)$ of a physical circuit, as illustrated in the following example:

Let us consider a constant-k band-pass filter illustrated in Fig. 2–13. As can be found in texts on filter theory,[(10)] the elements of the network

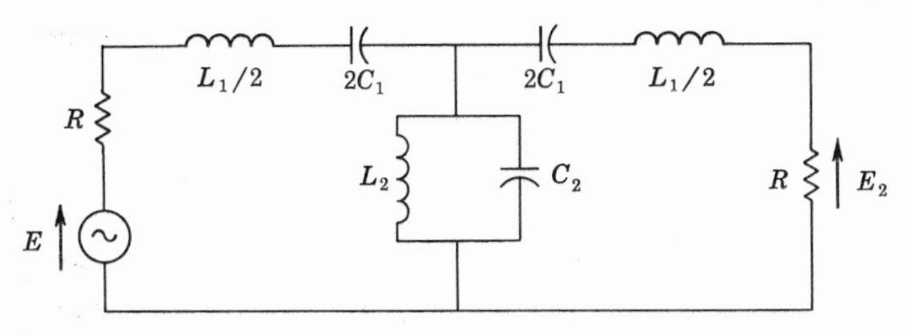

Fig. 2–13.

must be so determined that the impedance of each series arm of the T-section will be $Z_1/2 = jL_1(\omega^2 - \omega_0^2)/2\omega$ while that of the shunt branch is $Z_2 = \omega/[jC_2(\omega^2 - \omega_0^2)]$. The frequency $\omega_0/2\pi$ c.p.s. is the geometric mean of the cutoff frequencies and is related to the circuit elements by $\omega_0 = 1/\sqrt{L_1C_1} = 1/\sqrt{L_2C_2}$. The constant-$k$ condition requires

$$L_1/C_2 = L_2/C_1 = R^2.$$

The pass-band of the filter is found to be $2/\sqrt{L_1C_2}$.

Now let us assume we are concerned with the filter response over a very narrow band of frequencies so that $\omega \cong \omega_0$ and

$$\omega^2 - \omega_0^2 = (\omega + \omega_0)(\omega - \omega_0) \cong 2\omega_0(\omega - \omega_0).$$

Then $Z_1/2 \cong jL_1(\omega - \omega_0)$, and $Z_2 \cong 1/[j2C_2(\omega - \omega_0)]$. Now by ordinary alternating-current circuit methods

$$G(\omega) = \frac{E_2}{E} = \frac{Z_2R}{[R + (Z_1/2) + Z_2]^2 - Z_2^2} \tag{2-95}$$

and with the assumed approximations, (2–95) becomes $G_H(\omega)$ of the general theorem, i.e.,

$$G_H(\omega) = \frac{[1/j2C_2(\omega-\omega_0)]R}{\{R+jL_1(\omega-\omega_0)+[1/j2C_2(\omega-\omega_0)]\}^2-[1/j2C_2(\omega-\omega_0)]^2} \qquad (2\text{–}96)$$

written for $\omega > 0$. The same function of $(\omega+\omega_0)$ can be written for $\omega < 0$ and close to $-\omega_0$. $G_H(\omega)$ is here the gain of a fictitious network which coincides with the band-pass filter when ω is close to ω_0. Now if we replace $(\omega-\omega_0)$ by ω we obtain

$$G_L(\omega) = \frac{(1/j2C_2\omega)R}{[R+j\omega L_1+(1/j\omega C_2)]^2-(1/j2C_2\omega)^2} \qquad (2\text{–}97)$$

This is clearly the ratio of output to input voltage when $Z_1/2$, approximately equal to $jL_1(\omega-\omega_0)$, has been replaced by a new $Z_1/2$, equal to

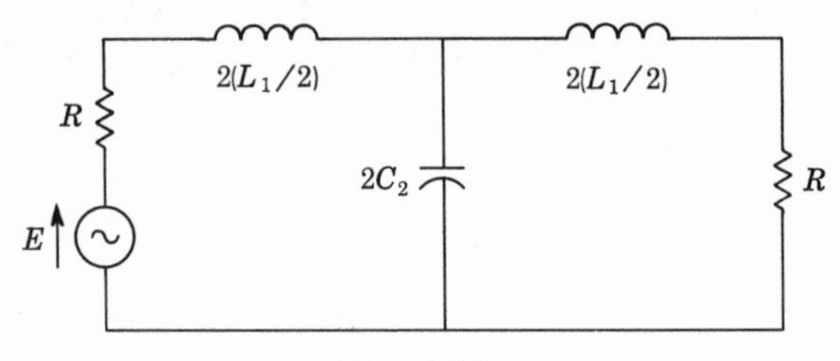

Fig. 2–14.

$j\omega L_1$, and when Z_2, approximately equal to $1/[j2C_2(\omega-\omega_0)]$ has been replaced by the new Z_2, equal to $1/j2C_2\omega$. We have then the constant-k low-pass filter of Fig. 2–14.

Comparison of Figs. 2–13 and 2–14 shows that C_1 and L_2 have each been made infinite, so that ω_0 has been replaced by zero, as occurred with ω_a in our earlier ideal-filter problem. (We recall that ω_a approximated the geometric mean of the cutoffs in that problem.) The cutoff of this low-pass filter is $1/\sqrt{L_1C_2}$ so that the pass band has half the bandwidth of the band-pass filter. This also corresponds to our finding for the ideal low-pass and band-pass filters.

Equations (2–96) and (2–97) illustrate the general principle given in equation (2–92). However, $G_H(\omega)$ given in (2–96) represents the ratio of complex output to input voltage of the band-pass filter only when the approximations preceding (2–95) are valid. Hence if a modulated a-c signal, whose frequency spectrum is essentially confined to a band close to ω_0, is applied to the band-pass filter, and if a voltage given by the envelope of this a-c signal is applied to the low-pass filter, the output of the low-pass filter will be given by the envelope of the band-pass filter output.

2-5 The Laplace Transformation

The Fourier integral theorem has been developed and used to determine the response of circuits whose alternating-current frequency characteristics were known. We shall now take the Fourier integral as a starting point from which to obtain the Laplace transformation. This transformation will form the basis of our later circuit analysis.

The Direct Laplace Transform

First, we shall limit our attention to functions which are zero for negative time. This limitation fits the viewpoint of transient analysis, for when a voltage or current is suddenly applied to a circuit, the instant of its application is designated as $t = 0$. The effects of any earlier phenomena are expressed as initial conditions. For example, let us say we are interested in the discharge of a capacitor after switching at an instant $t = 0$, in a certain network. The initial voltage across the capacitor is a datum of the problem (see Section 1–5, p. 20). The manner of build-up of this voltage prior to switching, i.e., during the time $t < 0$, is of no consequence. In view of this we shall apply the Fourier integral theorem to functions which have non-zero values only for time $t \geqq 0$.

The Fourier integral theorem as stated in (2–43, 46) can now be written

$$g(\omega) = \int_0^\infty f(t)e^{-j\omega t}\,dt \tag{2–98}$$

and

$$f(t) = \frac{1}{2\pi}\int_{-\infty}^\infty g(\omega)e^{j\omega t}\,d\omega \tag{2–99}$$

provided that the function $f(t)$ is zero for $t < 0$, that it satisfies Dirichlet's conditions for any finite interval in the range of time $t \geqq 0$, and that it has the property that

$$\int_0^\infty |f(t)|\,dt$$

is finite.

We now define a function $h(t)$ by

$$h(t) = f(t)e^{-ct} \tag{2–100}$$

By assigning a proper value to the real constant c, the Fourier integral of $h(t)$ can often be obtained, while that of $f(t)$ is obtainable, if at all, only through a limit process. A simple example will make this clear.

Let

$$
\begin{aligned}
f(t) &= 0 \quad \text{for} \quad t < 0 \\
f(t) &= t \quad \text{for} \quad t > 0
\end{aligned}
\tag{2–101}
$$

Now

$$\int_0^\infty |f(t)|\,dt = \int_0^\infty t\,dt$$

which is *not* finite. On the other hand $h(t) = te^{-ct}$, so that if we assign to c any positive value, then

$$\int_0^\infty |h(t)|\,dt = \int_0^\infty te^{-ct}\,dt = \frac{1}{c^2}$$

which is a finite result. Thus, when $c > 0$, the Fourier integral of $h(t)$ exists, since $h(t)$ satisfies the conditions of the Fourier integral theorem. The Fourier integral of $f(t)$ can only be obtained as the limit of the Fourier integral of $h(t)$ when c approaches zero. In general, this process is valid provided that the limit exists.(21) The factor e^{-ct} is called a *convergence factor*.* The Laplace transform retains this factor as part of its basic definition. In fact, while the Laplace transform of $f(t)$ can be separately defined, it may also be regarded as the Fourier integral of $h(t)$. Inserting $h(t)$ into the right side of (2–98) we find

$$\int_0^\infty h(t)e^{-j\omega t}\,dt = \int_0^\infty f(t)e^{-(c+j\omega)t}\,dt \tag{2–102}$$

* The use of the convergence factor and the meaning of the requirement that the limit exist may be clarified with the aid of examples. Let $f_1(t) = f_2(t) = 0$ for $t < 0$. Let $f_1(t) = 1$ and $f_2(t) = e^{at}$ for $t > 0$. The parameter, a, is real and positive. The Fourier integrals of $f_1\,e^{-ct}$ and $f_2\,e^{-ct}$ are easily found with the aid of (2–43) provided that $c > 0$ in the first case, and that $c > a$ in the second case. These Fourier integrals, or transforms, are respectively $g_1(\omega) = 1/(c+j\omega)$ and $g_2(\omega) = 1/[(c-a)+j\omega]$.

In the first case, the Fourier integral approaches a finite limit as c approaches zero for all values of ω except $\omega = 0$. Despite this singular point, the expression $1/j\omega$ is considered to be the Fourier integral of f_1. (Because this function becomes infinite at $\omega = 0$, special procedures are needed to show that $f_1(t)$ is obtained when (2–46) is applied to $1/j\omega$.)

The function f_2, above, is basically different. When c is made $\leqq a$, the Fourier transform

$$\int_{-\infty}^{\infty} f_2\,e^{-ct}\,e^{-j\omega t}\,dt$$

cannot be found and the expression $1/[(c-a)+j\omega]$ bears no relation to $f_2(t)$. Hence the limit does not exist and there is no suitable convergence factor.

Defining the complex variable, s, by $s = c+j\omega$, we have the usual form of the Laplace transform, namely

$$F(s) = \int_0^\infty f(t)e^{-st}\,dt \tag{2–103}$$

The letter F is used to denote the Laplace transform of f. That the integral in (2–103) yields a function of s is evident from the fact that t will be replaced by the limits zero and infinity when the integration is carried out with a specific function. The right-hand side of (2–103) is often expressed more concisely as $\mathcal{L}f(t)$.

The constant c, equal to $\mathcal{R}e\, s$, requires careful consideration. The process of the Laplace transformation can be valid only when a proper value of c can be found. Thus if $f(t) = e^{at^2}$ with $a > 0$, $\mathcal{L}f(t)$ does not exist, for

$$\int_0^\infty e^{at^2}e^{-ct}\,dt$$

is not finite for any value of c. For Laplace transformable functions we may define a number c' such that for $c > c'$,

$$\int_0^\infty |f(t)|e^{-ct}\,dt$$

is finite. Thus for the function (2–101), $c' = 0$. In general c' may be positive, zero, or negative depending on $f(t)$. Thus if $f(t) = 0$ for $t < 0$ and $f(t) = e^{\alpha t}$ for $t > 0$, then $c' = \alpha$. If α is positive, i.e., $f(t)$ is an increasing exponential, c' is positive; if α is zero, i.e., $f(t)$ is a unit-step function, c' is zero; and finally if α is negative, i.e., $f(t)$ is a decaying exponential, c' is negative. The only restriction on the constant c is that it be greater than c'.* If a value c' cannot be found, the function is not Laplace transformable.

The Inverse Transform

Let us now suppose that we have a transform $F(s)$ and seek the time-function to which it corresponds.† Since $F(s)$ is the Fourier transform of

* When the Laplace transform is defined, the real part of s can be generalized as a variable $\alpha > c'$.[8] The transform $F(s)$ will then be defined for all points in the complex plane which are to the right of c'. We have, however, disregarded such generalization in this section. When time-functions are found from their transforms, through the use of the inversion integral (2–107), values of $F(s)$ will be defined over the entire complex plane, s being taken as a complex variable, $s = \alpha+j\omega$. This will be carried out and justified in Chapter 3.

† One will ask whether the time-function is uniquely determined by the transform. Lerch's theorem demonstrates that if two functions $f(t)$ have the same Laplace transform they differ only at isolated points.[3, 6]

$h(t)$, we begin by applying (2–99), finding

$$h(t) = \frac{1}{2\pi} \int_{-\infty}^{\infty} F(s)e^{j\omega t}\,d\omega \qquad (2\text{–}104)$$

where $s = c+j\omega$ and $h(t) = f(t)e^{-ct}$ as before. In terms of $f(t)$, we then have

$$f(t)e^{-ct} = \frac{1}{2\pi} \int_{-\infty}^{\infty} F(s)e^{j\omega t}\,d\omega \qquad (2\text{–}105)$$

Now e^{+ct} does not vary with ω. Hence multiplication of (2–105) by this factor yields

$$f(t) = \frac{1}{2\pi} \int_{-\infty}^{\infty} F(s)e^{st}\,d\omega \qquad (2\text{–}106)$$

where $e^{st} = e^{ct}e^{j\omega t}$. Changing the variable of integration from ω to s, we find that the limits become $c-j\infty$ and $c+j\infty$, while $d\omega = (1/j)\,ds$, so that

$$f(t) = \frac{1}{2\pi j} \int_{c-j\infty}^{c+j\infty} F(s)e^{st}\,ds \qquad (2\text{–}107)$$

where $t \geqq 0$ and $c > c'$. From our derivation it is evident that $f(t)$ is presumed to be a Laplace transformable function, i.e., that a value c' exists such that for $c > c'$,

$$\int_{0}^{\infty} |f(t)|e^{-ct}\,dt$$

is finite and that $f(t)$, zero for negative time,* satisfies Dirichlet's conditions in any finite interval of time.

With $\mathcal{L}^{-1}F(s)$ to represent the right-hand side of (2–107), the Laplace transformation and its inverse can be expressed compactly thus:

$$\mathcal{L}f(t) = F(s) \quad \text{and} \quad \mathcal{L}^{-1}F(s) = f(t)$$

The right-hand side of (2–107) is also known as the *inversion integral.*

Comment on Fourier and Laplace Transforms

Although the Fourier and Laplace transforms are closely related, they do not, as might appear, replace each other on interchange of the variables s and $j\omega$.[21] A simple example will bring this out. We consider the two

* See footnote on p. 94, below.

time-functions $f_1(t)$ and $f_2(t)$:

$$f_1(t) = \begin{cases} -\frac{1}{2}e^{at} & \text{when } t < 0 \\ -\frac{1}{2}e^{-at} & \text{when } t > 0 \end{cases} \qquad (2\text{–}107a)$$

and

$$f_2(t) = \begin{cases} 0 & \text{when } t < 0 \\ \frac{1}{2}(e^{at} - e^{-at}) & \text{when } t > 0 \end{cases} \qquad (2\text{–}107b)$$

The real positive constant a is the same in both functions. The Fourier transform of $f_1(t)$ is obtained from (2–43) as

$$g(\omega) = \frac{a}{(j\omega)^2 - a^2} \qquad (2\text{–}107c)$$

The Laplace transform of $f_2(t)$ is obtained from (2–103), with $c > a$, as

$$F_2(s) = \frac{a}{s^2 - a^2} \qquad (2\text{–}107d)$$

These transforms differ from each other only in that s appears in one where $j\omega$ appears in the other. However, the two transforms represent entirely different time-functions. The basic reason for this result is evident: The integrals (2–103) and (2–107) for the Laplace transformation and its inverse require that the constant c be greater than the constant a when the time-function increases as e^{at}.

In general, if a function $f(t)$ equals zero for $t < 0$, its Laplace transform reduces to its Fourier transform when $\mathcal{Re}\, s = c = 0$, *provided* that $c' < 0$.[(8)] This criterion is justified on inspection of (2–107) and its derivation, where we see that unless $c' < 0$, we cannot choose $c = 0$ when we evaluate the inversion integral, if we are to obtain $f(t)$ equal to $\mathcal{L}^{-1}F(s)$. (See, however, footnote on page 88.)

The student familiar with complex-variable theory (see Chapter 3) will observe that if $F(s)$ is regular for $\mathcal{Re}\, s \geqq 0$, then c' is less than zero and c may be equated to zero when $F(s)$ is evaluated from its corresponding time-function. This follows from the fact that if $F(s)$ is regular at a point $s = \alpha + j\omega$, the direct transform (2–103) of the time-function $\mathcal{L}^{-1}F(s)$ converges for this value of s. Hence if $F(s)$ is regular in the right half-plane and on the $j\omega$ axis, $F(s)$ reduces to the Fourier integral of the time-function $\mathcal{L}^{-1}F(s)$ when s is replaced by $j\omega$, i.e., as c approaches zero.

The Laplace Transform Method of Electric Circuit Analysis

The Laplace transform method provides a basis for the analysis of electric circuits. Certain of its characteristics are common to other techniques of circuit analysis, while other characteristics are distinct advantages. The following is a broad outline of the manner in which the Laplace transformation will apply to the analysis of linear electric circuits with a finite number of lumped elements.

(A) If we take the Laplace transform (2–103) of both sides of an ordinary linear integro-differential equation with constant coefficients (see equations (1–5), (1–6), and (1–7) in Chapter 1), an algebraic equation results. The algebraic equation contains as unknowns the Laplace transforms of the unknown functions in the integro-differential equation. Hence instead of solving simultaneous integro-differential equations for instantaneous currents or voltages, we shall solve algebraic equations for the transforms of these currents or voltages.

(B) A time-function $f(t)$ with discontinuities is specified by separate expressions valid in each interval over which $f(t)$ is continuous. When such a function is Laplace transformable, its transform is given by a single expression (see under the heading *Time Delay Theorem*, p. 100 below). This results from the fact that the Laplace integral can be finite even though its integrand suffers discontinuities. Because of this property of the Laplace transformation, the response of a system subjected to a discontinuous driving function is easily obtained for the entire time range $0 < t < \infty$. Thus a separate integro-differential equation need not be written and solved for each range of time in which the driving function is continuous.

(C) Since the integral (2–103) has $t = 0$ as its lower limit, initial conditions will appear directly in the algebraic equations for the transforms of unknown voltages or currents. The use of transforms thus avoids the often irksome problem of evaluating constants of integration from initial values of current or voltage and their derivatives.

(D) The algebraic equations for the transforms of voltages and currents will have the same *form* as the equations for the complex voltages and currents of sinusoidal steady-state analysis. The letter s will replace $j\omega$, and terms arising from initial conditions will be treated as if they were transforms of applied e.m.f. or current sources. Hence the whole body of alternating-current theory—loop and node analysis, the impedance concept, network theorems, and two-port network coefficients—can be applied to voltage and current transforms as well as to the complex voltages and currents used in analysis of the sinusoidal steady state.

(E) When the Laplace transform of a desired circuit response is known, the corresponding time-function may be obtained either by

(1) evaluating the inversion integral (2–107) with the aid of the residue method, to be developed in the next chapter, or by

(2) expressing the transform as a sum of simpler, easily recognized or tabulated transforms by means of the partial fraction expansion presented in the next chapter.

(F) Network impedances will be expressed in terms of s rather than $j\omega$. The study of impedance as a function of a complex variable s is basic to most methods of network synthesis. Thus the viewpoint of the Laplace transformation can smoothly be carried over to the field of network synthesis.

The advantage of the Laplace transform method over other methods of circuit analysis is seen chiefly: in the ease of handling non-zero initial conditions, (C) above; in the ease of evaluating the inverse transform, (E) above; and in the fact that certain functions such as (2–101) are Laplace transformable, while their Fourier integrals can be obtained only with the aid of a convergence factor.[21]

For a detailed comparison of the Laplace transform and Heaviside methods, the reader is referred to Weber.[20]

2-6 Theorems of the Laplace Transformation

There are a number of theorems which facilitate the use of the Laplace transformation in electric circuit problems. When these theorems are derived, the uniqueness of the Laplace transformation will be used to advantage. This uniqueness follows from Lerch's theorem which states that two time-functions having the same transform may differ only at isolated points.[3,6] Our concern is with the values of functions where they are continuous and not at isolated points of discontinuity. Specifying a transform is, therefore, tantamount to stating its corresponding time-function. Theorems can, then, be derived by use of the direct Laplace transform equation (2–103), and conclusions drawn for the inverse process (2–107). For example, we shall show that if $F(s)$ is the transform of $f(t)$, then $(1/s)F(s)$ is the transform of the integral

$$\int_0^t f(\tau)\, d\tau$$

It will not be necessary to begin with $(1/s)F(s)$ in the integral (2–107). From the uniqueness property, we know the result may be read in either direction.

In each of the following theorems when $\mathcal{L}f(t)$ is used, it will be understood that we are limited to functions $f(t)$ which are Laplace transformable. By stating that $f(t)$ is *Laplace transformable*, we mean that $f(t)$ is zero for negative time,* must obey Dirichlet's conditions for any positive range of time, and must be such that a number c' may be found for which the integral

$$\int_0^\infty |f(t)|e^{-ct}\,dt$$

is finite when $c > c'$.

Let it also be understood that the initial value of $f(t)$, represented as $f(0+)$, shall mean the limit of $f(t)$ as t approaches zero through *positive* values.[6,8]†

Linearity Theorem

The *linearity theorem* of the Laplace transformation is stated by

$$\mathfrak{L}[af_1(t)+bf_2(t)] = a\mathfrak{L}f_1(t)+b\mathfrak{L}f_2(t) \qquad (2\text{–}108)$$

where a and b are constants. The proof of this theorem follows immediately from the definition of the Laplace transform (2–103), thus:

$$\mathfrak{L}[af_1(t)+bf_2(t)] = \int_0^\infty [af_1(t)+bf_2(t)]e^{-st}\,dt$$

$$= a\int_0^\infty f_1(t)e^{-st}\,dt + b\int_0^\infty f_2(t)e^{-st}\,dt = a\mathfrak{L}f_1(t)+b\mathfrak{L}f_2(t) \qquad (2\text{–}109)$$

From this result we may also conclude, bearing in mind the uniqueness of the transformation, that if we find a transform $aF_1(s)+bF_2(s)$, the corresponding time-function must be $af_1(t)+bf_2(t)$, provided that $\mathfrak{L}^{-1}F_1(s) = f_1(t)$ and $\mathfrak{L}^{-1}F_2(s) = f_2(t)$.

Differentiation Theorem

The Laplace transform of the derivative of a function is often required. The *differentiation theorem* is:

$$\mathfrak{L}\frac{d}{dt}f(t) = sF(s)-f(0+) \qquad (2\text{–}110)$$

where $\mathfrak{L}f(t) = F(s)$. The theorem (2–110) is valid provided that $f(t)$ is continuous for $t > 0$, and provided that $df(t)/dt$, as well as $f(t)$, is a Laplace transformable function.

* The view can also be taken that the values of $f(t)$ for $t < 0$ are irrelevant rather than zero, since the integration is over positive time only.[8]

† See footnote, p. 17, for definition of both $f(0+)$ and $f(0-)$.

Since $f(t)$ and/or its derivative will frequently exhibit a discontinuity at $t = 0$, we must consider the precise meaning of the theorem with regard to this point. By definition $\mathcal{L}df(t)/dt$ equals

$$\int_0^\infty [df(t)/dt]e^{-st}\,dt$$

The latter, however, is simply a brief way of writing[8]

$$\lim_{\substack{T\to\infty \\ \epsilon\to 0}} \int_\epsilon^T [df(t)/dt]e^{-st}\,dt$$

Hence the function symbolized as $df(t)/dt$ in (2–110) equals the slope of $f(t)$ for all positive values of t and, at $t = 0$, equals the limit of this slope as positive t reduces to zero. Hence, if we use the inverse transform $\mathcal{L}^{-1}[sF(s)-f(0+)]$ to obtain $df(t)/dt$ and evaluate the result at $t = 0$, we shall always obtain $\lim df(t)/dt$ as t approaches zero through positive values.

The theorem (2–110) is derived from the definition of the Laplace transform (2–103), thus:

$$\mathcal{L}\frac{d}{dt}f(t) = \int_0^\infty \left[\frac{d}{dt}f(t)\right]e^{-st}\,dt$$

$$= \int_0^\infty \left\{\left[\frac{d}{dt}f(t)e^{-st}\right] + sf(t)e^{-st}\right\}dt$$

$$= f(t)e^{-st}\Big|_{t=0}^{\infty} + sF(s) \qquad (2\text{–}110\text{a})$$

When $df(t)/dt$ has points of finite discontinuity, the integral will be broken into separate ranges, but the result (2–110a) will be unchanged since $f(t)$ is continuous by hypothesis.[6]

The theorem (2–110) follows from (2–110a) provided that

$$f(t)e^{-st}\Big|_{t=0}^{\infty}$$

vanishes at the upper limit. That this occurs is seen from the engineering argument that $f(t)$ represents a current or voltage which ordinarily will not grow more rapidly than e^{-st} will decay, with $\mathcal{R}e\ s$ sufficiently large. It also can be proved rigorously from the assumptions stated after (2–110).

From the assumption that f and df/dt are Laplace transformable, and from equation (2–110a), it is evident that

$$\lim_{t \to \infty} f(t)e^{-st}$$

exists, for otherwise $\mathcal{L}(df/dt)$ would not exist. There are, then, two possibilities:

$$\text{(A)} \quad \lim_{t \to \infty} |f(t)|e^{-ct} = 0$$

or

$$\text{(B)} \quad \lim_{t \to \infty} |f(t)|e^{-ct} > n$$

where n is a real, positive number, and c is the real part of s. The second possibility is easily eliminated. If (B) is assumed to be true, there is a value of time T such that for all $t \geqq T$, $|f(t)|e^{-ct} > n$. Hence we find

$$\int_0^\infty |f(t)|e^{-ct}\,dt \geqq \int_T^\infty |f(t)|e^{-ct}\,dt > \int_T^\infty n\,dt \to \infty$$

Possibility (B) then leads to the conclusion that

$$\int_0^\infty |f(t)|e^{-ct}\,dt$$

does not converge. But this contradicts the condition that $f(t)$ is Laplace transformable. Hence we accept the only remaining possibility, (A). This reduces (2–110a) to the theorem (2–110).

The foregoing proof establishes another fact. Suppose it is not known whether or not $\mathcal{L}(df/dt)$ exists. We can see from the derivation of (2–110a) and the reasoning following (A) and (B) that if $f(t)$ is continuous and has a Laplace transform, and if

$$\lim_{t \to \infty} f(t)e^{-st}$$

exists, this limit will be zero and therefore the derivative df/dt is Laplace transformable and its transform is given by (2–110).

The differentiation theorem may be illustrated for two functions, the one continuous at $t = 0$, the other exhibiting a discontinuity at this point.

Let

$$f(t) = \sin \omega t \quad \text{for} \quad t > 0 \tag{2–111}$$

and

$$g(t) = \cos \omega t \quad \text{for} \quad t > 0 \tag{2–112}$$

and, of course, let

$$f(t) = g(t) = 0 \quad \text{for} \quad t < 0 \tag{2–113}$$

Now

$$\mathcal{L}f(t) = \int_0^\infty e^{-st} \sin \omega t \, dt = \frac{\omega}{s^2 + \omega^2} \tag{2–114}$$

and

$$\mathcal{L}g(t) = \int_0^\infty e^{-st} \cos \omega t \, dt = \frac{s}{s^2 + \omega^2} \tag{2–115}$$

Applying the right-hand side of (2–110) to the transform of $\sin \omega t$ we obtain simply $s[\omega/(s^2+\omega^2)]$, for $\sin \omega t$ equals zero at $t = 0$. Comparing (2–114) and (2–115) we see that $s[\omega/(s^2+\omega^2)]$ is the transform of $\omega \cos \omega t$, i.e., of $d(\sin \omega t)/dt$. Now applying the right-hand side of (2–110) to the transform of $\cos \omega t$ we find two terms $s[s/(s^2+\omega^2)]-1$, where 1 is the value of $\cos \omega t$ at $t = 0$. This resulting transform is easily equated to $-\omega[\omega/(s^2+\omega^2)]$ which (see 2–114) is the transform of $-\omega \sin \omega t$, i.e., $d(\cos \omega t)/dt$.

In each case we observe that (2-110) yields a function whose value at $t = 0$ is the limit of the slope of the original function as t approaches zero through positive values.

Integration Theorem

The Laplace transformation of the indefinite integral

$$\int i \, dt$$

is given by the equation

$$\mathcal{L} \int f(t) \, dt = \frac{1}{s} F(s) - \frac{1}{s} \int^{0+} f(t) \, dt \tag{2–116}$$

where $\int^{0+}$ means the value of the indefinite integral as t approaches zero through positive values. For example, if the charge on a capacitance is written as

$$q = \int i \, dt$$

then

$$\int^{0+} i \, dt$$

represents the limiting value of q as t approaches zero through positive values, i.e., the initial charge q_0.(8,13)

In the statement of basic circuit laws, however, we have already separated out initial value terms. Recalling equations (1–15) and (1–10), we see that our circuit differential equations may contain

$$(1/C) \int_0^t i \, d\tau + v_0$$

or

$$(1/L) \int_0^t v \, d\tau + i_0$$

Since the integral will appear in these forms in the equations in this text, we shall confine our attention to the derivation of the Laplace transform of

$$\int_0^t f(\tau) \, d\tau$$

Hence we state the theorem(8,3)

$$\mathcal{L} \int_0^t f(\tau) \, d\tau = \frac{1}{s} F(s) \tag{2–116a}$$

provided that $\mathcal{L}f(t) = F(s)$. We shall assume the integral meets the requirements of the differentiation theorem. Before deriving equation (2–116a) it is of interest to consider the integral

$$\int_0^t f(\tau) \, d\tau$$

The letter τ represents time and is the variable of integration. Formally, $f(\tau)$ is obtained from the expression for $f(t)$, simply by replacing t by τ. The instant t is considered fixed *during the integration*. That the derivative of

$$\int_0^t f(\tau) \, d\tau$$

is $f(t)$ is easily demonstrated:

Let

$$g(t) = \int_0^t f(\tau) \, d\tau$$

Then by definition of a derivative

$$\frac{dg}{dt} = \lim_{\Delta t \to 0} \left[\frac{g(t+\Delta t)-g(t)}{\Delta t}\right] \tag{2–117}$$

i.e.,

$$\frac{dg}{dt} = \lim_{\Delta t \to 0} \left[\frac{\int_0^{t+\Delta t} f(\tau)\,d\tau - \int_0^t f(\tau)\,d\tau}{\Delta t}\right] \tag{2–117a}$$

By reference to Fig. 2–15, this is immediately seen to be

$$\frac{dg}{dt} = \lim_{\Delta t \to 0} \frac{\int_t^{t+\Delta t} f(\tau)\,d\tau}{\Delta t} \tag{2–118}$$

The area under the curve up to $t+\Delta t$, less that up to t, is clearly the area

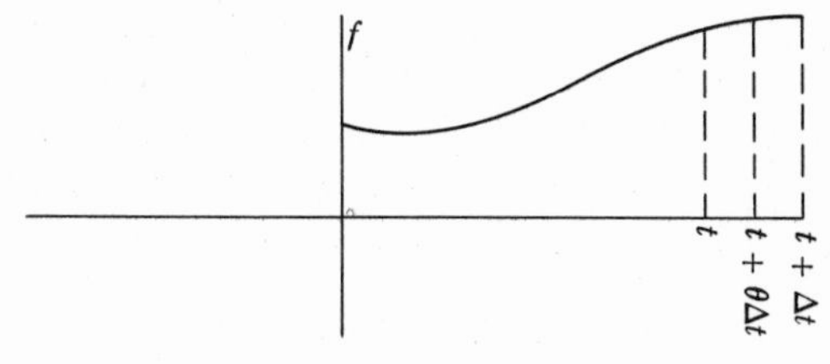

Fig. 2–15.

between t and $t+\Delta t$ as expressed by the numerator of (2–118). Now there must be one ordinate at, say, $t+\theta\Delta t$, of average height such that the area under the curve from t to $t+\Delta t$ is

$$f(t+\theta\Delta t)\Delta t = \int_t^{t+\Delta t} f(\tau)\,d\tau$$

where θ lies in the range $0 \leqq \theta \leqq 1$. Hence

$$\frac{dg}{dt} = \lim_{\Delta t \to 0} \frac{\Delta t\, f(t+\theta\Delta t)}{\Delta t} = f(t) \tag{2–119}$$

The integration theorem (2–116) is now very easy to demonstrate.

Let

$$G(s) = \mathfrak{L}g(t) = \mathfrak{L}\int_0^t f(\tau)\,d\tau \tag{2–120}$$

Now $g(t) = 0$ at $t = 0$ as can be seen from its definition. Hence from the differentiation theorem (2–110)

$$\mathfrak{L}\frac{d}{dt}g(t) = \mathfrak{L}f(t) = sG(s) \tag{2–121}$$

i.e.,

$$F(s) = sG(s) \tag{2–122}$$

whence

$$(1/s)F(s) = \mathfrak{L}\int_0 f(\tau)\,d\tau \tag{2–123}$$

Time Delay Theorem

When one function of time duplicates another, but appears at a later time T, their transforms are related by the factor e^{-sT}. This exponential has been termed a delay factor, or, in the language of Heaviside calculus, a shifting operator. We shall consider two time-functions, $f(t)$ and $f(t-T)$. The first is defined as zero for $t < 0$, while the second is zero for $t-T < 0$. Whatever the value of $f(t)$ at a certain instant, $f(t-T)$ takes the same value T seconds later. Thus $f(t-T)$ is simply $f(t)$ shifted in time by T seconds. We seek to prove that if

$$\mathfrak{L}f(t) = F(s) \tag{2–124}$$

then

$$\mathfrak{L}f(t-T) = F(s)e^{-sT} \tag{2–125}$$

The result follows from the direct Laplace transform (2–103):

$$\mathfrak{L}f(t-T) = \int_T^\infty f(t-T)e^{-st}\,dt \tag{2–126}$$

where the lower limit of the integral is T, since $f(t-T) = 0$ when $t < T$. Now replacing $(t-T)$ by χ in the integral of (2–126), we obtain

$$\mathfrak{L}f(t-T) = e^{-sT}\int_0^\infty f(\chi)e^{-s\chi}\,d\chi \tag{2–127}$$

The integral on the right is the Laplace transform of $f(t)$. The fact that it is written with χ in place of t does not alter the value of the integral. Hence (2–127) becomes (2–125) and the theorem is proved.

An important aspect of the Laplace transformation arises from the *time delay theorem* (2–125). The transform of a function of time with discontinuities is given by a single expression. As an example, let us consider the voltage pulse illustrated in Fig. 2–16. An expression for this voltage requires three separate equations, namely:

$$\left.\begin{aligned} v(t) &= 0 \quad \text{when} \quad t < 0 \\ v(t) &= V \quad \text{when} \quad 0 < t < T \\ v(t) &= 0 \quad \text{when} \quad T < t \end{aligned}\right\} \tag{2–128}$$

The transform of this function can be obtained by direct substitution in (2–103). However, the significance of the result will be clearer if we use

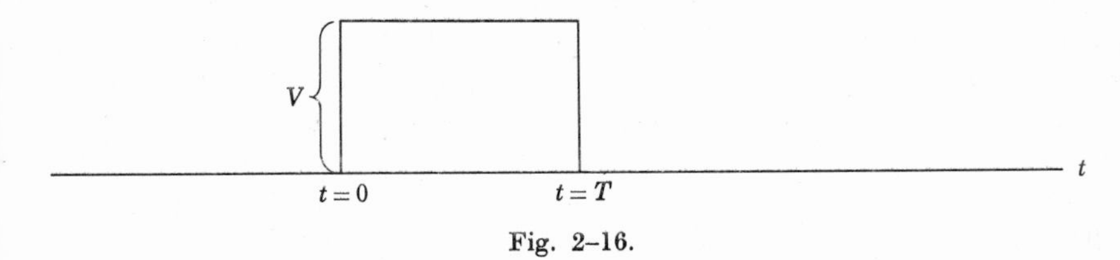

Fig. 2–16.

a different approach. The function plotted in Fig. 2–16 can be represented as a sum of two functions (1) and (2), shown in Fig. 2–17. The function (1) is continuous after $t = 0$. The function (2) is the negative of (1) but appears at $t = T$. Save for the minus sign, the second function duplicates the first and is shifted in time. The voltage V, applied

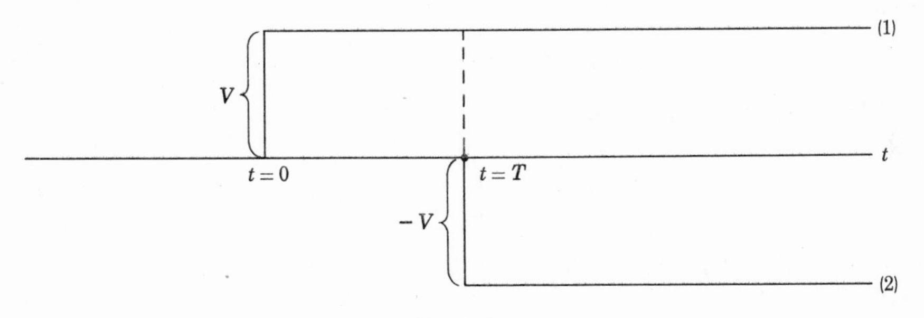

Fig. 2–17.

at $t = 0$, is known as a *step function* and occurs in many transient problems. The Laplace transform of the step function is easily obtained from (2–103):

$$\int_0^\infty Ve^{-st}dt = \frac{V}{s} \tag{2–129}$$

Now when the delay factor e^{-sT} is used, the negative step at $t = T$ must have as transform $-(V/s)e^{-sT}$. Since the superposition of these two steps is, in fact, the square pulse drawn in Fig. 2–16 and described by equation (2–128), we have at once

$$\mathcal{L}v(t) = \frac{V}{s} - \frac{V}{s}e^{-sT} \tag{2–130}$$

Thus the transform of the discontinuous function is given by a single expression. The same result will, of course, be obtained if we substitute $v(t)$ directly into (2–103) and evaluate the integral. In general, then, the Laplace transformation will represent discontinuous functions of time as a superposition of continuous functions, some of which are delayed, i.e., start at a time later than $t = 0$. It is, therefore, convenient to represent the basic discontinuous function, the *unit step*, by a symbol. We let $u(t-T)$ equal 0 for $(t-T) < 0$, and 1 for $(t-T) > 0$. Then, $u(t-T)$ is a *unit-step function* representing a discontinuity of height 1 at $t = T$.

The Transform of $f(t)e^{-\alpha t}$

Another theorem of some interest which can facilitate the solution of transient problems is: If

$$\mathcal{L}f(t) = F(s) \tag{2–131}$$

then

$$\mathcal{L}f(t)e^{-\alpha t} = F(s+\alpha) \tag{2–132}$$

The proof is immediate, for

$$\mathcal{L}f(t)e^{-\alpha t} = \int_0^\infty f(t)e^{-(s+\alpha)t}\,dt \tag{2–133}$$

and the integral on the right of (2–133) is the same function of $(s+\alpha)$ that

$$\int_0^\infty f(t)e^{-st}\,dt$$

is of s.

Because of the uniqueness of the transformation we can apply our conclusion in the opposite direction. Let us say we seek the time-function corresponding to the transform $V/(s+\alpha)$. Now V/s is the transform of a step function of height V appearing at the instant $t = 0$. Hence by the theorem (2–131 and 132) the time-function corresponding to $V/(s+\alpha)$ is $Ve^{-\alpha t}$ appearing at the instant $t = 0$.

Initial Value Theorem

This theorem yields the initial value of a time-function directly from its transform. The theorem states

$$\lim_{s \to \infty} sF(s) = \lim_{t \to 0} f(t) \tag{2–134}$$

provided that df/dt as well as $f(t)$ is Laplace transformable, that df/dt, finite in each continuous range of $f(t)$, approaches a finite limit at the end points of each such range, and that

$$\lim_{s \to \infty} sF(s)$$

exists.

The limit of $f(t)$ as t approaches zero is taken as t reduces to zero through positive values, and is the initial value $f(0+)$. Up to now $\mathscr{Re}\, s$ has been defined as a constant c. However, when taking the limit $sF(s)$ as s approaches infinity, we shall treat $\mathscr{Re}\, s$ as a variable.* Let it also be understood that as s approaches infinity, $\mathscr{Re}\, s$ approaches infinity.

We first consider the case in which $f(t)$ is continuous throughout the range $0 < t < \infty$, although a discontinuity may exist at $t = 0$.

From (2–103) and the differentiation theorem (2–110), we have

$$\int_0^\infty \frac{df}{dt} e^{-st} dt = sF(s) - f(0+) \tag{2–110b}$$

whence

$$\lim_{s \to \infty} \int_0^\infty \frac{df}{dt} e^{-st} dt = \lim_{s \to \infty} sF(s) - f(0+) \tag{2–135}$$

where $f(0+)$, being a constant, is unaffected by the limit process. Since the parameter, s, is independent of the variable of integration, the limit may be applied to the integrand prior to integration. We now recall that $\mathscr{Re}\, s \to \infty$, that $f(t)$ is continuous for all $t > 0$ so that (df/dt) is finite for all positive time, and that (df/dt) has finite limits as $t \to 0$ or ∞. Hence

$$\lim_{s \to \infty} [(df/dt)e^{-st}] = 0$$

for all $t > 0$. Since this holds for t arbitrarily small, the left side of (2–135) reduces to zero, yielding the theorem (2–134).

* For generalization of $\mathscr{Re}\, s$ to a variable, see Reference 8 and also Chapter 3.

The case in which $f(t)$ may have a discontinuity will now be considered. The nature of the discontinuities in $f(t)$ is stated after equation (2–134). In the course of the proof we shall obtain a more general differentiation theorem (see equation (2–140) below), of which (2–110) is a special case. For simplicity, we consider only one discontinuity at $t = T$ in addition to the one at $t = 0$. We define:

$$f(T-) = \lim_{\epsilon_1 \to 0} f(T - \epsilon_1)$$

and

$$f(T+) = \lim_{\epsilon_2 \to 0} f(T + \epsilon_2)$$

where ϵ_1 and ϵ_2 are both positive. We evaluate (essentially define)

$$\int_0^\infty (df/dt)e^{-st}\,dt$$

by the equation

$$\int_0^\infty \frac{df}{dt}e^{-st}\,dt = \int_0^T \frac{df}{dt}e^{-st}\,dt + \int_T^\infty \frac{df}{dt}e^{-st}\,dt \tag{2–136}$$

Because $f(t)$ is discontinuous at zero and at T, it is well to state explicitly the meaning of each of the integrals on the right side of (2–136), i.e.,

$$\int_0^T \frac{df}{dt}e^{-st}\,dt = \lim_{\substack{\epsilon \to 0 \\ \epsilon_1 \to 0}} \int_\epsilon^{T-\epsilon_1} \frac{df}{dt}e^{-st}\,dt \tag{2–137}$$

and

$$\int_T^\infty \frac{df}{dt}e^{-st}\,dt = \lim_{\substack{\epsilon_2 \to 0 \\ T' \to \infty}} \int_{T+\epsilon_2}^{T'} \frac{df}{dt}e^{-st}\,dt \tag{2–138}$$

where ϵ as well as ϵ_1 and ϵ_2 are positive. Each term on the right side of (2–136) is, now, easily evaluated by the method used in the derivation of (2–110). Hence

$$\begin{aligned}\int_0^\infty \frac{df}{dt}e^{-st}\,dt = {} & \lim_{\substack{\epsilon \to 0 \\ \epsilon_1 \to 0}} fe^{-st}\Big|_\epsilon^{T-\epsilon_1} + s \lim_{\substack{\epsilon \to 0 \\ \epsilon_1 \to 0}} \int_\epsilon^{T-\epsilon_1} fe^{-st}\,dt \\ & + \lim_{\substack{\epsilon_2 \to 0 \\ T' \to \infty}} fe^{-st}\Big|_{T+\epsilon_2}^{T'} + s \lim_{\substack{\epsilon_2 \to 0 \\ T' \to \infty}} \int_{T+\epsilon_2}^{T'} fe^{-st}\,dt\end{aligned} \tag{2–139}$$

Since f has only a finite discontinuity at $t = T$, the sum of the second and fourth terms becomes simply

$$s \int_0^\infty f e^{-st} dt$$

i.e., $sF(s)$. The sum of the first and third terms is easily evaluated as $f(T-)e^{-sT} - f(0+) - f(T+)e^{-sT}$. As mentioned after (2–110a), we may take

$$\lim_{T' \to \infty} f e^{-sT'}$$

to be zero on physical grounds. Hence we find

$$\int_0^\infty \frac{df}{dt} e^{-st} dt = sF(s) - f(0+) - Ke^{-sT} \qquad (2\text{–}140)^*$$

where $K = f(T+) - f(T-)$. Now when $s \to \infty$, $\mathcal{Re}\, s \to \infty$ as stipulated in the statement of the theorem. For this reason, the right-hand side of (2–140) approaches the value

$$\lim_{s \to \infty} sF(s) - f(0+)$$

In order to evaluate the limit of the left side of (2–140), we consider the means by which its value was determined. It is the value of the integral of $(df/dt)e^{-st}$ over the range of time $\epsilon < t < T - \epsilon_1$ added to the value of the same integral over the range of time $T + \epsilon_2 < t < \infty$. In each range df/dt is finite since $f(t)$ is continuous. We have stipulated with the statement of the theorem that df/dt approaches a finite limit at the end point of each range. Hence, since $\mathcal{Re}\, s \to \infty$,

$$\lim_{s \to \infty} (df/dt)e^{-st}$$

is zero. This holds for all values of ϵ, ϵ_1, and ϵ_2, however small. Hence the limiting value of each integral will be zero when ϵ, ϵ_1, and ϵ_2 reduce to zero. As s and its real part approach infinity, (2–140) becomes (2–134).

Interpretation in Terms of the Impulse Function

In the foregoing development the point of discontinuity at $t = T$ was approached from either side, and that at $t = 0$ from the right. In neither case was anything said regarding the derivative *at* points of discontinuity. The basic definition of a derivative, i.e.,

$$\lim_{\Delta t \to 0} (\Delta f / \Delta t)$$

yields two values at a point of discontinuity: the right-hand derivative

* See footnote, page 109.

obtained when Δt reduces to zero through positive values and the left-hand derivative obtained when Δt reduces to zero through negative values.[8] The engineer will be loath to stop here, however, since a discontinuity represents an instantaneous change and, therefore, suggests an infinite rate of change. This viewpoint stems from a recognition of the fact that the function $f(t)$ represents (in applied mathematics) a physical quantity such as voltage or current. A physical quantity does not, in general, suffer discontinuities, but may exhibit extremely rapid changes with corresponding time derivatives of very large magnitude. We, therefore, prefer to regard the discontinuity as an idealization or limiting case of extremely rapid change. With this end in mind, let us define

$$\left.\begin{aligned} g(t) &= f(T-) && \text{when} \quad t < T \\ g(t) &= f(T-) + K\frac{1}{\epsilon}(t-T) && \text{when} \quad T < t < T+\epsilon \\ \text{and} \quad g(t) &= f(T+) && \text{when} \quad T+\epsilon < t \end{aligned}\right\} \qquad (2\text{–}141)^*$$

where, as following (2–140), $K = f(T+) - f(T-)$. The function $g(t)$ changes in value by K in a time ϵ. As ϵ reduces to zero, the change in value of $g(t)$ from $f(T-)$ to $f(T+)$ approaches identity with the discontinuity in $f(t)$. The function $g'(t)$, i.e., dg/dt, is of interest.

$$\left.\begin{aligned} g'(t) &= 0 && \text{when} \quad t < T \\ g'(t) &= K\frac{1}{\epsilon} && \text{when} \quad T < t < T+\epsilon \\ g'(t) &= 0 && \text{when} \quad T+\epsilon < t \end{aligned}\right\} \qquad (2\text{–}142)$$

We observe that

$$\int_0^\infty g'(t)\,dt = \int_T^{T+\epsilon} K\frac{1}{\epsilon}\,dt = K\frac{1}{\epsilon}\epsilon = K$$

and note that this value is independent of ϵ, and is valid however small ϵ is chosen. We now define a unit impulse occurring at $t = T$ by the equation

$$Ku_0(t-T) = \lim_{\epsilon \to 0} g'(t) \qquad (2\text{–}143)$$

where $u_0(t-T)$ is the *unit impulse*, and K is termed the strength of the impulse. A unit impulse occurring at zero time is represented as $u_0(t)$,

* Other definining functions are also used to obtain the impulse function. See reference 20 at the end of the chapter.

and the time T is then replaced by zero in the equations defining $g'(t)$. The unit impulse has paradoxical properties: it equals zero for all time except the instant $t = T$, it is infinite at $t = T$, and its integral over all time is equal to 1. The impulse function is very useful, however, in problems where the time required for a very rapid change in a quantity is negligible (e.g., a problem involving a capacitance charging through leads whose resistance can be neglected). From equations (2–142) and (2–143) it is evident that an impulse function of strength K can, in physical problems, represent the derivative of $f(t)$ at a discontinuity where the value of $f(t)$ changes by K.

The Laplace transform of the impulse function is obtainable and facilitates the interpretation of equation (2–140). The function $g'(t)$, defined in (2–142), is Laplace transformable for any finite value of ϵ. Its transform is easily found by direct integration to be:

$$\mathcal{L}g'(t) = \frac{K}{\epsilon s}(1 - e^{-\epsilon s})e^{-sT} \qquad (2\text{–}144)$$

Now either by applying L'Hospital's rule to the fraction $(1 - e^{-\epsilon s})/\epsilon$, or by expressing $e^{-\epsilon s}$ in a power series, we find

$$\lim_{\epsilon \to 0} \mathcal{L}g'(t) = Ke^{-sT} \qquad (2\text{–}145)$$

Since ϵ is independent of t, the limit sign may be brought inside the transform symbol,* leading to

$$K\,\mathcal{L}u_0(t - T) = Ke^{-sT} \qquad (2\text{–}146)$$

where K, being a constant, is written outside the transform symbol.

On this basis Ke^{-sT} is recognized as the transform of an impulse of strength K occurring at $t = T$. The transform of an impulse of strength K occurring at $t = 0$ is then K.†

* The validity of this step may be questioned, since $g'(T) \to \infty$ as $\epsilon \to 0$. See the comments at the end of this subsection.

† A sequence of impulse functions of increasing order can be defined as corresponding to the transforms $1, s, s^2 \ldots$.[1] Each of these impulse functions occurs at $t = 0$ and is said to be of unit value. The first transform, 1, corresponds to the unit impulse discussed in the text. The transform s corresponds to the unit doublet at $t = 0$, which is defined as

$$\lim_{\epsilon \to 0} (1/\epsilon^2)[u(t) - 2u(t - \epsilon) + u(t - 2\epsilon)]$$

where u is the unit-step function defined on p. 102. We recognize that for $\epsilon > 0$,

$$(1/\epsilon^2)[u(t) - 2u(t - \epsilon) + u(t - 2\epsilon)]$$

represents a pair of pulses. The first pulse is of height $1/\epsilon^2$ during the interval $0 < t < \epsilon$. The second pulse follows during the interval $\epsilon < t < 2\epsilon$. The corresponding Laplace transform, $(1/\epsilon^2)[1 - 2\,e^{-\epsilon s} + e^{-2\epsilon s}]$, reduces to s as ϵ approaches zero.[8] Time-functions leading to impulses of higher order (unit triplet, etc.) are given in Reference 1; see also problem 2–8.

With the impulse function concept available, equation (2–140) can be interpreted. From the method of evaluation of

$$\int_0^\infty (df/dt)e^{-st}\,dt$$

it is evident that the right-hand side of (2–140) is the Laplace transform of a function which is equal to df/dt over the ranges of time $0 < t < T$, and $T < t < \infty$, and that the integral does not contain an impulse term. The terms $f(0+)$ and Ke^{-sT}, which represent impulses at $t = 0$ and $t = T$, must therefore be cancelled by terms in $sF(s)$. A simple illustration will clarify this interpretation:

Let

$$f(t) = e^{-\alpha t} \qquad 0 < t < T \tag{2–147}$$

$$f(t) = e^{-\alpha t}+1 \quad T < t < \infty \tag{2–148}$$

where α is a positive number.

Either by direct integration, or with the aid of the delay factor theorem (2–125)

$$\mathcal{L}f(t) = \frac{1}{s+\alpha} + \frac{1}{s}e^{-sT} \tag{2–149}$$

whence

$$sF(s) = \frac{s}{s+\alpha} + e^{-sT} \tag{2–150}$$

Or, by carrying out one step of a long-division of s by $(s+\alpha)$,

$$sF(s) = 1 - \frac{\alpha}{s+\alpha} + e^{-sT} \tag{2–151}$$

The term 1 represents a unit impulse at $t = 0$, and e^{-sT} represents a unit impulse at $t = T$. Now evaluating the right-hand side of (2–140) with the aid of (2–151), we find

$$sF(s) - f(0+) - Ke^{-sT} = -\frac{\alpha}{s+\alpha} \tag{2–152}$$

for $f(0+) = 1$ and $K = 1$ in the function $f(t)$, defined in (2–147, 148). The right-hand side of (2–152) is $\mathcal{L}df/dt$. We note that $-\alpha/(s+\alpha)$ is the transform of the derivative of $f(t)$ in the time ranges $0 < t < T$, and $T < t$. At the end points of each range we obtain for df/dt the limiting value of this derivative as the end point is approached from within the range. Thus the impulse terms $-f(0+)$ and $-Ke^{-sT}$ cancel the impulse terms contained within $sF(s)$. The same situation was observed in connection with (2–110), the differentiation theorem, when $f(t)$ was continuous save at $t = 0$. There it was also found that $\mathcal{L}^{-1}[sF(s)-f(0+)]$ yielded for df/dt a function which at $t = 0$ was lim df/dt as t approached zero through positive values.*

There is, of course, a certain lack of mathematical rigor in the use of the impulse function. The function g', defined for non-zero ϵ, is easily understood and clearly Laplace transformable. However, when ϵ approaches zero, g' increases without limit at one instant of time and vanishes for all other values of time. We have shown the integral of g' to be constant for all ϵ, but the meaning of the integral of this function when $\epsilon = 0$ may be questioned. The same question arises regarding the Laplace transform of g' when $\epsilon = 0$. It is, therefore, preferable to regard the impulse function as a short-hand notation used to approximate the time derivative during an extremely rapid change in a physical quantity.

We shall find that when the impulse function is used in problems, the result can easily be verified from the physical data of the particular problem at hand.

Final Value Theorem

The final value of a time-function, i.e.,

$$\lim_{t \to \infty} f(t)$$

can often be obtained directly from its transform. Since the statement of this theorem can be given much more effectively in terms of the properties of $F(s)$ as a function of a complex variable, both the theorem and its proof are reserved for Chapter 3.

Product of Two Transforms

The time-function corresponding to the product of two transforms may be obtained from the following theorem whose proof may be found in References 3, 8, and 20 at the end of this chapter.

If

$$F_1(s) = \mathcal{L}f_1(t) \tag{2–153}$$

and

$$F_2(s) = \mathcal{L}f_2(t) \tag{2–154}$$

* If we omit the last term of (2–140), we obtain an impulse function to represent the derivative at the discontinuity.

then

$$F_1(s)F_2(s) = \mathfrak{L}\int_0^t f_1(\tau)f_2(t-\tau)\,d\tau$$

$$= \mathfrak{L}\int_0^t f_1(t-\tau)f_2(\tau)\,d\tau \qquad (2\text{–}155)$$

Using the second form in (2–155), we note that if $F_1(s) = 1/s$, then

$$(1/s)F_2(s) = \mathfrak{L}\int_0^t f_2(\tau)\,d\tau$$

since $1/s$ is the transform of a step function of unit height. Thus we find the theorem (2–116a) to be a special case of the present one.

2-7 Summary

This chapter has introduced the Fourier series, Fourier integral, and Laplace transformation, and has shown how the first two of these lead to an extension of the reasoning and technique of alternating-current analysis to problems of a more general nature.

Dirichlet's conditions were stated and the Fourier series was presented in real and complex form. The Fourier series was then used to represent periodic voltage or current. The superposition principle was developed with the aid of a simple circuit problem, i.e., it was found that the response of a linear circuit to a periodic excitation could be obtained by first separately calculating the response corresponding to each term in the Fourier series for the excitation, and then superposing the results. Thus the Fourier series for the response was obtained through steady-state alternating-current calculation.

With the Fourier series and superposition principle available, the Fourier integral theorem was obtained, along with the relation between the Fourier transform of excitation and of response. The method of derivation involved an extension of the Fourier series base period to cover an infinite time range. The points at which the derivation lacked mathematical rigor were discussed, and references given for the student interested in a mathematically rigorous demonstration.

Certain applications of the Fourier integral theorem were presented: The criteria for distortionless transmission, i.e., the requisite alternating-current characteristics of an ideal transmission system, were obtained. Requirements for an ideal band-pass and an ideal low-pass filter were also found. The response of an ideal band-pass and ideal low-pass filter to a pulse of sinusoidal and of constant voltage were respectively calculated with certain approximations. A general relationship between high- and low-frequency circuits was discussed. In all these applications, the analysis was in terms of the over-all frequency characteristics of the network.

A still more general and effective tool for electric circuit analysis, the Laplace transformation, was next derived. The direct transform and the inversion integral were obtained. The value of the Laplace transformation as a basis for circuit analysis was discussed. A number of basic theorems of the Laplace transformation were then stated and derived. These included the theorems on linearity, differentiation, integration, time delay and initial value. The impulse function and its transform were also developed.

Problems

2-1. The function $v(t)$ is given by

$$v(t) = 0 \qquad \text{when} \quad -\frac{T}{2} < t < -\frac{kT}{2}$$

$$v(t) = \frac{2V}{kT}t \qquad \text{when} \quad -\frac{kT}{2} < t < \frac{kT}{2}$$

$$v(t) = 0 \qquad \text{when} \quad \frac{kT}{2} < t < \frac{T}{2}$$

where $0 < k < 1$.

(A) Does $v(t)$ satisfy Dirichlet's conditions in the interval $-T/2 < t < T/2$?

(B) Specify the points of discontinuity of $v(t)$.

(C) Discuss dv/dt at $t = \pm kT/2$, both from a strictly mathematical viewpoint and from a less rigid, "engineering" viewpoint.

(D) Let $v_1(t)$ be defined for $-\infty < t < \infty$. Let it be repetitive with period T, and let it be identical with $v(t)$ in the range $-T/2 < t < T/2$. Compare the Fourier series for $v_1(t)$ with that for $v(t)$.

2-2. Find the coefficient for the nth term in the Fourier series for $v(t)$ defined in Problem 2–1. Assume the real form.

2-3. (A) Find the coefficient α_n of the term $\alpha_n e^{jn\omega_1 t}$ in the complex form of the Fourier series.

(B) Show that the result reduces to $\alpha_0 = 0$ despite the factor $1/n^2$ in the general expression.

2-4. Let $a = kT$, and let a be constant as T increases without limit. By careful redefinition of variables, valid for large T, show that the series whose coefficients we found in Problem 2–3 becomes a Fourier integral for $v(t)$. Note that this is not a mathematically rigorous process.

2-5. Verify the result of problem 2-4 by using the Fourier integral theorem.

2-6. A number of functions are listed below. Answer the following questions regarding each one:

(NOTE: The statement that a function A is "represented" by another function B may be taken to mean that B uniquely determines A at all points at which A is continuous.)

(A) Can the function be represented by a Fourier series over a finite time interval?

(B) Can the function be represented by a Fourier series for all time, i.e., $-\infty < t < \infty$?

(C) Can the function be represented by a Fourier integral without introduction of a convergence factor?

(D) Can the function be represented by a Laplace transform?

(1) $f(t) = Ke^{at}$ when $0 < t < T$, $a > 0$ and real

$f(t) = 0$ when $t < 0$ and $t > T$

(2) $f(t) = Ke^{a(t-nT)}$ when $nT < t < (n+1)T$

with $n = 0, \pm 1, \pm 2, \ldots$

$a > 0$ and real

(3) $f(t) = Ke^{-a|t|}$ when $-\infty < t < \infty$ $a > 0$ and real

(4) $f(t) = Ke^{at}$ when $0 < t < \infty$ $a > 0$ and real

$f(t) = 0$ when $-\infty < t < 0$

2-7.

$$v(t) = 0 \quad \text{when} \quad t < 0$$

$$v(t) = \frac{V}{T}t \quad 0 < t < T$$

$$v(t) = \frac{V}{2} \quad T < t$$

(A) Evaluate $\mathcal{L}v(t)$, using the definition of the Laplace transform.

(B) Evaluate $\mathcal{L}v(t)$ by regarding it as a superposition of continuous time-functions.

(C) Evaluate $\mathcal{L}\, dv/dt$.

(D) Sketch $\mathcal{L}^{-1}\, dv/dt$.

2-8. Consider the function

$$v(t) = [u(t) - 4u(t-\epsilon) + 6u(t-2\epsilon) - 4u(t-3\epsilon) + u(t-\epsilon)]\frac{1}{\epsilon^4}$$

$$\text{where} \quad u(x) = 0 \quad \text{when} \quad x < 0$$

$$u(x) = 1 \quad \text{when} \quad x > 0$$

(A) Determine $\mathcal{L}v(t)$ for a given value of ϵ.

(B) Determine $\lim_{\varepsilon \to 0} \mathfrak{L}v(t)$.

(C) What order of impulse function does this represent?

(D) Compare the areas of the successive pulses when ϵ is greater than zero to the coefficients in the expansion of $(x+y)^3$.

2-9.

$$f_1(t) = 0 \qquad \text{when} \quad t < 0$$

$$f_1(t) = e^{-at} + e^{at^2} \qquad \text{when} \quad t > 0$$

$$f_2(t) = 0 \qquad \text{when} \quad t < 0$$

$$f_2(t) = e^{at} - e^{at^2} \qquad \text{when} \quad t > 0$$

$$f_3(t) = f_1(t) + f_2(t)$$

Let a be a real, positive constant.

(A) Is $f_1(t)$ Laplace transformable?

(B) Is $f_2(t)$ Laplace transformable?

(C) Is $f_3(t)$ Laplace transformable?

(D) Is it necessary for each of two functions to be Laplace transformable for their sum to be Laplace transformable?

(E) Is it sufficient for each of two functions to be Laplace transformable for their sum to be Laplace transformable?

2-10.

$$f(t) = e^{at} \sin \omega t \qquad \text{when} \quad t > 0$$

$$f(t) = 0 \qquad \text{when} \quad t < 0$$

(A) Evaluate $\mathfrak{L}f(t)$.

(B) If $F(s) = \mathfrak{L}f(t)$ where $s = \alpha + j\omega$, and if a is real and positive, does $\lim_{\alpha \to 0} F(s)$ equal the Fourier integral of $f(t)$?

(C) Answer (B) when a is real and negative.

References for Chapter 2

1. Campbell, G. A., and Foster, R. M., "Fourier Integrals for Practical Applications," *Bell Telephone System Monograph* B-584 (Sept. 1931).
2. Carslaw, H. S., *Introduction to the Theory of Fourier's Series and Integrals*, 3rd ed., Macmillan & Co., Ltd., London, 1930; reprinted by Dover Publications, Inc., New York, 1952.
3. Carslaw, H. S., and Jaeger, J. C., *Operational Methods in Applied Mathematics*, 2nd ed., Oxford University Press, New York, 1949.
4. Cherry, C., *Pulses and Transients in Communication Circuits*, Dover Publications, Inc., New York, 1950.
5. Churchill, R. V., *Fourier Series and Boundary Value Problems*, McGraw-Hill Book Co., Inc., New York, 1941.
6. Churchill, R. V., *Modern Operational Mathematics in Engineering*, McGraw-Hill Book Co., Inc., New York, 1944; *Operational Mathematics*, 2nd ed., 1958.

7. Courant, R., translated by McShane, E. J., *Differential and Integral Calculus*, Vols. I and II, Interscience Publishers, Inc. New York, [1936]–1938.
8. Gardner, M. F., and Barnes, J. L., *Transients in Linear Systems Studied by the Laplace Transformation*, John Wiley & Sons, Inc., New York, 1942.
9. Goldman, S., *Frequency Analysis, Modulation, and Noise*, McGraw-Hill Book Co., Inc., New York, 1948.
10. Guillemin, E. A., *Communication Networks*, Vols. I and II, John Wiley & Sons, Inc., New York, 1931, 1935.
11. Guillemin, E. A., *The Mathematics of Circuit Analysis*, John Wiley & Sons Inc., New York, 1949.
12. Lane, C. E., "Phase Distortion in Telephone Apparatus," *Bell System Tech. J.*, Vol. 9, pp. 493–521 (July 1930).
13. LePage, W. R., and Seely, S., *General Network Analysis*, McGraw-Hill Book Co., Inc., New York, 1952.
14. Sneddon, I. N., *Fourier Transforms*, McGraw-Hill Book Co., Inc., New York, 1951.
15. Sokolnikoff, I. S., and Sokolnikoff, E. S., *Higher Mathematics for Engineers and Physicists*, 2nd ed., Mc-Graw-Hill Book Co., Inc., New York, 1941.
16. Sullivan, W. L., "Analysis of Systems with Known Transmission-Frequency Characteristics by Fourier Integrals," *Elec. Eng.*, Vol. 61, pp. 248–256 (1942).
17. Thomson, W. T., *Laplace Transformation, Theory and Engineering Applications*, Prentice-Hall, Inc., New York, 1950.
18. Truxal, J. G., *Automatic Feedback Control System Synthesis*, McGraw-Hill Book Co., Inc., New York, 1955.
19. Valley, G. E., Jr., and Wallman, H., *Vacuum Tube Amplifiers*, McGraw-Hill Book Co., Inc., New York, 1948.
20. Weber, E., *Linear Transient Analysis*, Vol. I: *Lumped-Parameter Two-Terminal Networks*, John Wiley & Sons, Inc., New York, 1954.
21. Weber, E., *Linear Transient Analysis*, Vol. II: *Two-Terminal-Pair Networks. Transmission Lines*, John Wiley & Sons, Inc., New York, 1956.

Chapter 3

COMPLEX VARIABLE AND EVALUATION OF THE INVERSION INTEGRAL

The methods of the theory of functions of a complex variable have become of increasing importance to the analysis and design of electric networks. Evaluation of the inversion integral, criteria for the stability of active feedback networks, and various methods of network synthesis all lean heavily upon the theory of functions of a complex variable. In this chapter we shall begin with basic concepts and then develop theorems which find their application in the study of electric networks.

3-1 Complex Variable*

A complex number s may be represented in rectangular form as $s = \alpha + j\omega$ or alternatively in polar form by $|s|\underline{/\theta}$. The familiar relations $|s| = \sqrt{\alpha^2 + \omega^2}$ and $\theta = \tan^{-1}(\omega/\alpha)$ assure that both forms represent the same complex number. This in turn may be plotted as a point with rectangular coordinates α and ω or the equivalent polar coordinates $|s|$ and θ. When α or ω or both vary, s is termed a complex variable and the plane containing the plot of its values is called the s-plane. As a simple illustration of such a plot, let $\alpha^2 + \omega^2 = r^2$ where r is a constant. Then s lies on a circle in the s-plane as in Fig. 3-1.

3-2 Function of a Complex Variable

The variable F (usually complex) is said to be a function of the complex variable s, provided that to each value of s there corresponds one or more

* The notation $s = \alpha + j\omega$ is chosen in preference to $Z = x + jy$ for consistency with the rest of the text. In other chapters Z will represent impedance and will be a function of s. The letter ω is chosen for the imaginary part of s, since values of $s = j\omega$ will yield solutions to problems involving the sinusoidal steady state, and $\omega/2\pi$ will then represent a-c frequency. In this chapter, however, s, α, and ω may be thought of simply as three letters to represent any complex variable.

values of F. When only one value of F corresponds to each value of s, F is called a *single-valued* function. When more than one value of F is determined by each value of s, F is *multiple-valued*. Formally, the functional relationship is expressed as

$$F = F(s) \tag{3–1}$$

which is read simply "F is a function of s".

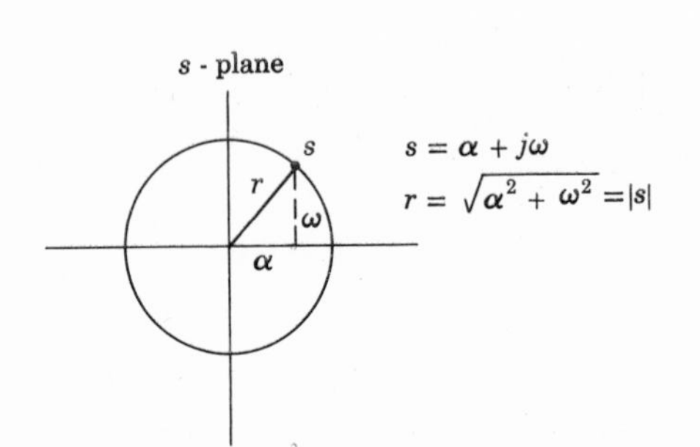

Fig. 3–1.

In most practical situations, the correspondence between F and s is expressed through an equation. Simple examples are

$$F = s^2 \tag{3–2}$$

and

$$F^2 = s \tag{3–3}$$

Equation (3–2) illustrates a single-valued function of s, since each value of s determines one value of F. Thus if $s = 5\underline{/\pi/3}$, F is uniquely determined as $25\underline{/2\pi/3}$. Equation (3–3) on the other hand illustrates a double-valued function. If $s = 25\underline{/2\pi/3}$ in that equation, F is given by either $5\underline{/\pi/3}$ or $5\underline{/4\pi/3}$.

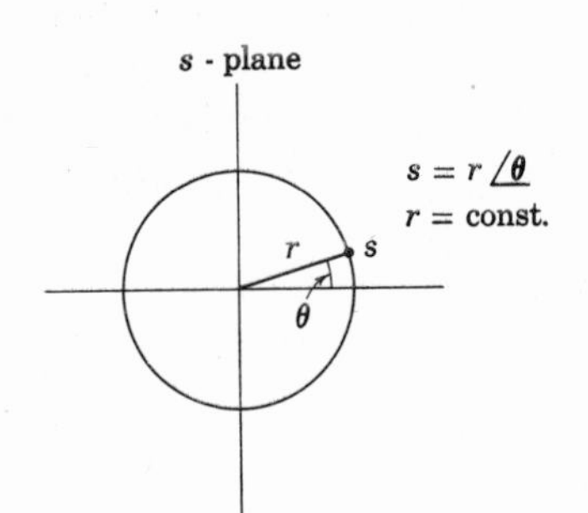

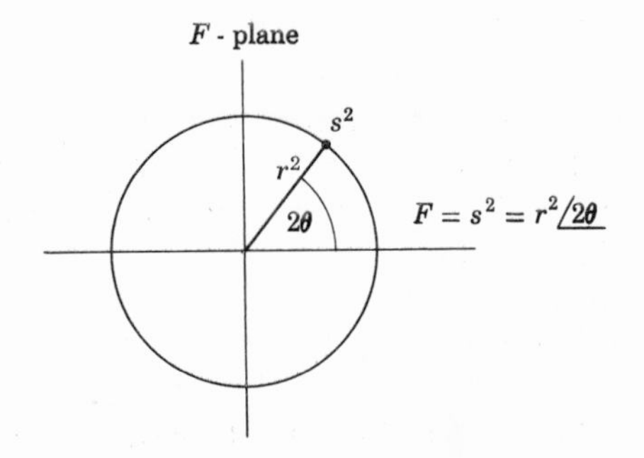

Fig. 3–2.

A graphical representation of a function of a complex variable requires more than one plane. The variation of s is drawn in the s-plane, while that of F is shown in the F-plane. As an illustration, suppose that s is confined to a circle as in Fig. 3–1. Then equation (3–2) may be represented in two planes as shown in Fig. 3–2.

3-3 Continuity

A function of a complex variable is continuous at a point, $s = a$, provided that

$$\lim_{s \to a} F(s) = F(a) \tag{3-4}$$

The requirement (3–4) must be examined in detail. First we note that (3–4) cannot be satisfied unless F can be evaluated at $s = a$; i.e., unless $F(a)$ exists, there will be a discontinuity at $s = a$. The function $F = 1/s$ illustrates a discontinuity of this type. Let the point a be chosen as the origin, i.e., $a = 0$. We observe that $F(0)$ cannot be evaluated, since infinity is not a number. The function $F = 1/s$ is, then, discontinuous at the origin, for it cannot satisfy (3–4) at this point. In general, points at which a function becomes infinite are points of discontinuity.

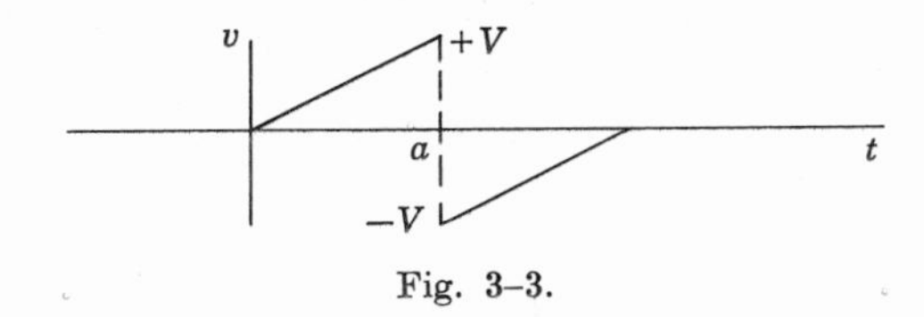

Fig. 3–3.

The requirement (3–4) also demands that $F(s)$ can be made arbitrarily close to $F(a)$ by a choice of s sufficiently close to a. The manner in which s approaches a must not alter the result. The significance of this requirement can best be understood by reference to a function of a real variable shown in Fig. 3–3. Without formal definitions, it is evident that $t = a$ is a point of discontinuity for the function v. If t approaches a from the left, v nears the value V; while if t approaches a from the right, v becomes $-V$. The essence of the discontinuity lies in the fact that the function v approaches different values depending upon the direction from which t moves toward a. Now, in the case of a complex variable, the requirement (3–4) means that $F(s)$ must approach $F(a)$ as s moves toward a from any direction in the complex plane.*

3-4 Derivative of a Function of a Complex Variable

The definition of the derivative of a function of a complex variable is entirely analogous to that of the derivative of a function of a real variable.

* When a function is defined only over a certain region, continuity at a point on the boundary of this region requires only that s approach a from any direction *within the region*. See Reference 2 at the end of this chapter.

If F is a function of the complex variable s, the derivative of F with respect to s at a point $s = a$ is defined

$$\left.\frac{dF}{ds}\right|_{s=a} = \lim_{\Delta s \to 0} \frac{F(a+\Delta s) - F(a)}{\Delta s} \tag{3–5}$$

It is implicit in the term *limit* that the result must not depend on the direction of Δs as it goes to zero. As an illustration, let us take a function which has a derivative at all finite points in the complex plane, e.g., $F = s^2$. We shall compute the limit (3–5) in three ways: with $\Delta s = \Delta\alpha$, then

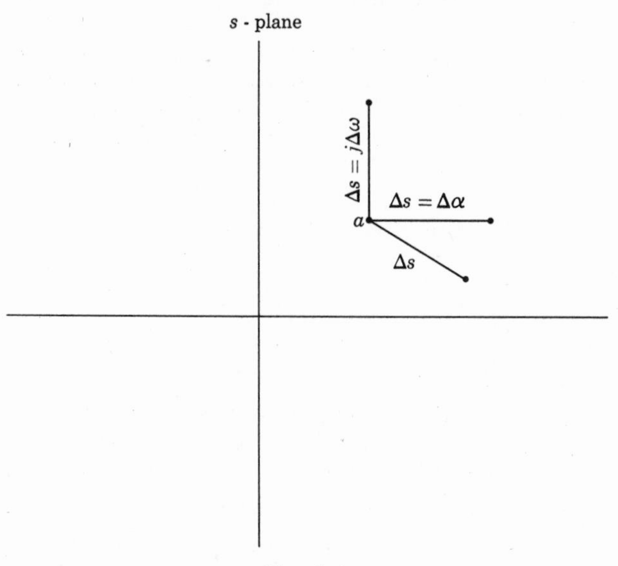

Fig. 3–4.

with $\Delta s = j\Delta\omega$, and finally with Δs in an arbitrary direction. The s-plane is shown in Fig. 3–4. When $\Delta s = \Delta\alpha$, equation (3–5) yields

$$\left.\frac{dF}{ds}\right|_{s=a} = \lim_{\Delta\alpha \to 0} \frac{(a+\Delta\alpha)^2 - a^2}{\Delta\alpha} = \lim_{\Delta\alpha \to 0} \frac{2a\Delta\alpha + \Delta\alpha^2}{\Delta\alpha} = 2a \tag{3–6a}$$

When $\Delta s = j\Delta\omega$:

$$\left.\frac{dF}{ds}\right|_{s=a} = \lim_{j\Delta\omega \to 0} \frac{(a+j\Delta\omega)^2 - a^2}{j\Delta\omega} = \lim_{j\Delta\omega \to 0} \frac{2aj\Delta\omega - \Delta\omega^2}{j\Delta\omega} = 2a \tag{3–6b}$$

In general, for any Δs

$$\left.\frac{dF}{ds}\right|_{s=a} = \lim_{\Delta s \to 0} \frac{(a+\Delta s)^2 - a^2}{\Delta s} = \lim_{\Delta s \to 0} \frac{2as\Delta s + \Delta s^2}{\Delta s} = 2a \tag{3–6c}$$

Since the limit is independent of the manner in which Δs approaches zero—as proven by (3–6c)—the function $F = s^2$ has a derivative at $s = a$, whose value is $2a$. Since the point a can be anywhere in the complex plane, the result is usually expressed by the statement that if $F = s^2$, $dF/ds = 2s$. It will be observed that the function $y = x^2$ yields a derivative of the same form, namely $dy/dx = 2x$. Now any single-valued function $F(s)$ which can be given *directly by an expression in s* must have a differentiation formula identical with that of the same function of a real variable[9] This follows because the differentiation formula will be derived through identical steps in the two cases. A few simple examples are

$$\frac{d}{ds}s^3 = 3s^2, \quad \frac{d}{ds}e^{st} = te^{st} \quad \text{and} \quad \frac{d}{ds}\sin st = t\cos st$$

t being constant in the last two instances.

It will be of interest to study a function which does not have a derivative at any point in the complex plane, namely[7]

$$F = s^* \tag{3–7}$$

where $s^* = \alpha - j\omega$, i.e., the conjugate of $s = \alpha + j\omega$. Hence if the point a is given by $\alpha_1 + j\omega_1$, then $F(a) = \alpha_1 - j\omega_1$. Now if $\Delta s = \Delta\alpha$, then $F(a+\Delta s) = F(\alpha_1 + \Delta\alpha + j\omega_1) = \alpha_1 + \Delta\alpha - j\omega_1$ while if $\Delta s = j\Delta\omega$, then $F(a+\Delta s) = F(\alpha_1 + j\omega_1 + j\Delta\omega) = \alpha_1 - j\omega_1 - j\Delta\omega$. If we attempt to evaluate a derivative, the definition (3–5) leads to the inconsistent results

$$\lim_{\Delta\alpha\to 0} \frac{(\alpha_1 + \Delta\alpha - j\omega_1) - (\alpha_1 - j\omega_1)}{\Delta\alpha} = \frac{\Delta\alpha}{\Delta\alpha} = 1 \tag{3–8}$$

while

$$\lim_{j\Delta\omega\to 0} \frac{(\alpha_1 - j\omega_1 - j\Delta\omega) - (\alpha_1 - j\omega_1)}{j\Delta\omega} = \frac{-j\Delta\omega}{j\Delta\omega} = -1 \tag{3–9}$$

Hence the derivative of the function $F = s^*$ does not exist at any point.

In our applications we shall generally be concerned with functions whose derivatives do not exist at particular points. Consider for example $F = 1/s$. The definition (3–5) yields

$$\left.\frac{dF}{ds}\right|_{s=a} = \lim_{\Delta s\to 0} \frac{\dfrac{1}{a+\Delta s} - \dfrac{1}{a}}{\Delta s} = -\frac{1}{a^2} \tag{3–10}$$

However, at the point $a = 0$, the limit (3–10) does not exist and the same must be said of $dF/ds|_{s=0}$. We shall find, however, that the way in which the function F varies close to the point $s = 0$ will be of considerable importance.

3-5 Analytic Functions

A function of a complex variable is *regular* in a region of the complex plane provided that it is single-valued and has a derivative at every point of the region. A function is regular at a point $s = a$ provided that it is regular in a small neighborhood of $s = a$. The point $s = a$ is included in its neighborhood, which consists of a small circular area with $s = a$ at its center.[11]

The term *analytic* can be used in two ways. Certain authors use this term as synonymous with *regular*.[2,22] Others use it as a designation of a function *regular in at least one region of the complex plane*.[11] Thus, according to the latter definition, a ratio of polynomials is described as an analytic function of a complex variable which is regular at all finite points of the complex plane except those at which the denominator is zero. The term *analytic function* will be used in the latter sense in this text.

A few illustrations will suffice to show the significance of these definitions. It was demonstrated in Section 3–4 that the single-valued function $F = s^2$ has a derivative at every finite point of the s plane. Hence it is regular at every point of the s plane (excluding $s = \infty$, however). On the other hand, the function $F = s^*$ was found not to have a derivative at any point. Hence the function $F = s^*$ is not regular anywhere and is not an analytic function according to either use of the term *analytic*. The function $F = 1/s$ was shown to have a derivative at all points of the s-plane except the origin. Clearly then this function is not regular at the origin. At any other point (even close to the origin) it is regular, since one can choose a neighborhood sufficiently small to exclude the origin while including the point in question. According to the second usage of the term *analytic* stated above, the function $F = 1/s$ may be termed an analytic function regular at all points of the s-plane save the origin.

The function

$$F = s^{3/2} \tag{3–11}$$

brings out the significance of the requirement that a function be regular at all points of a *neighborhood* of a particular point before it can be said to be regular at that point. At the point $s = 0$, $F = 0$ and from the definition of the derivative

$$\left.\frac{dF}{ds}\right|_{s=0} = \lim_{\Delta s \to 0} \frac{(0 + \Delta s)^{3/2} - (0)^{3/2}}{\Delta s} = \lim_{\Delta s \to 0} (\Delta s)^{1/2} = 0 \tag{3–12}$$

Hence the function and its derivative have the unique value zero at the origin. However, at points in any neighborhood including the origin, the function F is not single-valued, so that the function $F = s^{3/2}$ is not regular at the origin.

3-6 Cauchy–Riemann Equations

The Cauchy–Riemann partial differential equations interrelate the derivatives of the real and imaginary parts of an analytic function of a complex variable at any regular point of the function. We shall first derive these equations, and demonstrate that it is *necessary* that they hold in a region where $F(s)$ is regular.

Let the real and imaginary parts of F be called u and v. Since $s = \alpha + j\omega$, we must have

$$u = u(\alpha, \omega) \tag{3–13}$$

$$v = v(\alpha, \omega) \tag{3–14}$$

Now the function F may be differentiated with Δs taken parallel either to the α-axis or to the $j\omega$-axis. Hence the derivative of

$$F = u + jv \tag{3–15}$$

can be given by two alternative expressions. When Δs is taken parallel to the α-axis

$$\frac{dF}{ds} = \lim_{\Delta\alpha \to 0} \frac{F(s+\Delta\alpha) - F(s)}{\Delta\alpha} \tag{3–16}$$

Now $F(s+\Delta\alpha) = u(\alpha+\Delta\alpha, \omega) + jv(\alpha+\Delta\alpha, \omega)$, while $F(s) = u(\alpha, \omega) + jv(\alpha, \omega)$. We may, therefore, express (3–16) as a sum of two terms, namely:

$$\frac{dF}{ds} = \lim_{\Delta\alpha \to 0} \frac{u(\alpha+\Delta\alpha, \omega) - u(\alpha, \omega)}{\Delta\alpha} + j \lim_{\Delta\alpha \to 0} \frac{v(\alpha+\Delta\alpha, \omega) - v(\alpha, \omega)}{\Delta\alpha} \tag{3–16a}$$

Each of these terms defines a partial derivative, whence

$$\frac{dF}{ds} = \frac{\partial u}{\partial \alpha} + j\frac{\partial v}{\partial \alpha} \tag{3–17}$$

Now using

$$\frac{dF}{ds} = \lim_{j\Delta\omega \to 0} \frac{F(s+j\Delta\omega) - F(s)}{j\Delta\omega} \tag{3–18}$$

one obtains in an entirely similar manner

$$\frac{dF}{ds} = \frac{\partial v}{\partial \omega} - j\frac{\partial u}{\partial \omega} \tag{3–19}$$

Since F is regular where dF/ds is evaluated, the expressions for its derivative given by (3–17 and 19) are equivalent. Equating the real parts of these expressions to each other and the imaginary parts to each other leads to the *Cauchy–Riemann equations*

$$\frac{\partial u}{\partial \alpha} = \frac{\partial v}{\partial \omega} \tag{3–20}$$

and

$$\frac{\partial v}{\partial \alpha} = -\frac{\partial u}{\partial \omega} \tag{3–21}$$

It is therefore *necessary* that these relationships hold in any region in which the function is regular.

Conversely, in any region where the Cauchy–Riemann equations (3–20 and 21) are satisfied, $F(s)$ must be regular, provided that the four partial derivatives in these equations exist, and are continuous, at all points of the region.(19) To demonstrate this *sufficiency*, we write

$$dF = du + j\,dv \tag{3–22}$$

Now using the calculus of real variables

$$du = \frac{\partial u}{\partial \alpha}d\alpha + \frac{\partial u}{\partial \omega}d\omega \tag{3–23}$$

and

$$dv = \frac{\partial v}{\partial \alpha}d\alpha + \frac{\partial v}{\partial \omega}d\omega \tag{3–24}$$

From (3–22, 23, and 24) we have at once

$$dF = \left(\frac{\partial u}{\partial \alpha} + j\frac{\partial v}{\partial \alpha}\right)d\alpha + \left(\frac{\partial u}{\partial \omega} + j\frac{\partial v}{\partial \omega}\right)d\omega \tag{3–25}$$

Introducing the Cauchy–Riemann equations, (3–20 and 21), yields

$$dF = \left(\frac{\partial u}{\partial \alpha} - j\frac{\partial u}{\partial \omega}\right)d\alpha + \left(\frac{\partial u}{\partial \omega} + j\frac{\partial u}{\partial \alpha}\right)d\omega \tag{3–26}$$

which is easily shown to be equivalent to

$$dF = \left(\frac{\partial u}{\partial \alpha} - j\frac{\partial u}{\partial \omega}\right)(d\alpha + j d\omega) \tag{3-26a}$$

Now $d\alpha + jd\omega = ds$, and the direction of ds is entirely unrestricted. Hence

$$\frac{dF}{ds} = \frac{\partial u}{\partial \alpha} - j\frac{\partial u}{\partial \omega} = \frac{\partial u}{\partial \alpha} + j\frac{\partial v}{\partial \alpha} \tag{3-27}$$

Since the derivative has been evaluated in a manner independent of the direction of ds, the function is regular.

3-7 Singularities

A *singularity* or singular point of a function $F(s)$ is a point at which $F(s)$ is not regular. If $F(s)$ is regular at all other points in the neighborhood of a singular point, this point is termed an *isolated singularity.*

Poles

Consider a function $F(s)$ which increases without limit as s approaches s_0, but which is regular at all other points in a neighborhood of $s = s_0$. If a new function $G(s)$, defined as

$$G(s) = (s - s_0)^n F(s) \tag{3-28}$$

(where n is a positive integer), has a finite non-zero limit at s_0, the sigularity of $F(s)$ at s_0 is termed a *pole of order n*. A pole of order 1 is a *simple pole.** A few illustrations will clarify this terminology. Let us consider the function,

$$F(s) = \frac{1}{s}\frac{1}{(s+10)^3} \tag{3-29}$$

This function has a simple pole at $s = 0$ and a pole of order 3 at $s = -10$, for

$$\lim_{s\to 0} sF(s) = \frac{1}{10^3}$$

$$\lim_{s\to -10} (s+10)^3 F(s) = \frac{1}{-10}$$

both of which are finite.

* Although a *zero* of a complex function is not a singular point, it is conveniently defined here. If the function $1/F(s)$ has a pole of order n at s_0, the function $F(s)$ is said to have a *zero of order n* at this point. A zero of order 1 is termed a *simple zero.*

With transcendental functions the result may be less obvious. Let

$$F(s) = \frac{a}{s^2} \sin s \tag{3-30}$$

Evidently there is a pole at $s = 0$. In order to determine the order of this pole, express (3–30) as

$$F(s) = \frac{a}{s^2} s\left(1 - \frac{s^2}{3!} + \frac{s^4}{5!} - \cdots\right) \tag{3-31}$$

where sin s has been expanded in a series and s factored out. Now if $G(s) = sF(s)$,

$$\lim_{s \to 0} G(s) = a \tag{3-32}$$

Hence we have a simple pole at the origin.

Clearly if sin s in (3–30) were in the denominator of the expression, i.e., if $F(s)$ were equal to $a/(s^2 \sin s)$, we should find, on expansion of the sine function in its series, a triple-order pole at $s = 0$.

Essential Singularity

A function represented by a power series containing an infinite number of terms with increasing negative powers of $(s - s_0)$ is said to have an essential singularity at the point s_0.* For example if

$$F = \sinh \frac{1}{s} = \frac{1}{s} + \frac{1}{3!}\frac{1}{s^3} + \frac{1}{5!}\frac{1}{s^5} + \cdots \tag{3-33}$$

the function F has an essential singularity at $s = 0$. In a neighborhood of an isolated essential singularity, the function F can be shown(11) to approach any given value arbitrarily closely.

Branch Point

When dealing with a multiple-valued function such as the two-valued function F, defined by $F^2 = s$, one may, by restricting the range of $\underline{/s}$, define a single-valued function. Thus if $s = r\underline{/\theta}$, $F = r^{1/2}\underline{/\theta/2}$ where $-\pi/2 < \theta/2 < \pi/2$, *provided* that θ is restricted to lie in the range $-\pi < \theta < \pi$. This range is said to determine a branch of the function F. A second branch is obtained by confining θ to the range $\pi < \theta < 3\pi$, so that $\theta/2$ lies in the range $\pi/2 < \theta/2 < 3\pi/2$. If θ_1 be a value of θ between $-\pi$ and π, then $\theta_1 + 2\pi$ lies in the second range, i.e.,

$$\pi < (\theta_1 + 2\pi) < 3\pi$$

*We assume that the series converges when $0 < |s - s_0| < |a|$ and that s_0 is the center of, and the only singularity in, the circle of radius $|a|$.

Hence if $s = r\underline{/\theta_1 + 2\pi}$, $F = r^{1/2}\underline{/(\theta_1/2) + \pi}$, i.e., the negative of $r^{1/2}\underline{/\theta_1/2}$. Thus these two branches of the function correspond to the two roots of s. Clearly if θ be given values in the range $3\pi < \theta < 5\pi$, the first branch of the function will simply be repeated so that the equation $F^2 = s$ defines F as a two-valued function. The negative half of the real axis separates the two ranges of θ which yield these two branches and is, therefore, termed a *branch cut*.* Since θ must describe 2π radians to represent one branch of a function, two planes are required for θ to take on values determining both branches of F. Two such planes interconnected through the branch cut constitute a *Riemann surface* for the function F.

The interconnection is such that a point whose angle (in polar coordinates) passes from $-\pi$ to π on the first sheet of the Riemann surface moves through the branch cut to traverse the angles π to 3π on the second sheet of the Riemann surface. These planes also intersect each other through the branch cut, so that the point returns to the first sheet of the Riemann surface if it continues beyond the angle 3π. The origin is common to both sheets of this Riemann surface. The function F is, then, not single-valued in a neighborhood including the origin. Hence F is not regular at the origin, and the latter is a singularity termed a *branch point.* (The same may be said of the point at infinity.) More generally, if $F(s)$ is not single-valued in any neighborhood of $s = a$, the point a is termed a branch point.(11)

We have in the foregoing considered a particular double-valued function and its Riemann surface. Other multiple-valued functions may require Riemann surfaces of more than two sheets; in particular, $\ln s$ requires a Riemann surface with an infinite number of sheets. A more complete discussion of multiple-valued functions and the Riemann surface will be found in texts devoted entirely to functions of a complex variable.(2,11)

Of the three kinds of singularity discussed in this section, poles will be our major concern. The solution to transient problems involving linear, lumped, finite circuits with constant and, of course, real parameters will introduce ratios of polynomials in s with real, constant coefficients. The singularities of such ratios are poles. Transient and steady-state response will be directly related to the poles in the Laplace transform of the response. In this connection, it will be of interest to look ahead to Table 5–1 at the end of Section 5–5 in Chapter 5, where response has been classified in terms of location and order of the poles of the appropriate transform.

* The choice of branch cut is arbitrary. Any straight line or curve which does not cross itself, extending from the origin to infinity, can be used as branch cut.

The two other kinds of singularity (essential singularity and branch point) have been included in the present section for completeness.

3-8 Integration in the Complex Plane

The singularities of analytic functions are important in the evaluation of integrals of functions of a complex variable. These integrals are line integrals in the complex plane. In order to define line or contour integration for complex functions, let two points s_A and s_B be connected by a path in the s-plane, as illustrated in Fig. 3-5. Let the function $F(s)$ be regular at every point on this path. We now divide the path into n segments. The chord joining the end points of the kth segment defines a

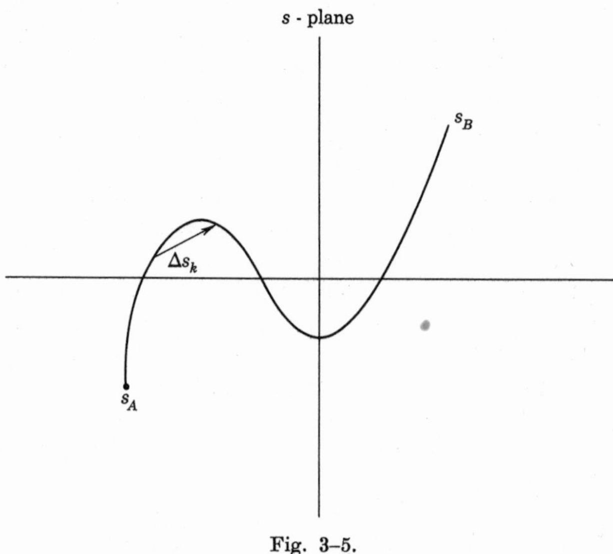

Fig. 3-5.

complex number Δs_k whose magnitude is the chord length and whose angle is that between the chord and the horizontal axis. Clearly, when Δs_k is small, it will nearly coincide with the corresponding segment of arc. Now let $F_k(s)$ be the value of $F(s)$ at some point in the kth segment of arc. The sum

$$\sum_{k=1}^{n} F_k(s)\Delta s_k$$

will approach a limit as the arc segments decrease toward zero, and their number becomes infinite. We therefore define the *line integral*

$$\oint_{s_A}^{s_B} F(s)ds = \lim_{\substack{\Delta s_k \to 0 \\ n \to \infty}} \sum_{k=1}^{n} F_k(s)\Delta s_k \tag{3-34}$$

When the path of integration is closed, i.e., when the end points s_A and s_B coincide, the line integral is called a *contour integral* and will be designated by the symbol used in example (3) below.

We shall perform three illustrative integrations. The first will emphasize the fact that Δs is complex, not simply a length of arc. The second will demonstrate that the line integral in the complex plane may be regarded as a generalization of the real integral. The third will yield a result essential to the proof of the residue theorem to be used in our applications to circuit problems.

(1) *Evaluate the following integral when* $F(s) = 1$.

$$\oint_{s_A}^{s_B} F(s)\,ds$$

The integral to be evaluated is simply

$$\oint_{s_A}^{s_B} ds$$

The sum (3–34) now becomes

$$\sum_{k=1}^{n} \Delta s_k$$

and, since complex numbers add vectorially, their sum is $s_B - s_A$ (a result independent of the limiting process). The integral, then, is a complex number whose magnitude and angle are those of the chord joining the points s_A to s_B.

(2) *The path of integration coincides with the horizontal axis, its end points being A and B as shown in Fig. 3–6. Express the integral of* $F(s)$ *over this path.*

At points on the axis of reals, the complex variable $s = \alpha + j\omega$ reduces to $s = \alpha$, and ds becomes $d\alpha$. The function $F(s)$ is simply $F(\alpha)$. If $F(\alpha)$ is complex, we obtain

$$\int_A^B \mathcal{R}e\, F(\alpha)\, d\alpha + j \int_A^B \mathcal{I}m\, F(\alpha)\, d\alpha$$

Each integral is real. If $F(\alpha)$ is real, the line integral reduces to the definite integral of the calculus of real variable,

$$\int_A^B F(\alpha)\, d\alpha$$

One may, therefore, regard integration with real variable as a special case of integration in the complex plane. This stems from the fact that real numbers constitute the limiting case of complex numbers which lie on the axis of reals.

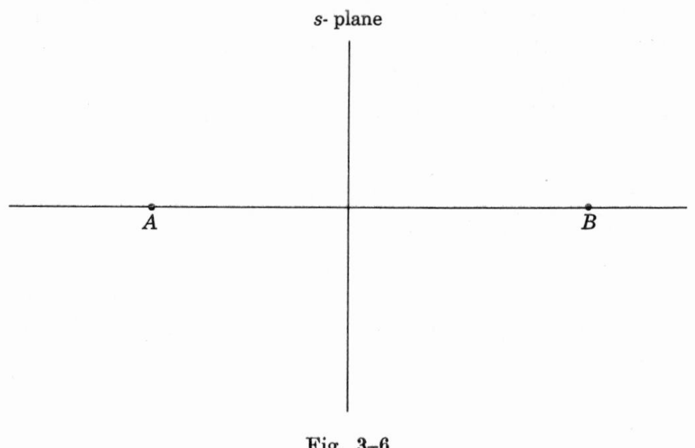

Fig. 3–6.

(3) $F(s) = 1/(s-a)^n$, *where n is an integer. The path of integration is a circle c about the point a, illustrated in Fig.* 3–7(a). *Evaluate*

$$\oint_c F(s)\, ds$$

Fig. 3–7(a) shows the path of integration of interest. Fig. 3–7(b) illustrates a new path c' obtained by the substitution of variable $w = s-a$. We have then:

$$\oint_c \frac{ds}{(s-a)^n} = \oint_{c'} \frac{dw}{w^n} \tag{3–35}$$

The contour c is a circle about a in the s-plane, while c' represents a circle about the origin in the w-plane. In each case the closed loop and arrowhead on the integral sign indicate that the integration is taken about a closed path in the counterclockwise direction. Expressing w in polar form, we have

$$w = |w|e^{j\theta} \tag{3–36}$$

Differentiating formally, while noting that $|w|$, the circle radius, is a constant, yields

$$dw = j|w|e^{j\theta}\,d\theta \tag{3-37}$$

This result may also be obtained geometrically.. The length of a small segment of arc is $|w|d\theta$. The direction of the tangent to this arc segment is $\theta+\pi/2$. These quantities are, in fact, the magnitude and angle of dw as given by (3–37).

Introducing (3–36 and 37) into the integral (3–35) yields

$$\oint_{c'} \frac{dw}{w^n} = \frac{j}{|w|^{n-1}} \int_0^{2\pi} e^{j(1-n)\theta}\,d\theta \tag{3-38}$$

When $n = 1$, the right-hand side of (3–38) becomes $2\pi j$. When $n \neq 1$,

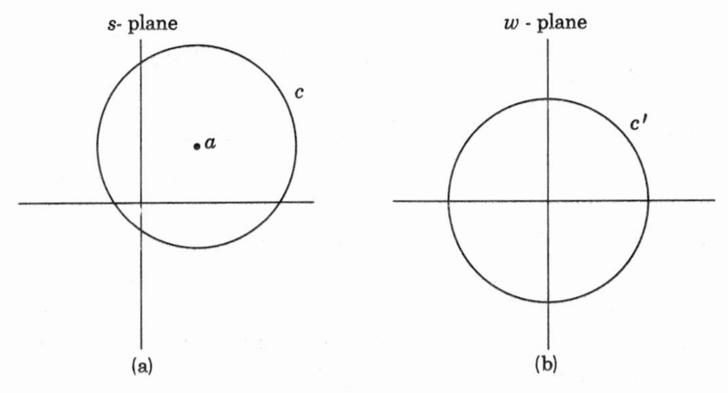

Fig. 3–7.

representation of $e^{j(1-n)\theta}$ in trigonometric form will show that the right-hand side of (3–38) is zero. Hence we have the general result,

$$\oint_c \frac{ds}{(s-a)^n} = \begin{cases} 2\pi j & \text{if} \quad n = 1 \\ 0 & \text{if} \quad n \neq 1 \end{cases} \tag{3-39}$$

provided that the path of integration is a circle with a as center, and provided that n is an integer.

3-9 Cauchy–Goursat Theorem

The Cauchy–Goursat theorem, essential to the evaluation of integrals in the complex plane, states that

$$\oint_c F(s)\,ds = 0 \tag{3-40}$$

provided that $F(s)$ is single-valued and regular within and on the closed contour c. One proof of this theorem refers to Green's theorem of real variable, which states

$$\int_c (P\,dx + Q\,dy) = \int_S \left(\frac{\partial Q}{\partial x} - \frac{\partial P}{\partial y}\right) dS \qquad (3\text{–}41)^*$$

where P and Q (functions of x, y) and their first partial derivatives are continuous on the surface S and its boundary c[2].

Now

$$F(s) = u + jv \qquad (3\text{–}42)$$

and since $ds = d\alpha + jd\omega$,

$$\oint_c F(s)\,ds = \oint_c (u+jv)(d\alpha + j\,d\omega) \qquad (3\text{–}43)$$

or

$$\oint_c F(s)\,ds = \oint_c (u\,d\alpha - v\,d\omega) + j\oint_c (v\,d\alpha + u\,d\omega) \qquad (3\text{–}44)$$

Applying Green's theorem (3–41) to each of the integrals on the right-hand side of (3–44) yields

$$\oint_c F(s)\,ds = \int_S \left(-\frac{\partial v}{\partial \alpha} - \frac{\partial u}{\partial \omega}\right) dS + j\int_S \left(\frac{\partial u}{\partial \alpha} - \frac{\partial v}{\partial \omega}\right) dS \qquad (3\text{–}45)$$

Since $F(s)$ is regular within and upon c, the Cauchy–Riemann equations (3–20 and 21) are valid and the right-hand side of (3–45) vanishes, proving the theorem.

In the preceding discussion it has been tacitly assumed that the region containing c, and throughout which $F(s)$ is regular, is *simply-connected*, i.e., is free of holes. In the next section, the means of applying the Cauchy theorem to a problem involving a *multiply-connected region*, i.e., a region containing one or more holes not belonging to the region, will be developed. The need for this development occurs naturally in the derivation of the Cauchy integral formula.

3-10 Cauchy Integral Formula†

If a function $F(s)$ is single-valued and regular at all points within and upon a closed contour c, its value at a point s_0 within the contour is

* Green's theorem is derived in References 4 and 12 in the list at the end of this chapter. The proof of (3–40), based on Green's theorem, was originated by Cauchy and requires that dF/ds be assumed continuous on S and its contour. This proof, together with Goursat's more general demonstration, is given in Reference 2. The reader will also be interested in the abridged forms of Goursat's proof given in References 6 and 18.

† See also References 2, 6, 9.

given by

$$F(s_0) = \frac{1}{2\pi j} \oint_c \frac{F(s)}{s - s_0} ds \tag{3-46}$$

Despite the pole of the integrand at $s = s_0$, this result may be demonstrated with the aid of the Cauchy–Goursat theorem. The given contour c, Fig. 3–8(a), is replaced by the contour $c + S_1 + c' + S_2$, Fig. 3–8(b). The area *enclosed* by the latter contour does not contain the point s_0. For convenience, c' is drawn as a circular arc with s_0 as center.

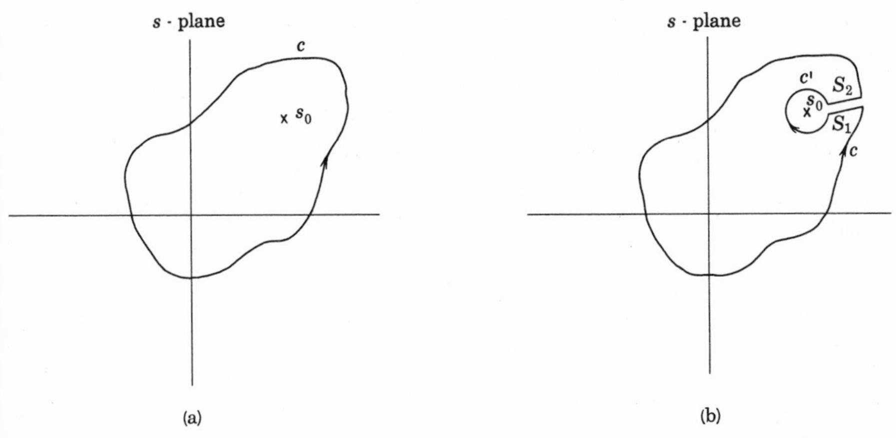

Fig. 3–8.

The cuts S_1 and S_2 in Fig. 3–8(b) are a means of extending the Cauchy–Goursat theorem to multiply-connected regions. Prior to the introduction of these cuts, the contours c and c' constitute the boundary of a *doubly-connected* region. The cuts are introduced to create a simply-connected region whose boundary is indicated by the arrowheads in Fig. 3–8(b). When a multiply-connected region is thus reduced to a simply-connected one by introduction of cuts, we must reiterate the requirement that $F(s)$ be single-valued, so that traversing a closed path does not bring us to a new value of the function.* Only when the function is single-

* The definition of the term *regular* included the requirement that a function regular at a point be single-valued in the neighborhood of that point. However we have seen that a multivalued function can be regular on its Riemann surface except at branch points. For this reason the requirement of single-valuedness is reiterated to make certain that functions which take on a new value after traversal of a closed path are not considered when the Cauchy–Goursat theorem is applied. This problem does not arise with a function regular throughout a simply-connected region.[11]

valued will the integrals along the cuts S_1 and S_2 cancel as required in the evaluation of (3–47).

Applying the Cauchy–Goursat theorem to the contour of Fig. 3–8(b), we find,

$$\oint_c \frac{F(s)}{s-s_0}ds + \int_{S_1} \frac{F(s)}{s-s_0}ds + \oint_{c'} \frac{F(s)}{s-s_0}ds + \int_{S_2} \frac{F(s)}{s-s_0}ds = 0 \qquad (3\text{–}47)$$

Now when S_1 and S_2 approach coincidence, the integrals over these straight lines must cancel. (Strictly speaking, the integrals over c and c' become integrals over closed paths only after S_1 and S_2 approach coincidence.) Reversing the direction of integration over the circle c' changes the sign of this integral, and (3–47) becomes

$$\oint_c \frac{F(s)}{s-s_0}ds = \oint_{c'} \frac{F(s)}{s-s_0}ds \qquad (3\text{–}48)$$

If $F(s)$ on the circle c' is represented as $F(s_0)+\Delta F$, equation (3–48) becomes

$$\oint_{c'} \frac{F(s)}{s-s_0}ds = \oint_{c'} \frac{F(s_0)}{s-s_0}ds + \oint_{c'} \frac{\Delta F}{s-s_0}ds \qquad (3\text{–}49)$$

Since $F(s_0)$ is a constant, the first of the integrals on the right side of (3–49) equals $2\pi jF(s_0)$ (see equation 3–39). The substitutions $(s-s_0) = Me^{j\theta}$ and $ds = jMe^{j\theta}d\theta$ reduce the second integral to

$$j\int_0^{2\pi} \Delta F\, d\theta$$

This integral vanishes as the radius of c' becomes arbitrarily small, for even the largest value of ΔF on c' will then approach zero. The equation (3–49) now reduces to the Cauchy integral formula (3–46).

The Cauchy integral formula leads to the conclusion that if a single-valued function of a complex variable is regular in a region, all its derivatives of any order exist in that region.

Let the function $F(s)$ be single-valued and regular on the closed contour c and the region which it bounds. Using (3–46) to express the value of $F(s)$ at a point $s_0+\Delta s$ lying within the contour c, we have

$$F(s_0+\Delta s) = \frac{1}{2\pi j}\oint_c \frac{F(s)}{s-(s_0+\Delta s)}ds \qquad (3\text{–}50)$$

Now combining (3–46) and (3–50) with the definition of the derivative

(3–5), and assuming that the limit may be placed inside the integral sign,* we find that

$$\left.\frac{dF}{ds}\right|_{s=s_0} = F'(s_0) = \frac{1}{2\pi j}\oint_c \lim_{\Delta s\to 0}\frac{F(s)}{\Delta s}\left(\frac{1}{s-s_0-\Delta s}-\frac{1}{s-s_0}\right)ds$$

or

$$F'(s_0) = \frac{1}{2\pi j}\oint_c \frac{F(s)}{(s-s_0)^2}ds \tag{3–51}$$

The expression for successive derivatives can be obtained in a similar manner; for the nth derivative at $s = s_0$:

$$F^{(n)}(s_0) = \frac{n!}{2\pi j}\oint_c \frac{F(s)}{(s-s_0)^{n+1}}ds \tag{3–52}$$

We see then that if a single-valued function is regular in a given region, derivatives of all orders may be obtained at any point of that region.

3-11 Taylor's Series and the Laurent Expansion Theorem

The Taylor series, familiar from the calculus of real variable, is also used in the calculus of functions of a complex variable. The Taylor expansion of the analytic function $F(s)$ about a point s_0 is valid at all points within a circle with s_0 as center, provided that $F(s)$ is regular within this circle (which clearly requires regularity at s_0 as well). The function $F(s)$ need not be regular on the circumference, which may be drawn through the nearest singularity to the point s_0.(11) This circle is then termed the *circle of convergence* of the Taylor series. We shall state the series, leaving proof of its convergence to References 2, 9, and 11 in the list at the end of this chapter. If s is a point within the circle of convergence drawn with s_0 as its center

$$F(s) = F(s_0)+(s-s_0)F'(s)+\frac{1}{2!}(s-s_0)^2F''(s)+\cdots \tag{3–53}$$

The derivatives at s_0, i.e., $F'(s_0)$, $F''(s_0)$, . . . may all be evaluated by the Cauchy integral formula of the preceding section.

Now suppose that a function $F(s)$ has only one singularity, a pole of order n at $s = s_0$, in a certain region of the s-plane. Fig. 3–9 illustrates several poles (marked $\times$) of a function $F(s)$. The entire region bounded by A contains but one singularity, at $s = s_0$, and $F(s)$ is regular in the region between contours A and B. The contour A is presumed to lie

* For a proof free of this assumption, see Reference 2.

entirely within the circle of convergence of the Taylor series for $G(s)$, defined below. The contour B is a circle about s_0.

Now let $G(s) = (s-s_0)^n F(s)$. Clearly $G(s)$ is regular on A and at all points within A, including the point s_0, where $G(s_0)$ is defined as

$$\lim_{s \to s_0} (s-s_0)^n F(s)$$

Taylor's series is, therefore, valid for $G(s)$ in the entire region bounded by A. Whence

$$G(s) = G(s_0) + (s-s_0)G'(s_0) + \frac{1}{2!}(s-s_0)^2 G''(s_0) + \cdots \tag{3-54}$$

Now if the point s lies in the region between boundaries A and B,

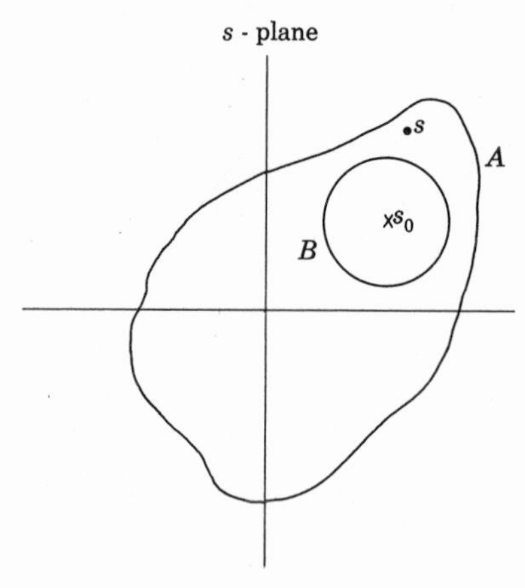

Fig. 3-9.

$s - s_0 \neq 0$. Division by $(s-s_0)^n$, therefore, does not destroy convergence of the series. Hence we write

$$F(s) = \frac{G(s)}{(s-s_0)^n} = \frac{G(s_0)}{(s-s_0)^n} + \frac{G'(s_0)}{(s-s_0)^{n-1}} + \cdots + \frac{G^{(n)}(s_0)}{n!}$$
$$+ (s-s_0)\frac{G^{(n+1)}(s_0)}{(n+1)!} + (s-s_0)^2 \frac{G^{(n+2)}(s_0)}{(n+2)!} + \cdots \tag{3-55}$$

Since all the derivatives of G at s_0 are constants, the notation can be considerably simplified by writing

$$F(s) = a_0 + a_1(s-s_0) + a_2(s-s_0)^2 + \cdots$$
$$+ \frac{b_1}{s-s_0} + \frac{b_2}{(s-s_0)^2} + \cdots + \frac{b_n}{(s-s_0)^n} \tag{3-56}$$

The series (3–56) is the Laurent expansion of $F(s)$ about its nth order pole at s_0. The series converges for values of s close to but not equal to s_0. The number of terms with negative powers of $(s-s_0)$ equals the order of the pole at $s = s_0$. The series of terms with positive powers of $s-s_0$ is infinite. If $F(s)$ is regular at $s = s_0$, the b's must vanish and (3–56) becomes the Taylor series (3–53). With the Laurent expansion, we shall develop the residue theorem, essential to the evaluation of integrals in the complex plane.

The preceding derivation yielded the Laurent expansion about a pole—the case of interest in this text. When the Laurent expansion is derived on a more general basis, however, it is found that it may contain either a finite or infinite series of terms with negative powers of $(s-s_0)$. The series is then used as a basis for defining both poles and essential singularities,[2,11] again provided that s_0 at the center of the circle B is the only singularity within and on B.

3-12 Evaluation of Contour Integrals by the Residue Method

The theory of functions of a complex variable presented in the preceding sections leads to a particularly simple and powerful procedure for contour integral evaluation. In order to develop this method, let us evaluate the integral of $F(s)$ over the contour c shown in Fig. 3–10(a). The function $F(s)$ is single-valued within and on c, and is regular there except at the points marked $\times$, which are poles. (One pole s_0'''' is shown outside of c in order to distinguish between the effect of poles outside and inside the contour.) We shall see that only the poles within the contour, at s_0', s_0'', and s_0''', are explicitly involved in the evaluation of the integral. Our first step is to consider integration over the new contour shown in Fig. 3–10(b). This new path bounds a simply-connected region and does not enclose the singularities of the function $F(s)$, so that the Cauchy–Goursat theorem applies and

$$\oint_{\substack{c+c'+c''\\+c'''\\+\text{straight}\\\text{lines}}} F(s)\,ds = 0 \tag{3–57}$$

As the members of each pair of straight lines approach coincidence, their contributions to the integral cancel, and at the same time the circular arcs, c', c'', and c''' become complete circles. Taking into account the direction of integration over each of these circles, we find

$$\oint_c F(s)\,ds = \oint_{c'} F(s)\,ds + \oint_{c''} F(s)\,ds + \oint_{c'''} F(s)\,ds \tag{3–58}$$

We shall now evaluate the integral of $F(s)$ over the circle c'. This may be carried out quite easily if $F(s)$ is represented by its Laurent expansion about the pole at $s = s_0'$, namely

$$F(s) = a_0' + a_1'(s-s_0') + a_2'(s-s_0')^2 + \cdots + \frac{b_1'}{s-s_0'} + \frac{b_2'}{(s-s_0')^2} + \cdots + \frac{b_n'}{(s-s_0')^n} \tag{3-59}$$

The coefficients are primed simply as a reminder that this is the expansion of $F(s)$ about the pole at s_0'. The terms with $(s-s_0')$ raised to positive

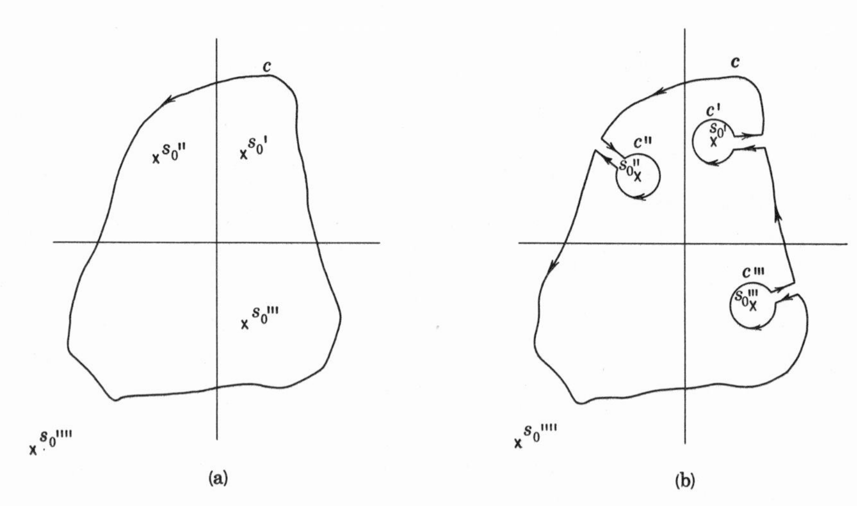

Fig. 3–10.

powers are all regular functions, both within and on the circle c'. Integration of each of these terms over c', therefore, yields zero by the Cauchy–Goursat theorem. The terms involving $(s-s_0')$ raised to negative powers are not regular at $s = s_0'$. However, since the integration is over a circle centered at s_0', we find, by reference to (3–39), that the first term yields $2\pi j b_1'$, while the remaining terms yield zero. Hence we conclude

$$\oint_{c'} F(s)\,ds = 2\pi j b_1' \tag{3-60}$$

Since the term $b_1'/(s-s_0)$ is the only term in the entire series which has not yielded zero upon integration, the coefficient b_1' is termed the *residue* of $F(s)$ at the pole at s_0'. Clearly, the Laurent expansion about the pole at s_0'' will yield

$$\oint_{c''} F(s)\,ds = 2\pi j b_1'' \tag{3-61}$$

and by the same reasoning we shall find again

$$\oint_{c'''} F(s)\,ds = 2\pi j b_1''' \tag{3-62}$$

The results (3–60, 61, and 62) applied to (3–58) show that

$$\oint_{c} F(s)\,ds = 2\pi j(b_1' + b_1'' + b_1''') \tag{3-63}$$

Since a closed path of integration may enclose any number of poles, (3–63) may be restated:

$$\oint_{c} F(s)\,ds = 2\pi j \cdot \text{(sum of the residues of } F(s) \text{ at the poles enclosed by } c) \tag{3-64}$$

where, except for a finite number of poles within c, the function $F(s)$ is regular within and on c.

3-13 Evaluation of Residues

The problem of integrating $F(s)$ over a closed contour, c, has now been reduced to that of evaluating the residue at each enclosed pole. This procedure will be very simple in many cases, particularly in problems involving electric circuits with lumped elements. We shall now develop formulas for residue evaluation in several situations:

(a) *$F(s)$ contains the factor $1/(s-s_0)$, no other factor having a pole at s_0.*

The residue at the simple pole of $F(s)$ at $s = s_0$ is easily determined. With the Laurent expansion for $F(s)$,

$$F(s) = [a_0 + a_1(s-s_0) + a_2(s-s_0)^2 + \cdots] + \frac{b_1}{s-s_0} \tag{3-65}$$

it is clear that b_1 may be found by multiplying both sides of (3–65) by $(s-s_0)$ and then evaluating the limit as s approaches s_0. All terms involving $(s-s_0)$ raised to a positive power will vanish, leaving

$$b_1 = \lim_{s \to s_0} (s-s_0)F(s) \tag{3-66}$$

An illustration of this procedure will be of interest. We wish to evaluate the integral

$$\oint_c \frac{e^{st}}{(s+5)(s^2+64)}\,ds$$

over the contour consisting of a semicircle of radius 7 and its diameter, illustrated in Fig. 3–11. The integrand is of a type which we shall encounter in circuit problems; the contour, c, will be somewhat different, however. The integrand contains simple poles at $s = -5$, $s = j8$, $s = -j8$. The pole at $s = -5$ is enclosed by the contour c. The residue of $F(s)$ at $s = -5$ is given by

$$\lim_{s\to -5}\left[(s+5)\frac{e^{st}}{(s+5)(s^2+64)}\right] = \frac{e^{-5t}}{25+64}$$

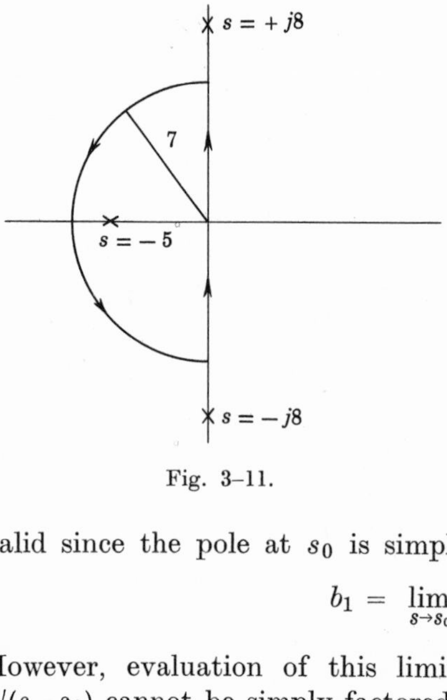

$s = +j8$

7

$s = -5$

$s = -j8$

Fig. 3–11.

We have at once

$$\oint_c \frac{e^{st}}{(s+5)(s^2+64)}ds = 2\pi j\frac{e^{-5t}}{89} \tag{3–67}$$

(b) *$F(s)$ contains a simple pole at $s = s_0$. It is not easy to factor $1/(s-s_0)$ out of the expression for $F(s)$.*

This problem arises in connection with lines consisting of a large number of identical sections in cascade—each section containing a circuit of lumped elements. The reasoning under (a) is still valid since the pole at s_0 is simple. Whence

$$b_1 = \lim_{s\to s_0}\left[(s-s_0)F(s)\right] \tag{3–68}$$

However, evaluation of this limit is complicated by the fact that $1/(s-s_0)$ cannot be simply factored out of $F(s)$. For convenience let us consider $F(s)$ as a fraction $N(s)/D(s)$, in which $N(s)$ and $D(s)$ are regular at $s = s_0$, and in which $N(s)$ does not equal zero at $s = s_0$. Clearly $D(s)$ must be zero at $s = s_0$, so that

$$\lim_{s\to s_0}\left[(s-s_0)N(s)/D(s)\right]$$

requires L'Hospital's rule for its evaluation. Differentiating the numerator and the denominator and then setting $s = s_0$, we obtain

$$\lim_{s\to s_0}\left[(s-s_0)F(s)\right] = \frac{\left[N(s)+(s-s_0)\dfrac{dN}{ds}\right]\Bigg|_{s=s_0}}{\left[\dfrac{d}{ds}D(s)\right]\Bigg|_{s=s}} \tag{3–69}$$

and the residue is given by

$$b_1 = \frac{N(s_0)}{\left[\dfrac{d}{ds}D(s)\right]\Bigg|_{s=s_0}} \tag{3–70}$$

It will be observed that the result (3–70) applies under the conditions of part (a) of this section as well.

In order to illustrate the use of (3–70), let us evaluate

$$\oint_c \frac{e^{st}}{\sin as}\,ds$$

where c is a circle of radius $\pi/2a$, about the origin, as illustrated in Fig. 3–12. The integrand has simple poles at $s = \pm n\pi/a$, where $n = 0, 1, 2, \ldots$. The contour, c, encloses only the pole at $s = 0$; the other poles lie

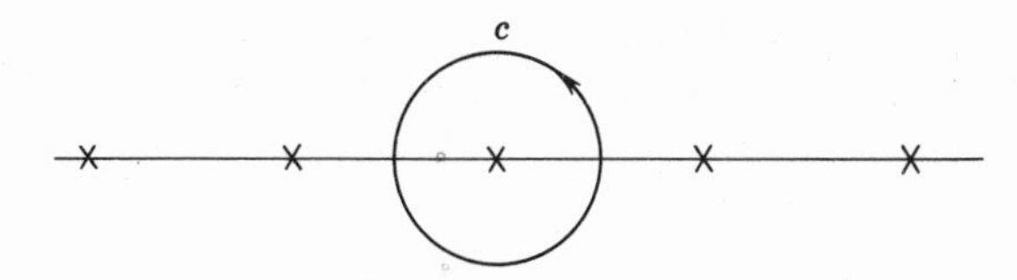

Fig. 3–12.

outside the circle. By use of (3–70), the residue of the integrand at $s = 0$ is seen to be

$$\lim_{s\to 0} \frac{e^{st}}{a \cos as} = \frac{1}{a}$$

and therefore

$$\oint_c \frac{e^{st}}{\sin as}\,ds = \frac{2\pi j}{a} \tag{3–71}$$

(c) *$F(s)$ contains a pole of order 2 at $s = s_0$.*

This problem will arise in connection with critically damped oscillatory circuits, and in cases where the "natural frequency" of a circuit coincides with that of the applied voltage or current source. The important point to bear in mind in evaluating a residue at a pole of higher order (i.e., 2 or more) is that the residue of the function is always the coefficient of $1/(s-s_0)$. When $F(s)$ contains a pole of order 2, its Laurent expansion will take the form

$$F(s) = a_0 + a_1(s-s_0) + a_2(s-s_0)^2 + \cdots + \frac{b_1}{s-s_0} + \frac{b_2}{(s-s_0)^2} \tag{3–72}$$

In order to determine b_1, knowing $F(s)$, we first multiply the series by $(s-s_0)^2$. The last two terms become $b_1(s-s_0)+b_2$. When the resulting series is differentiated with respect to s, b_2 vanishes and $(s-s_0)b_1$ reduces to b_1. All other terms will still contain the factor $(s-s_0)$ to the first or higher power. Hence in order to evaluate b_1, we simply take

$$\lim_{s\to s_0}\left[\frac{d}{ds}(s-s_0)^2F(s)\right]$$

This, then, is the residue of $F(s)$ at a second-order pole at the point s_0. The residue at a pole of any order is obtainable by the same general method. When the pole order is n,(9,14)

$$\operatorname*{Res}_{\text{at } s=s_0} F(s) = \frac{1}{(n-1)!}\lim_{s\to s_0}\frac{d^{n-1}}{ds^{n-1}}\left[(s-s_0)^nF(s)\right] \tag{3-72a}$$

As an illustration, let us consider the problem in part (a) of this section, but with $(s+5)^2$ in place of $(s+5)$ in the denominator of $F(s)$. The residue at this pole is given by

$$\lim_{s\to -5}\left[\frac{d}{ds}\frac{\cancel{(s+5)^2}e^{st}}{\cancel{(s+5)^2}(s^2+64)}\right] = \frac{89t+10}{89^2}e^{-5t}$$

We therefore obtain

$$\oint_c \frac{e^{st}}{(s+5)^2(s^2+64)}\,ds = 2\pi j\frac{89t+10}{89^2}e^{-5t} \tag{3-73}$$

where the path of integration is illustrated in Fig. 3–11, but the enclosed pole at $s = -5$ is of order 2. The significant fact to note in this result is that t appears as a factor as well as in the exponent. This will occur in transient problems involving second-order poles. In our later applications t will be time, not simply a parameter as in these illustrations.

3-14 Evaluation of the Inversion Integral by the Residue Method

When the Laplace transform $F(s)$ of a voltage or current has been determined, we shall seek the corresponding time-function $f(t)$. Chapter 2 demonstrated that $f(t)$ is given explicitly by the inversion integral (2–107), repeated here for convenience:

$$f(t) = \frac{1}{2\pi j}\int_{c-j\infty}^{c+j\infty} F(s)e^{st}\,ds \tag{2-107}$$

The Laplace transform of a time-function is obtained with $s = c+j\omega$.

If $f(t)$ is Laplace transformable, there exists a real number, c', such that when $c > c'$,

$$\int_0^\infty |f(t)| e^{-ct}\, dt$$

is finite. This condition was obtained in Chapter 2 (see also Reference 5, below). Up to this point, we have defined the direct transform $F(s)$ for values of s on the straight line $s = c + j\omega$. In order to apply the residue method to the integral (2–107), we shall first (a) extend the range of definition of $F(s)$, and (b) introduce a closed contour.

Generalization of Range of Definition of $F(s)$

In order to define the function F for values of s throughout the plane, we first consider the range

$$\alpha \geqq c \quad (\text{with } s = \alpha + j\omega)$$

In this range, the integral

$$\int_0^\infty f(t) e^{-st}\, dt$$

defines $F(s)$ as a regular function of a complex variable s.

In order to establish this statement, we note first that $F(s)$ exists for any value of α in the range of interest, for the only restriction on c is that it be greater than c'. Hence if $\alpha \geqq c$, $F(s)$ may be evaluated with c replaced by α, which of necessity is a larger number than c'. We shall now see that $F(s)$ is single-valued and differentiable for $\alpha \geqq c$:

$$(1)\quad \mathscr{Re}\, F(s) = \int_0^\infty f(t) e^{-\alpha t} \cos \omega t\, dt$$

and

$$\mathscr{Im}\, F(s) = -\int_0^\infty f(t) e^{-\alpha t} \sin \omega t\, dt$$

where α is constant during the integration and, since it is in the range specified above, may be used in place of c. Each of these integrals is a real, finite area under the curve of a single-valued time-function. Therefore *$F(s)$ is single-valued in the half-plane $\alpha \geqq c$.*

(2) We consider now the definition

$$\frac{dF}{ds} = \lim_{\Delta s \to 0} \frac{F(s + \Delta s) - F(s)}{\Delta s} \tag{3–74}$$

or

$$\frac{dF}{ds} = \lim_{\Delta s \to 0} \frac{1}{\Delta s}\left[\int_0^\infty f(t)e^{-(s+\Delta s)t}\,dt - \int_0^\infty f(t)e^{-st}dt\right] \tag{3-75}$$

Now we can combine the terms within the bracket into one integral, and, since Δs is constant during the integration, it can be brought under the integral sign. Hence

$$\frac{dF}{ds} = \lim_{\Delta s \to 0} \int_0^\infty f(t)\frac{e^{-(s+\Delta s)t} - e^{-st}}{\Delta s}\,dt \tag{3-76}$$

We shall place the limit sign inside the integral, omitting justification of this step.(17) Noting that

$$\lim_{\Delta s \to 0} \frac{e^{-(s+\Delta s)t} - e^{-st}}{\Delta s}$$

is simply

$$\frac{d}{ds}e^{-st}$$

which equals $-te^{-st}$, we find

$$\frac{dF}{ds} = \int_0^\infty -tf(t)e^{-st}\,dt \tag{3-77}$$

which is a happy result provided that this integral converges, i.e., provided that

$$\int_0^\infty t|f(t)|e^{-ct}\,dt$$

is finite. (We may use c instead of α since $\alpha \geqq c$.)

Let a real number, a, lie in the range

$$0 < a < c - c'$$

Then select T such that $e^{at} > t$ for $t > T$:

$$\int_T^\infty t|f(t)|e^{-ct}\,dt < \int_0^\infty e^{at}|f(t)|e^{-ct}\,dt = \int_0^\infty |f(t)|e^{-(c-a)t}\,dt \tag{3-78}$$

If $f(t)$ is Laplace transformable, the right-hand integral is finite, since $c - a > c'$. Therefore the lesser integral, at the left of (3-78), is also finite. (The range 0 to T adds only a finite number to the left-hand integral.) We therefore conclude that *the derivative dF/ds exists.*

In view of (1) and (2), above, $F(s)$ *is regular in the half-plane* $\alpha \geqq c$.

Before proceeding, it is well to note that (3–77) is also a theorem of the Laplace transformation, for it states that if $f(t)$ is Laplace transformable, and if $F(s)$ is its transform,

$$\mathcal{L}^{-1}\frac{dF}{ds} = -tf(t) \tag{3–79}$$

We now consider the range of s for which

$$\alpha < c$$

The half-plane $\alpha < c$ includes the region $\alpha \leqq c'$ so that $F(s)$ is not now defined by the direct Laplace transform. We therefore define a new function $F_1(s)$, given by precisely the same expression as $F(s)$, except that in $F_1(s)$ the variable s may take on any value $\alpha + j\omega$, while $F(s)$ is defined solely for the half-plane $\alpha \geqq c$. Clearly $F_1(s)$ is identical with

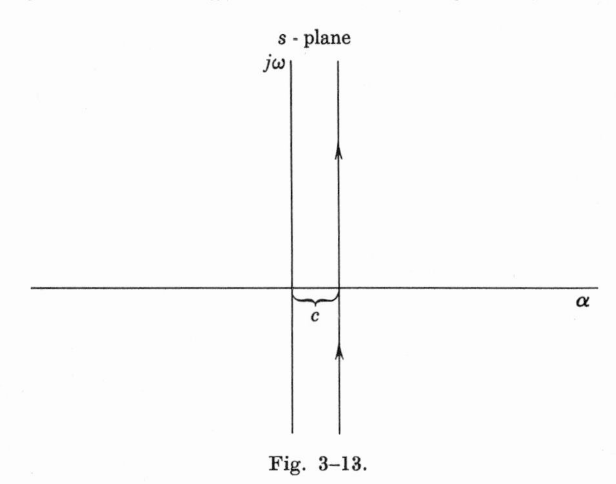

Fig. 3–13.

$F(s)$ for all values of s in the range $\alpha \geqq c$ and in particular on the line $c + j\omega$. However, our knowledge of the properties of $F_1(s)$ at points off this line will make the process of integration easier.

The reader familiar with the principle of analytic continuation will be interested in a slightly different statement which shows $F_1(s)$ to be the only function which reduces to $F(s)$ on the line $c + j\omega$. Consider, to the left of $c + j\omega$, the region R over which $F_1(s)$ is regular. (For example, if $F(s) = 1/s$, only the origin is excluded from R.) Now let $G(s)$ be some function regular in R and equal to $F(s)$ on $c + j\omega$. $G(s)$ is then said to be the analytic continuation of $F(s)$ in R. But there can be only one such function.(2) Therefore $F_1(s)$, equal to $F(s)$ for $\alpha \geqq c$, is equal to the analytic continuation of $F(s)$ in R.

A discussion of the principles of analytic continuation and of the analytic continuation of the transform of the unit step will be found in Reference 2 at the end of this chapter. The method of extension of the range of definition of a function through preservation of form is discussed in Reference 5.

Introduction of a Closed Contour

The path of integration (Fig. 3–13) is known as the *Bromwich contour* or *Bromwich path.* Since it is not closed, one wonders how the residue

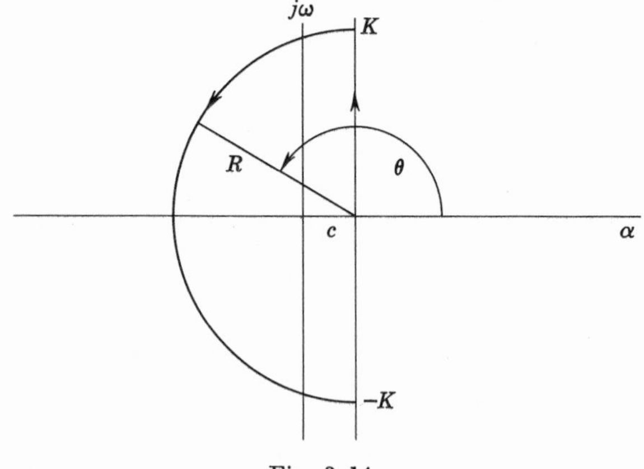

Fig. 3–14.

method will be applicable. Let us first recall the meaning of infinite limits in an integral, and write

$$\frac{1}{2\pi j}\int_{c-j\infty}^{c+j\infty} F_1(s)e^{st}\,ds = \lim_{K\to\infty}\frac{1}{2\pi j}\int_{c-jK}^{c+jK} F_1(s)e^{st}\,ds \tag{3–80}$$

Now in order to evaluate

$$\frac{1}{2\pi j}\int_{c-jK}^{c+jK} F_1(s)e^{st}\,ds$$

let us add the semicircular arc shown in Fig. 3–14 to the path from $-K$ to K. We now have a closed path. If $F_1(s)$ is regular on this path and if the only singularities of $F_1(s)$ are poles, we find at once

$$\frac{1}{2\pi j}\oint F_1(s)e^{st}\,ds = \frac{1}{2\pi j}\int_{-K}^{K} F_1(s)e^{st}\,ds + \frac{1}{2\pi j}\oint_{\substack{\text{semicircular}\\ \text{arc}}} F_1(s)e^{st}\,ds$$

$$= \sum \text{Res} \tag{3–81}$$

where Σ Res represents the sum of the residues of $F_1(s)$ at the poles enclosed by the contour consisting of the semicircular arc and its diameter. We shall now consider the limits of the terms in (3–81) when K and, therefore, the radius of the semicircular arc both become infinite. In the following subsection we shall demonstrate that if

$$\lim_{|s|\to\infty} |F_1(s)| = 0$$

the integral over the semicircular arc vanishes as the arc radius becomes infinite.(14) Hence when this condition is satisfied—and it will be satisfied in nearly all electric circuit problems—equation (3–81) reduces to

$$\frac{1}{2\pi j}\int_{c-j\infty}^{c+j\infty} F_1(s)e^{st}\,ds = \sum \text{Res} \qquad \text{(3–81a)}$$

where Σ Res now represents the sum of the residues at all poles of $F_1(s)$.

The Integral Over the Semicircular Arc Vanishes

We shall now prove that if(14)

$$\lim_{|s|\to\infty} |F_1(s)| = 0 \qquad \text{(3–82)}$$

and if

$$t > 0$$

then

$$\lim_{R\to\infty} \oint F_1(s)e^{st}\,ds = 0 \qquad \text{(3–82a)}$$

where the integration is taken over the semicircular arc of radius R shown in Fig. 3–14. The time t, real and positive, is a constant during the limit process. The angle θ is defined in the same figure. Now if $s' = s - c$, then $s' = R\cos\theta + jR\sin\theta = Re^{j\theta}$, and $ds' = jRe^{j\theta}\,d\theta$ for a particular value of R. Hence

$$\oint F_1(s)e^{st}\,ds = \int_{\pi/2}^{3\pi/2} F_1(s'+c)e^{(s'+c)t}jRe^{j\theta}\,d\theta \qquad \text{(3–83)}$$

Since the magnitude of an integral is less than or equal to the integral of the magnitude of the integrand,

$$\left|\oint F_1(s)e^{st}\,ds\right| \leq \int_{\pi/2}^{3\pi/2} \left|F_1(s'+c)e^{ct}e^{R(\cos\theta)t}e^{jR(\sin\theta)t}Rje^{j\theta}\right|\,d\theta \qquad \text{(3–84)}$$

i.e.,

$$\left| \oint F_1(s)e^{st}\,ds \right| \leqq \int_{\pi/2}^{3\pi/2} |F_1(s'+c)|e^{ct}e^{R(\cos\theta)t}R\,d\theta \tag{3–85}$$

where the factors of the integrand of (3–84) have been replaced by their magnitudes.

Now

$$\lim_{R\to\infty} |s| = \infty$$

since $s = s'+c$. Hence, using the condition (3–82),

$$\lim_{R\to\infty} |F_1(s'+c)|e^{ct} = 0$$

The factor e^{ct} is a constant with respect to R and cannot alter the limit. The meaning of this limit is that we can *always select R sufficiently large* to satisfy

$$|F_1(s'+c)|e^{ct} < \delta$$

where δ *is any positive number however small.* Using this fact in (3–85) leads to

$$\left| \oint F_1(s)e^{st}\,ds \right| < \delta \int_{\pi/2}^{3\pi/2} e^{Rt\cos\theta}R\,d\theta \tag{3–85a}$$

for sufficiently large values of R. The substitution of variable $\phi = \theta - \pi/2$ changes the form of this expression to

$$\left| \oint F_1(s)e^{st}\,ds \right| < \delta \int_0^{\pi} e^{-Rt\sin\phi}R\,d\phi \tag{3–86}$$

Now $\sin\phi$ goes through the same values between 0 and $\pi/2$ as between $\pi/2$ and π. These values are taken in opposite order, but the integral is the same over these two ranges. Hence (3–86) becomes

$$\left| \oint F_1(s)e^{st}\,ds \right| < 2\delta \int_0^{\pi/2} e^{-Rt\sin\phi}R\,d\phi \tag{3–87}$$

Using the inequality* $\sin\phi \geqq (2/\pi)\phi$ when $0 \leqq \phi \leqq \pi/2$, we can increase

* This inequality may be justified geometrically. The curve $\sin\phi$ and the straight line $(2/\pi)\phi$ meet at the points $\phi = 0$ and $\phi = \pi/2$. In the range of ϕ between these points, the second derivative of $\sin\phi$, namely $-\sin\phi$, is of constant sign. Hence there cannot be an additional intersection of the curve $\sin\phi$ and the straight line $(2/\pi)\phi$ between the points $\phi = 0$ and $\phi = \pi/2$, i.e., the straight line is a chord of the curve in the range $0 \leqq \phi \leqq \pi/2$. Finally since the second derivative, $-\sin\phi$, is negative throughout the range of interest, the curve $\sin\phi$ must lie above the straight line $(2/\pi)\phi$ in order to meet this straight line at the end points of the interval of interest.

the right-hand side of (3–87) by replacing $\sin\phi$ by $2\phi/\pi$ in the negative exponent, so that

$$\left|\oint F_1(s)e^{st}\,ds\right| < 2\delta\int_0^{\pi/2} e^{-R(2/\pi)\phi t}R\,d\phi \tag{3–88}$$

or

$$\left|\oint F_1(s)e^{st}\,ds\right| < \delta\pi(1-e^{-Rt})\frac{1}{t} \tag{3–89}$$

Since for any positive value of t, $(1-e^{-Rt})$ is less than 1,

$$\left|\oint F_1(s)e^{st}\,ds\right| < \frac{\pi\delta}{t} \tag{3–90}$$

Since with δ chosen arbitrarily small, the inequality holds if R is sufficiently large, and since t is a real positive constant, we have

$$\lim_{R\to\infty}\left|\oint F_1(s)e^{st}\,ds\right| = 0 \quad \text{for } t > 0 \tag{3–90a}$$

and (3–82a) is established.

The situation at the instant $t = 0$ is interesting, and its examination when $F_1(s)$ is a ratio of polynomials will be of value for later interpretation. Let the transform $F(s)$ be written in the form:

$$F_1(s) = \frac{a_0s^n+a_1s^{n-1}+\cdots+a_{n-1}s+a_n}{s^m+b_1s^{m-1}+\cdots+b_{m-1}s+b_m} \tag{3–90b}$$

where $a_0, a_1, \ldots, a_n$ and $b_1 \ldots b_m$ are all real. We consider two cases:

CASE 1: $m-n = 1$

At $t = 0$, the integral over the semicircular arc becomes

$$\lim_{R\to\infty}\oint F(s)\,ds$$

which, for $|s|$ large, can be written

$$\lim_{R\to\infty}\oint (a_0/s)\,ds$$

Now using the change of variable introduced after (3–82a), we require

$$\lim_{R\to\infty}\int_{\pi/2}^{3\pi/2}\frac{a_0}{(Re^{j\theta}+c)}jRe^{j\theta}\,d\theta$$

Again, for large R, c can be neglected when compared with $Re^{j\theta}$, so that the factors $Re^{j\theta}$ then cancel and the integral has the value $\pi j a_0$. This value becomes exact when R is infinite. Hence at $t = 0$ and with R infinite, equation (3–81) can be written

$$\frac{1}{2\pi j}\oint F_1(s)\,ds = \frac{1}{2\pi j}\int_{c-j\infty}^{c+j\infty} F_1(s)\,ds + \frac{1}{2\pi j}(\pi j a_0) \tag{3–90c}$$

Now since $m-n = 1$, the sum of the residues of $F(s)$ at its poles is a_0. (For proof, see footnote of Case 2.) We therefore find

$$\frac{1}{2\pi j}\int_{c-j\infty}^{c+j\infty} F_1(s)\,ds = a_0 - \frac{a_0}{2} = \frac{a_0}{2} \tag{3–90d}$$

Thus at $t = 0$, $\mathcal{L}^{-1}F(s) = a_0/2$.

Now consider $t > 0$. Since $F_1(s)$ satisfies (3–82), we have

$$\frac{1}{2\pi j}\int_{c-j\infty}^{c+j\infty} F_1(s)e^{st}\,ds = \frac{1}{2\pi j}\oint F_1(s)e^{st}\,ds \tag{3–90e}$$

The right-hand integral equals the sum of the residues at the poles of its integrand. From (3–72a) for the residue at a pole of any order, we see that, with appropriate constants set equal to zero, any one of these residues is a special case of $(k_1 + k_2t + \cdots + k_mt^{m-1})e^{bt}$ where b and the k's may be real, imaginary, complex, or zero. Now the limit of this function as t reduces to zero is k_1, i.e., the residue of $F_1(s)$. Thus the limit of $\mathcal{L}^{-1}F(s)$ as t reduces to zero through positive values is the sum of the residues of $F_1(s)$. This sum equals a_0, as pointed out above. With the notation $f(0-)$ and $f(0+)$ to represent limiting values of $f(t)$ as t approaches zero through negative and positive values, respectively, we now have for $f(t)$ equal to $\mathcal{L}^{-1}F(s)$

$$\begin{aligned} f(0-) &= 0 \\ f(0) &= \frac{a_0}{2} \\ f(0+) &= a_0 \end{aligned} \tag{3–90f}$$

The result for $f(0+)$ is confirmed by the initial value theorem (Section 2–6, equation 2–134). The value zero for $f(0-)$ results from the fact that $f(t)$ is understood to be zero for negative time. The result for $f(0)$ is the average value of $f(t)$ at the instant the discontinuity occurs. We recall from our derivation of the Laplace transformation that $F(s)$ is the Fourier transform of $f(t)e^{-ct}$, provided that $f(t) = 0$ for $t < 0$ and that

$$\int_0^\infty |f(t)|e^{-ct}\,dt$$

is finite. Hence it is to be expected that at a finite discontinuity we obtain the average of the "jump" in $f(t)$.

CASE 2: $m-n \geqq 2$

Here we may proceed in precisely the same manner as in Case 1. This time the integral over the semicircular arc

$$\oint F_1(s)\,ds$$

will vanish. The sum of the residues of $F_1(s)$ will be zero. (For proof, see footnote.*) We therefore find

$$\frac{1}{2\pi j}\int_{c-j\infty}^{c+j\infty} F_1(s)\,ds = 0 \tag{3–90g}$$

so that $f(t) = 0$ at $t = 0$. Following through the same argument as in Case 1, we now find that

$$\lim_{t\to 0} f(t) = 0$$

if t reduces to zero through positive values. Thus we now have for $f(t) = \mathcal{L}^{-1}F(s)$

$$f(0-) = f(0) = f(0+) = 0 \tag{3–90h}$$

* To prove that $\Sigma \operatorname{Res} F_1(s) = a_0$ when $m-n = 1$, and zero when $m-n \geqq 2$, we refer to the partial fraction theorem at the end of this chapter (Section 3–17). We take a particular case whose generalization will be obvious. Let

$$F_1(s) = \frac{a_0s^3+a_1s^2+a_2s+a_3}{s^4+b_1s^3+b_2s^2+b_3s+b_4} \tag{3–A}$$

Let the denominator have roots r_1, r_2, and r_4, the root r_2 being a double root. A partial fraction expansion of $F_1(s)$ takes the form

$$\frac{A_1}{s-r_1}+\frac{A_2}{s-r_2}+\frac{A_3}{(s-r_2)^2}+\frac{A_4}{s-r_4} = F_1(s) \tag{3–B}$$

As shown in Section 3–17, A_1, A_2, and A_4 are the residues of $F_1(s)$ at its poles at r_1, r_2, and r_4. Putting the left side of equation (3–B) over a common denominator D, we find:

$$\frac{A_1(s-r_2)^2(s-r_4)+A_2(s-r_1)(s-r_2)(s-r_4)+A_3(s-r_1)(s-r_4)+A_4(s-r_1)(s-r_2)^2}{D} = F_1(s) \tag{3–C}$$

Since D is identical with the denominator in (3–A), the numerator of the left side of (3–C) is identical with the numerator in (3–A). Hence the coefficient of s^3 in (3–C) equals a_0, i.e.,

$$A_1+A_2+A_4 = a_0 \tag{3–D}$$

But $A_1+A_2+A_4$ is the sum of the residues of $F_1(s)$ at its poles. We note that A_3, not a residue at a pole of $F_1(s)$, does not enter the sum equated to a_0.

Now the cases $m-n \geqq 2$ can be expressed by letting a_0 equal zero if $m-n = 2$, by letting a_0 and a_1 each equal zero if $m-n = 3$, etc. Then equation (3–D) yields

$$A_1+A_2+A_4 = 0 \tag{3–E}$$

Thus for $m-n \geqq 2$, the sum of the residues of $F_1(s)$ is zero.

This result for $f(0+)$ is also confirmed by the initial value theorem (Section 2–6, equation 2–134).

Summary of Section 3–14

In this section we have demonstrated the basic means of evaluating $f(t)$ from the equation

$$f(t) = \mathcal{L}^{-1}F(s)$$

The argument may be summarized as follows:

(a)
$$f(t) = \frac{1}{2\pi j}\int_{c-j\infty}^{c+j\infty} F(s)e^{st}\,ds$$

provided that $t \geqq 0$ and $c > c'$, the real constant c' having such a value that the condition $c > c'$ assures that

$$\int_0^\infty |f(t)|e^{-ct}\,dt$$

is finite. The integral of $F(s)e^{st}$ is regarded as a line integration along the Bromwich path.

(b) $F_1(s)$, formally identical with $F(s)$, is defined throughout the complex plane. The singularities of $F_1(s)$ lie to the left of the Bromwich path.

(c) If
$$\lim_{|s|\to\infty} |F_1(s)| = 0$$

the integral of $F_1(s)e^{st}$ over an infinite semicircle drawn to the left with the Bromwich path as diameter is zero for all $t > 0$.

(d) Because of (c) we find that if $F_1(s)$ is regular save for poles and if

$$\lim_{|s|\to\infty} |F_1(s)| = 0$$

the time-function $f(t)$ is equal to the sum of the residues at the poles of $F_1(s)e^{st}$ for all $t > 0$.

(e) If

$$F_1(s) = \frac{a_0s^n + a_1s^{n-1} + \cdots + a_n}{s^m + b_1s^{m-1} + \cdots + b_m}$$

and if $m - n = 1$, we have in addition to the statement (d) the further fact that $f(0+) = a_0$, i.e., $f(t)$ is discontinuous at $t = 0$, the "jump" being from 0 to a_0, *or if* $m - n \geqq 2$, we have in addition to (d) that $f(0+) = 0$, i.e., $f(t)$ is continuous at $t = 0$.

The residue method having been justified, we shall no longer require the subscript 1 in $F_1(s)$. We shall simply proceed as if $F(s)$ were defined for all points of the complex plane.

In this summary we have assumed that the function $F(s)$ is known to be a Laplace transform. In applications where the solution is an unknown time-function, this requires that the solution $f(t)$ be Laplace transformable. That the latter assumption has not led to error can be verified in specific cases by examining the solution to see whether it satisfies both the integro-differential equations of the problem and their boundary conditions.

3-15 Illustrations of the Evaluation of the Inversion Integral

While the mathematical background of the preceding section appears weighty, it leads to an effective and simple means of obtaining time-functions from their transforms. We shall now demonstrate this, using known functions of time. The method in which an unknown time-function is obtained by first finding its transform from electric circuit equations is reserved for the following chapter.

The Unit-Step Function

The unit-step function was the core of the Heaviside operational calculus, and is basic to all transient analysis. The superposition theorem (Chapter 1) demonstrates, in fact, that the response to a unit step determines the response to any applied voltage. Because of its importance and simplicity, we choose the unit step as our first illustration.

Let

$$f(t) = 0 \qquad \text{for} \qquad t < 0$$

and

$$f(t) = 1 \qquad \text{for} \qquad t > 0 \tag{3–91}$$

The Laplace transform of this function is easily found to be $F(s) = 1/s$. Let us now suppose that we are given $F(s)$, and obtain $f(t)$ from the inversion integral, i.e.,

$$f(t) = \frac{1}{2\pi j}\int_{c-j\infty}^{c+j\infty} \frac{1}{s}\, e^{st}\, ds \qquad \begin{matrix} c > 0 \\ t \geqq 0 \end{matrix} \tag{3–92}$$

At $t = 0$ the inversion integral yields $f(0) = 1/2$, i.e., half the discontinuity in $f(t)$ at this instant (see Section 3–14). (Note, here and in the following illustrations, that $f(0)$ does not have the same meaning as $f(0+)$. In this problem, $f(0+) = 1$.)

Clearly $1/s$ vanishes as $|s|$ approaches infinity, and is regular except for a simple pole at the origin; therefore, for $t > 0$ (but not at $t = 0$),

$$f(t) = \operatorname*{Res}_{\text{at } s=0} \frac{1}{s} e^{st} = \lim_{s \to 0} e^{st} = 1 \tag{3-93}$$

Since it is understood that $f(t) = 0$ for negative time it is clear that the equation (3–93) represents the unit-step function. It should be noted that, with the needed theorems already established, the actual work of obtaining the transform from its time-function is accomplished by the very simple step (3–93).

The Transform of $f(t) = e^{-\alpha_0 t}$, α_0 real, $t > 0$

The Laplace transform of this function can be obtained directly as $F(s) = 1/(s+\alpha_0)$.* While the coefficient α_0 may be positive or negative, we have written $f(t)$ in the form of a negative exponential since most practical problems deal with decaying transients. Now, given $F(s) = 1/(s+\alpha_0)$, let us find the corresponding time-function from the inversion integral, i.e.,

$$f(t) = \frac{1}{2\pi j} \int_{c-j\infty}^{c+j\infty} \frac{1}{s+\alpha_0} e^{st}\, ds \qquad \begin{array}{l} t \geqq 0 \\ c > -\alpha_0 \end{array} \tag{3-94}$$

Here again at $t = 0$ the inversion integral yields $f(0) = 1/2$, i.e., half the discontinuity in $f(t)$ at this instant. Also again, $1/(s+\alpha_0)$ clearly vanishes as $|s| \to \infty$, and is regular except for a simple pole at $s = -\alpha_0$, so that

$$f(t) = \operatorname*{Res}_{\text{at } s=-\alpha_0} \frac{1}{s+\alpha_0} e^{st} = \lim_{s \to -\alpha_0} e^{st} = e^{-\alpha_0 t} \quad \text{for} \quad t > 0 \tag{3-95}$$

The Transform of $f(t) = 1 - e^{-\alpha_0 t}$, α_0 real, $t > 0$

This function is, essentially, a unit step with a negative decaying exponential superimposed. The Laplace transform found by evaluating

$$\int_0^\infty (1 - e^{-\alpha_0 t}) e^{-st}\, dt$$

takes the form $F(s) = (1/s) - 1/(s+\alpha_0)$. However, in the course of a

* The subscript zero is included in the parameter α_0 in order to distinguish this constant from the variable α used to express s as $s = \alpha + j\omega$ when $F(s)$ is regarded as a function of a complex variable. We see that $F(s)$ has a pole at $s = -\alpha_0$, i.e., where $\alpha = -\alpha_0$ and $\omega = 0$, so that α_0 or its negative can also be regarded as a particular value of α. In a later subsection we express a sinusoid as $\cos \omega_0 t$ using the subscript zero with the corresponding situation in mind.

problem, we might well find this in the form $F(s) = \alpha_0/s(s+\alpha_0)$. Starting with the latter expression, let us find the time-function from

$$f(t) = \frac{1}{2\pi j}\int_{c-j\infty}^{c+j\infty}\frac{\alpha_0}{s(s+\alpha_0)}e^{st}\,ds \quad \text{for}\begin{cases} t \geqq 0 \\ c > 0 \quad \text{if } (-\alpha_0) < 0 \\ c > -\alpha_0 \text{ if } (-\alpha_0) > 0 \end{cases} \tag{3–96}$$

Here no discontinuity occurs at $t = 0$, for $f(0) = f(0+) = 0$ (see Section 3–14). Here again it is evident that the transform $\alpha_0/s(s+\alpha_0)$ has zero as its limit when $|s| \to \infty$, and is regular except at the simple poles $s = 0$ and $s = -\alpha_0$. Applying the residue method, therefore, we find

$$\operatorname*{Res}_{\text{at } s=0} \frac{\alpha_0}{s(s+\alpha_0)}e^{st} = \lim_{s\to 0}\frac{\alpha_0}{s+\alpha_0}e^{st} = 1 \tag{3–97}$$

and

$$\operatorname*{Res}_{\text{at } s=-\alpha_0} \frac{\alpha_0}{s(s+\alpha_0)}e^{st} = \lim_{s\to-\alpha_0}\frac{\alpha_0}{s}e^{st} = -e^{-\alpha_0 t} \tag{3–98}$$

Whence $f(t) = 1-e^{-\alpha_0 t}$ for $t > 0$.

A Suddenly Applied Cosine Wave:

$$f(t) = \begin{cases} 0 \text{ for } t<0 \\ \cos \omega_0 t \text{ for } t>0,\ \omega_0 \text{ real and } >0. \end{cases}$$

The constant ω_0 is given the subscript zero in order that it be distinguished from the variable ω used in defining s as $s = \alpha+j\omega$. The Laplace transform of $f(t)$ is obtained from

$$\int_0^\infty (\cos \omega_0 t)e^{-st}\,dt$$

and is given by $F(s) = s/(s^2+\omega_0{}^2)$. Let us again find the time-function starting with this transform as given. Then

$$f(t) = \frac{1}{2\pi j}\int_{c-j\infty}^{c+j\infty}\frac{s}{s^2+\omega_0{}^2}e^{st}\,ds \qquad \begin{matrix} c > 0 \\ t \geqq 0 \end{matrix} \tag{3–99}$$

At $t = 0$ the inversion integral yields 1/2, i.e., half the discontinuity in $f(t)$ at this instant. As in all previous cases, $F(s)$ vanishes when $|s| \to \infty$ and is regular except at simple poles to the left of c. The roots of $(s^2+\omega_0{}^2)$ are $j\omega_0$ and $-j\omega_0$, so that a simple pole occurs at each of these points on the imaginary axis. Writing $F(s)$ as $s/(s+j\omega_0)(s-j\omega_0)$, we find

$$\operatorname*{Res}_{\text{at } s=j\omega_0} \frac{se^{st}}{(s+j\omega_0)(s-j\omega_0)} = \lim_{s\to+j\omega_0} \frac{se^{st}}{(s+j\omega_0)} = \tfrac{1}{2}e^{+j\omega_0 t} \tag{3–100}$$

and

$$\operatorname*{Res}_{\text{at } s=-j\omega_0} \frac{se^{st}}{(s+j\omega_0)(s-j\omega_0)} = \lim_{s\to-j\omega_0} \frac{se^{st}}{(s-j\omega_0)} = \tfrac{1}{2}e^{-j\omega_0 t} \tag{3–101}$$

Since the residues at the poles are complex conjugates, their sum can be directly obtained as twice the real part of either residue, i.e.,

$$f(t) = 2\,\mathcal{R}e\,\tfrac{1}{2}e^{j\omega_0 t} = \cos\omega_0 t \quad t > 0 \tag{3–102}$$

The addition of the residues as complex conjugates to give a real function of time is not an accident of this illustration. Transient electric circuit problems have, as their final answers, expressions for instantaneous current or voltage. These must be real. We shall find, in fact, that when a pole of $F(s)$ occurs at a point off the real axis, another pole will occur at the conjugate point. The residues at these poles will then add to yield a real oscillatory time-function. Since this knowledge will facilitate the solution of many problems, we shall prove it as a theorem in a later section of this chapter.

The Impulse Function

The impulse function was defined and discussed in Chapter 2, where it was found that the transform of an impulse of strength K occurring at the instant $t = 0$ is given by

$$\mathcal{L}Ku_0(t) = K \tag{3–103}$$

Clearly this transform cannot reduce to zero as $|s|$ approaches infinity. Hence the impulse function will not be obtained from its transform by the residue method. One simply recognizes that a constant represents the transform of an impulse.

A simple illustration will show the technique of obtaining an impulse function from its transform. Let

$$f(t) = Ku_0(t) + Me^{-\alpha_0 t} \text{ with } t > 0$$

From (3–103) and (2–103) the transform of this time-function is seen to be $F(s) = K + [M/(s+\alpha_0)]$. However in problems involving transforms we shall not always have $F(s)$ conveniently split into two terms. Therefore starting with the form

$$F(s) = \frac{Ks + K\alpha_0 + M}{s + \alpha_0} \tag{3-104}$$

we observe that

$$\lim_{|s|\to\infty} |F(s)| \neq 0$$

so that a residue evaluation has not been justified. Noting that s is of equal degree in numerator and denominator, we perform one step of a long-division, yielding $F(s) = K + [M/(s + \alpha_0)]$. The inverse transform of the constant k is the impulse function $Ku_0(t)$. The second term satisfies

$$\lim_{|s|\to\infty} |M/(s + \alpha_0)| = 0$$

and is regular save for the simple pole at $s = -\alpha_0$. Hence the residue method is applicable, yielding

$$\operatorname*{Res}_{\text{at } s=-\alpha_0} \frac{M}{s + \alpha_0} e^{st} = \lim_{s\to-\alpha_0} Me^{st} = Me^{-\alpha_0 t} \tag{3-105}$$

Combining the inverse transforms of the two terms, we obtain

$$f(t) = Ku_0(t) + Me^{-\alpha_0 t} \tag{3-106}*$$

The foregoing result may be stated more generally. Let $N(s)/D(s)$ be a ratio of polynomials with real coefficients and of equal degree. Since

$$\lim_{|s|\to 0} |N/D| \neq 0,$$

use of the residue method has not been justified. One step of a long-division, however, produces two readily transformable terms, namely $K + (N_1/D)$ where N_1 is of degree one less than D. The constant K is the transform of an impulse function $Ku_0(t)$, and $\mathcal{L}^{-1}(N_1/D)$ is easily found by the residue method.

It is interesting to note, however, that, in the mechanics of obtaining the answer, one can omit the formal division process. The term K is, clearly, the ratio of the coefficients of the highest powers of s in N and

* Because the impulse function is defined as only a limit of a Laplace transformable function (see Chapter 2), there will be some question as to the justification of this technique. However, in an electric circuit problem the result can always be verified by seeing whether the solution reduces to a correct value as t approaches zero from the positive side.

in D. The remainder N_1 need not be obtained, for if s_0 is a root of D, then

$$\operatorname*{Res}_{\text{at } s=s_0} (N_1/D)e^{st}$$

is equal to

$$\operatorname*{Res}_{\text{at } s=s_0} [(N/D)-K]e^{st}$$

which in turn is equal to

$$\operatorname*{Res}_{\text{at } s=s_0} (N/D)e^{st}$$

since Ke^{st} does not have a pole at s_0.

Transform Containing the Delay Factor e^{-sT}

In Chapter 2 it was demonstrated that if

$$\mathcal{L}f(t) = F(s) \qquad t > 0 \tag{3–107}$$

then

$$\mathcal{L}f(t-T) = F(s)e^{-sT} \qquad t-T > 0 \tag{3–108}$$

In terms of the inversion integral, we find that if

$$\frac{1}{2\pi j}\int_{c-j\infty}^{c+j\infty} F(s)e^{st}\,ds = f(t) \qquad \begin{matrix} t \geqq 0 \\ c > c' \end{matrix} \tag{3–109}$$

then

$$\frac{1}{2\pi j}\int_{c-j\infty}^{c+j\infty} F(s)e^{-sT}e^{st}\,ds = f(t-T) \qquad \begin{matrix} t-T \geqq 0 \\ c > c' \end{matrix} \tag{3–110}$$

The latter result is immediately obvious if we rewrite (3–110) as

$$\frac{1}{2\pi j}\int_{c-j\infty}^{c+j\infty} F(s)e^{sx}\,ds = f(x) \qquad \begin{matrix} x \geqq 0 \\ c > c' \end{matrix} \tag{3–111}$$

where $x = t-T$.

Clearly (3–111) must yield the same function of x that (3–109) yields of t. Since $f(t)$, (3–109), is zero for negative time, then $f(x)$, (3–111), is zero for negative x, i.e., for $t < T$. Hence if the inversion integral of $F(s)$ can be evaluated by any method, the time-function corresponding to $F(s)e^{-sT}$ is directly known.

As an illustration consider the transform $[1/(s+\alpha_0)]e^{-sT}$. We have seen in an earlier subsection that the inversion integral

$$(1/2\pi j)\int_{c-j\infty}^{c+j\infty}[1/(s+\alpha_0)]e^{st}\,ds$$

can be evaluated by the residue method to yield:

$$f(t) = \begin{cases} 0 & \text{for } t < 0 \\ e^{-\alpha_0 t} & \text{for } t > 0 \end{cases}$$

From this we can now conclude that

$$\frac{1}{2\pi j}\int_{c-j\infty}^{c+j\infty}\frac{1}{s+\alpha_0}e^{-sT}e^{st}\,ds = \begin{cases} 0 & \text{for } t < T \\ e^{-\alpha_0(t-T)} & \text{for } t > T \end{cases} \tag{3-112}$$

and of course the integral yields 1/2 at $t = T$, i.e., half the discontinuity in $f(t)$ occurring at this instant.

3-16 A Few Special Theorems Applicable to Electric Circuit Analysis

We now consider a number of theorems concerning the complex function $F(s)$ which will greatly facilitate the analysis of lumped electric circuits.

(a) *The Poles of $F(s)$ are either real or occur in conjugate pairs.*

This theorem is easily demonstrated under the hypothesis that $F(s)$ is a ratio of polynomials in s with real coefficients. We shall find that the equations of linear, lumped, finite networks with constant parameters result in functions of this type. $F(s)$ may be the Laplace transform of a current or voltage; later, when we define impedance and admittance as functions of s, we shall find that these, too, satisfy the hypothesis of this theorem. In order to prove the theorem, let the superscript * denote complex conjugate, i.e., the conjugate of s is s^*. If, in the expression for $F(s)$, we replace each s by s^*, we obtain $F(s^*)$. But since all coefficients of powers of s are real by hypothesis, replacement of s by s^* means that every j in the ratio of polynomials $F(s)$ is replaced by $-j$. Hence $F(s)$ itself is replaced by its conjugate. This may be expressed compactly by

$$F(s^*) = [F(s)]^* \tag{3-113}$$

Now let s_0 be a pole of $F(s)$. Since infinity is not a number, we express this by

$$\frac{1}{F(s_0)} = 0 \tag{3-114}$$

Since $s_0{}^*$ is the conjugate of s_0,

$$\frac{1}{F(s_0{}^*)} = \frac{1}{[F(s_0)]^*} = 0^* = 0 \tag{3–115}$$

where we have used (3–113) and (3–114) and the fact that the conjugate of zero is zero.

Hence we conclude that if s_0 is a pole of $F(s)$, the conjugate of s_0 is also a pole of $F(s)$. It need hardly be added that if s_0 is real, it is its own conjugate. An illustration of this theorem was given by the transform of $\cos \omega_0 t$, i.e., $s/(s^2+\omega^2)$; both $j\omega_0$ and $-j\omega_0$ are poles of this fraction.

(b) *The residues of $F(s)e^{st}$ at conjugate poles of $F(s)$ are themselves complex conjugates.*

Let us suppose that the point s_0 is a pole of $F(s)$, and, again, that $F(s)$ is a ratio of polynomials in s with real coefficients. Then by the previous theorem the conjugate point $s_0{}^*$ is also a pole of $F(s)$. Clearly both s_0 and $s_0{}^*$ are poles of $F(s)e^{st}$. Letting b_1 be the residue of $F(s)e^{st}$ at the pole s_0, and b_2 be the residue of the same function at $s_0{}^*$, we shall demonstrate that $b_2 = b_1{}^*$.

As shown in Fig. 3–15, we use two circles of equal radius with s_0 and $s_0{}^*$ as their respective centers. The radii must be chosen sufficiently small so that, except for s_0 and $s_0{}^*$, there are no poles within or on the circles. This is always possible since the poles of $F(s)e^{st}$ will occur only at isolated points. Select any point on the circle A which surrounds s_0, and the conjugate point on the circle B which surrounds $s_0{}^*$. (The points marked $\times$ on the figure illustrate a possible pair of such conjugates.) Now starting at $\times$ on circle A, integrate $F(s)e^{st}$ over this circle, describing it in the positive, i.e., counterclockwise, sense. Starting at $\times$ on the circle B, integrate $F(s)e^{st}$ in the negative, i.e., clockwise, direction. Then by the residue theorem we have

$$\oint_A F(s)e^{st}\,ds_A = 2\pi j b_1 \tag{3–116}$$

and

$$\oint_B F(s)e^{st}\,ds_B = -2\pi j b_2 \tag{3–117}$$

Now, to each point on the path A, there corresponds a conjugate point on the path B. Also, as indicated on the figure, to each element ds_A of A, there corresponds a conjugate element ds_B of B. Hence

$$\oint_B F(s)e^{st}\,ds_B = \oint_A F(s^*)e^{s^*t}\,ds_A{}^* \tag{3–118}$$

i.e., if we traverse A, replacing each point by its conjugate and each arc element by its conjugate, we have, in fact, the integral over B. From the nature of $F(s)$, discussed in the previous theorem, (3–118) becomes

$$\oint_B F(s)e^{st}\,ds_B = \oint_A [F(s)e^{st}]^*\,ds_A^* \tag{3–119}$$

Since an integral is the limit of a sum, and since the conjugate of a sum equals the sum of the conjugates of its terms, (3–119) can be written

$$\oint_B F(s)e^{st}\,ds_B = \left[\oint_A F(s)e^{st}\,ds_A\right]^* \tag{3–120}$$

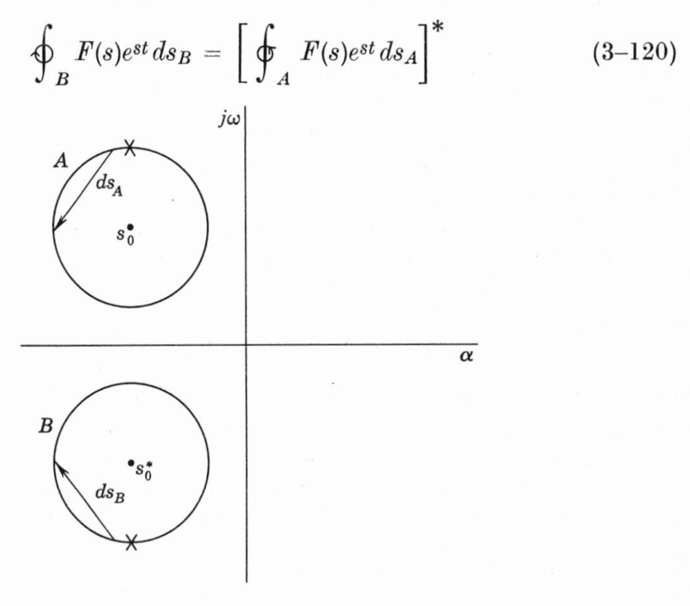

Fig. 3–15.

Referring to (3–117) and (3–116), we have

$$-2\pi j b_2 = [2\pi j b_1]^* \tag{3–121}$$

or

$$-2\pi j b_2 = -2\pi j b_1^* \tag{3–122}$$

and

$$b_2 = b_1^* \tag{3–123}$$

We have thus shown that the residues of $F(s)e^{st}$ at conjugate poles of $F(s)$ are themselves conjugates. It should also be noted that the proof is valid for a pole of any order. Use of this theorem can often halve the work in a residue evaluation, for when the poles of $F(s)$ are not real they occur in conjugate pairs. The sum of the residues for a pair of conjugate poles becomes

$$\operatorname*{Res}_{\text{at } s=s_0} F(s)e^{st} + \operatorname*{Res}_{\text{at } s=s_0{}^*} F(s)e^{st} = 2\,\mathcal{R}e \operatorname*{Res}_{\text{at } s=s_0} F(s)e^{st} \tag{3-124}$$

We can, therefore, evaluate the residue at one pole of each conjugate pair and then simply take twice its real part. An easy illustration of this theorem was seen in equations (3–99 to 102).

(c) *The presence of poles and zeros within a closed contour may often be detected graphically.*(1)

A theorem basic to the Nyquist stability criterion for feedback networks will now be derived. As a general theorem of complex functions, it is included in the present chapter.

Writing $F(s)$ for a function of a complex variable which may have poles and zeros, we consider the integral over a closed path of $d \ln F(s)/ds$. The result will lead to a procedure for the detection of poles and zeros within the closed path. Needless to say, the path of integration must be one on which the integrand is regular. We consider

$$\oint \frac{d}{ds} \ln F(s)\, ds = \lim_{A\to B} \int_A^B \frac{d}{ds} \ln F(s)\, ds \tag{3-125}$$

When the points A and B coincide, the integral over the open path with A and B as end points becomes the integral over the closed path on the left side of the equation. If we let $w = \ln F(s)$, it is evident that the integrand on either side in (3–125) is simply dw and the right-hand integral is directly evaluated as

$$\ln F(s) \Big|_{s=A}^{s=B}$$

Inserting these limits and using the form for the logarithm of a complex number, we find

$$\oint \frac{d}{ds} \ln F(s)\; ds = \lim_{A\to B} \left[\ln |F(B)| - \ln |F(A)| + j\{\underline{/F(B)} - \underline{/F(A)}\}\right] \tag{3-126}$$

Now when B and A coincide, the first two terms cancel; the angles, however, will differ by the number of times $F(s)$ encircles the origin in the F-plane. Hence if $F(s)$ encircles the origin in the F-plane T times in a counterclockwise direction, when s traverses its closed path once in the same direction, we have

$$\oint \frac{d}{ds} \ln F(s)\, ds = j2\pi T \tag{3-127}$$

Thus the value of the integral is obtained by a graphical procedure.

We shall now evaluate this integral in another manner, which will relate T to the number of poles and zeros of $F(s)$ enclosed by the path of s.

First the integrand (3–125) is put in another form with the aid of

$$\frac{d \ln F(s)}{ds} = \frac{F'(s)}{F(s)} \tag{3–128}$$

where $F'(s)$ is the derivative of F with respect to s. Now if s_1 is a pole of order n of $F(s)$, and if $G(s) = (s-s_1)^n F(s)$, then $G(s)$ has neither pole nor zero at this point. In a similar manner, a zero of order m is defined by the fact that if $H(s) = F(s)/(s-s_2)^m$, then $H(s)$ has neither a zero nor pole at $s = s_2$ when $F(s)$ has a zero of order m at $s = s_2$. Solving for $F(s)$ in each case, we find that $F'(s)/F(s)$ may be expressed by

$$\frac{F'(s)}{F(s)} = \frac{G'(s)}{G(s)} - \frac{n}{s-s_1} \tag{3–129}$$

and

$$\frac{F'(s)}{F(s)} = \frac{H'(s)}{H(s)} + \frac{m}{s-s_2} \tag{3–130*}$$

From the first of these expressions it is clear that if $F(s)$ has a pole of order n at $s = s_1$, then $F'(s)/F(s)$ has a simple pole at s_1. The residue of $F'(s)/F(s)$ at the point s_1 is $-n$. The second expression demonstrates that if $F(s)$ has a zero of order m at $s = s_2$, then $F'(s)/F(s)$ has a simple pole at $s = s_2$. The residue of $F'(s)/F(s)$ at the point s_2 is m. Let N = the number of poles enclosed by the path of integration, counting an nth order pole n times. Let M = the number of zeros enclosed by the path of integration, counting an mth order zero m times. Then using the residue theorem we have

$$\oint \frac{F'(s)}{F(s)} ds = 2\pi j(M-N) \tag{3–131}$$

Since $F'(s)/F(s)$ is simply another form of $d \ln F(s)/ds$, the right-hand sides of (3–131) and (3–127) are equal, yielding the theorem

$$T = M - N \tag{3–132}$$

The left-hand side of (3–132) is the number of times $F(s)$ encircles the F-plane origin by moving counterclockwise when s traverses the closed path in the s-plane with the same direction of rotation. The right-hand side of (3–132) is the number of zeros less the number of poles of $F(s)$

* It becomes evident here that the path of integration must not go through poles or zeros of $F(s)$.

enclosed by the path in the s-plane (a pole or zero of higher order being counted as many times as its order).

This theorem leads to a graphical means of determining the presence of poles or zeros of a function in a region of the complex plane. One must be careful, however, to avoid ambiguous results. Let us suppose that the plot of $F(s)$ corresponding to a closed path in the s-plane does not encircle the origin of the F-plane. The only safe conclusion from such a result would be that the number of poles equals the number of zeros enclosed by the path in the s-plane (each pole or zero weighted by its order). However in many problems one may know that $F(s)$ has no poles in the region enclosed by the path in the s-plane; then the plot proves without ambiguity the absence of zeros.

(d) *Final Value Theorem*[5,21]

The final value theorem offers a means, in certain cases, of obtaining

$$\lim_{t\to\infty} f(t)$$

directly from the expression for s times the Laplace transform of $f(t)$. The presentation of the theorem has been deferred until this point, since its most useful statement is given in terms of $sF(s)$ as a function of a complex variable.

Let a function $f(t)$, continuous for $t > 0$, and its first derivative $df(t)/dt$ be Laplace transformable. Further we require that the function $sF(s)$, where $F(s) = \mathcal{L}f(t)$, be regular except that poles may occur to the left of the j-axis.* We shall demonstrate that

$$\lim_{s\to 0} sF(s) = \lim_{t\to\infty} f(t) \tag{3–133}$$

For the given function $f(t)$, we have the Laplace transform of the derivative (see equation 2–110):

$$\int_0^\infty \frac{df(t)}{dt} e^{-st}\,dt = sF(s) - f(0+) \tag{3–134}$$

Now let s approach zero on both sides:

$$\int_0^\infty \frac{df(t)}{dt}\,dt = \lim_{s\to 0} sF(s) - f(0+) \tag{3–135}$$

where the constant $f(0+)$ is unaffected by the limit process. On the left

* This condition also implies that the theorem is not valid if $sF(s)$ approaches ∞ as s approaches ∞. Since s may approach ∞ in any direction, a pole at $s = \infty$ would violate the requirement that no poles of $sF(s)$ be found on or to the right of the j-axis.

side, s is reduced to zero before the integration is carried out, since s is simply a parameter independent of the integration variable.

We now consider the transform of df/dt. Since $sF(s)-f(0+)$ is regular save for poles, and since it does not represent an impulse function,* the residue method will yield df/dt. Since the only singularities are poles to the left of the j-axis, df/dt must consist of exponentially decreasing terms (see also development of table on relation between pole location and time-function, Chapter 5, Section 5–5). We therefore conclude that

$$\int_0^\infty (df/dt)\,dt$$

is finite. Hence equation (3–135) becomes

$$\lim_{t\to\infty} f(t)-f(0+) = \lim_{s\to 0} sF(s)-f(0+) \tag{3–136}$$

which leads directly to the theorem (3–133).

Several examples will suffice to illustrate the theorem and its limiting condition. Let

$$F(s) = \frac{2s+\alpha_0}{s(s+\alpha_0)} \tag{3–137}$$

where α_0 is a positive number. Then $sF(s)$ has only one pole at $s = -\alpha_0$. According to the final value theorem (3–133),

$$\lim_{t\to\infty} f(t) = 1 \tag{3–138}$$

which is a correct result since $f(t) = 1+e^{-\alpha_0 t}$. Now if α_0 is zero, the theorem applies, for $sF(s) = 2$, so that no pole occurs, and (3–133) yields

$$\lim_{t\to\infty} f(t) = 2 \tag{3–139}$$

which is clearly a correct result. If, on the other hand, α_0 is negative, i.e., $e^{-\alpha_0 t}$ is a rising exponential, $sF(s)$ has a pole to the right of the j-axis and the theorem yields a false result.

The transform

$$F(s) = \frac{s+\alpha_0}{(s+\alpha_0)^2+\omega_0{}^2} \tag{3–139a}$$

* A simple illustration will clarify this statement. Let $f(t) = e^{-\alpha_0 t}$ with $\alpha_0 > 0$. Then $F(s) = 1/(s+\alpha_0)$ and $sF(s) = s/(s+\alpha_0)$, a transform which has a numerator and denominator of equal degree and, therefore, represents a time-function including an impulse term. However $sF(s)-f(0+) = [s/(s+\alpha_0)]-1 = -\alpha_0/(s+\alpha_0)$, a transform which does not represent an impulse.

affords further interesting illustrations. With $\alpha_0 > 0$ and $\omega_0 \neq 0$, the poles of $sF(s)$ lie to the left of the j-axis. We find that

$$\lim_{s\to 0} sF(s) = 0$$

a correct result, for (3–139a) is the transform of $e^{-\alpha_0 t}\cos\omega_0 t$, which reduces to zero when t increases without limit. If, however, $\alpha_0 = 0$ and $\omega_0 \neq 0$, the poles of $sF(s)$ occur on the j-axis, so that the theorem cannot apply. In this case we find again

$$\lim_{s\to 0} sF(s) = 0$$

but this is now an erroneous result since

$$\lim_{t\to\infty} \cos\omega_0 t$$

does not exist. If both $\alpha_0 = 0$ and $\omega_0 = 0$, we have $F(s) = 1/s$, $sF(s)$ has no poles, and

$$\lim_{s\to 0} sF(s) = 1$$

the correct limit for the unit step.

3-17 Partial Fractions

The method of partial fractions is often used to express a Laplace transform as a sum of simpler transforms. The partial fraction method can be developed in a general manner with the aid of the Laurent expansion.[20] Let $F(s)$ be regular save for a number of poles including one of order m at $s = a$, and another of order n at $s = b$. Now define a new function $F_1(s)$ by

$$F_1(s) = F(s) - \frac{k_1}{s-a} - \frac{k_2}{(s-a)^2} - \cdots - \frac{k_m}{(s-a)^m} \tag{3–140}$$

where k_r, with $r = 1, 2, \ldots, m$, is the coefficient of $1/(s-a)^r$ in the Laurent expansion of $F(s)$ about its pole at $s = a$.

We can easily show that the new function $F_1(s)$ does not have a pole at $s = a$, has a pole of order n at $s = b$, and cannot have a pole at any point at which $F(s)$ is regular: The function $F_1(s)$ is given by an infinite power series in $(s-a)$ at all points *where the Laurent expansion of $F(s)$ is valid.* In particular this is true at s arbitrarily close to the point a, so that

$$\lim_{s\to a} F_1(s) = a_0$$

where a_0 is the constant term in the power series; hence $F_1(s)$ does not have a pole at $s = a$. Since $F(s)$ has a pole of order n at $s = b$, while the summation

$$\sum_{r=1}^{m} k_r/(s-a)^r$$

is finite at this point, it is evident from (3–140) that $F_1(s)$ has an nth order pole at $s = b$. Similar inspection of the right-hand side of (3–140) confirms, at once, that $F_1(s)$ does not have a pole at any value of s at which $F(s)$ is regular.

We now define

$$F_2(s) = F_1(s) - \frac{l_1}{s-b} - \frac{l_2}{(s-b)^2} - \cdots - \frac{l_n}{(s-b)^n} \tag{3–141}$$

where l_q, with $q = 1, 2, \ldots, n$, is the coefficient of $1/(s-b)^q$ in the Laurent expansion of $F_1(s)$ about its pole at $s = b$. By precisely the same reasoning we have used in connection with $F_1(s)$, it is evident that the new function $F_2(s)$ does not have a pole at $s = b$. Examination of the right-hand side of (3–141) shows clearly that $F_2(s)$ is also regular at $s = a$ and at any point at which $F(s)$ is regular. Combining (3–140) and (3–141), we have at once

$$F(s) = F_2(s) + \frac{k_1}{s-a} + \frac{k_2}{(s-a)^2} + \cdots + \frac{k_m}{(s-a)^m}$$
$$+ \frac{l_1}{s-b} + \frac{l_2}{(s-b)^2} + \cdots + \frac{l_n}{(s-b)^n} \tag{3–142}$$

where, as seen above, $F_2(s)$ is regular at $s = a$ and at $s = b$ and at all points at which $F(s)$ is regular.

Clearly, the foregoing process can be continued until all poles of $F(s)$ are "extracted". The typical coefficient k_r is given by

$$k_r = \frac{1}{(m-r)!}\left[\frac{d^{(m-r)}}{ds^{(m-r)}}(s-a)^m F(s)\right]_{s=a} \tag{3–143}$$

When $r = 1$, we have the expression for the residue of $F(s)$ at $s = a$. Equation (3–143) can be justified directly from (3–142). Upon multiplication of (3–142) by $(s-a)^m$, we obtain

$$(s-a)^m F(s) = (s-a)^m \left[F_2(s) + \sum_{q=1}^{n} \frac{l_q}{(s-b)^q}\right]$$
$$+ \sum_{r'=1}^{m} k_{r'}(s-a)^{m-r'} \tag{3–144}$$

The left-hand side is regular at $s = a$, so that all its derivatives exist and (3–143) can be evaluated. The first term on the right-hand side of (3–144) is regular at $s = a$, and its $(m-r)$th derivative will contain the factor $(s-a)^{m-r}$, so that this derivative is zero at $s = a$. The second term on the right-hand side, namely the summation

$$\sum_{r'=1}^{m} k_{r'}(s-a)^{m-r'}$$

can easily be shown to yield the value $k_r(m-r)!$ for the $(m-r)$th derivative at $s = a$. The equation (3–143) then follows directly on division of both sides by $(m-r)!$ (The typical coefficient l_q is obtained analogously.)

The function we have termed $F_2(s)$ merits consideration. Clearly if $F(s)$ contains R poles instead of two, the process developed above can be carried out until all poles are "extracted" from the function, and the remaining function may then be termed $F_R(s)$, where R is the number of poles in $F(s)$.

Since $F_R(s)$ is regular at any point of the s-plane (with a possible exception at $s = \infty$), $F_R(s)$ can be represented by the power series

$$F_R(s) = \sum_{k=0}^{N} a_k s^k \tag{3–145}$$

where N may or may not be finite.

We note also that

$$\lim_{s\to\infty} F(s) = \lim_{s\to\infty} F_R(s) \tag{3–146}$$

Now let us suppose that $F(s)$ is a ratio of polynomials in s, i.e.,

$$F(s) = \frac{N(s)}{D(s)} \tag{3–147}$$

in which N and D do not have common factors. We write at once

$$F(s) = F_R(s) + \sum_{i=1}^{m} \frac{A_i}{(s-a)^i} + \sum_{j=1}^{n} \frac{B_j}{(s-b)^j} + \dots \tag{3–148}$$

where $a, b, \dots$ are the roots of $D(s)$, where $m, n, \dots$ represent the order of the poles of $F(s)$ at $a, b, \dots$, and where R represents the number of roots of $D(s)$ and the number of summations on the right-hand side of (3–148).

Certain special cases are of particular interest for the work of this text:

CASE 1. *$N(s)$ is of lower degree than $D(s)$*

Then,

$$\lim_{s\to\infty} (N/D) = 0$$

and

$$\lim_{s\to\infty} F_R(s) = 0$$

Since F_R is given by the power series (3–145), it follows that $F_R = 0$ for all values of s (i.e., all coefficients in its power series are zero).

CASE 2. *$N(s)$ and $D(s)$ are of equal degree*

Then,

$$\lim_{s\to\infty} [N(s)/D(s)] = K \quad \text{a constant.}$$

Hence

$$\lim_{s\to\infty} F_R = K$$

Comparison with the power series (3–145) indicates that $a_0 = K$, and that all other coefficients are zero, i.e., $F_R = K$. Incidentally, K is the ratio of the coefficients of the highest power of s in N and in D. The quantity K may be obtained by one step of a long division, i.e., $(N/D) = K + (N_1/D)$, where N_1 is lower in degree than D. We note also that if (N/D) is a Laplace transform, K is the transform of an impulse function.

An Application of the Partial Fraction Method

The application of the partial fraction method, like that of the residue method, is far simpler than its theoretical justification. In order to illustrate the partial fraction technique, let it be supposed that we seek the inverse transform

$$f(t) = \mathcal{L}^{-1}F(s) \tag{3–149}$$

where

$$F(s) = \frac{s^3+s^2+s+2}{(s+1)(s+2)^2}$$

We suppose, also, that we know or have previously established that

$$\mathcal{L}^{-1}\frac{1}{s+a} = e^{-at} \tag{3–150}$$

and

$$\mathcal{L}^{-1}\frac{1}{(s+b)^2} = t\,e^{-bt} \tag{3–151}$$

and

$$\mathcal{L}^{-1}1 = u_0(t) \tag{3–152}$$

where $u_0(t)$ is a unit impulse occurring at $t = 0$.

Since the unknown transform is a ratio of polynomials of equal degree, we have Case 2 of the foregoing development. With one step of a long-division, the expression for $F(s)$ is easily written as

$$F(s) = 1 - \frac{4s^2 + 7s + 2}{(s+1)(s+2)^2} \tag{3–153}$$

Now comparing with (3–148), we have $F_R = 1$ and

$$F(s) = 1 + \frac{k_1}{(s+1)} + \frac{l_1}{(s+2)} + \frac{l_2}{(s+2)^2} \tag{3–154}$$

The coefficients k_1, l_1, and l_2 are found from (3–143). In order to determine k_1, we let $m = 1$, $r = 1$ in that equation. Then

$$k_1 = (s+1)\left[1 - \frac{4s^2 + 7s + 2}{(s+1)(s+2)^2}\right]\bigg|_{s=-1} \tag{3–155}$$

or $k_1 = 1$.

In order to determine l_1, we let $m = 2$, $r = 1$, whence

$$l_1 = \frac{d}{ds}\left\{(s+2)^2\left[1 - \frac{4s^2 + 7s + 2}{(s+1)(s+2)^2}\right]\right\}\bigg|_{s=-2} \tag{3–156}$$

or $l_1 = -5$.

The coefficient l_2 is found with $m = 2$ and $r = 2$, so that

$$l_2 = (s+2)^2\left[1 - \frac{4s^2 + 7s + 2}{(s+1)(s+2)^2}\right]\bigg|_{s=-2} \tag{3–157}$$

or $l_2 = 4$.

It should be noted that the constant term 1 in the square brackets of (3–155), (3–156), and (3–157) contributes nothing to the values of k_1, l_1, or l_2. Thus the values of k_1, l_1, and l_2 are the same whether we apply (3–143) to $F(s)$ as above or simply to the term

$$(4s^2 + 7s + 2)/(s+1)(s+2)^2.$$

The transform can now be written

$$F(s) = 1 + \frac{1}{s+1} - \frac{5}{s+2} + \frac{4}{(s+2)^2} \tag{3–158}$$

Now from (3–150), (3–151), and (3–152), we have at once

$$f(t) = u_0(t) + e^{-t} - (5-4t)e^{-2t} \tag{3–159}$$

3-18 Summary

This chapter has developed some of the basic ideas and theorems of the theory of functions of a complex variable, with a view to using the resulting techniques in the analysis of electric circuit problems.

The terms *complex variable* and *function* were defined, the concepts of *continuity* and the definition of the *derivative* were developed. Analytic functions were defined with particular attention given to the use of the terms *regular* and *analytic*. A derivation of the *Cauchy–Riemann equations* and a discussion of the *singularities* of a function of a complex variable followed.

The fundamentals of integration in the complex plane were then presented. These included *contour integration*, the *Cauchy–Goursat theorem*, and the *Cauchy integral formula*, and were followed by the *Taylor* and *Laurent series*, leading directly to the evaluation of contour integrals by the *residue method*.

The complex variable theory presented in this chapter was applied to the *inversion integral* of the Laplace transformation. The residue method of evaluation of the inversion integral was developed together with the conditions which justify this method. The residue method was then applied to the evaluation of the inversion integral of several functions. The means of treating a transform of a time-function containing an impulse term was also illustrated. Here the residue method was not directly applicable. Several special theorems of complex functions, useful in electric circuit analysis, were derived.

The *partial fraction expansion*, useful for expressing a transform as a sum of simpler transforms, was derived with the aid of the Laurent series. This method of derivation yielded the expansion in the most general possible form.

With the material of this chapter as background, we shall develop the various techniques and methods of electric network analysis for both transient and steady-state problems. The residue method of evaluation of the inversion integral will prove more than a powerful tool for solving transient problems—it will add to a fundamental understanding of network response.

Problems

3-1. Which of the following functions is continuous at the origin of the complex plane?

(A) $\sin s$ (B) $\sin(1/s)$ (C) $1/s$ (D) e^{as} (E) $\sin |s|$.

3-2. With the aid of the Cauchy–Riemann equations, determine which of the functions listed in Problem 3–1 is regular at the origin of the complex plane.

3-3. (A) Which of the functions in Problem 3–1 is analytic (i.e., regular in some region of the complex plane)?

(B) Which has a simple pole at the origin?

(C) Which has an essential singularity at the origin? NOTE: The power series expansion for the sine may prove helpful.

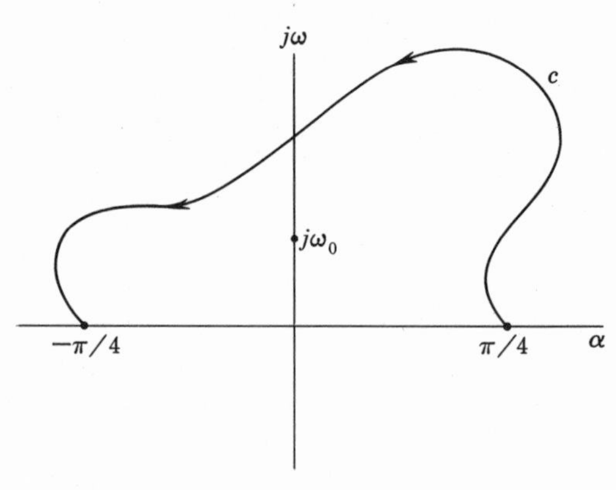

Problem 3–4.

3-4. (A) If $F(s)$ is regular at $s = s_1$, show that $F(s-k)$ is regular at $s = s_1+k$.
(B) Evaluate

$$\oint_c \sin(s-j\omega_0)\, ds$$

where the path c, the direction of integration along it, and the point $j\omega_0$ are shown in the figure.

3-5. Evaluate

$$\oint_c \frac{2s\, ds}{s^2+\omega_0{}^2}$$

where the path c, the direction of integration along it, and the point $j\omega_0$ are shown in the figure for Problem 3–4.

3-6. Solve each of the following equations for $f(t)$:

(A)
$$\mathcal{L}f(t) = \frac{1}{s^n}$$

(B)
$$\mathcal{L}f(t) = \frac{1}{(s+a)^n}$$

where a is a real, positive constant

(C)
$$\mathcal{L}f(t) = \frac{1}{(s+a)^2(s+b)}$$

where a and b are real, positive constants

(D)
$$\mathcal{L}f(t) = \frac{s^3}{(s+a)(s+b)}$$

3-7. (A) A voltage $v(t)$ given by

$$v(t) = 0 \text{ when } t < 0$$
$$\text{and } v(t) = V \text{ when } t > 0$$

is applied to the input terminals of a certain linear, lumped, finite circuit with constant parameters. The circuit is initially at rest. As is commonly the case, it is found that the Laplace transform I of the input current is given by

$$I = \frac{V}{s}\frac{N(s)}{D(s)}$$

where:

(1) $sD(s)$ is a polynomial in s (with real constant coefficients) of degree $m+1$.

(2) $N(s)$ is a polynomial in s with real constant coefficients.

(3) The degree of $N(s)$ is less than $m+1$.

(4) No root of $N(s)$ equals a root of $sD(s)$, and the poles of I are all simple.

Show, with the aid of the residue method, that

$$i(t) = V\frac{N(0)}{D(0)} + \sum_{r=1}^{m} \frac{VN(s_r)}{s_rD_1(s_r)}e^{s_rt}$$

where

$$D_1(s_r) = \lim_{s\to s_r} \frac{D(s)}{s-s_r}$$

and where s_r is a root of $D(s)$ with $r = 1, 2, \ldots, m$. This result is known as the

Heaviside expansion theorem. Many circuits meet the requirements of this theorem.

(B) What will happen if $\mathcal{R}e\, s_r > 0$ for one or more values of r?

(C) Could $s_r = 0$ for any value of r, i.e., $r = 1, 2, \ldots, m$?

3-8. Establish as a lemma, using the residue method, that

$$\mathcal{L}^{-1} \frac{A}{s-a} = Ae^{at}$$

provided that A and a are constants. With this result known, use the partial fraction theorem to establish the Heaviside expansion theorem, stated in Problem 3–7.

3-9. A ratio of polynomials in s with real constant coefficients (and with numerator of lesser degree than denominator) has 10 poles. These occur in the left half of the s-plane. Three of these poles occur at points in the second quadrant of the s-plane (not on the axes).

(A) State the largest number which is less than or equal to the degree of the denominator. Under what circumstances is this number less than the degree of the denominator?

(B) How many of these poles are real?

(C) How many residues of $[N(s)/D(s)]e^{st}$ are complex?

(D) Is the sum of the residues of $[N(s)/D(s)]e^{st}$ real or complex?

3-10. A certain current $i(t)$ is given by

$$i(t) = \mathcal{L}^{-1} \frac{N(s)}{D(s)}$$

where N and D are polynomials in s with real constant coefficients and N is lower in degree than D. With the results obtained in Problems 3–6 and 3–7 as a guide, state whether or not $i(t)$ will increase without limit in each of the cases given below:

(A) All poles of $N(s)/D(s)$ are simple, none occurs to the right of the $j\omega$ axis.

(B) Some poles are multiple, but none occurs on or to the right of the $j\omega$ axis.

(C) A multiple pole occurs at the origin.

(D) A multiple pole occurs on the $j\omega$ axis.

(E) A simple pole occurs in the right half-plane.

(See also Table 5–1, p. 239).

References for Chapter 3

1. Bode, H. W., *Network Analysis and Feedback Amplifier Design*, D. Van Nostrand Co., Inc., Princeton, N.J., 1945.
2. Churchill, R. V., *Introduction to Complex Variables and Applications*, McGraw-Hill Book Co., Inc., New York, 1948.
3. Churchill, R. V., *Modern Operational Mathematics in Engineering*, McGraw-Hill Book Co., Inc., New York, 1944; *Operational Mathematics*, 2nd ed., 1958.

4. Fich, S., *Transient Analysis in Electrical Engineering*, Prentice-Hall, Inc., New York, 1951.
5. Gardner, M. F., and Barnes, J. L., *Transients in Linear Systems Studied by the Laplace Transformation*, John Wiley & Sons, Inc., New York, 1942.
6. Guillemin, E. A., *The Mathematics of Circuit Analysis*, John Wiley & Sons, Inc., New York, 1949.
7. Hildebrand, F. B., *Advanced Calculus for Engineers*, Prentice-Hall, Inc., New York, 1949.
8. LePage, W. R., and Seely, S., *General Network Analysis*, McGraw-Hill Book Co., Inc., New York, 1952.
9. McLachlan, N. W., *Complex Variable and Operational Calculus with Technical Applications*, Cambridge University Press, 1939; *Complex Variable Theory and Transform Calculus with Technical Applications*, 2nd ed., 1953.
10. McLachlan, N. W., *Modern Operational Calculus with Applications in Technical Mathematics*, Macmillan & Co., Ltd., London, 1948.
11. Nehari, Z., *Conformal Mapping*, McGraw-Hill Book Co., Inc., New York, 1952.
12. Osgood, W. F., *Advanced Calculus*, The Macmillan Co., New York, 1925.
13. Phillips, E. G., *Functions of a Complex Variable with Applications*, 3rd ed., Oliver and Boyd Ltd., Edinburgh, and Interscience Publishers, Inc., New York, 1945; 8th ed., 1957, reprinted 1958.
14. Pipes, L. A., *Applied Mathematics for Engineers and Physicists*, McGraw-Hill Book Co., Inc., New York, 1946; 2nd ed., 1958.
15. Ritt, J. F., *Theory of Functions*, King's Crown Press, New York, 1947.
16. Rothe, R., Ollendorff, F., and Pohlhausen, K., editors, *Theory of Functions as Applied to Engineering Problems*, Technology Press, Massachusetts Institute of Technology, Cambridge, 1942.
17. Seshu, S., and Balabanian, N., *Linear Network Analysis*, John Wiley & Sons, Inc., New York, 1959.
18. Thomson, W. T., *Laplace Transformation, Theory and Engineering Applications*, Prentice-Hall, Inc., New York, 1950.
19. Titchmarsh, E. C., *The Theory of Functions*, 2nd ed., Oxford University Press, New York, 1939.
20. Tuttle, D. F., Jr., *Network Synthesis. Vol. I*, John Wiley & Sons, Inc., New York, 1958.
21. Weber, E., *Linear Transient Analysis, Vol. I: Lumped-Parameter Two-Terminal Networks*, John Wiley & Sons, Inc., New York, 1954.
22. Weber, E., *Electromagnetic Fields, Theory and Applications, Vol. I: Mapping of Fields*, John Wiley & Sons, Inc., New York, 1950.
23. Weber, E., *Linear Transient Analysis, Vol. II: Two-Terminal-Pair Networks. Transmission Lines*, John Wiley & Sons, Inc., New York, 1956.

Chapter 4

ELECTRIC CIRCUIT LAWS IN TERMS OF THE LAPLACE TRANSFORMATION

The laws relating the instantaneous current and voltage for each type of circuit element were stated in Chapter 1. For example, at any instant the current in a pure inductance is related to the voltage across it by

$$v = L\frac{di}{dt} \tag{4-1}$$

For the special case of the sinusoidal steady state, this rule takes the form

$$V = j\omega LI \tag{4-2}$$

in which V and I are complex numbers and $j\omega L$ is termed the impedance of the coil. The second equation has the advantage of being algebraic. Its use of complex numbers compresses the essential facts of alternating-current variation, namely amplitude and phase, into one simple equation.

With the aid of the Laplace transformation we shall be able to replace the circuit law (4–1) by an algebraic equation regardless of the form of current and voltage variation. With this purpose in mind, the current-voltage law for each type of circuit element will be used to obtain a law relating the Laplace transform of the voltage to the Laplace transform of the current. From this result we shall formulate the general methods of loop and node analysis in terms of Laplace transforms of the voltages and currents in an electric network. The problem involving the sinusoidal steady state will then appear as a very simple special case of the general circuit problem.

The Laplace transformation, which forms the basis of the material in this chapter, was derived from the Fourier integral in Chapter 2 (Section 2–5). For convenience it is restated here:

The Laplace transform of a time-function $f(t)$, written as $F(s)$, is given by

$$F(s) = \mathcal{L}f(t) = \int_0^\infty f(t)e^{-st}\,dt \tag{4-3}$$

where $s = c+j\omega$ and the real constant c is chosen greater than the real constant c' so that

$$\int_0^\infty |f(t)|e^{-c't}\,dt$$

is finite. The transform $F(s)$ exists provided that $f(t)$ is zero for $t < 0$,* that $f(t)$ satisfies Dirichlet's conditions over any finite interval, and that the constant c' can be found. It is often convenient to write f and F in place of $f(t)$ and $F(s)$, respectively.

If the transform of a certain time-function is known, the time-function from which it came is given by

$$f = \mathcal{L}^{-1}F = \frac{1}{2\pi j}\int_{c-j\infty}^{c+j\infty} Fe^{st}\,ds \tag{4-4}$$

where $t > 0$, $s = c+j\omega$, and $c > c'$. As demonstrated in Chapter 3, however, the integral may be evaluated with the function F regarded as a function of the complex variable s equal to $\alpha+j\omega$, and with no further restriction on the range of α.

The transformation (4-3) applied to each type of circuit element yields an algebraic relationship between the transform of the voltage across the element and the transform of the current through it. The Laplace transformation will also lead to an extension of the impedance concept, so that it will be applicable in many transient problems as well as in steady-state problems.

4-1 Voltage-Current Transform Relationships for Circuit Elements

Resistance

At any instant, the voltage across a resistance is related to its current by Ohm's law:

$$v = Ri \tag{4-5}$$

* See, however, footnote to Section 2-6, second paragraph.

Taking the Laplace transform of both sides of (4–5), we have, by the linearity theorem (Section 2–6), or by direct application of (4–3),

$$V = Ri \tag{4–6}$$

where V and I are respectively the voltage and current transforms, related precisely by Ohm's law, as are the instantaneous current and voltage in (4–5). R can still be called the resistance and we also write

$$I = \frac{1}{R}V \tag{4–6a}$$

calling $1/R$ the conductance. The latter form, though obvious, is listed separately, as it will fit into the pattern of circuit relationships which form the basis of node analysis.

*Self-Inductance**

At any instant the voltage across an inductance is related to the rate of change of current in it by

$$v = L\frac{di}{dt} \tag{4–1}$$

Taking the Laplace transform of each side, we have, by the definition (4–3),

$$V = L\int_0^\infty \frac{di}{dt}e^{-st}\,dt \tag{4–7}$$

The value of this transform is given by the differentiation theorem (2–110) of Chapter 2 as

$$V = LsI - Li_0 \tag{4–8}$$

where i_0 is the value of the initial current in the inductance (see Section 1–5). The theorem (4–8) is a form of (2–110) and applies provided that v and i are Laplace transformable, and that i is continuous. These conditions are generally met in physical problems. (A sudden discontinuity in coil current† is sometimes assumed when the arc following opening of a switch is of short duration. This case requires special consideration. See Section 1–5, and again in the present chapter, Section 4–4 for treatment of discontinuity in determining i_0.)

Equation (4–8), if solved for I, yields the form

$$I = \frac{1}{Ls}V + \frac{1}{s}i_0 \tag{4–8a}$$

* The discussion of *mutual inductance* has been reserved for Chapter 5, where it can be carried out more effectively with the aid of loop and node analysis.

† This, of course, implies instantaneously infinite voltage.

Equation (4–8a), like (4–6a), is written because it fits the pattern of relations which form the basis of node analysis.

Equations (4–8) and (4–8a) have the advantage of being algebraic and of expressing the initial current directly. If the derivative relationship (4–1) were to be used in a problem, the current i_0 would appear in the answer only after the process (often involved) of evaluating constants of integration. This process was illustrated in Chapter 1 (Section 1–7).

In order to have a terminology which will lead to a convenient procedure for electric network analysis, let us first consider the case where $i_0 = 0$. Then (4–8) and (4–8a) become

$$V = LsI \tag{4–9}$$

$$I = \frac{1}{Ls}V \tag{4–9a}$$

Equation (4–9) is identical in form with (4–2) but contains Ls in place of the alternating-current impedance $Lj\omega$. Hence Ls is also termed *impedance* and $1/Ls$ *admittance*. In words, equation (4–9) reads "voltage transform equals impedance times current transform" while (4–9a) asserts "current transform equals admittance times voltage transform." With the use of this terminology derived from the special case (4–9 and 9a), the term Li_0 in (4–8) remains to be interpreted. This term may be regarded as equivalent to the transform of an applied e.m.f. The constant Li_0 is, in fact, the transform of an impulse voltage (see Section 2–6) of precisely the strength required to establish the current i_0 in the inductance instantaneously at $t = 0$. In the absence of i_0, then, the inductance is completely described by the impedance Ls. When i_0 is present, however, the coil terminals are the end points of a combination of e.m.f. source and impedance, the transform of the potential difference between these terminals being given by (4–8). In a similar manner, the term $(1/s)i_0$ in equation (4–8a) will be interpreted as a current source of strength i_0. (Note that $\mathfrak{L}^{-1}(1/s)i_0 = i_0$ for $t > 0$.)

Capacitance

The charge q on a capacitance C is at any instant proportional to the voltage across it, as expressed by the relation

$$q = Cv \tag{4–10}$$

The rate of increase of charge on the capacitance is the current flowing to it, so that differentiation of (4–10) yields

$$i = C\frac{dv}{dt} \tag{4–11}$$

Comparison of (4–11) with (4–1) shows them to be the same mathematical relationship except that i and v are interchanged and C replaces L. Because these equations embody the same law, though with interchange of quantities, they are called *duals*.* Any mathematical procedure beginning with (4–11) must yield the dual of the result of the same procedure beginning with (4–1). Thus if, starting with (4–11), we follow the same step as in proceeding from (4–7) to (4–8), we must obtain the dual of (4–8), namely:

$$I = -Cv_0 + CsV \tag{4–12}$$

where v_0 is the initial value of the voltage across the capacitance (see Chapter 1). It is evident on physical grounds that both i and v will be Laplace transformable functions and that v will be continuous. Hence the conditions of the differentiation theorem of Chapter 2 are met. (A sudden discontinuity in capacitive voltage, caused, say, by applying a voltage source across a capacitance with resistanceless leads, will require special consideration. See Sections 1–5 and 4–4.) Equation (4–12), if solved for V, yields

$$V = \frac{1}{Cs}I + \frac{1}{s}v_0 \tag{4–12a}$$

Equations (4–12) and (4–8) are duals, as are the pair (4–12a) and (4–8a).

Here, as in the case of the inductance, the Laplace transformation has replaced the calculus relationship by an algebraic one and expressed the initial condition explicitly. As with the inductance, we consider the special case in which the initial condition is zero, i.e., $v_0 = 0$. Then (4–12) and (4–12a) become

$$I = CsV \tag{4–13}$$

and

$$V = \frac{1}{Cs}I \tag{4–13a}$$

These are entirely analogous to

$$I = Cj\omega V \tag{4–14}$$

$$V = \frac{1}{Cj\omega}I \tag{4–14a}$$

Hence, we term Cs the *admittance* and $1/Cs$ the *impedance* of a capacitance. As with the inductance, we have arrived at the terms *admittance* and

* See the subsection The Duality Principle, in Section 1–4 for definition of duality.

impedance from the special case of the zero initial condition. The term Cv_0 in (4–12) remains to be interpreted. This term may be regarded as equivalent to the transform of an applied current. The constant Cv_0 is, in fact, the transform of an impulse current (see Section 2–6) of precisely the strength required to establish the voltage v_0 across the capacitance instantaneously at $t = 0$. In the absence of v_0, then, the pure capacitor is completely described by the admittance Cs. When v_0 is present, however, the capacitor terminals are the end points of a combination of current source and admittance, the transform of the capacitive current being given by (4–12). In a similar manner, the term $(1/s)v_0$ in (4–12a) will be interpreted as an e.m.f. source of strength v_0. (Note that $\mathcal{L}^{-1}(1/s)v_0 = v_0$ for $t > 0$.)

The reader will observe that the principle of duality has made possible almost identical discussion of the capacitance and inductance relationships. It was merely necessary to interchange the terms *voltage* and *current*, and the terms *capacitance* and *inductance*.

4-2 Kirchhoff's Laws Applied to Current and Voltage Transforms

Voltage Law

Kirchhoff's voltage law(Section 1–1) states that the sum of the voltage-increases (or decreases) in a specified direction around any closed path is

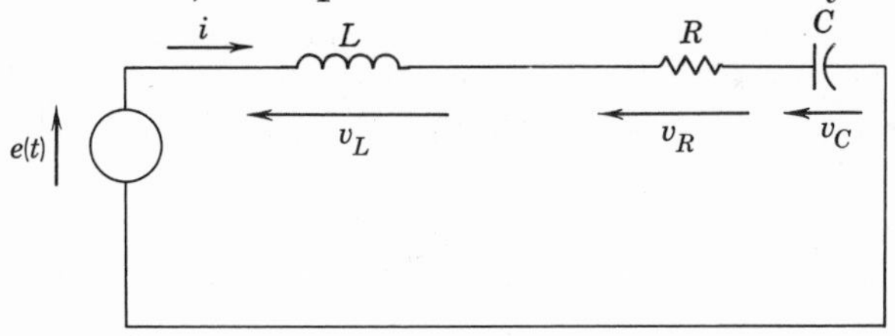

Fig. 4–1.

zero at any instant. In order to express this as a law relating transforms of voltages,[4] we consider a specific case capable of easy generalization. Let the path be that shown in Fig. 4–1. Using Kirchhoff's voltage law and writing v_L, v_R, and v_C, respectively, for the instantaneous voltages across L, R, and C, with the reference direction of each v taken opposite to that of e, we obtain

$$e = v_L + v_R + v_C \tag{4–15}$$

Taking the Laplace transform of both sides of (4–15) and using (4–8, 6, and 12a) for the transforms of the respective terms, we find (with i_0 and v_0 the initial values of i and v_C)

$$E = -Li_0 + LsI + RI + \frac{1}{Cs}I + \frac{1}{s}v_0 \tag{4–16}$$

Now with $E_m = E + Li_0 - (1/s)v_0$, the last equation becomes

$$E_m = LsI + RI + \frac{1}{Cs}I \tag{4–16a}$$

In a more general network where the elements of the loop (Fig. 4–1) are common to other loops in the network, the I's in the separate terms of equations (4–16) and (4–16a) will be unequal. If we call E_m a *modified e.m.f. transform*, and terms such as LsI, RI, and $(1/Cs)I$ *impedance-voltage transforms*, Kirchhoff's voltage law can be stated for the Laplace transforms of the voltages in a closed path:

> In any closed path in an electric network, the modified e.m.f. transform equals the sum of the impedance-voltage transforms.*

This statement of Kirchhoff's voltage law forms a basis for writing the loop equations in an electric network directly in terms of Laplace transforms. Since terms representing initial quantities are included on the e.m.f. side of the equation, we simply sum the impedance-voltage transforms. However when the voltage across a particular element is sought, the Laplace transform of that voltage must again involve the initial condition. Thus while the transform of the current in the inductance of Fig. 4–1 follows directly from Kirchhoff's voltage law as stated, or from equation (4–16a), as

$$I = \frac{E_m}{Ls + R + \dfrac{1}{Cs}} \tag{4–17}$$

the transform of the voltage across this inductance is

$$V_L = \frac{E_m Ls}{Ls + R + \dfrac{1}{Cs}} - Li_0 \tag{4–18}$$

The latter equation is a direct application of equation (4–8).

* The signs of the transforms follow easily from the signs of the instantaneous functions which they represent.

Current Law

Kirchhoff's current law (Chapter 1) states that at any instant the sum of the currents flowing out of any point in an electric network equals zero. In order to express this as a law relating transforms of currents, we again consider a specific case capable of easy generalization. Let the branches C, R, and L be connected to a current source of strength $i(t)$ as in Fig. 4–2. Applying Kirchhoff's current law to the junction P, we have

$$i(t) = i_C + i_R + i_L \tag{4–19}$$

at any instant, the symbols being defined in Fig. 4–2. Taking the Laplace

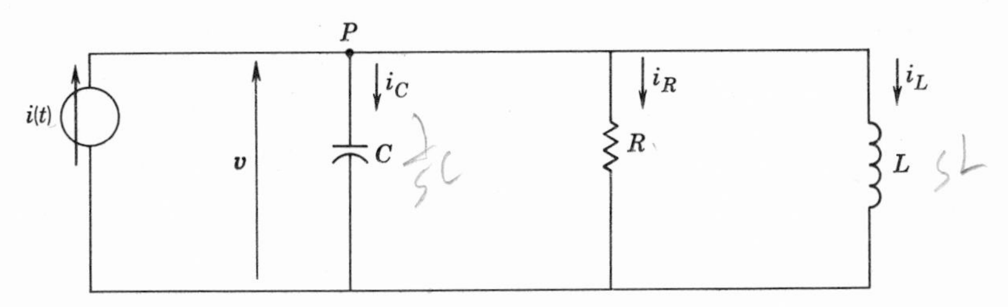

Fig. 4–2.

transform of both sides and using equations (4–12), (4–6a), and (4–8a) for the respective terms, we obtain (with v_0 and i_0 the initial values of v and i_L)

$$I = -Cv_0 + CsV + \frac{1}{R}V + \frac{1}{Ls}V + \frac{1}{s}i_0 \tag{4–20}$$

Now with $I_m = I + Cv_0 - (1/s)i_0$, the last equation becomes

$$I_m = CsV + \frac{1}{R}V + \frac{1}{Ls}V \tag{4–20a}$$

In a more general network where the elements radiate from P (Fig. 4–2) to separate points in the network, the V's in the separate terms of (4–20) and (4–20a) will be unequal. If we call I_m a *modified source-current transform* and terms such as CsV, $(1/R)V$, and $(1/Ls)V$ *admittance-current transforms*, Kirchhoff's current law can be stated for the Laplace transforms of currents at a node or junction point:

> At any node in an electric network, the modified source-current transform equals the sum of the admittance-current transforms.*

* See footnote, preceding page.

This statement of Kirchhoff's current law forms a basis for writing the node equations of an electric network directly in terms of Laplace transforms. Since terms representing initial quantities are included on the current-source side of the equation, we simply sum the admittance-current transforms. However, when the current through a particular element is sought, the Laplace transform of that current must again involve the initial condition. Thus while the transform of the voltage across the capacitance of Fig. 4–2 follows directly from Kirchhoff's current law as stated, or from equation (4–20a), as

$$V = \frac{I_m}{Cs + \dfrac{1}{R} + \dfrac{1}{Ls}} \tag{4–21}$$

the transform of the capacitive current is

$$I_C = \frac{I_m Cs}{Cs + \dfrac{1}{R} + \dfrac{1}{Ls}} - Cv_0 \tag{4–22}$$

The latter is a direct application of (4–12).

The reader will observe a high degree of identity of language in the discussion of the current and voltage laws. This has been used in order to emphasize again the duality principle in network theory.

4-3 Parallel-Series Combinations as Single Impedances

In problems involving the sinusoidal steady state, where initial conditions are not involved, circuit elements in parallel or series are commonly replaced by equivalent single impedances. The question naturally arises as to whether this obvious simplification will be of use in the application of Kirchhoff's current and voltage laws to current and voltage transforms. With this objective, the word *impedance* will be defined as the ratio of voltage transform to current transform when that ratio can be given in terms of circuit parameters and the complex variable s. *Admittance* is the ratio of current transform to voltage transform under the same circumstances.

Since the initial condition plays the role of an e.m.f. transform or a source-current transform, it is evident that elements connected in series and parallel combinations cannot be represented as single impedances or admittances when non-zero initial conditions must be taken into account. However, in the important case of zero initial conditions, equivalent impedances or admittances may be computed to represent parallel or series combinations in precisely the same manner as in problems involving the sinusoidal steady state. This point is illustrated in Fig. 4–3.

Let us suppose we seek the currents in the circuit of Fig. 4–3 for all time after the switch S opens. At the instant immediately after the switch opens, the current in the inductance will be i_0 and equal in value to the current immediately before switching. The voltage across the

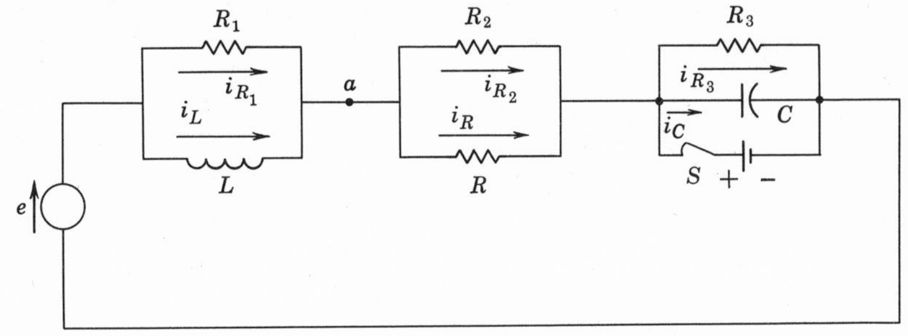

Fig. 4–3.

capacitance will be v_0 and also equal to the value of that voltage immediately before switching. With S open, there are four closed paths in the network, but for our immediate purpose only three need be considered, namely, those formed by L and R_1, R and R_2, and C and R_3. Taking the positive direction of current flow to the right, and identifying current transforms by the same subscripts used for currents in the figure, application of Kirchhoff's voltage law to the three loops in question leads to the equations

$$Li_0 = LsI_L - R_1 I_{R_1} \tag{4–23a}$$

$$0 = RI_R - R_2 I_{R_2} \tag{4–23b}$$

$$-\frac{v_0}{s} = \frac{1}{Cs} I_C - R_3 I_{R_3} \tag{4–23c}$$

Now if I is the transform of the current to the right at the point a, Kirchhoff's law yields

$$I = I_R + I_{R_2} \tag{4–24}$$

If R_p be defined by $1/R_p = (1/R) + (1/R_2)$, then (4–23b) and (4–24) can easily be used to show that

$$IR_p = I_R R = I_{R_2} R_2 \tag{4–24a}$$

As in alternating-current theory, then, we can regard R and R_2 together as a single resistance R_p and use this in calculating the current transforms in the network. However, if we attempt to do the same thing with the R_1–L and R_3–C parallel combinations, we find that it cannot be done, for the left sides of equations (4–23a) and (4–23c) contain Li_0 and $-v_0/s$. Thus the ratios of voltage transform to current transform for the R_1–L and R_3–C combinations depend on initial current and voltage values rather than on the circuit elements themselves. An equivalent situation occurs in alternating-current circuit theory where impedance is not defined for parallel branches containing an independent* source of e.m.f.

Now, suppose in Fig. 4–3 we remove the battery across the capacitance and put an open switch in series with the e.m.f. e. Both the voltage across the capacitance and the current in the coil will decay to zero. Closing the switch in series with e then yields the important special case of zero initial conditions, i.e., $i_0 = 0$ in (4–23a) and $v_0 = 0$ in (4–23c). These relations can be treated in a manner entirely analogous to the steps based on (4–23b). For this special case, there results

$$1/(Z_p)_L = (1/Ls) + (1/R_1)$$

and

$$1/(Z_p)_C = Cs + (1/R_3)$$

where $(Z_p)_L$ and $(Z_p)_C$ are the impedances of the R_1–L and R_3–C combinations. Hence, if initial values are zero, the previous circuit becomes a single-loop problem in which the current transform I is solved by the equation

$$E = (Z_p)_L I + R_p I + (Z_p)_C I.$$

The same problem, of course, is involved in the matter of combining elements connected in series as a single admittance. For example, the transform of the voltage across the branch in Fig. 4–3(a) is

Fig. 4–3(a).

$$V = RI + LsI - Li_0$$

where the voltage reference direction is taken opposite to the current reference direction. If $i_0 = 0$, $I/V = 1/(R+Ls) = Y$, while if $i_0 \neq 0$, we cannot describe this branch as a single admittance.

4-4 Simplified Treatment of Initial Conditions

The discussion of initial conditions in Section 1–5 referred to two situations. The simpler and more common situation was that in which Kirchhoff's laws for the circuit after switching were satisfied only if current in inductance, and voltage across capacitance, were continuous

* We shall see in Chapters 5 and 6, however, that a dependent e.m.f. or current source, such as μEg in the vacuum-tube linear equivalent circuit, does not bar use of the impedance concept.

at the instant of switching. In such cases, the condition of the circuit prior to switching yielded the necessary initial values.

The second case discussed in Chapter 1 was that in which the values of current or voltage just before switching could not satisfy the equations valid for the circuit after switching. A limiting process was developed, which yielded values of current and voltage discontinuities valid for ideal circuits (see Section 1–5, for assumptions involved and for definition of ideal L, R, C, and switch).

A simpler approach, again assuming ideal circuits, is possible when the Laplace transform method is used.[1,4,5] The value of current in inductance, and of voltage across capacitance, just prior to switching may be inserted as initial values in the Laplace transform equations. The resulting solution reduces to a correct limit as t approaches zero through positive values, i.e., at $t = 0+$. The justification for this in Reference 5 is in terms of charge Q and its time derivative.* A demonstration is included, however, that when the circuit equations are written in terms of current and when the initial value of charge Q_0 is taken as the value of Q just prior to switching, an impulse current term appears in the solution of the circuit equations. The strength of the impulse is equal to the charge discontinuity at $t = 0$. (Needless to say, when Q is continuous at the instant of switching, the impulse term is of zero strength, i.e., does not occur.)

Clearly, if we seek the voltage across an inductance, we should again expect an impulse term to appear in the solution when a current discontinuity occurs. Let $i(0-)$ and $i(0+)$ be respectively the values of current just before and just after switching, i.e., the limits of i as t approaches zero from the left and right, respectively. We consider the identity

$$\mathcal{L}^{-1}[LsI - Li(0-)] \equiv \mathcal{L}^{-1}[LsI - Li(0+)] + \mathcal{L}^{-1}[Li(0+) - Li(0-)] \quad (4\text{–}25)$$

The inverse transform $\mathcal{L}^{-1}[LsI - Li(0+)]$ is, by the differentiation theorem (Section 2–6), equal to $L(di/dt)$ for $t > 0$. The term

$$\mathcal{L}^{-1}L[i(0+) - i(0-)]$$

is the impulse function $L[i(0+) - i(0-)]u_0(t)$, the strength of which is equal to the discontinuity of flux linkage in the inductance.

When a discontinuity must occur, it is not easy in general to justify the choice of initial values from the circuit condition just prior to switching, i.e., at $t = 0-$. However, in specific problems the result may be verified directly from the circuit differential equations valid for positive time. In certain instances, verification will be obvious, as when an ideal e.m.f. source is suddenly applied to an ideal capacitance. In other cases,

* The general development concerns networks with applied e.m.f.'s (excluding impulse e.m.f.'s applied to purely capacitive circuits). See also Reference (1).

the values of current or voltage at $t = \epsilon$, where ϵ is small and positive, may be obtained by integrating the differential equations from time zero to time ϵ, as illustrated in Section 1–5. This gives a means of verification which is independent of the impulse function and its transform. Essentially we assume a continuous change in an interval which reduces to zero.

4-5 Examples of Transient Problems in Simple Circuits

Before taking up the general methods of loop and node analysis, we shall develop several examples to demonstrate the mechanics of the Laplace transform method. In these examples, the application of Kirchhoff's laws to the circuit will be evident, so that it will be unnecessary to refer to the general form of loop and node analysis. However, important procedures involved in the use of the Laplace transform method will be illustrated.

Step Voltage Applied to an RC Circuit with Initially Charged Capacitance

The voltage applied to the circuit of Fig. 4–4 is given by the equations $e(t) = 0$ for $t < 0$, and $e(t) = E$ for $t > 0$. The capacitance is assumed to be charged to a voltage v_{C0} prior to the instant $t = 0$. Kirchhoff's voltage law, here, requires that the voltage v_C be continuous at the instant of switching, since a sudden change in this quantity implies infinite current, and hence infinite iR. The latter is incompatible with Kirchhoff's voltage law (as well as with reasonable energy considerations, of course). Calling the transform of the applied voltage $E(s)$ and using relations (4–6) and (4–12a) for the resistance and capacitance, we have

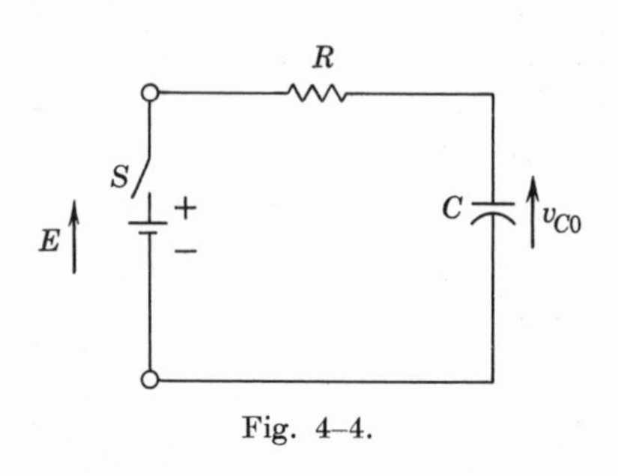

Fig. 4–4.

$$E(s) = RI + \frac{1}{Cs}I + \frac{v_{C0}}{s} \tag{4–26}$$

Now $E(s)$ equals E/s, and the term v_{C0}/s simply modifies the e.m.f. transform; therefore

$$\frac{E}{s} - \frac{v_{C0}}{s} = RI + \frac{1}{Cs}I \tag{4–26a}$$

whence the current transform I is

$$I = \frac{E - v_{C0}}{R} \frac{1}{s + \frac{1}{RC}} \tag{4–26b}$$

The time-function corresponding to the transform I can be evaluated by the residue method of Chapter 3. The transform I, regarded as a function of the complex variable s, equal to $\alpha + j\omega$, is seen to be regular except at a simple pole at $s = -1/RC$, so that

$$i = \operatorname*{Res}_{\text{at } s=(-1/RC)} Ie^{st} = \lim_{s \to -(1/RC)} \left(s + \frac{1}{RC}\right) Ie^{st} = \frac{E - v_{C0}}{R} e^{-(t/RC)} \tag{4–27}$$

Step Voltage Applied to the Circuit of Fig. 4–5

C_1 and C_2 in Fig. 4–5 are uncharged prior to application of the step voltage. The voltage across the capacitance C_2 must be continuous at

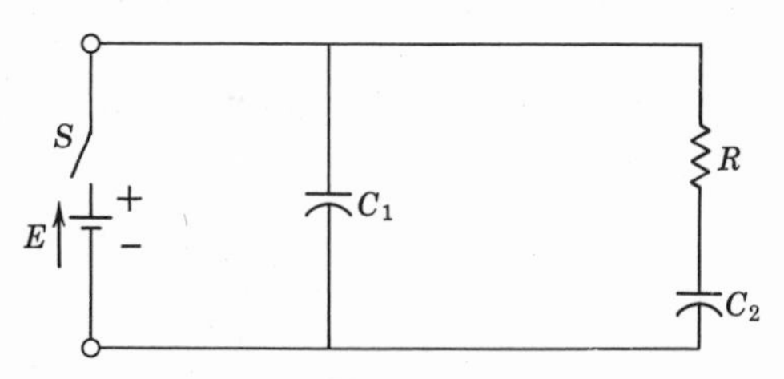

Fig. 4–5.

the instant of switching if Kirchhoff's voltage law is to be satisfied for the loop consisting of E, R, and C_2. (Any assumption other than continuity would result in an infinite voltage across the resistance R.) On the other hand, the voltage across C_1 must be discontinuous at the instant of switching, for Kirchhoff's voltage law applied to the closed path formed by the source and C_1 after switching cannot be consistent with the assumption of continuity of voltage across C_1 at the instant of switching. However, following the method discussed in Section 4–4, we write the Laplace transform equations with $v_{C_10} = v_{C_20} = 0$. That the solution (with the aid of an impulse term) will lead to correct values for $t > 0$ will be seen below.

The admittance of this circuit is given by

$$Y = C_1 s + \frac{1}{R + \frac{1}{C_2 s}} \tag{4–28}$$

or

$$Y = \frac{RC_1C_2s^2 + (C_1 + C_2)s}{RC_2s + 1} \tag{4–28a}$$

The transform of the current i delivered by the e.m.f. source is then

$$I = \frac{E}{s}Y \tag{4–29}$$

where E/s is the Laplace transform of the applied unit step, so that

$$I = \frac{E}{s}\,\frac{RC_1C_2s^2 + (C_1 + C_2)s}{RC_2s + 1} \tag{4–30}$$

The numerator and denominator of $I(s)$ are polynomials of equal degree. In order to have a form for which we have justified the residue method (see Section 3–14), we perform one step of a long-division, which yields

$$I = EC_1 + \frac{EC_2}{RC_2s + 1} \tag{4–31}$$

or

$$I = EC_1 + \frac{E}{R\left(s + \dfrac{1}{RC_2}\right)}$$

We note that the partial fraction theorem as developed in Section 3–17, equation (3–148), yields precisely the same result.

We observe that the second term of (4–31) is regular save for the simple pole at $s = -1/RC_2$ and clearly satisfies the condition

$$\lim_{|s|\to\infty} |F(s)| = 0$$

Hence the time-function which it represents can be found by the residue method.

Recalling that a constant is interpreted as the transform of an impulse, we find

$$i = EC_1u_0(t) + \frac{E}{R}\,e^{-(t/RC_2)} \tag{4–32}$$

where the first term on the right-hand side is an impulse of strength EC_1 and the second is the residue of $Ee^{st}/R[s + (1/RC_2)]$ at the simple pole at the point $s = -1/RC_2$.

The terms of (4–32) are easily interpreted. The term $(E/R)e^{-t/RC_2}$ is clearly the solution to the differential equation for the current in the

RC_2 branch of the circuit of Fig. 4–5. The impulse term, then, represents the current to the capacitance C_1 alone. The integral

$$\int_0^\infty u_0(t)\,dt$$

is equal to 1, so that the capacitance is charged to EC_1 coulombs at E volts. This charge and the corresponding voltage are present at any positive time t, however small. Hence, Kirchhoff's voltage equation $E = v_{C_1}$ for the loop consisting of source E and capacitance C_1 is satisfied for all positive time. Thus, although the initial value zero was used for the voltage across C_1 in the Laplace transform equation, the solution yields a correct charge on, and voltage across, the capacitance C_1 at the instant $t = 0+$. The current, which is the time derivative of charge, contains an impulse term.

In connection with the initial condition for C_1, it is also of interest to assume a resistance R_1 in series with C_1. With R_1 present, Kirchhoff's voltage law requires that the voltage across C_1 shall be continuous at the instant of switching. Hence, under this condition, v_{C_10} is zero both at $t = 0-$ and at $t = 0+$. This holds for all values of R_1, however small, and as R_1 reduces to zero the transform becomes the expression (4–30) used above.

It should, perhaps, be mentioned that in this problem one could avoid the step involving long-division by solving for the current in each branch of the circuit separately, and then adding the two branch currents to obtain the source current. However, one purpose of this illustrative problem was to demonstrate the fact that whenever one solves a network problem and obtains a transform with polynomials of equal degree in numerator and denominator, the division step is necessary before evaluation of the inverse transform. This division step is needed to obtain the constant term in the transform. Thus, in general, if $F(s) = N/D$, and N and D are polynomials of equal degree in s, we express $F(s)$ as $K + (N_1/D)$. The constant K, as we have seen, is the transform of the impulse in the response occurring at $t = 0$, and the term (N_1/D) is the transform of the response for $t > 0$. It is interesting to recall from Sections 3–15 and 3–17 that

$$\sum \text{Res}\,(N_1/D)e^{st} = \sum \text{Res}\,(N/D)e^{st}$$

and that the terms in the partial fraction expansion of (N_1/D) are identical with those in the expansion of (N/D) save for the constant K. Hence it is not necessary to obtain (N_1/D) explicitly. However, it is desirable to have this term as a simpler function than (N/D) and as the term which actually is the transform of the time-function for $t > 0$.

A Step Current Applied to the Circuit of Fig. 4–6

We shall now solve for the voltage v which appears across the input terminals aa' of the circuit of Fig. 4–6 after opening of the switch S. As usual, ideal circuit elements are assumed and arcing will be ignored in the solution. The resistance R_1 has been included in the figure in order to avoid ambiguity of the direct-current path when the switch S is closed. When R_1 is reduced to zero, this circuit and that of Fig. 4–5 become duals. Their equations are the same save for interchange of the letters v and i, L and C, R and $1/R$ (i.e., G).

The switch S, Fig. 4–6, opens at the instant $t = 0$. Prior to this, the current in each inductance is zero. The current in L_2 must be continuous

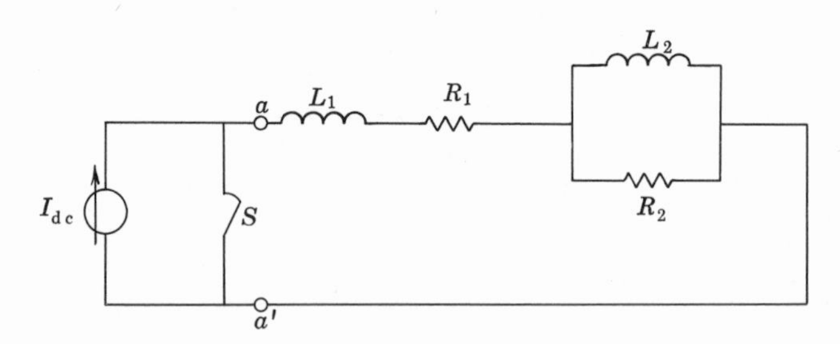

Fig. 4–6.

at the instant of switching. Any other assumption would violate Kirchhoff's current law, for a discontinuity in the current in L_2 would create an infinite voltage across R_2 and, therefore, an infinite current in R_2. This is inconsistent with the current law at the node at either end of L_2 and R_2. The current in L_1, however, must be discontinuous at the instant of switching. The assumption of zero current in L_1 when t is positive would violate Kirchhoff's current law at the junction of L_1 and the current source $I_{\text{d.c.}}$. However, proceeding along the lines of our previous discussion, we shall write the equation for the Laplace transform V of the voltage v with $i_{L_1 0} = i_{L_2 0} = 0$, i.e., the value of these currents just prior to switching. That the solution with the aid of an impulse term will lead to correct values for $t > 0$ will be seen below. The Laplace transform of v is

$$V = \left(L_1 s + R_1 + \frac{R_2 L_2 s}{R_2 + L_2 s}\right) \frac{I_{\text{d.c.}}}{s} \tag{4–33}$$

When the quantity in parentheses is multiplied by $I_{\text{d.c.}}/s$, the first term becomes a constant, the second term will have a simple pole at $s = 0$, while the third term will have a simple pole at $s = -R_2/L_2$. Hence we have immediately

$$V = L_1 I_{\text{d.c.}} u_0(t) + R_1 I_{\text{d.c.}} + R_2 I_{\text{d.c.}} e^{-(R_2/L_2)t} \tag{4-34}$$

The first term is an impulse function and represents the inverse transform of the constant $L_1 I_{\text{d.c.}}$. The latter two terms have been easily evaluated from (4–33) by the residue method (Sections 3–13 and 14).

The terms of (4–34) are readily interpreted. For $t > 0$, the voltage across R_1 is $R_1 I_{\text{d.c.}}$ so that $I_{\text{d.c.}}$ is the current in R_1. The current in R_2 is clearly

$$I_{\text{d.c.}} e^{-(R_2/L_2)t}$$

while the current in L_2 follows, immediately, from the voltage across it as

$$(1/L_2) \int_0^t I_{\text{d.c.}} R_2 e^{-(R_2/L_2)\tau} \, d\tau$$

i.e.,

$$I_{\text{d.c.}}[1 - e^{-(R_2/L_2)t}]$$

This current approaches zero as t reduces to zero through positive values. The integral

$$\int_0^\infty u_0(t) \, dt$$

is equal to 1, so that the flux linkage at L_1 is $L_1 I_{\text{d.c.}}$ with a current of $I_{\text{d.c.}}$ amperes. This flux linkage and corresponding current are present at any positive time, however small. Thus, although the initial value zero was used for the current in L_1 in the Laplace transform equation, the solution yields a correct current at the instant $t = 0+$. The voltage across L_1, which is proportional to the time derivative of the current, is expressed by means of the impulse function.

Flux Linkage and Charge

The circuits of Figs. 1–4(d) and 1–6(b) of Chapter 1 reveal an interesting physical interpretation of our method of choosing initial values for the Laplace transform equations. In the circuit of Fig. 1–4(d), the Laplace transform of the current after the switch S opens is found from

$$\frac{E}{s} = (R_1 + L_1 s) I_1 + (R_2 + L_2 s) I_2 - L_2 \frac{E}{R_2} \tag{4-35}$$

with $I_1 = I_2$.

The currents just prior to switching were E/R_2 in L_2 and zero in L_1. Hence, following the method discussed in the present chapter, we have taken L_2E/R_2 as the only initial value term. However, let it be argued that currents just *after* switching, at the instant $t = 0+$, are certainly correct initial values. These current values are

$$i_1(0+) = i_2(0+) = EL_2/R_2(L_1+L_2)$$

as obtained in Chapter 1 (see equation 1–25a). From the identity (1–26) it is immediately evident that these values introduce no change in the Laplace transform equation (4–35) above! This result is to be expected if one observes that the term $-Li_0$ in the transform of $L\,di/dt$ is equal in magnitude to flux linkage. Hence if flux linkage for the entire loop is continuous at the instant of switching, the values of current in the inductances at $t = 0-$ must lead to the same transform equations as the values of current in the inductances at $t = 0+$. For the voltage across each inductance, however, the solution obtained from $i(0-)$ as initial current contains an impulse term, which does not appear if $i(0+)$ is used. The strength of this impulse equals the change in flux linkage in each inductance (see equation 4–25 in Section 4–4).

The dual circuit of Fig. 1–6(b) reveals a similar situation. The voltage across any one of the branches of this circuit after S closes is found from the Laplace transform equation

$$\frac{I}{s} = (G_1+C_1s)V_1+(G_2+C_2s)V_2-C_2\frac{I}{G_2} \qquad (4\text{–}36)$$

with $V_1 = V_2$.

The voltages just prior to switching were I/G_2 across C_2 and zero across C_1. Hence C_2I/G_2 is taken as the only initial value term. However, as with the dual inductive circuit, let it be argued that the voltages at the instant $t = 0+$ are certainly correct initial values, that is

$$v_{C_1}(0+) = v_{C_2}(0+) = IC_2/G_2(C_1+C_2)$$

as obtained in Chapter 1 (see equation 1–30). From the identity (1–31) it is clear that this assumption introduces no change in the Laplace transform equation (4–36) above. This result is to be expected if one observes that the term $-Cv_0$ in the transform of $C\,dv/dt$ is, in magnitude, equal to charge. Hence if the total charge on the capacitances C_1 and C_2 is continuous at the instant of switching, the values of voltage across each capacitance at $t = 0-$ must lead to the same transform equations as the values of voltage across each capacitance at $t = 0+$. For the current to each capacitance, however, the solution obtained from

$v_C(0-)$ as initial voltage contains an impulse term. The strength of this impulse equals the change in charge on each capacitance.

In the circuits of Fig. 4–5 and 4–6, the ideal sources create the charge and flux discontinuities in C_1 and L_1 respectively. Since, by its definition (see Chapter 1), the ideal e.m.f. source (Fig. 4–5) can supply unlimited current, it can evidently supply the impulse current necessary to charge the capacitance C_1 instantaneously. Since, by its definition, the ideal current source (Fig. 4–6) can maintain unlimited voltage across its terminals, it can evidently supply the impulse voltage necessary for the sudden creation of current and flux linkage in L_1. In these cases the justification of the assumption of initial values from the circuit condition at $t = 0-$ lies in the fact that the solution satisfies the circuit equations at $t = 0+$.*

A Sinusoidal Voltage Replaces the Direct Voltage Applied to the Circuit of Fig. 4–5

Let a sinusoidal voltage source replace the direct voltage in Fig. 4–5. At the instant the switch is closed, the applied voltage is beyond its peak and passing through the value $V_m \cos\phi$, i.e., the applied voltage can be represented as $V_m \cos(\omega t+\phi)$ where $t = 0$ at the instant the switch closes.

We first observe that the Laplace transform of $V_m \cos(\omega t+\phi)$ can be evaluated by (4–3) with the aid of Peirce's integral tables,[(6)] if we first expand $\cos(\omega t+\phi)$ as the sum of two angles. The value of the transform is $V_m(s \cos\phi - \omega \sin\phi)/(s^2+\omega^2)$. This expression is complicated. By temporarily further complicating the problem, we shall find a much simpler means of obtaining the desired solution: Consider that we also apply to the circuit the voltage $V_m \sin(\omega t+\phi)$ whose transform is $V_m(s \sin\phi + \omega \cos\phi)/(s^2+\omega^2)$. Then if $Y(s)$ be the admittance of the circuit, which is assumed to be initially at rest, the transforms of the currents due to the cosine and sine voltages are respectively,

$$I = V_m Y(s) \frac{s \cos\phi - \omega \sin\phi}{s^2+\omega^2} \tag{4–37}$$

and

$$I' = V_m Y(s) \frac{s \sin\phi + \omega \cos\phi}{s^2+\omega^2} \tag{4–38}$$

If we now define a new transform $\bar{I}$ as

$$\bar{I} = I + jI' \tag{4–39}$$

* In the absence of derivatives, we may simply write the circuit equations at $t = \epsilon$ (with $0-$ initial values) and let $\epsilon \to 0$.

direct substitution shows that $\overline{I}$ can be expressed in the concise form

$$\overline{I} = \frac{(s+j\omega)(\cos\phi + j\sin\phi)}{s^2+\omega^2} V_m Y(s) \tag{4-40}$$

or

$$\overline{I} = \frac{\overline{V}}{s-j\omega} Y(s) \tag{4-41}$$

where $\overline{V} = V_m e^{j\phi}$. $\overline{I}$ is a much simpler transform than I or I'.

Taking the inverse transform of both sides of (4–39) yields, by the linearity theorem (Section 2–6),

$$\mathfrak{L}^{-1}\overline{I} = \mathfrak{L}^{-1}I + j\mathfrak{L}^{-1}I' \tag{4-42}$$

Since $\mathfrak{L}^{-1}I$ and $\mathfrak{L}^{-1}I'$ are each the current resulting from the application of a *real voltage* to the circuit, each is a *real function of time*. $\mathfrak{L}^{-1}I'$, being multiplied by j, is then the imaginary part of $\mathfrak{L}^{-1}\overline{I}$ while $\mathfrak{L}^{-1}I$ is the real part of $\mathfrak{L}^{-1}\overline{I}$. Hence if we define $\overline{i(t)}$ as the inverse transform of $\overline{I}$, we have that

$$\mathcal{R}e\,\overline{i(t)} = i(t) \tag{4-43}$$

where $i(t)$ is the current which flows in response to $V_m \cos(\omega t + \alpha)$ applied at $t = 0$. The advantage of this method is that, as we have noted, $\overline{I}$ is a simpler transform than I, and its inverse is therefore more easily obtained.

Consider now the circuit of Fig. 4–5 to which we apply (in place of the direct voltage source shown)

$$V_m \cos(\omega t + \phi).$$

Using the method given above, we can write

$$\overline{I} = \frac{V_m e^{j\phi}}{s-j\omega}\,\frac{RC_1C_2s^2 + (C_1+C_2)s}{RC_2s+1} \tag{4-44}$$

where the latter factor is the admittance Y of the circuit as found earlier (see 4–28). Here again we find equal degree of s in numerator and denominator, for the voltage $V_m \cos\phi$ is suddenly applied to the capacitance C_1 at the instant $t = 0$.* After one step of a long-division, we find a constant

* If $\phi = \pm\pi/2$, then $V_m \cos\phi = 0$, i.e., the source is connected to the circuit at an instant when the source voltage is zero. Hence we do not expect an impulse term, and the constant term in equation (4–46) might be suspect. We note, however, that $V_m C_1 e^{\pm j\pi/2}$ is a pure imaginary. Hence the impulse function which it represents, namely $\pm jV_mC_1u_0(t)$ cannot contribute to $\mathcal{R}e\,\overline{i(t)}$, which is the current we seek.

term (representing an impulse) and another term, in which the numerator is of lower degree than the denominator. Thus

$$\bar{I} = V_m e^{j\phi}\left[C_1 + \frac{C_2 s + j\omega R C_1 C_2 s + j\omega C_1}{(s - j\omega)(RC_2 s + 1)}\right] \tag{4-45}$$

or

$$\bar{I} = V_m e^{j\phi}\left[C_1 + \frac{C_2 s}{(s - j\omega)(RC_2 s + 1)} + \frac{j\omega C_1}{(s - j\omega)}\right] \tag{4-46}$$

where the third term results from factoring $j\omega C_1$ out of the last two terms in the numerator with the result that $(RC_2 s + 1)$ cancels out.

Hence

$$\overline{i(t)} = V_m e^{j\phi}\left[C_1 u_0(t) + \operatorname*{Res}_{\text{at } s=j\omega} \frac{s e^{st}}{R(s - j\omega)\left(s + \dfrac{1}{RC_2}\right)} + \operatorname*{Res}_{\text{at } s=-(1/RC_2)} \frac{s e^{st}}{R(s - j\omega)\left(s + \dfrac{1}{RC_2}\right)} + \operatorname*{Res}_{\text{at } s=j\omega} \frac{j\omega C_1 e^{st}}{(s - j\omega)}\right] \tag{4-47}$$

Since in each case we have simple poles, the residues are directly evaluated and, after slight simplification of the resulting terms, we have

$$\overline{i(t)} = V_m\left[e^{j\phi} C_1 u_0(t) + \frac{e^{j(\omega t + \phi)}}{R + \dfrac{1}{j\omega C_2}} + \frac{e^{-(t/RC_2)} e^{j\phi}}{R(1 + j\omega R C_2)} + j\omega C_1 e^{j(\omega t + \phi)}\right] \tag{4-48}$$

An alternative means of evaluating the transform is to expand the expression for $\bar{I}$ in partial fractions (Section 3–17), so that the terms other than the constant would be of the simple form $A/(s + \alpha)$.

Since $i(t) = \mathscr{Re}\,\overline{i(t)}$, we have

$$i(t) = V_m C_1 (\cos\phi) u_0(t) + \frac{V_m}{\left[R^2 + \left(\dfrac{1}{\omega C_2}\right)^2\right]^{1/2}} \cos(\omega t + \phi - \psi_1) + \frac{V_m e^{-(t/RC_2)}}{R[1 + (\omega C_2 R)^2]^{1/2}} \cos(\phi - \psi_2) + V_m \omega C_1 \cos\left(\omega t + \phi + \frac{\pi}{2}\right) \tag{4-49}$$

where

$$\psi_1 = \tan^{-1}\frac{\dfrac{-1}{\omega C_2}}{R}$$

and

$$\psi_2 = \tan^{-1}\frac{\omega C_2 R}{1}$$

Each term in (4–49) is the real part of the corresponding term in (4–48). The real part has been obtained from each term by taking its magnitude and multiplying by the cosine of its angle, the magnitude being the product of the magnitudes of the separate factors and the angle being the sum of the angles of the separate factors.

The physical interpretation of the separate terms is evident and of interest. The first term is an impulse current which charges the capacitance C_1 with charge $V_m C_1 \cos \phi$; this occurs almost instantaneously (the mathematical solution omits the word "almost"). The second term is the steady-state sinusoidal current in the RC branch and, as we expect, has a peak value equal to the voltage peak divided by the magnitude of the impedance; this current leads the voltage by the magnitude of the angle of the impedance (note that $-\psi_1$ is positive). The third term represents the transient current in the RC branch. The last term is the steady-state sinusoidal current to the capacitance C_1.

A Single Direct-Current Pulse Applied to an RC Circuit

The square current pulse of Fig. 4–7(a) is applied to the series RC circuit in Fig. 4–7(b) by the current source in the latter figure. (Fig. 4–7(c) will be considered at the end of this discussion.)

The Laplace transform of the applied current is, by equation (4–3), given by the integral

$$\int_0^{\infty} i(t)e^{-st}\,dt$$

Since $i(t)$ equals zero for $t > T$ and since it is equal to the constant value $I_{\text{d.c.}}$ during the interval $0 < t < T$, the integral in (4–3) becomes

$$I(s) = \int_0^T I_{\text{d.c.}}e^{-st}\,dt \tag{4–50}$$

The transform of the square pulse was also found in connection with the delay factor theorem in Section 2–6, where it was seen that the square pulse can be regarded as the superposition of two step-functions. The first of these appears at the instant $t = 0$, while the second is of equal magnitude, and opposite sign, and appears at $t = T$. Hence either by (4–50), or by use of the delay factor of the Laplace transformation, we obtain

$$I(s) = \frac{I_{\text{d.c.}}}{s} - \frac{I_{\text{d.c.}}}{s} e^{-sT} \tag{4–51}$$

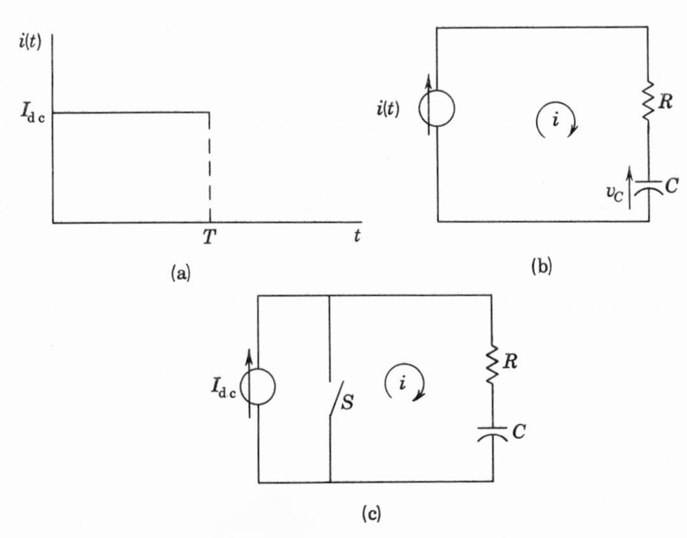

Fig. 4–7. $i(t)$ in Fig. (b) is given by Fig. (a).

In the present problem we seek the voltage v_C across the capacitance C. If the initial voltage across the capacitance is zero, we have at once

$$I(s)\frac{1}{Cs} = V_C \tag{4–52}$$

where $V_C = \mathfrak{L}v_C$.

The combination of (4–51) and (4–52) yields

$$V_C = \frac{I_{\text{d.c.}}}{C}\frac{1}{s^2} - \frac{I_{\text{d.c.}}}{C}\frac{1}{s^2} e^{-sT} \tag{4–53}$$

The Laplace transform V_C consists of two terms. In each a double pole appears at $s = 0$; the second contains in addition the delay factor e^{-sT}

(see Section 2–6). Although the algebra of the solution is easy, the general method will be clearer if we define:

$$v_{C1}(t) = \mathfrak{L}^{-1}\frac{I_{\text{d.c.}}}{Cs^2} \tag{4–54}$$

$$v_{C2}(t) = \mathfrak{L}^{-1}\frac{I_{\text{d.c.}}}{Cs^2}e^{-sT} \tag{4–55}$$

By the delay factor theorem, we have

$$\begin{aligned} v_{C2}(t) &= 0 && \text{for } t < T \\ v_{C2}(t) &= v_{C1}(t-T) && \text{for } t > T \end{aligned} \tag{4–56}$$

The time-function $v_{C1}(t)$ is easily evaluated as the residue of $(I_{\text{d.c.}}/Cs^2)e^{st}$ at the double pole at $s = 0$ (Section 3–13):

$$v_{C1}(t) = \frac{I_{\text{d.c.}}}{C}\frac{d}{ds}e^{st}\bigg|_{s=0} \qquad \text{when } t > 0 \tag{4–57}$$

or

$$v_{C1}(t) = \frac{I_{\text{d.c.}}}{C}t \qquad \text{when } t > 0 \tag{4–58}$$

Now from equation (4–56) we have at once

$$v_{C2}(t) = \frac{I_{\text{d.c.}}}{C}(t-T) \qquad \text{when } t > T \tag{4–59}$$

From (4–58) and (4–59), the voltage across the capacitance is

$$v_C = \frac{I_{\text{d.c.}}}{C}tu(t) - \frac{I_{\text{d.c.}}}{C}(t-T)u(t-T) \tag{4–60}$$

where the unit-step function $u(t)$ is 0 for negative time, and 1 for positive time. The function $u(t-T)$ is 0 when $t-T$ is negative, and 1 when $t-T$ is positive. The voltage $v_C(t)$, therefore, is represented by the first term of (4–60) during the interval $0 < t < T$, and by both terms for time $t > T$. These terms and their resultant are shown graphically in Fig. 4–8.

The solution shows the voltage across the capacitance as constant and equal to $I_{\text{d.c.}}T/C$ for all time after the instant $t = T$; this results from the assumption of the ideal current source $i(t)$. An ideal current source must be regarded as of infinite impedance, so that when the strength, i, of the current source is zero, we have simply an open circuit, and the capacitance cannot discharge. If we assume the circuit of Fig. 4–7(c), on the other hand, with S closed for $t < 0$, open for $0 < t < T$, and closed for $T < t$, we have a new circuit and a new problem at the instant $t = T$.

Let $t' = t-T$. Then

$$I = -\frac{v'_{C0}}{R}\frac{1}{s+\dfrac{1}{RC}} \tag{4–61}$$

where v'_{C0} is the value of voltage across the capacitance at the instant

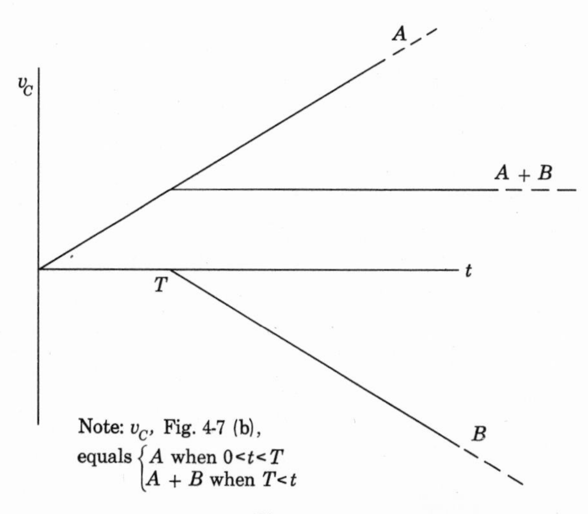

Fig. 4–8.

$t' = 0$, so that $v'_{C0} = I_{\text{d.c.}}T/C$. Since the Laplace transform of the voltage across a capacitance is $I(1/Cs)+(v_{C0}/s)$, we find

$$V_C = \frac{I_{\text{d.c.}}T}{C}\frac{1}{s+\dfrac{1}{RC}} \tag{4–62}$$

as the transform of the voltage $v_C(t')$ across the capacitance in the circuit of Fig. 4–7(c) after S closes at $t = T$. Hence, evaluating the residue of Ie^{st} at the simple pole at $s = -1/RC$ (see Section 3–13), we find

$$v_C(t') = \frac{I_{\text{d.c.}}T}{C}e^{-(1/RC)t'} \tag{4–63}$$

with $t' = t-T > 0$.

4-6 Summary

The application of the Laplace transformation to the analysis of linear electric circuits was introduced in this chapter. For each circuit element the law relating instantaneous voltage and current was expressed as a law relating voltage and current transforms. Kirchhoff's voltage and current laws were then formulated as laws for the Laplace transforms of voltage and current. In order to do this, it was helpful to regard transform terms arising from non-zero initial conditions as e.m.f. or current source transforms (e.g., a transform term such as Li_0 was treated as if it were the transform of an applied e.m.f.).

The concept of impedance $Z(s)$ as a ratio of transforms $V(s)/I(s)$ was introduced. With the aid of an example, it was demonstrated that such an impedance could have meaning only for a circuit initially at rest, as well as free of independent e.m.f. and current sources.* The admittance $Y(s)$ was defined with similar restrictions.

The determination of initial data was discussed, both for the case where Kirchhoff's laws require continuity of voltage and/or current at the instant of switching, and for the case where Kirchhoff's laws indicate that a readjustment of pre-switching values, along with a voltage or current impulse, accompany switching.

Several problems were worked out to demonstrate techniques which are needed when the Laplace transform is used in transient analysis. These problems illustrated:

(a) The choice of initial values for insertion into the transform equations.

(b) The means of handling transforms when numerator and denominator are of equal degree.

(c) The use of the transform $Ve^{j\phi}/(s-j\omega)$ in order to represent an alternating e.m.f.

(d) The use of the delay factor in the representation of both a discontinuous source and the resulting response of the circuit.

(e) The evaluation of a circuit response when its transform contains a double pole.

In all of these illustrations, an extremely simple circuit was chosen, so that attention might be focused entirely on the problem of obtaining the transform of the applied voltage or current and then the inverse transform of the resulting voltage or current. This is the primary problem of what is generally termed *transient analysis*. In many cases, however, the

* See the footnote on p. 184.

electric circuit itself is sufficiently complex to make its study (even with simple applied voltages) worthy of special attention. This is the primary problem of *electric network analysis.*

Kirchhoff's laws in transform terms will be used in the next chapter to formulate the methods of *loop* and *node analysis*, which are basic to electric network analysis. With these methods, the equations relating the voltage and current transforms can be obtained directly in any circuit problem. The methods of loop and node analysis will be applicable to any linear electric network, whether passive or active, and whether we seek a transient or simply the sinusoidal steady-state solution.

Problems

4-1. A step voltage of height V is applied to the input terminals of a circuit. The Laplace transform of the current through the input terminals is I, given by

$$I = \frac{N(s)}{D(s)} = \left[Z_1 + \frac{1}{Y_2 + Y_3} + Z_4\right]^{-1}\left(\frac{V}{s}\right)$$

where Z_1 and Z_4 are the impedances of a resistance and capacitance, respectively, and $1/(Y_2+Y_3)$ is the impedance of a parallel combination of a resistance and an inductance.

(A) State the initial value of the current in the inductance included in the circuit.

(B) State the initial value of the voltage across the capacitance in the circuit.

(C) If the initial value of i, i.e., of $\mathcal{L}^{-1}I$, is 0.5 ampere, compare the degrees of $N(s)$ and $D(s)$

4-2. The circuit in the figure is in a steady state with the switch S closed. The current source provides a direct current I. At $t = 0$, the switch S opens.

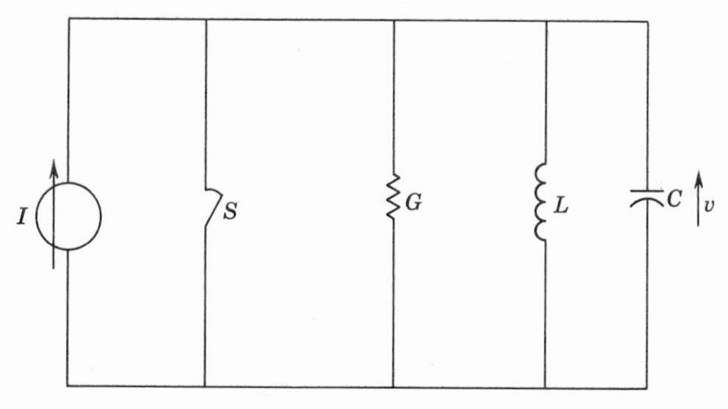

Problem 4–2.

Derive the Laplace transform of the voltage v and obtain the condition under which v will vary in an oscillatory manner. (Assume that a small R is in series with L and can be neglected after S opens.)

4-3. The voltage applied to a series RL circuit initially at rest is given by

$$v(t) = 0 \qquad t < 0$$

$$v(t) = Ve^{-at} \qquad 0 < t < T$$

$$v(t) = 0 \qquad T < t$$

where $a \neq R/L$.

(A) Find $\mathcal{L}v(t)$ and show that $v(t)$ may be obtained as a superposition of two functions, the first continuous for $t > 0$ and the second continuous for $t > T$.

(B) Find the current $i(t)$ in the circuit.

4-4. Solve Problem 4–3(B) assuming $R/L = a$.

4-5. The circuit in the figure is initially at rest. A step voltage of height V is applied to its input terminals at the instant $t = 0$. Does the Laplace

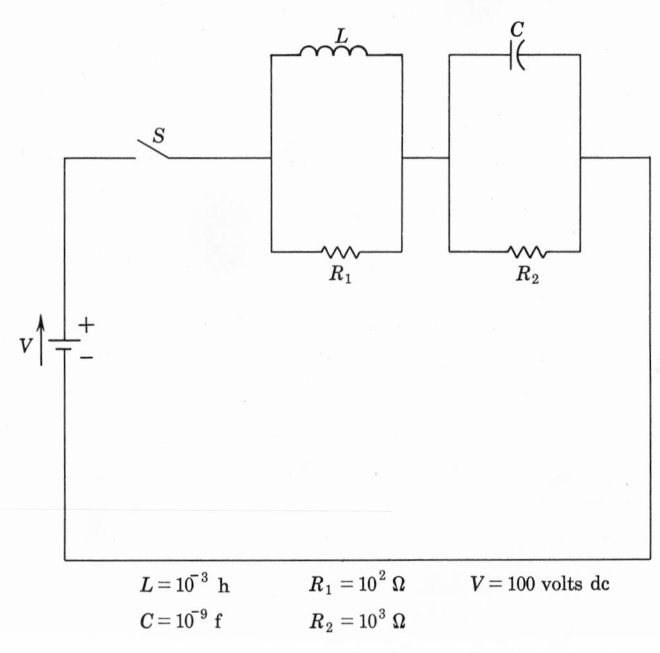

Problem 4–5.

transform I of the input current meet the requirements of the Heaviside expansion theorem as stated in Problem 3–7 (A) of Chapter 3?

4-6. The voltage $v(t)$ is applied to the circuit in the figure. The initial current in the inductance is zero. The voltage v_C across the capacitance is initially equal to V. The voltage $v(t)$ is:

$$v(t) = 0 \qquad \text{when} \quad t < 0$$

$$v(t) = V\left(1 - \frac{t}{T}\right) \qquad \text{when} \quad 0 < t < T$$

$$v(t) = 0 \qquad \text{when} \quad T < t$$

Find the current $i(t)$ for $t > 0$.

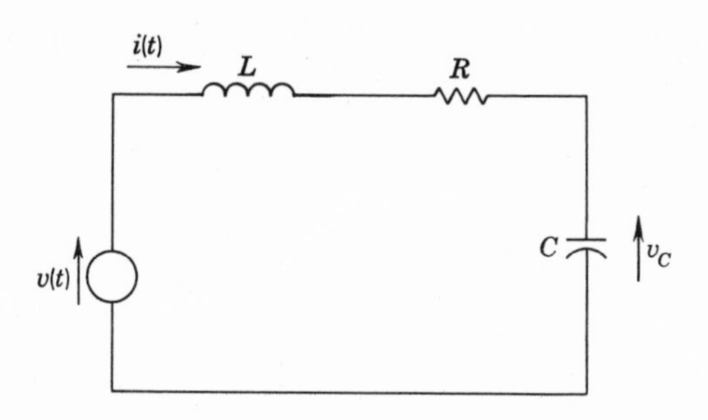

Problem 4–6.

4-7. Solve for the voltages v_1 and v_2 of Problem 1–6 in Chapter 1. Use the Laplace transform method as developed in the present chapter. Is it, now, necessary to eliminate one unknown before solving the differential equations?

4-8. Solve for the voltages v_1 and v_2 of Problem 1–7 in Chapter 1. Use the Laplace transform method as developed in the present chapter.

4-9. (A) Consider the voltages v_a and v_b, across the current source and across the inductance, respectively, in the circuit of Problem 1–8, Chapter 1. Express the transforms of these voltages when $t > 0$. In doing this, arbitrarily use values at $t = 0-$ as if they were initial values. *Note:* v_a here is v_{a_2} of the figure for Problem 1–8.

(B) Apply the initial value theorem to $\mathfrak{L}v_a$ and $\mathfrak{L}v_b$ in order to determine $v_a(0+)$ and $v_b(0+)$. Compare with $v_a(0+)$ and $v_b(0+)$ as found in Problem 1–8 of Chapter 1.

(C) From the values of $v_a(0+)$ and $v_b(0+)$, find $i_L(0+)$ and compare with $i_L(0-)$.

4-10. (A) Obtain the equations for the transforms V_a and V_b in Problem 4–9, but now use values at $t = 0+$ as initial values. Are the expressions for V_a and V_b altered?

(B) Use the transform V_a, and use the value of the charge on C_1 at $t = 0-$ as initial charge. Find the impulse current which charges C_1. Show that this puts a correct value of charge on C_1 at $t = 0+$.

(C) Show that the charge on C_2 at $t = 0-$ is simply redistributed between C_1 and C_2 instantaneously upon closure of the ideal switch.

References for Chapter 4

1. Carslaw, H. S., and Jaeger, J. C., *Operational Methods in Applied Mathematics*, 2nd ed., Oxford University Press, New York, 1949.
2. Gardner, M. F., and Barnes, J. L., *Transients in Linear Systems Studied by the Laplace Transformation*, John Wiley & Sons, Inc., New York, 1942.
3. Goldman, S., *Transformation Calculus and Electrical Transients*, Prentice-Hall, Inc., New York, 1949.
4. Jaeger, J. C., *An Introduction to the Laplace Transformation with Engineering Applications*, Methuen & Co., Ltd., London, 1949.
5. Jaeger, J. C., "Switching Problems and Instantaneous Impulses." *Phil. Mag.*, Ser. 7, Vol. 36, pp. 644–651, 1945.
6. Peirce, B. O., *A Short Table of Integrals*, Ginn & Company, Boston, 1910.
7. Pipes, L. A., *Applied Mathematics for Engineers and Physicists*, McGraw-Hill Book Co., Inc., New York, 1946; 2nd ed., 1958.
8. Weber, E., *Transient Analysis of Electrical Networks*, New York University, Engineering Defense Program, 1941.
9. Weber, E., *Linear Transient Analysis, Vol. I: Lumped-Parameter Two-Terminal Networks*, John Wiley & Sons, Inc., New York, 1954.

Chapter 5

LOOP AND NODE ANALYSIS, POLES AND ZEROS

The methods of loop and node analysis presented in this chapter are followed by a study of pole-zero distributions and their effects. From loop and node analysis we obtain both Laplace transforms of voltage and current and the usual complex voltage and current of sinusoidal steady-state analysis. The pole-zero distribution study summarizes the transient and steady-state effects of the Laplace transforms obtained, and leads to certain general network properties.

Both loop and node analyses result from the direct application of Kirchhoff's laws to electric networks. The equations of loop analysis treat the network in terms of the voltage law, while those of node analysis describe the network in terms of the current law. In both methods, the number of equations can be reduced if parallel and series circuit elements are combined to form single impedances or admittances wherever possible (see Section 4–3).

A useful preliminary to the development of the loop or node method is a discussion of voltage and current generators. This is carried out in the following section.

5-1 Voltage and Current Generators

The ideal e.m.f. or voltage source and the ideal current source were each defined in Section 1–4. A physical generator is commonly represented as an ideal voltage source in series with an impedance, or as an ideal current source in parallel with an admittance. The first combination may be termed a *voltage generator*, and the second a *current generator*. Either combination is linear and serves to approximate a physical generator.

The equivalence of voltage and current generators (with proper choice of values) will now be demonstrated in terms of Laplace transforms.

Although it is certainly not necessary to use this equivalence in a network analysis, it is very often extremely convenient to do so.[9,19]

In Fig. 5–1(a), E and E_1 are the Laplace transforms of the e.m.f. and terminal voltage, respectively, of a voltage generator applied to the network N. The current into the network has the Laplace transform I_1 shown on the figure. We shall demonstrate that the transform E_1' in Fig. 5–1(b) equals E_1 in Fig. 5–1(a), and that I_1' in Fig. 5–1(b) equals I_1 in Fig. 5–1(a). We assume only that the network N is the same in each figure, that all voltages and currents are Laplace transformable, and that the box labeled Z is initially at rest so that the impedance Z of this box can be defined.

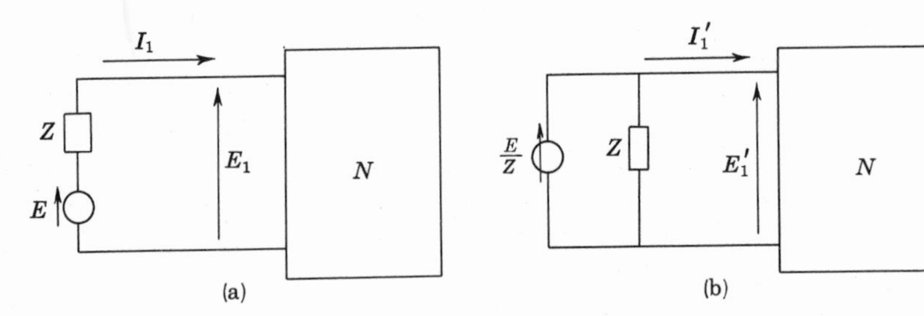

Fig. 5–1.

From Fig. 5–1(a),

$$E_1 = E - I_1 Z \tag{5–1}$$

Whatever the nature of the network N, I_1 must be a function of E_1, so that substituting $f(E_1)$ for I_1 yields

$$E_1 = E - Zf(E_1) \tag{5–2}$$

Now e_1, the instantaneous terminal voltage of the source, is a single-valued function of time, so that its transform E_1 is uniquely determined.* Hence $f(E_1)$ must be of such a nature that (5–2) has only one solution.

From application of Kirchhoff's current law to the circuit in Fig. 5–1(b),

$$\frac{E}{Z} = \frac{E_1'}{Z} + I_1' \tag{5–3}$$

or

$$E_1' = E - I_1' Z \tag{5–3a}$$

* It is, of course, also true that E_1 is uniquely determined even when e_1 has points of finite discontinuity.

Since N is the same in both figures, $I_1' = f(E_1')$ and f is the same function as above; therefore (5–3a) becomes

$$E_1' = E - Zf(E_1') \tag{5-4}$$

Comparing (5–2) and (5–4), we see that E_1 and E_1' are solutions of the same equation. We have shown that this equation has only one solution. Hence

$$E_1' = E_1 \tag{5-5}$$

and

$$I_1' = I_1 \tag{5-6}$$

Therefore the voltage and current generators in Fig. 5–1 are equivalent.

Two situations are encountered when this result is to be applied in network analysis:

CASE 1. *An ideal voltage source is in series with an impedance or an ideal current source is shunted by an admittance.* The combination of ideal voltage source and series impedance or ideal current source and shunt admittance can then be regarded as a voltage generator or current generator, respectively. If it appears to be desirable, a generator of either type can be replaced by its equivalent of the other type.

CASE 2. *An ideal voltage source or an ideal current source appears in the network, but we do not find an impedance in series with the ideal voltage source or an admittance shunting the ideal current source.* In this event the conversion is not easily expressed, as will immediately be evident if Z is replaced by zero in Fig. 5–1. Artifices are possible, however. One may, for example, replace an ideal voltage source in the circuit diagram by a combination of ideal source and series resistance R. This combination may in turn be replaced by an equivalent current generator. The resistance R can then be reduced to zero in the expression for the final answer to the problem. In a similar manner, one might introduce a conductance, G, across an ideal current source and allow G to go to zero in the expression for the final result. Other artifices are possible,(9) Whether we use such artifices or keep the ideal source in our equations will depend both on the particular problem and on personal inclination. It is important to note, however, that it is possible (whether or not it is always easy or desirable) to represent the sources applied to a network as either all current or all voltage sources. Thus if we wish to derive a theorem applicable to linear networks generally, we may write our equations in terms of only one type of source (i.e., all voltage or all current) without incurring any loss of generality.

5-2 Loop Analysis*

The method of loop analysis is best developed through an example of a three-loop circuit designed to bring out the main points in the practical application of the method. The final form of the result will be such as to make extension to the n-loop case evident.

In Fig. 5–2, attention is drawn to three closed paths and the subscripts on the branch currents indicate to which closed path each belongs.

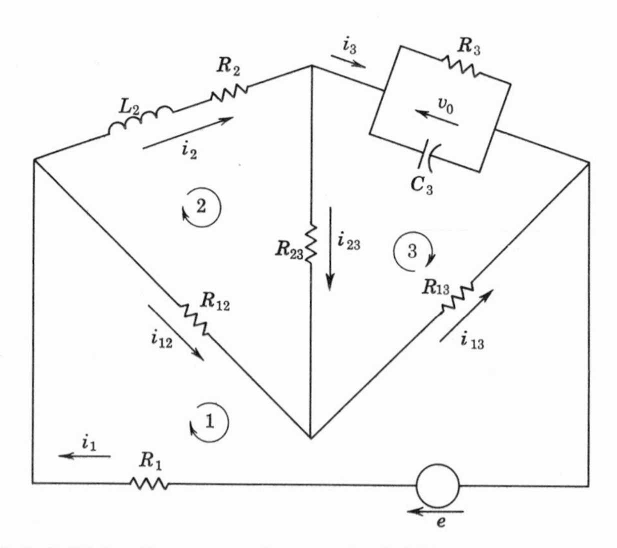

Fig. 5–2. Initial voltage across C_3, $v_o = 0$. Initial current in L_2, $i_{2o} \neq 0$.

Hence two subscripts are used when a current flows in a circuit element common to two closed paths or loops.

Since the initial voltage across C_3 is zero, we define the ratio of the transform of the voltage across the parallel combination of R_3C_3 to the transform of the current i_3 which enters the combination, as an impedance Z_C. Evidently $Z_C = R_3(1/C_3s)/[R_3 + (1/C_3s)] = R_3/(1 + R_3C_3s)$. If this initial voltage were not zero, however, it would be incorrect to use Z_C, and R_3C_3 would be treated as a fourth loop in the network. The direct application of Kirchhoff's voltage and current laws for voltage and

* The words *mesh* and *loop* can be used interchangeably to designate a closed path in a network.[21] Another approach is to use the word *mesh* to refer only to the holes in a network which has been drawn without crossing wires.[6] In the present chapter, the boundary of such a hole is termed a *simple loop*.

current transforms leads to six equations:

$$E = R_1I_1+R_{12}I_{12}+R_{13}I_{13} \tag{5-7}$$

$$Li_{20} = (R_2+L_2s)I_2+R_{23}I_{23}-R_{12}I_{12} \tag{5-8}$$

$$0 = Z_CI_3-R_{13}I_{13}-R_{23}I_{23} \tag{5-9}$$

$$0 = -I_1+I_{12}+I_2 \tag{5-10}$$

$$0 = -I_2+I_{23}+I_3 \tag{5-11}$$

$$0 = -I_{12}+I_{13}-I_{23} \tag{5-12}$$

If I_{12}, I_{23}, and I_{13} are eliminated by substitution, equations (5–7, 8, and 9) can be put into the general form of loop analysis, namely

$$E_1 = Z_{11}I_1+Z_{12}I_2+Z_{13}I_3 \tag{5-7a}$$

$$E_2 = Z_{21}I_1+Z_{22}I_2+Z_{23}I_3 \tag{5-8a}$$

$$E_3 = Z_{31}I_1+Z_{32}I_2+Z_{33}I_3 \tag{5-9a}$$

where $E_1 = E$, $E_2 = Li_{20}$, $E_3 = 0$ and with the definitions

$$Z_{11} = R_1+R_{12}+R_{13} \qquad Z_{12} = -R_{12} = Z_{21}$$

$$Z_{22} = (R_2+L_2s)+R_{23}+R_{12} \qquad Z_{23} = -R_{23} = Z_{32}$$

$$Z_{33} = Z_C+R_{13}+R_{23} \qquad Z_{31} = -R_{13} = Z_{13}$$

The forms (5–7a, 8a, and 9a) are arrived at by direct algebraic substitution and factoring. However, the coefficients have a physical significance which justifies naming them. The coefficient Z_{11} is the ratio of e.m.f. transform to current transform in loop 1, when loops 2 and 3 are open-circuited. Hence Z_{11} is termed the *self-impedance* of loop 1. From the same viewpoint, Z_{22} and Z_{33} are the self-impedances, respectively, of loops 2 and 3. Each coefficient with unequal subscripts (e.g., Z_{12} or Z_{13}) is equal to either the impedance of a branch common to the two loops indicated by these subscripts, or the negative of this common impedance. The positive sign holds when the loop currents in the common branch are drawn in the same direction, while the negative sign holds when these are oppositely directed. These coefficients are often termed *mutual impedances.*(5,17) Some authors, however, prefer the term *coefficient of impedance* or *copedance* for all the Z coefficients in the loop equations.(9) When a network contains coils coupled by magnetic flux, mutual impedance terms such as $\pm MsI$ appear in the loop equations. The sign conventions discussed in Chapter 1 for coils coupled by mutual magnetic flux will apply again when loop currents flow through the coils.

The relation $Z_{rs} = Z_{sr}$ is a fundamental property of passive circuits consisting of bilateral elements. When the method of loop analysis is applied to linear vacuum-tube and transistor circuits, the coefficients in the equations will no longer be subject to this restriction.*

It will be observed that the self- and mutual impedances in the loop equations have been written as if the circuit elements were initially at rest. Initial quantities (i_0 in inductance or v_0 across capacitance) enter the loop equations as e.m.f. transforms and do not appear in the self- and mutual impedance coefficients. It is important to note, however, that each circuit element with an initial condition must appear explicitly and cannot be lumped to form an impedance with other parallel elements.

The functions E_1, E_2 and E_3 are the e.m.f. transforms in each loop. The first is the transform of the applied e.m.f., the second is an e.m.f. transform arising from an initial condition,† while the third is zero in the illustration used. All three cases may arise in any loop analysis problem. The current transforms I_1, I_2 and I_3 may now be termed loop current transforms.

Number of Loop Equations

The development given above leads directly to an expression for the number of loops and the number of equations required in a loop analysis[2] of a *one-part network*, i.e., a network in which each node is connected to each other node by at least one path through branches of the network.[21] The number of unknown current transforms to be found is identical with the number of branches B in the entire network. All but one of the N nodes in the network are used for the application of Kirchhoff's current law. One of these nodes is not used, as the Kirchhoff's current relation obtained from it will be derivable from the relations already found at the other nodes. Hence we begin with B equations for the unknown branch current transforms, and use the $N-1$ current relations at the nodes to eliminate $N-1$ of the unknowns, leaving $B-(N-1) = B-N+1$ equations to be solved. These were shown in the example of the bridge circuit to be the loop equations. Hence the number of loops needed is $B-N+1$.

If two portions of a network are coupled only through mutual magnetic flux linking two coils, and have no common node, they are called *separate parts*. The relation we have just found applies to each separate part of

* In exceptional cases, the symmetrically placed off-diagonal coefficients may be equal in an electronic circuit, but the equality will depend on circuit arrangement and values of circuit elements, and is a property of the particular case.

† If the inductance were in a mutual branch between loops, the e.m.f. transform Li_0 would appear in more than one equation, with appropriate sign.

a network. Hence if a network consists of r separate parts, we can write the number of loops to be used in each part: $B_1 - N_1 + 1$ for the first part, $B_2 - N_2 + 1$ for the second part, and similarly for the remaining parts, and there will be $(B_1 - N_1 + 1) + (B_2 - N_2 + 1) + \cdots + (B_r - N_r + 1)$ equations or loops required. Now since the total number of branches in the network is $B = B_1 + B_2 + \cdots + B_r$ and the total number of nodes in the network is $N = N_1 + N_2 + \cdots + N_r$, we see that addition of the number of loops for each part leads to $B - N + r$ as the expression for the number of loops needed in a network of r parts.[3]

When using this expression, one should bear in mind that the number of branches and nodes will depend on how many elements are combined into single impedances. Generally one should, wherever possible, combine elements into single impedances, and thus reduce the number of branches and the required number of equations. It was possible to do this, for example, with the parallel RC combination in the bridge of Fig. 5–2, because the initial voltage across C_3 was zero.

Conditions for Choice of Loops

The foregoing development shows that the loop equations can be derived from the branch current equations. It is generally preferable, however, to select loops directly. This may be done provided that:

(a) the number of loops selected equals $B - N + 1$, for each separate part of the network, and
(b) the equations for the chosen loops are independent, i.e., no one equation may be derivable from one or more of the others.

That it is *necessary* to satisfy condition (a) has been shown in the preceding subsection, where, beginning with B equations for the branch currents and eliminating $(N - 1)$ current-law equations from these, we were left with $(B - N + 1)$ voltage-law equations. The necessity of condition (b) is obvious, since if the equations are not independent, it is impossible to solve for all the unknown loop currents.

Let us now demonstrate that (a) and (b) are *sufficient* to assure the correct determination of each of the branch currents in the network. If condition (b) is satisfied, the loop-current equations can be solved and the loop currents are then known. At each branch of the circuit these loop currents can be superposed and branch currents then evaluated. It remains to show, however, that these branch currents are correct. We note first that these branch currents will satisfy Kirchhoff's voltage law for each loop for which we have drawn a loop current. We note also that superposition of loop currents leads to branch-current values which satisfy

Kirchhoff's current law at each node. If now condition (a) is also satisfied, we see that our B branch currents have satisfied the $(B-N+1)$ Kirchhoff's voltage-law equations as well as the $(N-1)$ current-law equations. If we take it as axiomatic that these B Kirchhoff's-law equations yield a unique solution for the B branch currents, we conclude that loops chosen in a manner consistent with (a) and (b) yield correct branch-current values.

Choice of Simple Loops in a Planar Network

A very common network is the *planar* or *flat* network. This is defined as a network which can be drawn on a plane without any crossing branches.(21) Such a network, when so drawn, has the appearance of a fish net. The holes in the net (here termed *meshes**) are said to be bounded by *simple loops*. We shall demonstrate that these simple loops meet both the requirements (a) and (b) in the preceding subsection. For ease of discussion, we assume a network of one part.

In order to demonstrate that requirement (a) is met, let us draw the simple loops in order, and number these in the order drawn as loop 1, 2, . . ., m, surrounding mesh 1, 2, . . ., m, respectively. Now let β_1 be the number of branches bounding mesh 1. Let β_2 be the number of branches bounding mesh 2 except for those on the common boundary with mesh 1. In the same way, let β_r be the number of branches bounding mesh r which are not on the common boundaries of meshes 1, 2, . . ., $(r-1)$. Clearly, the total number of branches in the network is then

$$B = \sum_{r=1}^{m} \beta_r \tag{5-13}$$

Now let η_1 be the number of nodes at the end points of the branches in loop 1. Let η_2 be the number of nodes in loop 2 which are not also nodes of loop 1, and again η_r will be the number of nodes in loop r which are not nodes of loops 1, 2, . . ., $(r-1)$. Clearly, the total number of nodes in the network is

$$N = \sum_{r=1}^{m} \eta_r \tag{5-14}$$

Now consider each branch as a line drawn out from a node. From the node at the further end of this branch, a second branch is drawn, and so forth. For the first loop drawn in this way, we find one new branch to each node, so that $\beta_1 = \eta_1$. When the second loop is drawn, however,

* See the footnote at the beginning of Section 5–2.

its first branch starts from a node in the first loop, so that we find $\beta_2 = \eta_2+1$, i.e., the number of new branches exceeds the number of new nodes by 1. The same reasoning applies to each successive loop, so that $\beta_r = \eta_r+1$ when $r \neq 1$. We now arrive at a relationship between the number of branches and the number of nodes in a planar network:

$$\sum_{r=1}^{m} \beta_r = \left(\sum_{r=1}^{m} \eta_r\right) + (m-1) \tag{5-15}$$

since each of the m β's, except the first, exceeds the corresponding η by 1. The last relationship can also be written as

$$B = N+m-1$$

or

$$m = B-N+1 \tag{5-16}$$

Thus the simple loops of a planar network yield the correct number of loop equations, i.e., condition (a) is met.

We now investigate condition (b), i.e., the independence of the equations.[6] If simple adjacent loops are drawn in a planar network, each new loop will have at least one branch not in any of the previously selected loops. Hence when the corresponding loop equations are written, each will have one coefficient which is not in any way related to the coefficients in the preceding equations. Now consider equation k in such a set of simultaneous equations. Obviously it cannot be derived from one or more of the first $(k-1)$ equations, since it contains at least one coefficient which is in no way related to the coefficients in the previous equations. Suppose now that we attempt to derive equation k from one or more preceding and succeeding equations, or from one or more succeeding equations alone. Of these equations, the last one will contain at least one coefficient unrelated to those in the others. The term containing this coefficient cannot, therefore, be eliminated. Further, since this coefficient is also unrelated to those of equation k, we cannot derive that equation. It follows, since k is any one of the equations, that no one equation in the set of loop equations obtained from the simple loops of a planar network can be derived from the others, i.e., we have a set of independent simultaneous equations.

A More General Method for Choosing Loops: The Tree

A more general method of selecting loops in each separate part of a network is available. This method, designated by the word *tree*, applies equally well to planar and to *non-planar* networks (the latter are networks which cannot be drawn on a plane without branches crossing).

While one may not always obtain the easiest choice of loops in this manner, the method will be certain to satisfy the requirements (a) and (b) for proper selection of loops. For simplicity of statement, we shall consider a network of only one part.

A *tree* is drawn on the network diagram. A *tree* consists of a set of branches joining all the nodes of the network but not forming any closed loops. Thus any branch of the network which is not part of the tree joins two nodes touched by the tree. Further, one can travel from one of these nodes to the other through branches of the tree without lifting pencil from paper. Hence a set of loops can be drawn, each going through a branch of the network which is not part of the tree, and each then closed by branches of the tree only. Each loop so drawn contains one branch which does not belong to any other loop. This is the branch not included in the tree. Hence one term in each loop equation contains a coefficient which does not appear in any of the other equations. Therefore, no one of these loop equations can be derived from the others. The equations so obtained are, thus, independent; i.e., condition (b) is satisfied.

The number of loops, m, equals the number of branches not included in the tree. The number of branches in the tree is one less than the number of nodes in the network (the first branch joins two nodes, and each additional branch goes to an additional node). We find then that the number of loops equals the total number of branches, B, less the number in the tree (i.e., less $N-1$). Hence we have $m = B-N+1$, which satisfies condition (a).

Loop Analysis in Active Circuits: (1) *Application of Loop Analysis to a Vacuum-Tube Circuit*

Let a signal voltage $e_s(t)$ be applied to a grounded-plate triode (cathode follower)* (Fig. 5–3), and let $e_s(t)$ be sufficiently small for the linear vacuum-tube equivalent circuit to be valid. We shall assume in this problem (and other vacuum-tube circuit problems involving transients) that the response to the signal $e_s(t)$ can be represented adequately when capacitances are included with the equivalent circuit as in Fig. 5–3(b). This implies that the Fourier spectrum of the signal shows negligible amplitude outside the frequency range in which the equivalent circuit is valid, or, alternatively, that only the response corresponding to this frequency range is to be calculated.

* Fig. 5–3 follows, with modifications, Fig. 6–9 of Seely,[13] by permission of McGraw-Hill Book Company, Inc. See also References 12 and 20.

Since only the variations from the quiescent tube values are of interest, the capacitances are regarded as initially at rest. Although we shall solve for voltage rather than current, it is evident that impulse currents to the capacitors will accompany the sudden application of a finite ideal voltage source, so that the term "at rest" applies to the circuit condition just prior to switching, i.e., at $t = 0-$.

Since the circuit is regarded as initially at rest, we can compute an impedance between cathode and plate, namely

$$Z_K = R_K(1/Cs)/[R_K + (1/Cs)] = R_K/(1 + R_K Cs).$$

If the loops are chosen as indicated, loop 1 has no mutual impedance with loop 2 or 3. This will mean that only two equations will require simultaneous solution.

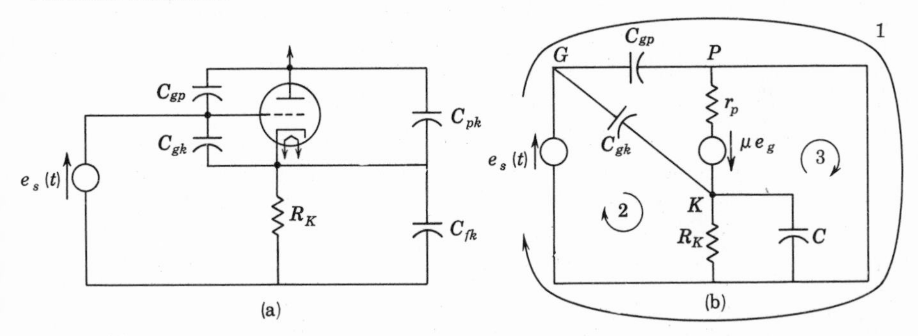

Fig. 5–3. All capacitance initially uncharged: $C = C_{pk} + C_{fk}$. Since the equivalent circuit is valid only for small changes from the quiescent tube values, the word "uncharged" is also to be understood in this sense. (See credit footnote, p. 214.)

First, treating e_g as if it were a known e.m.f. and using

$$Z_{11} = \frac{1}{C_{gp}s} \qquad Z_{12} = 0 = Z_{21}$$

$$Z_{22} = Z_K + \frac{1}{C_{gk}s} \qquad Z_{23} = -Z_K = Z_{32}$$

$$Z_{33} = r_p + Z_K \qquad Z_{31} = 0 = Z_{13}$$

we obtain the following equations relating the current and voltage transforms:

$$E_s = \frac{1}{C_{gp}s} I_1 \tag{5–17}$$

$$E_s = \left(Z_K + \frac{1}{C_{gk}s}\right) I_2 - Z_K I_3 \tag{5–18}$$

$$-\mu E_g = -Z_K I_2 + (r_p + Z_K) I_3 \qquad (5\text{–}19)$$

where E_s and E_g are the Laplace transforms of e_s and e_g, respectively. Now E_g is not actually the transform of a known e.m.f., but is linearly dependent on E_s which is the transform of e_s, the given signal voltage. The applied voltage e_s is termed an *independent source,* while μe_g may be termed a *dependent source.** Hence E_g must be expressed in terms of E_s, and using

$$E_s = (I_2 - I_3) Z_K + E_g \qquad (5\text{–}20)$$

changes (5–19) into

$$-\mu E_s = -Z_K(1+\mu) I_2 + [r_p + Z_K(1+\mu)] I_3 \qquad (5\text{–}21)$$

Consideration of (5–18) and (5–21) illustrates the simple but basic difference, mentioned previously, between the loop equations of an active circuit and those of a passive circuit consisting of bilateral elements, namely that the relation $Z_{rs} = Z_{sr}$ need not hold for the active circuit. We observe that Z_{23} is equal to $-Z_K$ in (5–18) while Z_{32} in (5–21) is equal to $-(1+\mu)Z_K$, so that symmetrically placed coefficients in the equation are no longer equal.

We shall now solve a transient problem and a sinusoidal steady-state problem with the aid of these equations. The transient problem is: Find the output voltage $e_o(t)$ if $e_s(t)$ is a step voltage of height V. The sinusoidal steady-state problem is: Find the complex output voltage if the voltage $e_s(t)$ is a sinusoidal signal and the system is in the steady state. In both problems, signal and response are, of course, superposed on quiescent values. In each case we first solve equations (5–18) and (5–21) algebraically for $(I_2 - I_3)Z_K$. After solving for I_2 and I_3 and representing $1/Z_K$ by its expression $(1/R_K) + Cs$, we find, with $g_m = \mu/r_p$,

$$(I_2 - I_3) Z_K = \frac{r_p(g_m + C_{gk}s)}{r_p(C_{gk} + C)s + \dfrac{r_p}{R_K} + (1+\mu)} E_s \qquad (5\text{–}22)$$

When $e_s(t)$ is a step voltage applied at $t = 0$, its transform is $E_s = V/s$. The transform of the output voltage is equal to $(I_2 - I_3)Z_K$, and has simple poles at $s = 0$ and at $s = -\alpha$, where

$$\alpha = [1 + (1+\mu)(R_K/r_p)]/[R_K(C_{gk} + C)].$$

The output voltage $e_o(t)$ can be evaluated by the residue method (Chapters

* The term *controlled source* is often used in place of dependent source.

3 and 4) as

$$e_o(t) = \sum \text{Res}\left[\frac{V}{C_{gk}+C}\cdot\frac{g_m + C_{gk}s}{s\left[s+\dfrac{1+(1+\mu)(R_K/r_p)}{R_K(C_{gk}+C)}\right]}e^{st}\right] \qquad (5\text{–}23)^*$$

The expression multiplied by e^{st} in (5–23) is equal to the right-hand side of (5–22) with V/s substituted for E_s, and with the fraction in (5–22) put in convenient form for evaluation by the residue method. Alternatively, we may express the transform as a sum of two easily recognized transforms with the aid of the partial fraction theorem (Chapter 3). We thus find

$$e_o(t) = \frac{\mu V R_K}{r_p + (1+\mu)R_K}(1-e^{-\alpha t}) + \frac{VC_{gk}}{C_{gk}+C}e^{-\alpha t} \qquad (5\text{–}24)$$

with $t > 0$, where $e_o(t)$ is the deviation from the quiescent value of the voltage across R_K.

It is of interest to note that equation (5–24) yields $VC_{gk}/(C_{gk}+C)$ as the value of $e_o(t)$ at the instant $t = 0+$. Thus, the two stray capacitances have acted as a voltage divider. The instantaneous voltage change in $e_o(t)$ from 0 at $t = 0-$ to $VC_{gk}/(C_{gk}+C)$ at $t = 0+$ is accompanied by impulse current to the capacitances. For large values of t, $e_o(t)$ is given by the coefficient of $(1-e^{-\alpha t})$ in equation (5–24).

We now solve the second problem, namely that of finding the steady-state sinusoidal output voltage. The answer is given by (5–22) provided that we re-define symbols. Let $s = j\omega$, let I_2 and I_3 be complex currents, and let E_s, taken as phase reference, represent the applied sinusoidal signal. Then E_o, the complex output voltage, follows from equation (5–22):

$$E_o = \frac{r_p(g_m + j\omega C_{gk})}{r_p(C_{gk}+C)j\omega + \dfrac{r_p}{R_K} + (1+\mu)}E_s \qquad (5\text{–}25)$$

The direct relation between the transform equation (5–22) and the solution to the sinusoidal steady-state problem (5–25) occurs because the equivalent circuit is initially at rest. Basically we have used the fact that each impedance $Z(s)$ in the transform analysis becomes an identical function of $j\omega$ in the alternating-current analysis. More generally, we see that Kirchhoff's laws apply equally to complex voltages and currents of alternating-current analysis, and to voltage and current transforms.

* The symbol Σ Res means, of course, the sum of the residues of the function at its poles.

In the special case where $C_{gk} \cong 0 \cong C$, (5–25) reduces to

$$E_o = \frac{\mu R_K}{r_p + (1+\mu)R_K} E_s \qquad (5\text{–}25a)$$

Loop Analysis in Active Circuits: (2) *Application of Loop Analysis to a Transistor Circuit*

The preceding paragraphs have dealt with the application of loop analysis to the linear equivalent circuit of the vacuum tube. The trans-

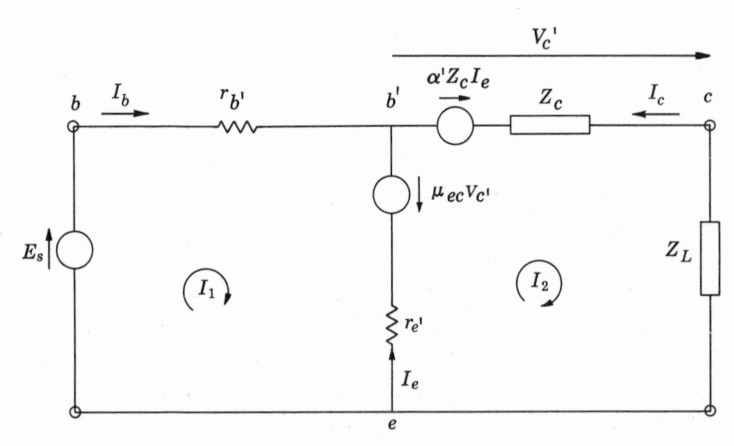

$Z_c = 1/(g_c' + sC_c)$ See Reference[11]

The branch $b'c$ can also be drawn in the equivalent form[1]

b' $\alpha' Z_c I_b$ $Z_c(1-\alpha')$ c

where I_e has been replaced by $-(I_b + I_c)$

Fig. 5–4.

istor is another active circuit device which can be operated linearly. Because of the intricate physical theory of the transistor, a number of different equivalent circuits have been developed.[11,15] Fig. 5–4* shows

* The circuit of Fig. 5–4 of this chapter corresponds to the circuit in Fig. 4 of Reference 11, where, however, the circuit is drawn for the common base connection and one of the internal sources is represented as a current source. Such a circuit is also shown in common base configuration in Fig. 2.14 of Reference 15, but with approximation mentioned in the accompanying text of that reference. A more general circuit (drawn for both the common base and common emitter connection) is shown in Fig. 1 of Reference 1. This circuit is also valid at higher frequencies. The last reference indicates, in addition, where resistance should be added to the given circuit.

a low-frequency equivalent for a junction transistor drawn for the common emitter connection.(1,11,15) An ideal e.m.f. source, as a small signal, and a load impedance have been added to the transistor equivalent.

It is of interest to note that the equivalent circuit of Fig. 5–4 has more than the four parameters necessary for its specification (see theory of two-port networks, Chapter 7). However, this circuit has the advantage that its parameters are directly related to physical properties of the transistor: as such, they are termed *device parameters*.(11)

Since the equivalent circuit is specified for low frequencies,* we assume the sinusoidal steady state in the following equations. Hence the letter s (see Fig. 5–4) represents $j\omega$, and each voltage and current symbol stands for a complex number specifying the r.m.s. value and phase of the corresponding voltage or current. When the response to a transient signal is desired, an equivalent circuit valid over a sufficient frequency range should be used. This frequency range should cover the non-negligible portion of the Fourier spectrum of the transient.

The loop equations for the circuit drawn in Fig. 5–4 follow:

$$E_s + \mu_{ec} V_c' = (r_b' + r_e')I_1 - r_e' I_2 \tag{5–25b}$$

$$-\mu_{ec} V_c' + \alpha' Z_c I_e = -r_e' I_1 + (r_e' + Z_c + Z_L) I_2 \tag{5–25c}$$

In order to have only two unknowns in these two equations, we introduce the subsidiary relations:

$$I_c = -I_2,\ I_e = I_2 - I_1, \text{ and } V_c' = \alpha' Z_c I_e + Z_c I_c.$$

These lead to the form

$$E_s = (r_b' + r_e' + \mu_{ec}\alpha' Z_c) I_1 - [r_e' + \mu_{ec}(\alpha' - 1) Z_c] I_2 \tag{5–25d}$$

$$0 = -[r_e' + \alpha'(\mu_{ec} - 1) Z_c] I_1 + [r_e' + (1 - \alpha')(1 - \mu_{ec}) Z_c + Z_L] I_2 \tag{5–25e}$$

Here, as with the vacuum-tube circuit, we find $Z_{12} \neq Z_{21}$.

5-3 Node Analysis

The method of node analysis uses Kirchhoff's current law to solve for the unknown node potentials. The network is described in terms of admittances instead of impedances. The equations are of the same form as those of loop analysis, but will be fewer in number and easier to set up in many applications.

* See Reference 1 for an equivalent circuit valid over a broader frequency range.

Development of the Node Method

The node method of analysis will be developed with use of the circuit in Fig. 5-5 as an example. The bridge circuit is the same as that used in developing loop analysis. The elements are given new subscripts, as the numerical ones used for loop analysis are of little utility here. The generator is represented as a current source, shunted by R_G, as this is equivalent to an e.m.f. source in series with R_G. The strength of the current source is $i(t)$, the transform of which is I. The initial conditions

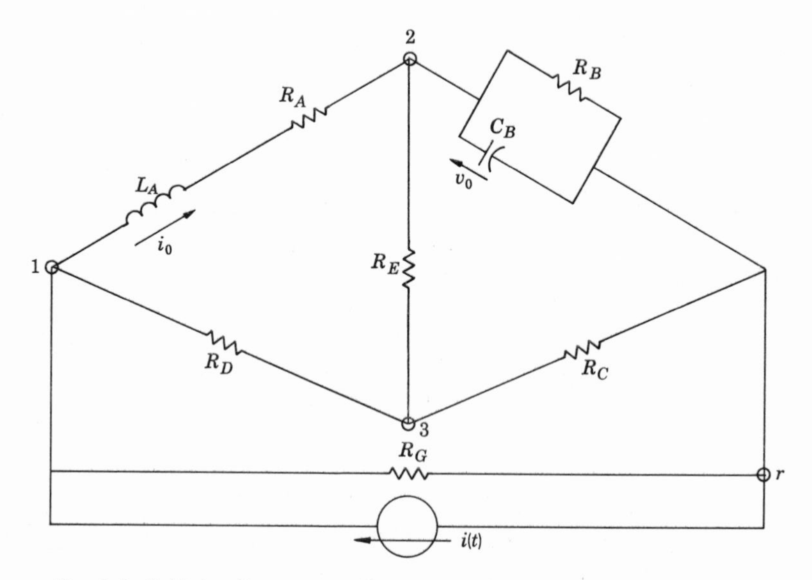

Fig. 5-5. Initial voltage across C_B, $v_o \neq 0$. Initial current in L_A, $i_o = 0$.

assumed are different from those in the loop case, simply to have a better example for development of the node method. Since the initial current in L_A is zero, we may replace the branch L_A, R_A by the single admittance $Y_A = 1/(L_As+R_A)$ so that we have a three-node problem. If there were an initial current in L_A, the junction of L_A and R_A would be an additional node requiring an additional equation.

Letting V_1, V_2, and V_3 be the transforms of the node potentials relative to the reference node r, and applying Kirchhoff's current law to the current transforms at each node, we write directly

$$I = \frac{1}{R_G}V_1 + Y_A(V_1 - V_2) + \frac{1}{R_D}(V_1 - V_3) \tag{5-26}$$

$$C_B v_0 = \left(sC_B + \frac{1}{R_B}\right) V_2 + Y_A(V_2 - V_1) + \frac{1}{R_E}(V_2 - V_3) \qquad (5\text{-}27)$$

$$0 = \frac{1}{R_C} V_3 + \frac{1}{R_D}(V_3 - V_1) + \frac{1}{R_E}(V_3 - V_2) \qquad (5\text{-}28)$$

By factoring V_1, V_2, and V_3, we may put these equations into the general form

$$I_1 = Y_{11}V_1 - Y_{12}V_2 - Y_{13}V_3 \qquad (5\text{-}29)$$

$$I_2 = -Y_{21}V_1 + Y_{22}V_2 - Y_{23}V_3 \qquad (5\text{-}30)$$

$$I_3 = -Y_{31}V_1 - Y_{32}V_2 + Y_{33}V_3 \qquad (5\text{-}31)$$

where $I_1 = I, \quad I_2 = C_B v_0, \quad I_3 = 0,$

and $Y_{11} = (1/R_G) + Y_A + (1/R_D),$

$Y_{22} = sC_B + (1/R_B) + Y_A + (1/R_E),$

$Y_{33} = (1/R_C) + (1/R_D) + (1/R_E),$

and $Y_{12} = Y_A = Y_{21}, \quad Y_{23} = (1/R_E) = Y_{32},$

and $Y_{31} = (1/R_D) = Y_{13}.$

The admittances Y_{11}, Y_{22}, and Y_{33} are called the *self-admittances* of nodes 1, 2, and 3, respectively. The self-admittance of a node is the admittance between it and the reference node when all the other nodes are shorted to the reference. The admittances Y_{12}, Y_{23}, etc., are simply the admittances of the branches joining nodes 1 to 2, 2 to 3, etc. These are often termed *mutual admittances*,[(2)] while some authors prefer the term *coefficients of admittance* or, more briefly, *comittances* for all the coefficients in the node equations.[(9)] Since all node potentials are measured relative to the reference node, the potential of the latter is zero (relative to itself); one does not, therefore, need an equation to solve for the reference node potential. Hence if N is the total number of nodes in a network consisting of one part, the required number of node equations is $N-1$. Since this rule holds for each part of a network consisting of r parts, the number of node equations in an r-part network is

$$(N_1 - 1) + (N_2 - 1) + \cdots + (N_r - 1) = N - r$$

where $N_1, N_2, \ldots, N_r$ are the numbers of nodes in the respective parts, and N is the total number of nodes in the r-part network.

Initial Conditions in Node Analysis

It will be observed that the self- and mutual admittances in the node equations have been written as if the circuit elements were initially at rest. When initial voltage v_0 appears across a capacitance, or initial current i_0 flows in an inductance, the initial quantity gives rise to a current source transform applied to the terminals of the element. Further, the terminals of the element with the initial condition must be nodes, i.e., such an element cannot be combined in series with other circuit elements.

Node Analysis of a Circuit Containing an Ideal E.M.F. Source

An ideal e.m.f. source cannot be converted directly into a meaningful equivalent current source. When this conversion is attempted, the result is an ideal source of infinite current shunted by a short circuit. The node equations may, however, be written in terms of ideal e.m.f. sources in the network. The end points of an e.m.f. source are nodes, say k and k', and the source adds the equation $e(t) = v_{k'} - v_k$ or, in terms of transforms, $E = V_{k'} - V_k$.

As a simple illustration consider the circuit of Fig. 5–5(a), where node 1

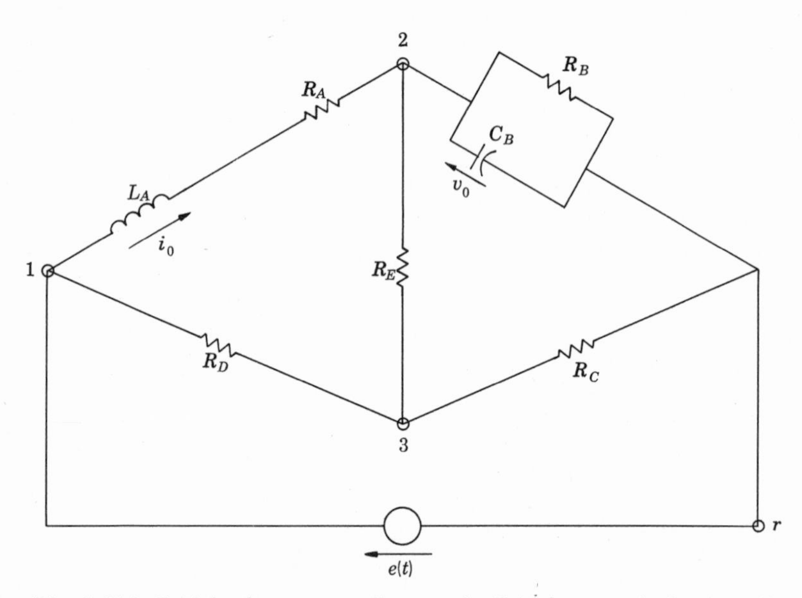

Fig. 5–5(a). Initial voltage across C_B, $v_o \neq 0$. Initial current in L_A, $i_o = 0$.

and the reference node represent k' and k. The node equations become

$$E(s) = V_1 \tag{5–32}$$

$$C_B v_0 = -Y_{21}V_1 + Y_{22}V_2 - Y_{23}V_3 \tag{5–33}$$

$$0 = -Y_{31}V_1 - Y_{32}V_2 + Y_{33}V_3 \tag{5–34}$$

These equations immediately reduce to two equations for the two unknown node potential transforms, namely

$$Y_{21}E(s)+C_Bv_0 = Y_{22}V_2 - Y_{23}V_3 \quad (5\text{–}35)$$

$$Y_{31}E(s) = -Y_{32}V_2 + Y_{33}V_3 \quad (5\text{–}36)$$

where

$$Y_{22} = 1/(L_As+R_A)+(1/R_E)+sC_B+(1/R_B)$$
$$Y_{33} = (1/R_C)+(1/R_E)+(1/R_D)$$
$$Y_{21} = 1/(L_As+R_A)$$
$$Y_{31} = 1/R_D \quad \text{and} \quad Y_{32} = Y_{23} = 1/R_E$$

When the ideal e.m.f. source occurs between two nodes, k and k', neither of which has been chosen as reference node, the situation is somewhat more complicated than in the preceding example. When Kirchhoff's current law is applied to each node, the current through the ideal e.m.f. source is an additional unknown. Correspondingly, the additional equation $E = V_{k'} - V_k$ is available.

If one prefers to have only current sources, in order to retain the standard form of the node equations, as in (5–29) to (5–31), an artifice may be used, as suggested in Section 5–1.

Example of the Node Method Applied to an Active Circuit

We shall again solve the problem in which a signal voltage $e_s(t)$ is applied to a grounded-plate triode with non-negligible capacitances. The equivalent circuit can be drawn, Fig. 5–6(a), with the equivalent generator μe_g replaced by a current source represented by arrows.

The transform of the indicated current source into the cathode is $\mu E_g/r_p = g_mE_g$, where E_g is the transform of varying grid potential relative to cathode potential. Taking the ground as reference node, and the grid and cathode as nodes 1 and 2 respectively, and noting that $E_s \equiv V_1$, it is evident that we have but one node potential for which to solve, and hence only one equation, namely

$$g_m(E_s - V_2) = -Y_{21}E_s + Y_{22}V_2 \quad (5\text{–}37)$$

or

$$(g_m + Y_{21})E_s = (g_m + Y_{22})V_2 \quad (5\text{–}38)$$

where $E_s - V_2 = E_g$, $Y_{21} = sC_{gk}$, and

$$Y_{22} = (1/R_K)+(1/r_p)+sC+sC_{gk}.$$

Hence

$$V_2 = \frac{g_m + sC_{gk}}{g_m + \dfrac{1}{R_K} + \dfrac{1}{r_p} + sC + sC_{gk}} E_s \tag{5-39}$$

where $E_s = V/s$ when e_s is a step voltage of height V. Equation (5–39) will prove to be identical with (5–22) when numerator and denominator

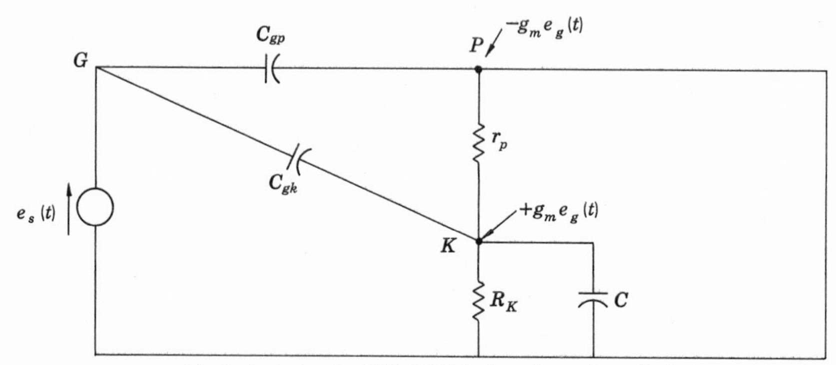

Equivalent circuit of Fig. 5-3(b) in form for node analysis.

(a)

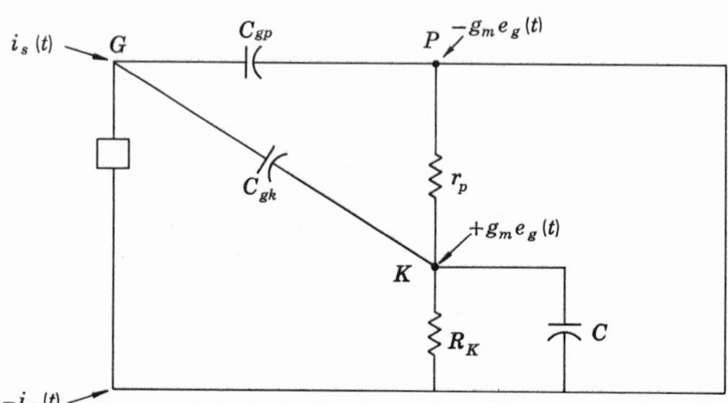

Same equivalent circuit as in (a), but with source impedance Z_s

Note: $\mathfrak{L} i_s(t) = I_s = \dfrac{E_s}{Z_s}$

(b)

Fig. 5–6.

of the fraction are multiplied by r_p, and $g_m r_p$ is replaced by μ. Equation (5–22), it will be recalled, is the solution for the transform of the output voltage in the same problem, obtained by the loop method. Here, as in many cases the node method has required less algebra.

A Problem Involving Two Unknown Node Potentials in an Active Circuit

In order to have a problem more representative of the general form of node analysis, let us assume a source impedance in series with $e_s(t)$. With the voltage source replaced by a current source, the equivalent circuit becomes that shown in Fig. 5–6(b), with G and K again as nodes 1 and 2.

The transform of the current into node 1, supplied by the current source, is $I_s = E_s/Z_s$ while that into node 2 is $g_m E_g = g_m(V_1 - V_2)$. In this case, V_1 is not known, so that we have two equations, namely

$$I_s = Y_{11}V_1 - Y_{12}V_2 \tag{5–40}$$

$$g_m(V_1 - V_2) = -Y_{21}V_1 + Y_{22}V_2 \tag{5–41}$$

Since V_1 and V_2 are unknown node potential transforms, equation (5–41) is written

$$0 = -(Y_{21} + g_m)V_1 + (Y_{22} + g_m)V_2 \tag{5–42}$$

where the coefficients of the equations (5–40) and (5–42) are:

$$Y_{11} = \frac{1}{Z_s} + C_{gp}s + C_{gk}s$$

$$Y_{22}' = Y_{22} + g_m = \frac{1}{r_p} + \frac{1}{R_K} + g_m + C_{gk}s + Cs$$

and

$$Y_{12} = sC_{gk} \qquad \text{while} \quad Y_{21}' = Y_{21} + g_m = sC_{gk} + g_m$$

The node potential transforms may be obtained by solution of equations (5–40) and (5–42). These equations differ in form from the node equations for a passive circuit consisting of bilateral elements, in that the symmetrically placed off-diagonal coefficients, i.e., Y_{12} and Y_{21}', are unequal. Such asymmetry characterizes the node equations for active circuits in the same way that it characterized the loop equations for active circuits.

5-4 Coils Coupled by Mutual Magnetic Flux—Loop and Node Methods

The method of solving problems involving coils coupled by mutual magnetic flux by loop or node analysis requires separate treatment.

In Fig. 5–7, v_1 and v_2 are the instantaneous potentials of nodes 1 and 2 relative to the common reference indicated by the ground symbol. They are also, in this case, the instantaneous voltages across coils 1 and 2 respectively. In a problem where nodes 3 and 4 are not tied to the same point, one need merely replace v_1 by $v_1 - v_3$, and v_2 by $v_2 - v_4$. In that case at least one of the nodes 3 and 4 is not a reference node when the network consists of one part. If nodes 3 and 4 belong to separate parts of the network, each of these nodes can, but need not, be the reference for its part.

The basic equations for Fig. 5–7 are:

$$v_1 = L_1 \frac{di_1}{dt} + M \frac{di_2}{dt} \tag{5–43}$$

and

$$v_2 = M \frac{di_1}{dt} + L_2 \frac{di_2}{dt} \tag{5–44}$$

where L_1 and L_2 are the self-inductances of coils 1 and 2, while M is their

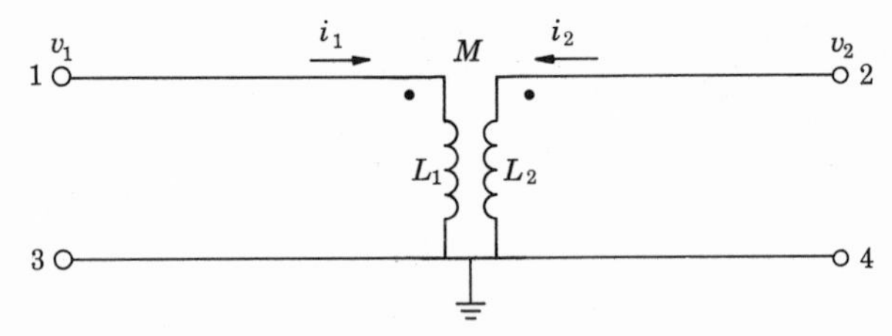

Fig. 5–7.

mutual inductance. Comparing the terms of (5–43) and (5–44) with those of equations (4–1) and (4–8), we see that taking Laplace transforms of both sides of (5–43) and (5–44) leads to

$$V_1 = L_1 s I_1 + M s I_2 - L_1 i_{10} - M i_{20} \tag{5–45}$$

$$V_2 = M s I_1 + L_2 s I_2 - L_2 i_{20} - M i_{10} \tag{5–46}$$

where i_{10} is the initial value of the current i_1, while i_{20} is the initial value of the current i_2.

The relations (5–45) and (5–46) are the basic relations for use in a loop analysis of an electric circuit containing coils coupled by mutual magnetic flux. The terms $L_1 i_{10}$ and $M i_{20}$ are effectively e.m.f. transforms in the left-hand loop, while $L_2 i_{20}$ and $M i_{10}$ are e.m.f. transforms in the right-hand loop.

In order to have a convenient form for node analysis, equations (5–45) and (5–46) must be solved for I_1 and I_2. The result, after necessary simplification, is

$$I_1 = \frac{L_2}{L_1 L_2 - M^2} \frac{1}{s} V_1 - \frac{M}{L_1 L_2 - M^2} \frac{1}{s} V_2 + \frac{1}{s} i_{10} \tag{5–47a}$$

$$I_2 = -\frac{M}{L_1L_2-M^2}\frac{1}{s}V_1+\frac{L_1}{L_1L_2-M^2}\frac{1}{s}V_2+\frac{1}{s}i_{20} \qquad (5\text{–}48a)$$

The quantities $-(1/s)i_{10}$ and $-(1/s)i_{20}$ may be regarded as current transforms applied between node 1 and the reference node, and node 2 and the reference node, respectively.

The coefficients in these equations will have a more evident significance if we note that the mutual inductance M may be written as $M = k(L_1L_2)^{1/2}$ where k is the coefficient of coupling and lies in the range $0 < k < 1$. Then

$$I_1 = \frac{1}{1-k^2}\frac{1}{L_1s}V_1-\frac{k}{1-k^2}\frac{1}{(L_1L_2)^{1/2}s}V_2+\frac{1}{s}i_{10} \qquad (5\text{–}47b)$$

$$I_2 = -\frac{k}{1-k^2}\frac{1}{(L_1L_2)^{1/2}s}V_1+\frac{1}{1-k^2}\frac{1}{L_2s}V_2+\frac{1}{s}i_{20} \qquad (5\text{–}48b)$$

Now if $k = 0$, i.e., if the coils are completely isolated, the equations reduce, as they should, to

$$I_1 = \frac{1}{L_1s}V_1+\frac{1}{s}i_{10} \qquad (5\text{–}47c)$$

$$I_2 = \frac{1}{L_2s}V_2+\frac{1}{s}i_{20} \qquad (5\text{–}48c)$$

Hence we see that, in the presence of coil 2, the self-admittance of coil 1 is increased by the factor $1/(1-k^2)$, and the self-admittance of coil 2 in the presence of coil 1 is also increased by the same factor.

Interpretation of the special case $M = (L_1L_2)^{1/2}$ in (5–47a) and (5–48a), or $k = 1$ in (5–47b) or (5–48b), is not immediately obvious, for under this condition the denominators of the admittances go to zero. The condition $k = 1$ implies maximum flux linkage, so that the voltage induced in L_2 should be related to that in L_1 simply by the turns ratio of the coils. We therefore expect that (5–45) and (5–46) are not truly independent relationships in this limiting case. While the physical argument supplies motivation for a proof and reassurance as to its conclusion, it is preferable to see precisely how the equations are interrelated. If we replace M by $(L_1L_2)^{1/2}$ in (5–45) and (5–46) and attempt to solve for the current transforms, the equations become

$$V_1+L_1i_{10}+(L_1L_2)^{1/2}i_{20} = L_1sI_1+(L_1L_2)^{1/2}sI_2 \qquad (5\text{–}45a)$$

$$V_2+L_2i_{20}+(L_1L_2)^{1/2}i_{10} = (L_1L_2)^{1/2}sI_1+L_2sI_2 \qquad (5\text{–}46a)$$

Attempting to solve for I_1 by determinants, we write

$$I_1 = \frac{\begin{vmatrix} V_1+L_1i_{10}+(L_1L_2)^{1/2}i_{20} & (L_1L_2)^{1/2}s \\ V_2+L_2i_{20}+(L_1L_2)^{1/2}i_{10} & L_2s \end{vmatrix}}{\begin{vmatrix} L_1s & (L_1L_2)^{1/2}s \\ (L_1L_2)^{1/2}s & L_2s \end{vmatrix}} \tag{5–49}$$

Now the determinant in the denominator has the value

$$L_1L_2s^2 - L_1L_2s^2 = 0$$

Since I_1 is the transform of a current (which must be finite and Laplace transformable), we know that I_1 is finite. Hence we conclude that the numerator determinant is also zero. Expanding it then leads to the equation

$$\begin{aligned} &V_1L_2s + L_1L_2si_{10} + (L_1L_2)^{1/2}L_2si_{20} \\ &\quad - V_2(L_1L_2)^{1/2}s - L_2(L_1L_2)^{1/2}si_{20} - L_1L_2si_{10} = 0 \end{aligned} \tag{5–50}$$

or, canceling terms,

$$V_1L_2s - V_2(L_1L_2)^{1/2}s = 0 \tag{5–50a}$$

whence

$$\frac{V_1}{V_2} = \left(\frac{L_1}{L_2}\right)^{1/2} = \frac{N_1}{N_2} \tag{5–50b}$$

where N_1/N_2 is the turns ratio of the transformer and where we have used the fact that the inductance of a coil of constant shape is proportional to the square of the number of its turns.(17) If the ratio of the transforms is equal to the turns ratio, a real constant, it is evident that the instantaneous voltages are in the same ratio.

If now the relationship (5–50b) is substituted into (5–45) and (5–46), it is easy to show that (5–45) and (5–46) become, in this case, the same equation. Hence in the case of a transformer with maximum flux linkage, we can solve for I_1 and I_2 in terms of V_1, V_2, and the initial conditions, using equations (5–45) and (5–50b) and the relationship between V_2 and I_2 determined by the load on the secondary side. The latter relationship will be $V_2/(-I_2) = Z_2$ if a load impedance Z_2 can be defined.

It is of interest to note that the assumption of maximum flux linkage, introduced above, has not made the transformer ideal. The assumptions needed to obtain the ideal transformer relationships from the relationships of coils coupled by mutual magnetic flux are stated in Section 1–4, where the ideal transformer concept is developed.

Illustration: Node Analysis of a Circuit Containing Coils Coupled by Mutual Magnetic Flux

In order to illustrate the node analysis of a circuit containing coils coupled by mutual inductance, consider the circuit of Fig. 5–8. An ideal current source is applied to the first or input node,* and the output voltage transform (across the capacitance C_2) will be obtained. The circuit is assumed initially at rest, so that an easy reinterpretation of symbols will yield the steady-state solution when the applied current source is sinusoidal. The equations will first be set up for a general case, and resonance conditions will then be introduced.

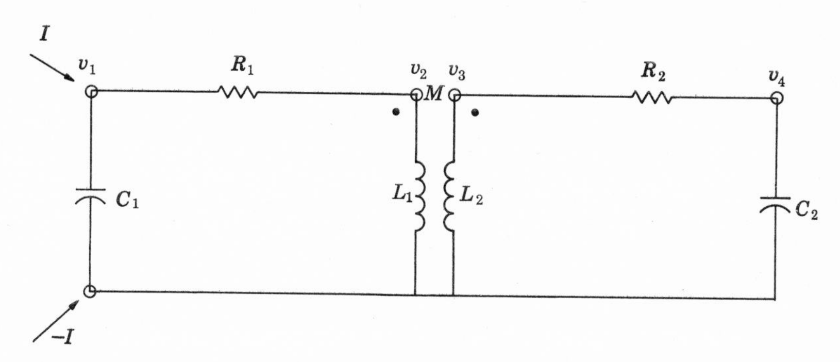

Fig. 5–8.

In the doubly tuned circuit shown in Fig. 5–8, the resistors R_1 and R_2 are included to account for energy loss; the capacitances C_1 and C_2 can include stray capacitance. The current source of instantaneous strength i, with transform I, is applied at node 1. Since the initial charge on C_1 and C_2 is zero, we can represent R_2 and C_2 in series by the admittance $Y_2 = C_2s/(1+R_2C_2s)$. The three node equations then become

$$I = \left(\frac{1}{R_1} + C_1s\right)V_1 - \frac{1}{R_1}V_2 - 0V_3 \tag{5–51}$$

$$0 = -\frac{1}{R_1}V_1 + \left(\frac{1}{\sigma^2L_1s} + \frac{1}{R_1}\right)V_2 - \frac{k}{\sigma^2(L_1L_2)^{1/2}s}V_3 \tag{5–52}$$

$$0 = -0V_1 - \frac{k}{\sigma^2(L_1L_2)^{1/2}s}V_2 + \left(\frac{1}{\sigma^2L_2s} + Y_2\right)V_3 \tag{5–53}$$

where $\sigma^2 = 1-k^2$.

* The other end of the current source is connected to the reference node.

Solving for the voltage transform V_3 yields, after considerable algebraic simplification,

$$V_3 = \frac{Ik(L_1L_2)^{1/2}s(1+R_2C_2s)}{A_0s^4+A_1s^3+A_2s^2+A_3s+A_4} \tag{5-54}$$

where

$$A_0 = \sigma^2 L_1L_2C_1C_2$$

$$A_1 = R_1C_1L_2C_2+R_2C_2L_1C_1$$

$$A_2 = L_1C_1+L_2C_2+R_1R_2C_1C_2$$

$$A_3 = R_1C_1+R_2C_2$$

$$A_4 = 1$$

The voltage transform across the capacitance C_2 is $V_4 = V_3/(1+R_2C_2s)$. The denominator of (5–54) simplifies considerably if we introduce the substitutions

$$L_1C_1 = \frac{1}{{\omega_m}^2} = L_2C_2$$

$$Q_1 = \frac{\omega_m L_1}{R_1}$$

$$Q_2 = \frac{\omega_m L_2}{R_2}$$

$$Q_g = (Q_1Q_2)^{1/2} \quad Q_a = \tfrac{1}{2}(Q_1+Q_2) \quad b = Q_g/Q_a$$

The first of these relations states the fact that both sides of the circuit are tuned to the same frequency. The output voltage transform (across C_2) is then determined as

$$V_4 = \frac{I\dfrac{k}{\sigma^2}(L_1L_2)^{1/2}s}{\left(\dfrac{s}{\omega_m}\right)^4+\dfrac{2}{\sigma^2 bQ_g}\left(\dfrac{s}{\omega_m}\right)^3+\dfrac{1}{\sigma^2}\left(2+\dfrac{1}{{Q_g}^2}\right)\left(\dfrac{s}{\omega_m}\right)^2+\dfrac{2}{\sigma^2 bQ_g}\left(\dfrac{s}{\omega_m}\right)+\dfrac{1}{\sigma^2}} \tag{5-55}$$

Normalization

Introducing the change in variable $s' = s/\omega_m$, we obtain

$$V_4(s) = V_4'(s') = \frac{I\frac{k}{\sigma^2}(L_1L_2)^{1/2}\omega_m s'}{s'^4 + \frac{2}{\sigma^2 b Q_g}s'^3 + \frac{1}{\sigma^2}\left(2 + \frac{1}{Q_g{}^2}\right)s'^2 + \frac{2}{\sigma^2 b Q_g}s' + \frac{1}{\sigma^2}} \qquad (5\text{–}55\text{a})^*$$

This substitution involves a slight change in the expression for the time-function $v_4(t)$. The inversion integral states

$$v_4(t) = \frac{1}{2\pi j}\int_{c-j\infty}^{c+j\infty} V_4(s)e^{st}\,ds \qquad (5\text{–}56)$$

Again introducing $s = \omega_m s'$ and noting that $ds = \omega_m\,ds'$, we find

$$v_4(t) = \frac{\omega_m}{2\pi j}\int_{c'-j\infty}^{c'+j\infty} V_4'(s')e^{\omega_m s't}\,ds' \qquad (5\text{–}56\text{a})$$

or

$$v_4'(t') = \frac{1}{2\pi j}\int_{c'-j\infty}^{c'+j\infty} V_4'(s')e^{s't'}ds' \qquad (5\text{–}56\text{b})$$

where $t' = \omega_m t$, and $c' = c/\omega_m$. Comparing (5–56a) and (5–56b), we find

$$v_4(t) = \omega_m v_4'(t') \qquad (5\text{–}56\text{c})$$

We see then that, corresponding to the normalization of the complex variable s, there also occurs normalization of the time variable.

The function $V_4(s)$ is regular save for poles. These poles lie to the left of the Bromwich path, $c + j\omega$, in the s-plane (Section 3–14). Since ω_m is a real, positive number, $V_4'(s')$ is regular save for poles to the left of the path $c' + j\omega'$ in the s'-plane. Clearly $F'(s')$ also satisfies

$$\lim_{|s'|\to\infty} |F'(s')| = 0$$

Hence the residue method is applicable to the evaluation of the integral on the right-hand side of (5–56b).

* The notation $V_4'(s')$ is based on the following argument. Clearly the right-hand side of (5–55a) is a function of s'. However, it is not $V_4(s')$, since this symbol would imply replacement of each s by s' in the expression for $V_4(s)$. This would not give the right-hand side of (5–55a).

An analysis by which we may obtain or approximate roots for the 4th-degree denominator is omitted as it is felt to lie outside the main subject of this text. When the roots are known, the residue method may be applied directly in order to obtain the time-function, or a partial fraction expansion may first be used to simplify the transform.

The Sinusoidal Steady-State Solution

Suppose the applied current source to be a pure sinusoid represented by the complex number I. The steady-state solution will be obtained from (5–55) upon replacement of s by $j\omega$. The complex output voltage V_4 is then

$$V_4 = \frac{I \dfrac{k}{\sigma^2}(L_1 L_2)^{1/2} j\omega}{\left(\dfrac{\omega}{\omega_m}\right)^4 - \dfrac{1}{\sigma^2}\left(2 + \dfrac{1}{Q_g^2}\right)\left(\dfrac{\omega}{\omega_m}\right)^2 + \dfrac{1}{\sigma^2} + j\dfrac{2}{\sigma^2 b Q_g}\left[\dfrac{\omega}{\omega_m} - \left(\dfrac{\omega}{\omega_m}\right)^3\right]} \tag{5–57}$$

When the applied current source is at the resonant frequency of the double-tuned circuit, i.e., when $\omega = \omega_m$

$$V_4 = \frac{I \dfrac{k}{\sigma^2}(L_1 L_2)^{1/2} j\omega_m}{1 - \dfrac{1}{\sigma^2}\left(2 + \dfrac{1}{Q_g^2}\right) + \dfrac{1}{\sigma^2}} \tag{5–58}$$

Substituting $(1-k^2)$ for σ^2, and M for $k\sqrt{L_1 L_2}$, we find

$$V_4 = \frac{-j\omega_m M I Q_g^2}{1 + k^2 Q_g^2} \tag{5–59}$$

at the resonant frequency.

5-5 Classification of Circuit Response in Accordance with Location and Order of Poles

Each time-function obtained in the present chapter and in the previous one was a special case of $\mathcal{L}^{-1}[N(s)/D(s)]e^{-sT}$ where, in many cases, the delay factor e^{-sT} was equal to 1, since T was equal to 0. In all cases, $N(s)$ and $D(s)$ were polynomials in s with real constant coefficients—a consequence of the fact that these problems concerned linear, lumped, finite circuits with constant and (necessarily) real parameters. Again in all cases, $\mathcal{L}^{-1}N(s)/D(s)$ was evaluated and time delay, when present, was introduced as a second step.

Now the ratio $N(s)/D(s)$ may be replaced, in all these cases, by

$$K + [N_1(s)/D(s)]$$

where:

(a) $K = 0$, and $N_1(s) \equiv N(s)$ if N is of lower degree than D, or
(b) $K \neq 0$, and N_1 is of lower degree than D, if N is of equal degree with D.

In case (b), K is recognized as the transform of an impulse function. In both (a) and (b), N_1 is of lower degree than D and, according to Section 3–14, $\mathcal{L}^{-1}N_1(s)/D(s)$ is equal to the sum of the residues at the poles of $[N_1(s)/D(s)]e^{st}$ for all $t > 0$. We see then that there is a direct tie

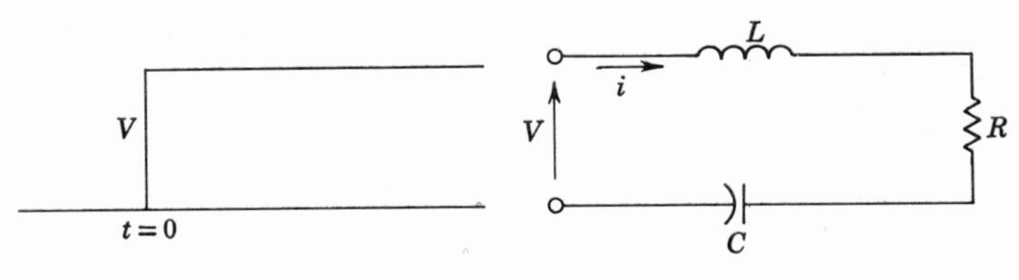

Fig. 5–9.

between transform poles and time-function. We shall now classify circuit response in accordance with the poles which arise. These poles may be simple or of higher order, and may occur at real, imaginary, or complex values of s.

The response of a series RLC circuit to an applied step voltage illustrates, for various values of the parameters, the major types of transient and steady-state response. It should be noted, however, that the tie between transform pole and time response does not depend on the particular circuit used as illustration. If now a step voltage is applied to the circuit as illustrated in Fig. 5–9 with no initial charge on the capacitance and no initial current in the inductance, the Laplace transform of the current is

$$I = \frac{V}{L}\,\frac{1}{s^2 + 2\alpha_0 s + \omega_0^2} \tag{5–60}$$

where

$$\alpha_0 = \frac{R}{2L} \quad \text{and} \quad \omega_0^2 = \frac{1}{LC}$$

The nature and location of the poles of this expression depend on the circuit parameters. When the denominator is factored in terms of its roots, we have

$$I = \frac{V}{L}\frac{1}{[s+\alpha_0-(\alpha_0^2-\omega_0^2)^{1/2}][s+\alpha_0+(\alpha_0^2-\omega_0^2)^{1/2}]} \tag{5-61}$$

We shall now consider various cases which arise as we vary the circuit parameters:

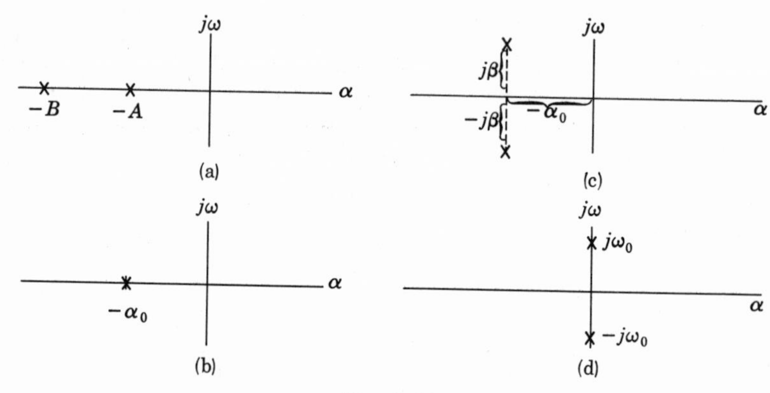

Fig. 5–10.

CASE 1. $\alpha_0^2 > \omega_0^2$, *simple poles on left-half real axis.*

In this instance, we have two simple poles on the left half of the real axis as illustrated in Fig. 5–10(a). With the definitions

$$A = \alpha_0-(\alpha_0^2-\omega_0^2)^{1/2}$$

and

$$B = \alpha_0+(\alpha_0^2-\omega_0^2)^{1/2}$$

the transform becomes

$$I = \frac{V}{L}\frac{1}{(s+A)(s+B)} \tag{5-62}$$

yielding the response

$$i = \frac{V}{L}\,\frac{1}{B-A}\,(e^{-At}-e^{-Bt}) \quad \text{with} \quad t \geqq 0 \tag{5-63}$$

Since A and B are each real and positive, each term alone illustrates the rule that the time-function corresponding to a simple pole on the left-half real axis is a decaying exponential.

CASE 2. $\alpha_0^2 = \omega_0^2$, *double pole on left-half real axis.*

With the circuit parameters adjusted to make $(\alpha_0^2 - \omega_0^2)^{1/2}$ vanish, the transform of the current becomes

$$I = \frac{V}{L}\frac{1}{(s+\alpha_0)^2} \tag{5-64}$$

We have then a double pole at $s = -\alpha_0$ as illustrated in Fig. 5–10(b). Evaluating the residue at this double pole, we find the current to be

$$i = \frac{V}{L}\left(\frac{d}{ds}e^{st}\right)\bigg|_{s=-\alpha_0} = \frac{V}{L}te^{-\alpha t} \quad \text{with} \quad t \geqq 0 \tag{5-65}$$

Thus we see that the time-function corresponding to a double pole on the left-half real axis rises as t for small values of time and then falls off exponentially for larger time values when $e^{-\alpha t}$ dominates.

CASE 3. $\alpha_0^2 < \omega_0^2$, *complex conjugate poles in left half-plane.*

When the resistance is reduced so that $\alpha_0^2 < \omega_0^2$, it is convenient to use

$$(\alpha_0^2 - \omega_0^2)^{1/2} = j(\omega_0^2 - \alpha_0^2)^{1/2}$$

Letting $\beta = (\omega_0^2 - \alpha_0^2)^{1/2}$, we find that the transform of the current becomes

$$I = \frac{V}{L}\frac{1}{(s+\alpha_0-j\beta)(s+\alpha_0+j\beta)} \tag{5-66}$$

the two simple poles being illustrated in Fig. 5–10(c). Since these poles are conjugates, the residues at these poles are also conjugates, as shown in Section 3–16, part (b). We therefore have:

$$i = 2\frac{V}{L}\mathscr{Re}\frac{e^{-(\alpha_0+j\beta)t}}{2j\beta} = \frac{V}{L\beta}e^{-\alpha_0 t}\sin\beta t \quad \text{with} \quad t \geqq 0 \tag{5-67}$$

Thus when a transform contains a pair of simple poles which are complex conjugates, the corresponding term in the time-function will be oscillatory with exponential decay, or decreasing envelope.

The same circuit yields further illustrations of the relation between transform pole and circuit response if we take extreme parameter values.

CASE 3A. $\alpha_0 = 0,\ j(\omega_0^2 - \alpha_0^2)^{1/2} = j\omega_0$.

This case is realized if the resistance in the circuit is set equal to zero. We now have conjugate poles on the $j\omega$-axis as illustrated in Fig. 5–10(d).

The transform of the response becomes

$$I = \frac{V}{L}\frac{1}{(s+j\omega_0)(s-j\omega_0)} \tag{5-68}$$

Again since the poles are at conjugate points, we have

$$i = \frac{V}{L} 2\,\mathscr{Re}\,\frac{e^{j\omega_0 t}}{2j\omega_0} = \frac{V}{\omega_0 L}\sin\omega_0 t \quad \text{with} \quad t \geqq 0 \tag{5-69}$$

Thus, a pair of simple poles on the $j\omega$-axis corresponds to a sinusoidal steady-state response.

CASE 3B. $\alpha_0 = 0$, $\omega_0 = 0$ *(with $C = \infty$ and L finite).*

These parameter values are obtained if we replace both the capacitance and the resistance by short circuits. We have then a step voltage applied to an ideal inductance. The current transform reduces to the form

$$I = \frac{V}{Ls^2} \tag{5-70}$$

which has a double pole at the origin. The resulting current is then

$$i = \frac{V}{L}\left(\frac{d}{ds}e^{st}\right)\bigg|_{s=0} = \frac{V}{L}t \quad \text{with} \quad t \geqq 0 \tag{5-71}$$

This response is an increasing transient. An increasing transient, of course, either destroys the circuit or changes its parameters so that the result given above can be valid only for an ideal inductance. Equation (5-71) illustrates the important rule that a double pole at the origin corresponds to a linearly increasing transient.

CASE 4. $L = 0$, $C = \infty$.

These parameter values reduce the circuit to an ideal resistance. The current transform

$$I = \frac{V}{R}\frac{1}{s} \tag{5-72}$$

has a simple pole at the origin, and the response

$$i = \frac{V}{R} \quad \text{with} \quad t > 0 \tag{5-73}*$$

* From the initial value theorem or the discussion in Section 3-14, we note that when $N(s)$ is lower in degree than $D(s)$ by 2 or more, there is no discontinuity in $f(t)$ at time $t = 0$. This was the case in the preceding illustrations of this subsection, where each current solution was given for $t \geqq 0$. In (5-72) we have the transform of a time-function with a discontinuity at $t = 0$, for $N(s)$ is only one less in degree than $D(s)$. We therefore specify the time-function for $t > 0$ rather than $t \geqq 0$.

is well known without the aid of transform theory. Thus a simple pole at the origin corresponds to a steady-state d-c response.

Conjugate Double Poles on Imaginary Axis

In cases 2 and 3, we have seen the effect of double poles on the real axis. We now consider double poles on the axis of imaginaries. In order to do this, we again use the RLC circuit with $R = 0$, but apply a sinusoidal voltage at the resonant frequency of the circuit, i.e., $V_m \sin \omega_0 t$. The transform of the current is then

$$I = \frac{V_m \omega_0}{(s^2 + \omega_0^2)} \frac{s}{L(s^2 + \omega_0^2)} \tag{5–74}$$

Factoring yields

$$I = \frac{V_m \omega_0}{L} \frac{s}{(s + j\omega_0)^2 (s - j\omega_0)^2} \tag{5–75}$$

where one factor of each double pole arises from the circuit impedance and one from the factored denominator of the voltage transform

$$V_m \omega_0 / (s^2 + \omega_0^2)$$

The current i is then given by the expression

$$i = 2 \frac{V_m \omega_0}{L} \mathcal{R}e \frac{d}{ds} \frac{s e^{st}}{(s + j\omega_0)^2} \bigg|_{s = j\omega_0} \tag{5–76}$$

The right-hand side of (5–76) represents twice the real part of the residue of Ie^{st} at its double pole at $s = j\omega_0$. Evaluation of the right-hand side of (5–76) yields

$$i = \frac{V_m}{2L} t \sin \omega_0 t \quad \text{with} \quad t \geqq 0 \tag{5–77}$$

The solution (5–77), like (5–71), is an increasing transient.

Conjugate Double Poles in Left Half-Plane

In order to observe the effect of double poles at conjugate points in the left half of the complex plane, let us apply the voltage $V_m e^{-\alpha_0 t} \sin \beta t$, to the RLC circuit of the previous illustrations. Here again $\alpha_0 = R/2L$, $\omega_0^2 = 1/LC$, and $\beta = \sqrt{\omega_0^2 - \alpha_0^2}$ with $\omega_0^2 > \alpha_0^2$. The Laplace transform of the applied voltage is then

$$\mathcal{L} V_m e^{-\alpha_0 t} \sin \beta t = \frac{V_m \beta}{(s + \alpha_0 - j\beta)(s + \alpha_0 + j\beta)} \tag{5–78}$$

Division by the circuit impedance yields the current transform

$$I = \frac{V_m \beta}{L} \frac{s}{(s+\alpha_0+j\beta)^2(s+\alpha_0-j\beta)^2} \tag{5–79}$$

where it will be observed that the selection of α_0 and β as the parameters in the damped sinusoidal voltage has resulted in a pair of double poles in the current transform. These are located at $s = -\alpha_0 - j\beta$ and at $s = -\alpha_0 + j\beta$. The current is then given by

$$i = 2\,\mathscr{Re}\, \frac{d}{ds} \frac{V\beta}{L} \frac{se^{st}}{(s+\alpha_0+j\beta)^2}\bigg|_{s=-\alpha_0+j\beta} \tag{5–80}$$

the derivative evaluated at the pole $s = -\alpha_0 + j\beta$ being the residue of Ie^{st} at this point. Carrying out the differentiation, evaluating the real part of the result, and simplifying, lead to

$$i = \frac{V_m}{2\beta L}\left[(\alpha_0{}^2+\beta^2)^{1/2} te^{-\alpha_0 t}\cos(\beta t+\phi+\pi) + \frac{\alpha}{\beta} e^{-\alpha_0 t}\cos\left(\beta t + \frac{\pi}{2}\right)\right] \tag{5–81}$$

where

$$\phi = \tan^{-1}\frac{\beta}{-\alpha_0}\quad, \text{ with } t \geqq 0$$

The first term is a sinusoid whose amplitude is damped by the factor $e^{-\alpha_0 t}$, but also multiplied by the factor t. The presence of the factor t results from the necessary differentiation of e^{st} with respect to s when the residue of Ie^{st} is evaluated at a double pole. The factor $e^{-\alpha_0 t}$ results from the fact that the pole was located α_0 to the left of the $j\omega$-axis.

Pole in the Right Half-Plane

It will be observed that all poles considered in this section have been on the imaginary axis or in the left half-plane. That a pole in the right half-plane corresponds to an exponentially increasing time-function is seen from the relation

$$\mathcal{L}^{-1}\frac{1}{s-a} = e^{at} \quad \text{with} \quad t > 0 \tag{5–82}$$

which may be verified by taking the residue of $e^{st}/(s-a)$ at the simple pole at $s = a$. Such an exponentially increasing transient can arise only in a circuit containing an energy source, and occurs with unstable feedback circuits.

From the foregoing illustrations, we see that when

$$f(t) = \mathcal{L}^{-1}N_1(s)/D(s)$$

with the polynomial $N_1(s)$ lower in degree than the polynomial $D(s)$, the form of the function $f(t)$ is determined by the nature and location of the poles of $N_1(s)/D(s)$. This relationship, independent of the particular circuit used as illustration, is summarized in Table 5–1.

TABLE 5–1

LOCATION AND TYPE OF POLE	FORM OF CORRESPONDING TIME-FUNCTION (Contribution to the total response due to the pole or poles specified)
A. Poles to left of $j\omega$*-axis*	*A. Exponential decay*
1. Simple pole on real axis.	1. Exponential decay unmodified.
2. Multiple pole on real axis.	2. Exponential decay modified by factor with positive powers of t. (Modifying factor is of form (a) below.)
3. Conjugate pair (simple) off real axis.	3. Exponential decay modified by oscillatory factor.
4. Conjugate pair (multiple of order n) off real axis.	4. Exponential decay modified by factor with oscillatory terms each multiplied by power of t. (Modifying factor is of form (b) below.)
B. Poles on $j\omega$*-axis*	*B. No exponential factor*
1. Simple pole at origin.	1. Steady-state d-c.
2. Conjugate pair (simple) off origin.	2. Steady-state a-c.
3. Multiple pole at origin.	3. Increasing transient. (See form (a) below.)
4. Conjugate pair (multiple of order n) off origin.	4. Increasing oscillatory transient. (See form (b) below.)
C. Poles to right of $j\omega$*-axis*	*C. Exponential increase* (Exponential may again be modified in accordance with location and order of pole(s).

$$(a) = \sum_{i=0}^{n-1} a_i t^i \qquad (b) = \sum_{i=0}^{n-1} a_i t^i \cos(\omega_0 t + \phi_i)$$

5-6 Pole-Zero Distribution of Network Functions[2]

A *network function* may be defined as any ratio between the Laplace transform of a signal and the Laplace transform of the response of a network which is initially at rest. Examples of network functions are: driving-point (i.e., input) impedance and admittance, Z_{IN} and Y_{IN}, transfer impedance and admittance, Z_T and Y_T, voltage gain, etc.

These functions are obtained through the solution of the loop or the node equations. With an ideal e.m.f. source as the only independent source applied to a circuit initially at rest, one finds Δ_l/Δ_{l11} as the driving-point impedance.* Here Δ_l is the determinant of the loop equations and Δ_{l11} is the minor obtained by striking out row 1 and column 1 of Δ_l. We have supposed the loops to be so chosen that only the single loop current i_1 passes through the source. If we replace the ideal e.m.f. source, above, with an ideal current source as the only independent source applied to the circuit initially at rest, the node equations yield Δ_n/Δ_{n11} as the driving-point admittance.* (The subscript n indicates that the determinant and its minor are based on the node equations.) We have here supposed the nodes to be so numbered and the reference node so chosen that the current source is connected between the reference node and node 1, and points toward node 1. Transfer impedance and admittance may be expressed in a similar manner. Minors of elements with unequal subscripts will appear. We may find a sum of two minors in the denominator, e.g., an output voltage transform in a transfer admittance I/V_o

* The validity of Δ_l/Δ_{l11} and Δ_n/Δ_{n11} as formulas for driving-point impedance and admittance depends on the fact that each of these ratios is obtained from a set of equations in which only one known quantity, the applied source, appears in only one equation, the first one. It is, therefore, necessary that each dependent or controlled source be expressed in terms of response. Thus the e.m.f. transform μE_g in a vacuum-tube equivalent circuit may be expressed as $\mu Z_{gk} I$ [2] where I, the transform of the current from grid to cathode, may consist of one or more loop current transforms, and Z_{gk} is the impedance between grid and cathode. A circuit not containing Z_{gk} may, for the purpose of general theory, be regarded as a limiting case in which Z_{gk} is infinite. In such circuits it is sometimes possible to express μE_g in terms of current transforms and circuit parameters without introducing an impedance Z_{gk}. The node equations present less difficulty, since E_g appears as a difference of two node potential transforms.

The transistor equivalent circuit also involves dependent sources. We have seen these sources expressed in terms of loop currents in a basic transistor equivalent circuit (equations 5-25d and e).

One may in a particular problem handle dependent sources in a manner other than that described above. In such a case, driving-point impedance and admittance will not be given by the simple ratios Δ_l/Δ_{l11} and Δ_n/Δ_{n11}.

may be a difference of two node potential transforms with neither node chosen as potential reference.

Any element of the determinant of the loop or node equations consists of one or more terms of the form αs^k where $k = \pm 1$ or 0, and where α is *real*. We therefore find that the network functions of linear, lumped, finite networks with constant parameters can be written as ratios of polynomials with real coefficients. (All that is required is expanding the determinants in the ratio defining the function, clearing fractions of negative powers of s, and being sure not to multiply numerator and denominator by a complex or imaginary factor.)[14]

The poles and zeros of a ratio of polynomials with real coefficients are either real or occur in conjugate pairs. (The proof for poles, Section 3–16(a), can easily be altered to show that the conclusion also holds for zeros.)

Beyond this, the pole-zero distribution of network functions is intimately related to the problem of stability. An electric network may be called *stable* if none of its loop currents and none of its node potentials increase without limit after the application of a current or voltage impulse. Specifically, the impulse may be applied at $t = 0$ and the response is to be finite or zero for all $t > 0$.* The advantage of this definition or criterion may be seen in two ways. Since a voltage or current impulse is gone immediately after its application, we examine the subsequent behavior of the network "on its own," i.e., without driving function. An equivalent argument may be advanced on a purely mathematical basis. Since the transform of an impulse is a constant, the only poles in the transform of the response arise from the nature of the network itself.

We shall see below that a network which proves to be stable with an applied voltage impulse may not prove stable with an applied current impulse. The reverse situation may also occur. The voltage impulse leaves a network with a short circuit across its input terminals for all $t > 0$, and the current impulse leaves an open circuit at the input terminals for all $t > 0$. Essentially, then, the choice of source determines which of *two* networks is considered: the given network with shorted input terminals, or the given network with open input terminals.

We now seek the pole-zero configuration of a driving-point impedance Z_{IN} of a stable network. Let the network N, Fig. 5–11(a), be at rest, and, at the instant $t = 0$, let an ideal source of impulse voltage $K_V u_0(t)$ be

* If the response is an impulse, whether of first or second order, it is zero for $t > 0$ (although not at $t = 0$). Such a response is, therefore, consistent with stability as here defined.

applied to the input terminals 1–0. The Laplace transform I_1, equal to $\mathcal{L}i_1$, is then

$$I_1 = K_V \frac{1}{Z_{IN}} \tag{5–83}$$

The zeros of Z_{IN} are the poles of I_1. If i_1 does not increase without limit for $t > 0$, we conclude with the aid of the table in the preceding section* that:

(a) The zeros of Z_{IN} are not in the right half-plane.
(b) The zeros of Z_{IN} on the $j\omega$-axis are simple. (See footnote, p. 123.)

By implication, we have required that the network N be stable *with a short circuit across its input terminals.* This implication becomes obvious

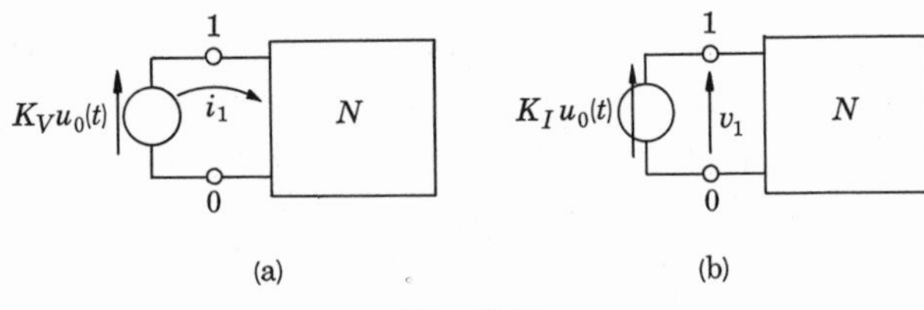

Fig. 5–11.

when we consider that to these terminals we have connected the ideal e.m.f. impulse $K_V u_0(t)$ which equals zero for all $t > 0$.

So far nothing has been learned concerning the poles of Z_{IN}. Let us consider, first, the circuit of Fig. 5–11(b). This circuit is identical with that of Fig. 5–11(a) and at rest, but now a current impulse is applied at the instant $t = 0$. We find at once

$$V_1 = K_I \frac{1}{Y_{IN}} \tag{5–84}$$

where $V_1 = \mathcal{L}v_1$ and Y_{IN} is the driving-point admittance. The zeros of Y_{IN} are the poles of V_1. With the aid of Table 5–1 we see that if v_1 does not increase without limit for $t > 0$,

(c) The zeros of Y_{IN} are not in the right half-plane.
(d) The zeros of Y_{IN} on the $j\omega$-axis are simple.

* Table 5–1 is for polynomial-ratios which are proper fractions. If any $1/Z$ (or $1/Y$) is improper, division yields a proper fraction whose poles are poles of $1/Z$ (or $1/Y$) and which yields the response for $t > 0$. Thus use of the table ignores impulse response at $t = 0$. If we assume condition (b) or (d) on this page applies at $j\infty$, we find $1/Z$ (or $1/Y$) may have a simple (but not a higher-order) pole at ∞. With a simple pole at ∞, the response to an impulse will in general include impulses of first and second order. These, however, are zero for $t > 0$.

With the applied ideal current source equal to zero for $t > 0$, we have clearly required that the network N be stable with *its input terminals open-circuited.*

The relation $Z_{IN} = 1/Y_{IN}$ may now be used to draw conclusions regarding the poles of the driving-point impedance Z_{IN} and the driving-point admittance Y_{IN}. If the network is stable with its input terminals open-circuited, it follows from (c) and (d) that:

(e) The poles of Z_{IN} are not in the right half-plane.
(f) The poles of Z_{IN} on the $j\omega$-axis are simple.

If the network is stable with its input terminals short-circuited, we find from (a) and (b) that:

(g) The poles of Y_{IN} are not in the right half-plane.
(h) The poles of Y_{IN} on the $j\omega$-axis are simple.

Since a passive network does not contain an energy source, it satisfies our definition of stability when its input terminals are either open- or short-circuited, so that for a passive network (a), (b), (c), (d), (e), (f), (g) and (h) are always satisfied.

We now examine the transfer impedance and admittance functions Z_T and Y_T. (We again assume the circuit at rest prior to $t = 0$.) If I_r be the Laplace transform of any loop current other than i_1, Fig. 5–11(a) yields

$$I_r = \frac{K_V}{Z_T} \tag{5–85}$$

so that if the network is stable (with input terminals short-circuited) the zeros of Z_T satisfy the restrictions (a) and (b) stated for the zeros of Z_{IN}. If V_q be the Laplace transform of any potential difference in the network other than v_1, Fig. 5–11(b) yields

$$V_q = \frac{K_I}{Y_T} \tag{5–85a}$$

so that if the network is stable (with input terminals open), the zeros of Y_T satisfy the restrictions (c) and (d) stated for the zeros of Y_{IN}.

We have no conclusions regarding the poles of the transfer impedance Z_T, or the poles of the transfer admittance Y_T. These may, in fact, be in the right half-plane. As an example we note that each voltage ratio of Fig. 5–16 is proportional to the reciprocal of a transfer impedance, so that the zeros in the right half-plane in that figure represent poles of a transfer impedance.

In the foregoing we have seen that a stable circuit which remains stable when its input terminals are open-circuited or short-circuited may yield simple zeros and poles on the $j\omega$-axis. For certain purposes (see, for example, Section 5–9), it is convenient to define the following circuits of a more restricted type:[2,18]

A *minimum-reactance impedance* is a passive-circuit driving-point impedance with no poles on the $j\omega$-axis. The reciprocal of such an impedance is a *minimum-reactance admittance.*

A *minimum-susceptance admittance* is a passive-circuit driving-point admittance with no poles on the $j\omega$-axis. The reciprocal of such an admittance is a *mimimum-susceptance impedance.*

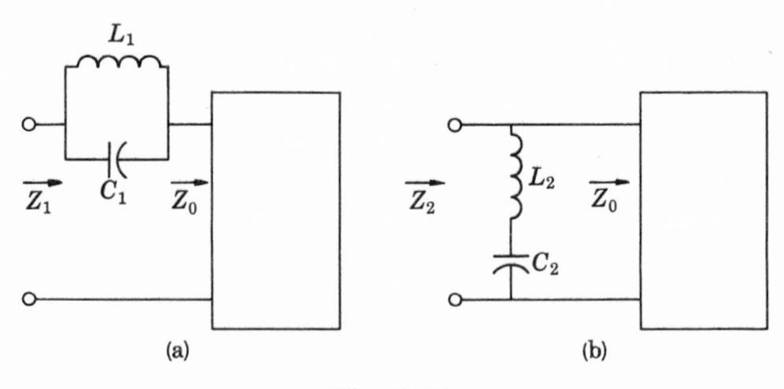

Fig. 5–12.

A driving-point impedance may be only minimum-reactance or only minimum-susceptance, or it may be both. An equivalent statement, of course, applies to the driving-point admittance.

The significance of these definitions may be seen from Fig. 5–12 where the impedance Z_0 is assumed to be a minimum-reactance, minimum-susceptance impedance. The impedance Z_1 of Fig. 5–12(a) is not minimum-reactance, for it has a pole at $\omega = 1/\sqrt{L_1C_1}$. Again, the impedance Z_2 of Fig. 5–12(b) is not minimum-susceptance, because of the zero at $\omega = 1/\sqrt{L_2C_2}$.

Comment on Definition of Impedance and Admittance Functions

Comparatively recent definitions[22,14] of *driving-point* and *transfer impedance* and *admittance* define each as a *response ratio*, i.e., as a ratio of response transform to excitation transform. If a single applied current source produces a voltage v across two terminals of a network which is initially at rest, the ratio of transforms, V/I, is a driving-point or transfer impedance depending upon the location of v. Correspondingly, application of a voltage source leads to I/V as a driving-point or transfer admittance. The specification of source and response in these definitions is opposite to that often used[2,9] as well as to that used in this book (see equations (5–83, 84, 85, 85a) and the accompanying discussion).

With this in mind, let us re-examine our conclusions in order to see whether or not they apply to the newer definitions. It is easy to show that our conclusions with regard to driving-point impedance and admittance remain unaltered: that is, we can show that statements (a), (b), (g), and (h) still hold provided that the network remains stable with short-circuited input terminals, and statements (c), (d), (e), and (f) are again valid for a network which remains stable with open input terminals. However, with the newer definitions these statements are obtained in a different sequence from that used earlier. Thus if we apply a current impulse to the network and find a stable response, the equation $V = K_I Z$ establishes (e) and (f.) The statements (c) and (d), and (a), (b), (g), and (h) may now be justified by the student. (See Problem 5–7 at the end of this chapter.)

The situation regarding transfer impedance and admittance, however, is less comfortable. For convenience, let us call any voltage or current not across or through the input terminals, an output voltage or current. When transfer impedance is defined as a *response function*, one takes the ratio of output voltage (response) to input current (excitation). Correspondingly, transfer admittance becomes the ratio of output current (response) to input voltage (excitation). Let us call these response functions Z_T' and Y_T', reserving the symbols Z_T and Y_T for transfer impedance and admittance as used in our prior discussion. We now note that $Z_T' = 1/Y_T$ and $Y_T' = 1/Z_T$. However, Z_T and Y_T are *not* reciprocals of each other, and Z_T' and Y_T' are *not* reciprocals of each other. We find, using $V = K_I Z_T'$, that if a network is stable with its input terminals open, the poles of Z_T' do not occur in the right half-plane and, if on the $j\omega$-axis, they are simple. This is the restriction previously found for the zeros of Y_T. Again if a network is stable with its input terminals short-circuited, the equation $I = K_V Y_T'$ shows that the poles of Y_T' do not occur in the right half-plane and, if on the $j\omega$-axis, they are simple. This is the restriction previously found for the zeros of Z_T.

5-7 The Sinusoidal Steady State—s-Plane Poles and Zeros

In Section 5–5 circuit response was classified in accordance with location and order of poles. We saw that a steady sinusoid resulted when a conjugate pair of simple poles occurred on the $j\omega$-axis. We now turn to a more detailed study of the sinusoidal steady state. Specifically, we shall note the importance of poles and zeros off the $j\omega$-axis in determining the nature of steady-state response.

Equations (4–41) and (4–43) yield the current response to an applied voltage, $V_m \cos(\omega_1 t + \phi)$. The subscript 1 has been added to ω to distinguish this fixed value of ω_1 from the variable ω to be used subsequently. With this minor change, the equations (4–41) and (4–43) are:

$$\bar{I} = \frac{\bar{V}}{s - j\omega_1} Y(s) \tag{5–86}$$

and

$$i(t) = \mathcal{R}e\, \overline{i(t)} \tag{5–87}$$

where $\bar{V} = V_m e^{j\phi}$, and where

$$\overline{i(t)} = \mathcal{L}^{-1}\bar{I} \tag{5–87a}$$

These equations apply only to circuits which are initially at rest. The current $i(t)$ is, of course, the entire response, including transient terms as well as the steady sinusoidal terms. Clearly $Y(s)$ may be replaced by other network functions (input or transfer impedance, voltage gain, etc.), depending upon the nature of signal and response.

The function $\overline{i(t)}$, (5–87a), may be evaluated by the residue method (see Section 3–14), or the transform $\bar{I}$ may first be simplified with the aid of the partial fraction theorem (Section 3–17). With either method, we see that if $Y(s)$ is regular at $s = j\omega_1$, the transform $\bar{I}$ has a simple pole at this point, and the inverse transform $\overline{i(t)}$ will contain a term equal to $\bar{V}Y(j\omega_1)e^{j\omega_1 t}$. With the aid of (5–87) we now find that $i(t)$ contains the steady sinusoidal term $i_s(t)$, given by:

$$i_s(t) = \mathcal{R}e\, \bar{V}Y(j\omega_1)e^{j\omega_1 t} \tag{5–88}$$

If, on the other hand, $Y(s)$ has a pole of *any* order at $s = j\omega_1$, we obtain an increasing transient in place of a steady sinusoid (see Table 5–1, p. 239).

The circuit of Fig. 5–13 affords a simple illustration of equation (5–88). In this circuit

$$Y(s) = \frac{1}{Ls + R + \dfrac{1}{Cs}} \tag{5–89}$$

With equation (5–88) and $\bar{V}$ replaced by $V_m e^{j\phi}$, we have at once

$$i_s(t) = \mathcal{R}e \frac{V_m e^{j\phi}}{R + j\left(\omega_1 L - \dfrac{1}{\omega_1 C}\right)} e^{j\omega_1 t} \tag{5–90}$$

or

$$i_s(t) = \frac{V_m}{\sqrt{R^2+\left(\omega_1 L - \dfrac{1}{\omega_1 C}\right)^2}} \cos(\omega_1 t + \phi - \psi) \tag{5-91}$$

where

$$\psi = \tan^{-1}\left(\frac{\omega_1 L - \dfrac{1}{\omega_1 C}}{R}\right)$$

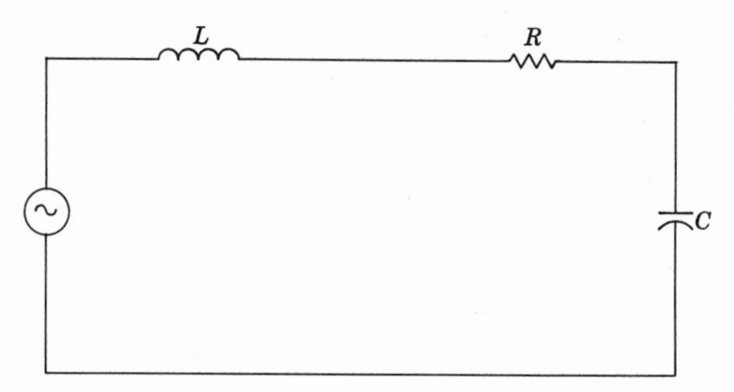

Fig. 5-13.

5-8 Pole-Zero Plot for Specific Circuits

We now note that since polynomials can be factored in terms of their roots, the constants which characterize a ratio of polynomials are the numerator roots (zeros), the denominator roots (poles), and a single multiplying factor. Thus we may write a ratio of polynomials, $Y(s)$, in the form (in which equal numerator and denominator factors have been cancelled)

$$Y(s) = A\,\frac{(s-s_1)(s-s_3)\cdots(s-s_{2m+1})}{(s-s_2)(s-s_4)\cdots(s-s_{2n})} \tag{5-92}$$

This expression may be regarded as entirely general if we admit that the roots need not be unequal and that one or more of these roots may be zero. It is evident from a glance at (5-92) that specification of $s_1, s_2, s_3, \ldots$ and the constant A determines Y for any value of the variable s. Normalizing, we find, then, that the function $Y(s)/A$ is completely determined by its poles $s_2, s_4, \ldots$ and its zeros $s_1, s_3, \ldots$. Now if $Y(s)$ is a network function, for example an admittance, we are particularly interested in its values on the $j\omega$-axis, since these determine the sinusoidal steady-state behavior of the network. Equation (5–92) becomes

$$Y(j\omega) = A\,\frac{(j\omega - s_1)(j\omega - s_3)\cdots(j\omega - s_{2m+1})}{(j\omega - s_2)(j\omega - s_4)\cdots(j\omega - s_{2n})} \tag{5–93}$$

and we are in a position to study the variation of Y on the $j\omega$-axis in terms of its poles and zeros.

Series Resonant Circuit

The series resonant circuit is commonly used to illustrate the analysis of the variation of an admittance on the $j\omega$-axis.[6,16,19] The circuit is shown in Fig. 5–13. With the constants $\alpha_0 = -R/2L$ and $\omega_0 = 1/\sqrt{LC}$ we find

$$Y(s) = \frac{1}{L}\,\frac{s}{s^2 + 2\alpha_0 s + \omega_0{}^2} \tag{5–94}$$

When $\omega_0{}^2$ is greater than $\alpha_0{}^2$, it is convenient, as in Section 5–5, to define $\beta = \sqrt{\omega_0{}^2 - \alpha_0{}^2}$ where β is real and positive. Then

$$Y(s) = \frac{1}{L}\,\frac{s}{(s + \alpha_0 - j\beta)(s + \alpha_0 + j\beta)} \tag{5–95}$$

and on the $j\omega$-axis the function $LY(s)$ becomes

$$LY(j\omega) = \frac{j\omega}{(j\omega + \alpha_0 - j\beta)(j\omega + \alpha_0 + j\beta)} \tag{5–96}$$

The poles of this expression are indicated by $\times$'s in Fig. 5–14. The arrows (or phasors) a, b, and c represent the complex numbers $(j\omega - 0)$, $[j\omega - (-\alpha_0 + j\beta)]$, and $[j\omega - (-\alpha_0 - j\beta)]$.* Since $\alpha_0{}^2 + \beta^2 = \omega_0{}^2$, it is evident that if ω_0 is held constant and R permitted to vary so that α_0 lies in the range $0 < \alpha_0 < \omega_0$, the poles of $Y(j\omega)$ lie on a semicircle of radius ω_0. Since R and, therefore, α_0 are positive, the locus of the poles cannot cross the $j\omega$-axis and the semicircle lies in the left half-plane. The points $\pm j\omega_0$ represent limiting values for the roots which occur when $R = 0$. The value of R for which α_0 equals ω_0 yields a double pole on the real axis. For larger values of R, for which $\alpha_0 > \omega_0$, β is imaginary and $j\beta$ real, so that we have simple real axis poles rather than the complex roots shown in Fig. 5–14.

One use of the pole-zero plot becomes apparent when a high Q circuit is assumed. Noting that the Q of a coil at resonance is defined as $\omega_0 L/R$,

* Fig. 5–14 is drawn for the case $\omega = \omega_0$.

one easily finds $\alpha_0 = \omega_0/2Q$. Thus for large Q, $\beta \simeq \omega_0$ and ω_0 is approximately at the same height above the real axis as the pole $-\alpha_0+j\beta$. If, now, ω varies over a small range of values centered at ω_0, the phasors a and c may be treated as substantially constant so that the variation of $Y(j\omega)$ is given by the phasor b. It is interesting to note that, under these assumptions, if ω is equal to $\omega_0 \pm \alpha$, the phasor b is $\sqrt{2}\,\alpha$ in length. Hence the impedance is $\sqrt{2}$ times its value at resonance, and the points $j(\omega_0+\alpha)$ and $j(\omega_0-\alpha)$ represent frequencies at which the average power

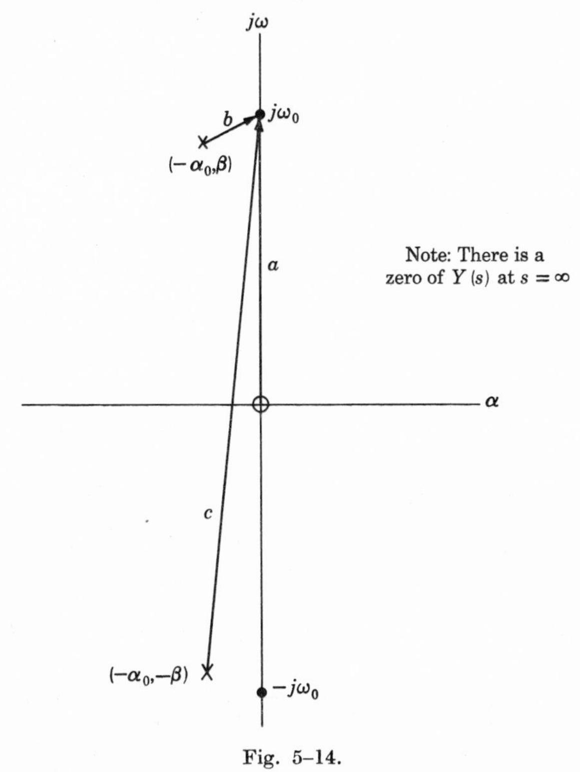

Fig. 5–14.

delivered to R is half that delivered at the resonant frequency, i.e., the half-power points.

All-Pass Lattice

The pole-zero plot for the all-pass or constant resistance lattice, Fig. 5–15, is of interest.[2,19] When, as in the figure, the resistance R is connected to the output terminals of the lattice, the input impedance equals

R at all frequencies; hence the name *constant resistance lattice* (see also discussion of characteristic and image impedances in Section 7–11). This property holds not only for $Z(j\omega)$ but for any $Z(s)$, provided that the impedance of each series arm of the lattice is $Z(s)$ and that the impedance of each shunt arm is $R^2/Z(s)$.

When the product of the input impedances of two networks is a constant, R^2, the networks are said to be *inverse networks*. When $R^2 = 1$, they are termed *reciprocal networks*.* Thus the series and shunt arms of the constant resistance lattice are inverse networks. The design of the inverse of a given impedance is a basic problem in network synthesis and

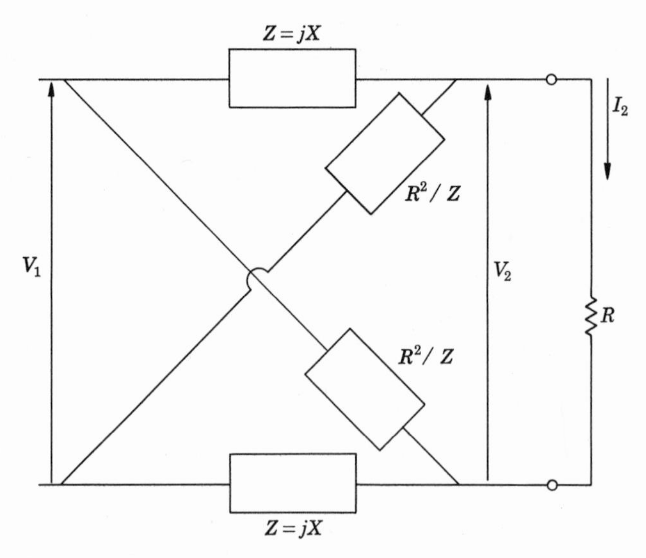

Fig. 5–15. $Z = jX$ for $s = j\omega$ only. Shunt arm impedances each equal R^2/Z for all s.

is discussed in References 2, 5, 7, and 18 listed at the end of this chapter.

A loop analysis of the circuit in Fig. 5–15 yields after some simplification

$$\frac{V_2}{V_1} = \frac{1 - Z_n(s)}{1 + Z_n(s)} \tag{5–97}$$

where $Z_n(s) = Z(s)/R$.

Now if $s = j\omega_1$, V_2 and V_1 may be interpreted as complex voltages of sinusoidal steady-state analysis. If in addition $Z = jX$ on the $j\omega$-

* The term *reciprocal* is also used in a different sense to identify networks which obey the reciprocity theorem. See Section 7–1, footnote to definition of *reciprocal twoport*.

axis, as indicated in Fig. 5–15, we find

$$\frac{V_2}{V_1} = \frac{1-jX_n}{1+jX_n} \tag{5–98}$$

where $X_n = X/R$.

From (5–98) we see at once that

$$\left|\frac{V_2}{V_1}\right| = 1 \tag{5–99}$$

Since this relation holds for all values of ω, the network is termed an *all-pass network*. We note, of course, that the output and input voltages differ in phase, so that the network offers a means of obtaining phase shift without attenuation.

The pole-zero configuration of an all-pass lattice is determined by the reactance X. However, much can be learned from general considerations which do not specify the particular reactance X to be used. These considerations are, in fact, of broader significance than the particular problem at hand.

As a first step we shall demonstrate a theorem regarding the even and odd character of the real and imaginary parts of network functions on the $j\omega$-axis. Basic to the proof is the fact that our network functions are ratios of polynomials in s with real coefficients (see Section 5–6). When $s = j\omega$, a function Z may be represented as

$$Z(j\omega) = R(\omega)+jX(\omega) \tag{5–100}$$

where R and X are the real and imaginary parts of Z. If ω is replaced by its negative in (5–100), we find

$$Z(-j\omega) = R(-\omega)+jX(-\omega) \tag{5–101}$$

If instead we replace j by its negative in (5–100), we find

$$Z(-j\omega) = R(\omega)-jX(\omega) \tag{5–102}$$

The left-hand sides of (5–101) and (5–102) are identical because $Z(j\omega)$ is a function in which $j\omega$ is the only variable, so that reversing the sign of j is identical in effect with reversing the sign of ω. From (5–101) and (5–102) we have at once

$$R(\omega) = R(-\omega) \tag{5–103}$$

$$X(\omega) = -X(-\omega) \tag{5–104}$$

Thus the real part of Z is even on the $j\omega$-axis, while the imaginary part is odd on that axis.

Now the impedance Z in our all-pass lattice reduces to jX on the $j\omega$-axis, i.e., it is ideally reactive. For this impedance, (5–100) and (5–102) yield

$$Z(j\omega) = jX(\omega) \tag{5–105}$$

and

$$Z(-j\omega) = -jX(\omega) \tag{5–106}$$

We now find

$$Z(j\omega) = -Z(-j\omega) \tag{5–107}$$

Further, if $j\omega$ is replaced by s in the expression for Z, we find

$$Z(s) = -Z(-s) \tag{5–108}$$

Hence, if the real part of Z is zero on the imaginary axis, Z is an odd function of s. We see then that if $Z_n(s)$ in equation (5–97) represents an ideally reactive network, replacement of s by its negative is equivalent to replacement of the right-hand side of (5–97) by its reciprocal. We conclude, therefore, that if a pole of V_2/V_1 occurs at s_1, a zero occurs at $-s_1$.

The ratio V_2/V_1 is the reciprocal of Z_T/R where Z_T is the transfer impedance V_1/I_2 in Fig. 5–15. The circuit of Fig. 5–15 is passive and, therefore, stable. The zeros of Z_T, then, cannot lie in the right half-plane (see Section 5–6). The current i_2 cannot be sustained without a driving function because of the non-zero rate of energy dissipation $i_2{}^2R$. Hence the zeros of Z_T cannot lie on the $j\omega$-axis. Thus the zeros of Z_T or the poles of V_2/V_1 lie in the half-plane to the left of the $j\omega$-axis.

As a result of these considerations, we find that the ratio V_2/V_1 is characterized by the following pole-zero arrangement. If a pole occurs in the second quadrant at $-\alpha+j\beta$, another is found at the conjugate point $-\alpha-j\beta$. In addition, a zero appears at $\alpha-j\beta$ and at the conjugate point to this one, $\alpha+j\beta$. The real axis acts as a mirror, the image of a pole or zero being a pole or zero at the conjugate point. The imaginary axis acts as a different sort of mirror, the image of a pole being a zero an equal distance to the right, and the image of a zero being a pole an equal distance to the left.

Figs. 5–16(a) and (b) show two examples of the all-pass lattice and the corresponding pole-zero configuration. In each case the dotted lines represent phasors. Each phasor is a factor in the expression for V_2/V_1, so that the sum of their angles, *with proper signs*, yields $\angle V_2 - \angle V_1$ at any value of ω. (Note that in Fig. 5–16(a) we have an additional π radians or 180° because of the minus sign in the expression for $(V_2/V_1)|_{s=j\omega}$.)

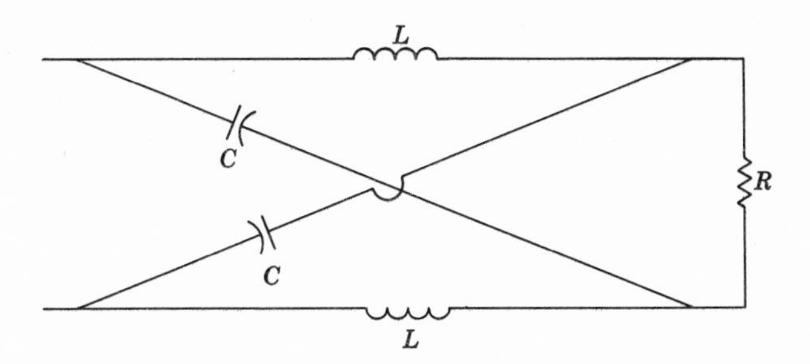

$$R^2 = \frac{L}{C}, \omega_0^2 = \frac{1}{LC}$$

$$\frac{V_2}{V_1} = -\frac{s-\omega_0}{s+\omega_0}, \left.\frac{V_2}{V_1}\right|_{s=j\omega} = -\frac{j\omega-\omega_0}{j\omega+\omega_0}$$

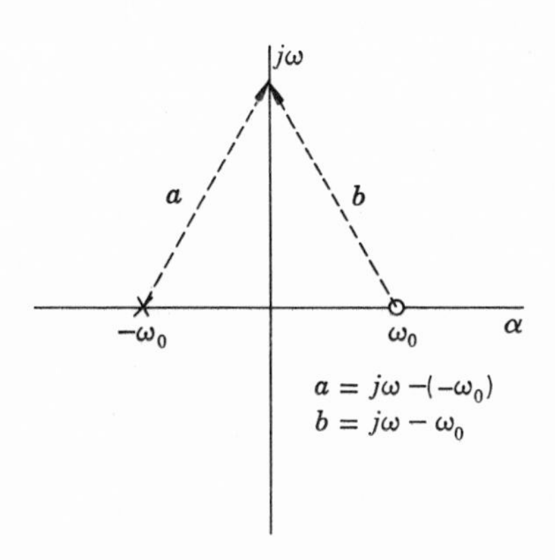

Fig. 5–16(a).

5-9 Relation Between Real and Imaginary Parts of the Driving-Point Impedance Z(jω)[2, 7, 18]

The real and imaginary parts of the driving-point impedance $Z(j\omega)$, used in sinusoidal steady-state analysis, are not entirely independent. The relationship is revealed when $Z(j\omega)$ is regarded as a special case of the more general function $Z(s)$. In the following development, $Z(s)$ is assumed to be a minimum-reactance impedance. On the $j\omega$-axis we have the form $Z(j\omega) = R(\omega)+jX(\omega)$. Two properties of $X(\omega)$ will be useful. These are

$$X(\infty) = 0 \tag{5–109}$$

$$X(0) = 0 \tag{5–110}$$

Since $X(\omega)$ is a ratio of polynomials in ω, we may write

$$X(\infty) = \lim_{\omega\to\infty} k\omega^n$$

Since $X(\omega)$ is an odd function (see equation 5–104), n is an odd number.

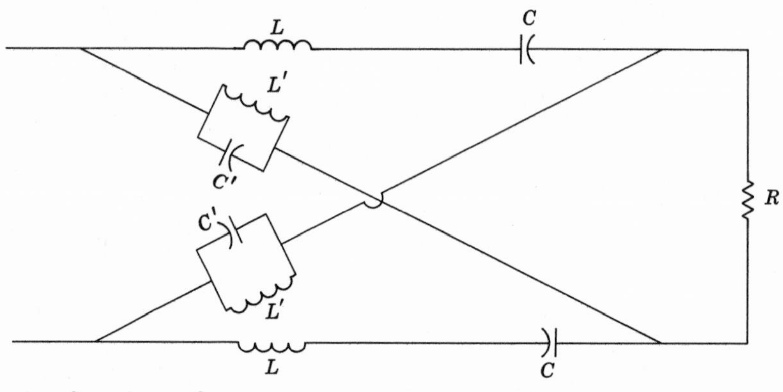

$L' = R^2 C,\ C' = L/R^2$

$$\frac{V_2}{V_1} = \frac{s^2 - 2\alpha_0 s + \omega_0^2}{s^2 + 2\alpha_0 s + \omega_0^2} = \frac{(s + r_1)(s + r_2)}{(s - r_1)(s - r_2)}$$

$$\left.\frac{V_2}{V_1}\right|_{s=j\omega} = \frac{(j\omega + r_1)(j\omega + r_2)}{(j\omega - r_1)(j\omega - r_2)}$$

$\omega_0^2 = 1/LC,\ \alpha_0 = R/2L$

$r_1 = -\alpha_0 + j\beta$

$r_2 = -\alpha_0 - j\beta$

where $\beta = \sqrt{\omega_0^2 - \alpha_0^2}$

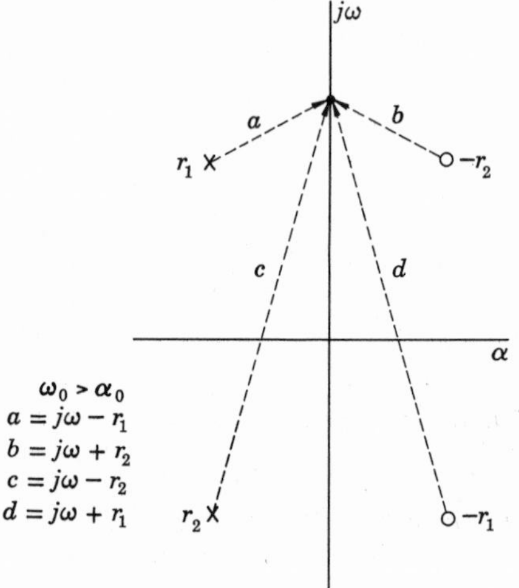

Fig. 5–16(b).

Since Z is minimum reactance, we cannot have a pole at $j\infty$, so that n must be negative and we have (5–109). We may also write

$$X(0) = \lim_{\omega\to 0} k'\omega^m$$

Repetition of the arguments given above shows that m is positive, and (5–110) is established.

In order to obtain the relationship between the real and imaginary parts of Z with a minimum of difficulty, we define

$$A(s) = \frac{Z(s) - Z(j\omega_0)}{s - j\omega_0} \tag{5–111}$$

where ω_0 is any fixed point on the $j\omega$-axis and where Z, as stated, is a minimum reactance impedance. Now the numerator of $A(s)$ is a ratio of

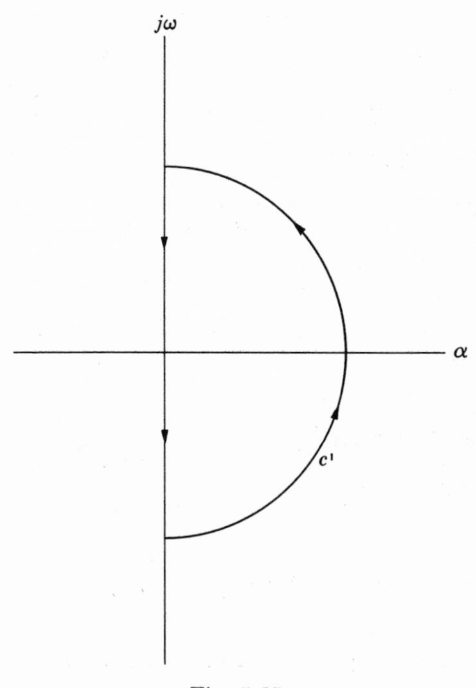

Fig. 5–17.

polynomials without singularities on the $j\omega$-axis or in the right half-plane. Further, this numerator has a zero at $s = j\omega_0$, so that the denominator, $s - j\omega_0$, does not introduce a pole. The Cauchy–Goursat theorem (Section 3–9), therefore, applies to the closed contour, Fig. 5–17, and

$$\oint \frac{Z(s) - Z(j\omega_0)}{s - j\omega_0} ds = 0 \tag{5–112}$$

On the semicircular arc, the magnitude of s is constant, so that the polar form $|s|e^{j\theta}$ yields $ds = j|s|e^{j\theta}\,d\theta$ (see Section 3–8, discussion of equations 3–36 and 3–37). We now find, with c' representing the semicircular arc, that

$$\lim_{|s|\to\infty} \oint_{c'} \frac{Z(s)-Z(j\omega_0)}{s-j\omega_0}\,ds = \lim_{|s|\to\infty} \int_{-\pi/2}^{\pi/2} \frac{Z(s)-Z(j\omega_0)}{|s|e^{j\theta}-j\omega_0}\,j|s|e^{j\theta}\,d\theta$$

$$= j[Z(\infty)-Z(j\omega_0)] \int_{-\pi/2}^{\pi/2} d\theta = j\pi[Z(\infty)-Z(j\omega_0)] \qquad (5\text{–}113)$$

With the aid of (5–112) we have for the integral along the $j\omega$-axis

$$\int_{-j\infty}^{j\infty} \frac{Z(j\omega)-Z(j\omega_0)}{j\omega-j\omega_0}\,dj\omega = j\pi[Z(\infty)-Z(j\omega_0)] \qquad (5\text{–}114)$$

If we integrate with respect to ω instead of $j\omega$, equation (5–114) becomes

$$\int_{-\infty}^{\infty} \frac{Z(j\omega)-Z(j\omega_0)}{\omega-\omega_0}\,d\omega = j\pi[Z(\infty)-Z(j\omega_0)] \qquad (5\text{–}114\text{a})$$

where it is understood that $Z(j\omega)$ must be expressed as $R(\omega)+jX(\omega)$ before the integration can be carried out. Now writing (5–114a) in terms of real and imaginary parts, dividing both sides by π, and introducing (5–109), we have

$$\frac{1}{\pi}\int_{-\infty}^{\infty} \frac{R(\omega)-R(\omega_0)}{\omega-\omega_0}\,d\omega = X(\omega_0) \qquad (5\text{–}115)$$

and

$$\frac{1}{\pi}\int_{-\infty}^{\infty} \frac{X(\omega)-X(\omega_0)}{\omega-\omega_0}\,d\omega = R(\infty)-R(\omega_0) \qquad (5\text{–}116)$$

We therefore conclude that for a minimum reactance impedance:

(a) The reactance at any one frequency, $\omega_0/2\pi$ c.p.s., is determined by specification of the resistance at all frequencies.

(b) The resistance at any one frequency, $\omega_0/2\pi$ c.p.s., is determined by specification of (1) the resistance at infinite frequency and (2) the reactance at all frequencies.

Two special cases are of interest. When $\omega_0 = 0$, equation (5–116) yields, with the aid of (5–110),

$$\frac{1}{\pi}\int_{-\infty}^{\infty} \frac{X(\omega)}{\omega}\,d\omega = R(\infty)-R(0) \qquad (5\text{–}117)$$

and, since $X(\omega)$ is odd (see 5–104), $X(\omega)/\omega$ is even, so that (5–117) yields

$$\frac{2}{\pi}\int_0^{\infty} \frac{X(\omega)}{\omega} d\omega = R(\infty) - R(0) \tag{5–118}$$

Thus the resistance change between zero and infinite frequency is measured by the area under the curve of $X(\omega)/\omega$.

A second special case is obtained if we multiply (5–115) by ω_0 and take the limit of both sides as ω_0 increases without limit. We find

$$-\frac{1}{\pi}\int_{-\infty}^{\infty} [R(\omega) - R(\infty)]\, dw = \lim_{\omega_0 \to \infty} \omega_0 X(\omega_0) \tag{5–119}$$

The resistance $R(\omega)$ is even (see 5–103), as is the constant $R(\infty)$, so that equation (5–119) becomes

$$-\frac{2}{\pi}\int_0^{\infty} [R(\omega) - R(\infty)]\, d\omega = \lim_{\omega_0 \to \infty} \omega_0 X(\omega_0) \tag{5–120}$$

Now we consider a minimum reactance impedance, which as a result of capacitance across its input terminals, has the property

$$\lim_{\omega_0 \to \infty} Z = \lim_{\omega_0 \to \infty} j\left(-\frac{1}{\omega_0 C}\right) = 0 \tag{5–121}$$

where $j(-1/\omega_0 C)$ is the approximate value of Z for large ω. We then find, using $R(\infty) = 0$, that

$$\frac{2}{\pi}\int_0^{\infty} R(\omega)\, d\omega = \frac{1}{C} \tag{5–122}$$

This result is known as the *resistance integral theorem.*

The relations developed between the real and imaginary components of a minimum reactance impedance show that the behavior of a network function on the $j\omega$-axis depends on its properties as a function of the complex variable s. The same fact was clear in a simpler situation in Section 5–8, where the behavior of a series resonant circuit and of an all-pass lattice was seen to depend on the location of poles and zeros in the complex plane.

There are a number of additional relations between the real and imaginary components of network functions. These will be found in such sources as References 2, 7, and 18.

5-10 Summary

This chapter dealt with the development of loop and node analysis and with the significance of the poles and zeros of complex functions arising in network problems. It was possible, since Kirchhoff's laws were stated in terms of Laplace transforms in Chapter 4, to present the loop and node circuit equations directly in terms of Laplace transforms of current and voltage. These equations were easily reinterpreted for sinusoidal steady-state problems. The interchange of equivalent voltage and current sources in terms of transforms was presented as an aid in loop and node analysis.

The loop equations were developed through a specific example designed to bring out their general form. The role of non-zero initial conditions was also studied with the help of this example. The expression for the correct number of loop equations for any circuit was derived. Methods of selecting loops to yield equations which would be independent, as well as correct in number, were presented and justified. It was shown that the simple loops of a planar network yield independent equations which are correct in number. It was also shown that with the aid of a *tree* we can properly choose the loops in any network, planar or non-planar. The distinction between the loop equations of passive circuits consisting of bilateral elements, and the loop equations of active circuits was brought out, and active circuits were illustrated with both a vacuum-tube and a transistor equivalent circuit.

The advantage of the node method of analysis for vacuum-tube circuits was seen through an example. The node analysis of a circuit containing an ideal e.m.f. was also demonstrated. The loop and node equations for coils coupled through mutual magnetic flux were worked out as a separate topic, with inclusion of the case of perfectly coupled coils. An example of the node analysis of a circuit containing mutual inductance was then carried out.

In the final sections of this chapter, circuit response was classified in accordance with the location and order of the poles of the Laplace transforms representing response; the possible distributions of poles and zeros of network functions were considered; the significance of poles and zeros in steady-state analysis was studied; and the relationship between the real and imaginary parts of a minimum reactance driving-point impedance was derived, with the resistance integral theorem obtained as a special case.

Problems

5-1. The circuit in the figure shows branch currents and loop currents. For the purpose of this problem, do *not* replace the parallel resistors R_3 and R_7 by a single resistance.

(A) Write the Kirchhoff voltage and current law equations in terms of branch currents.

(B) Eliminate the branch currents I_4, I_5, and I_6. Retain I_1, I_2, I_3+I_7, and I_7. When this is carried out, the identity $R_3 I_3 \equiv R_3(I_3+I_7)-R_3 I_7$ will be useful.

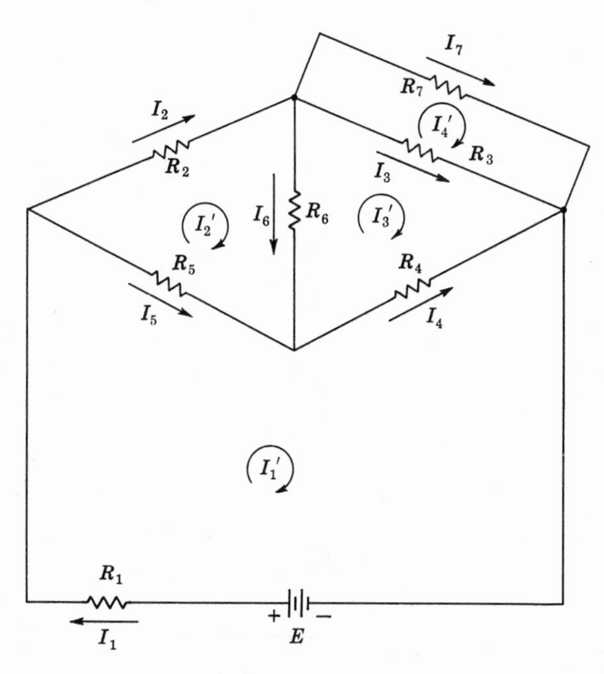

Problem 5–1.

(C) Identify the retained currents with the loop currents I_1', I_2', I_3', and I_4'.

(D) Are the loop equations for I_1', I_2', I_3', and I_4' independent? (Justify your answer.)

(E) Is it necessary, for independence of loop equations, to have at least one branch in each loop which is not common to any other loop?

5-2. A certain tree is drawn on a one-part network. Loops are then chosen in the manner discussed in this chapter in connection with the tree. How many sets of such loops can be drawn, or is the choice of loops unique?

5-3. Draw a tree and show the corresponding choice of loops for a network of each of the following types:

(A) Series circuit
(B) Parallel circuit
(C) Series–parallel circuit
(D) Non-series–parallel but planar circuit
(E) Non-planar circuit.

5-4. The figure shows the linear equivalent of a vacuum-tube circuit. The susceptance of interelectrode capacitances and the reactance of a blocking capacitor have been neglected. Obtain the gain, defined as E_L/E_s by means of loop analysis.

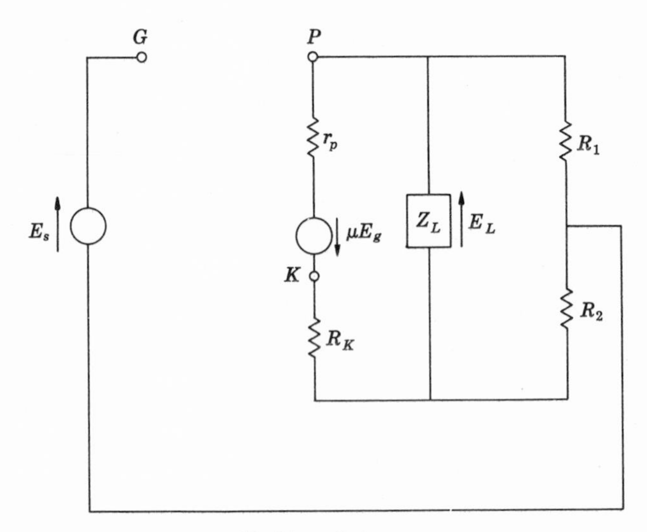

Problem 5–4.

5-5. Repeat Problem 5–4 but use node analysis.

5-6. The input current response to a unit-step voltage is calculated for each of several circuits. The e.m.f. source is ideal. In each case we find that for t greater than zero, the response consists of one term. For circuits (a), (b), (c), and (d), the response is, respectively, (a) Ke^{-10t}, (b) Kt, (c) Ke^{10t}, (d) $Ke^{-10t} \sin \omega_0 t$.

(A) Which circuits are stable? Use the term *stable* as defined in this chapter.

(B) Do these circuits remain stable when their input terminals are short-circuited?

(C) For each stable case, sketch a possible circuit.

5-7. Let driving-point impedance and admittance be defined as response functions (see comment at the end of Section 5–6). Starting with these definitions, establish statements (a), (b), (c), (d), (e), (f), (g), and (h) of Section 5–6. Note that (e) and (f) have been established in the comment referred to above.

5-8. The circuit in the figure consists of passive bilateral elements. No mutual inductance is present. Defining transfer impedance as $Z_T = E/I$ where the transforms E and I are shown in the figure, prove that none of the poles of Z_T

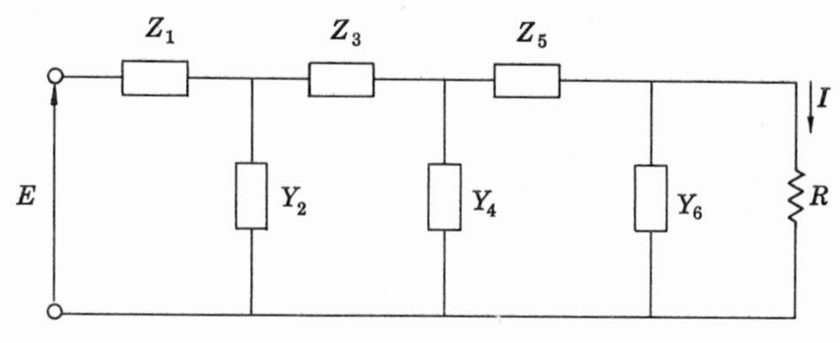

Problem 5-8.

lie in the right half-plane. (Note that with this definition of Z_T, only zeros are excluded from the right half-plane by the stability requirement in the general case.)

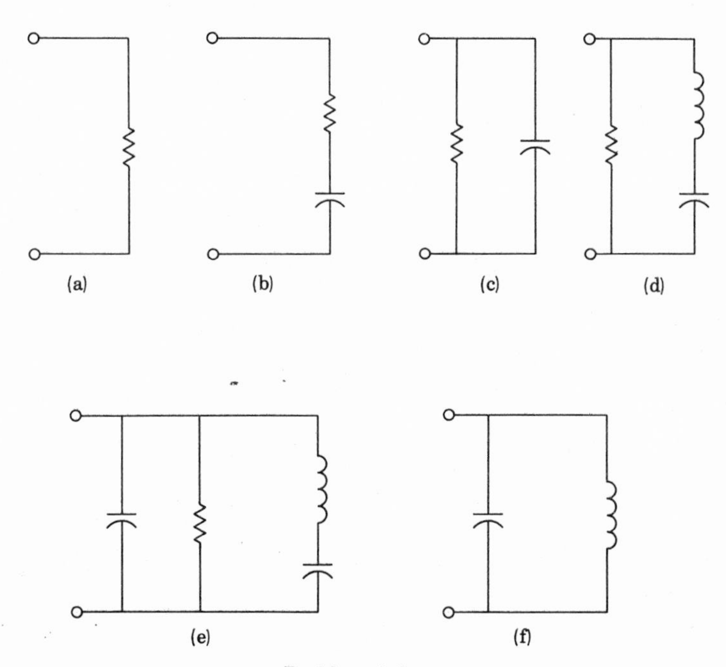

Problem 5-9.

5-9. To which of the circuits in the figure does the resistance integral theorem apply? Justify each answer.

5-10. The figure shows a linear equivalent circuit of a grounded-cathode tube in which grid-plate interelectrode capacitance and source impedance have been neglected. The impedance Z includes the parallel combination of load impedance, the plate resistance r_p, and the plate-cathode interelectrode capacitance. Assume Z to be minimum reactance. If the magnitude of the real component of the gain is greater than a real constant K over the frequency range $0 < f < f_1$, prove that $f_1 K < (g_m/4C)$ where C is the parallel combination of plate-cathode interelectrode capacitance and any other capacitance between plate and cathode.

NOTE: Grid-cathode impedance is not shown in the figure since it cannot affect the gain with the approximations stated above.

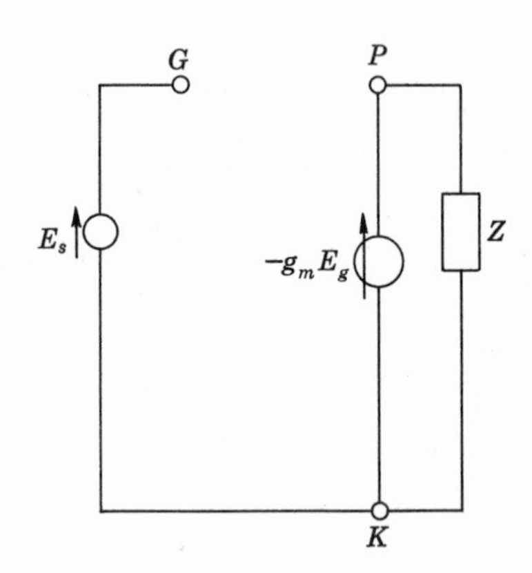

Problem 5–10.

References for Chapter 5

1. Blecher, F. H., "Design Principles for Single Loop Transistor Amplifiers," IRE *Trans. Circuit Theory*, Vol. CT-4, pp. 145–156 (Sept. 1957).
2. Bode, H. W., *Network Analysis and Feedback Amplifier Design*, D. Van Nostrand Co., Inc., Princeton, N.J., 1945.
3. Gardner, M. F., and Barnes, J. L., *Transients in Linear Systems*, John Wiley & Sons, Inc., New York, 1942.
4. Goldman, S., *Transformation Calculus and Electrical Transients*, Prentice-Hall, Inc., New York, 1949.
5. Guillemin, E. A., *Communication Networks*, Vols. I and II, John Wiley & Sons, Inc., New York, 1931, 1935.
6. Guillemin, E. A., *Introductory Circuit Theory*, John Wiley & Sons, Inc., New York, 1953.
7. Guillemin, E. A., *Synthesis of Passive Networks*, John Wiley & Sons, Inc., New York, 1957.
8. LeCorbeiller, P., *Matrix Analysis of Electric Networks*, Harvard University Press, Cambridge, 1950.
9. LePage, W. R., and Seely, S., *General Network Analysis*, McGraw-Hill Book Co., Inc., New York, 1952.

10. Members of the Staff of the Department of Electrical Engineering, Massachusetts Institute of Technology, *Applied Electronics*, John Wiley & Sons, Inc., New York, 1943; Gray, T. S., *Applied Electronics*, 2nd ed., John Wiley & Sons, Inc., New York 1954.
11. Pritchard, R. L., "Electric-Network Representation of Transistors—A. Survey," IRE *Trans. Circuit Theory*, Vol. CT-3, pp 5–21 (March 1956).
12. Reich, H. J., *Theory and Application of Electron Tubes*, 2nd ed., McGraw-Hill Book Co., Inc., New York, 1944.
13. Seely, S., *Electron-Tube Circuits*, McGraw-Hill Book Co., Inc., New York, 1950; 2nd ed., 1958.
14. Seshu, S., and Balabanian, N., *Linear Network Analysis*, John Wiley & Sons, Inc., New York, 1959.
15. Shea, R. F., Editor, *Transistor Circuit Engineering*, John Wiley & Sons, Inc., New York, 1957.
16. Skilling, H. H., *Electrical Engineering Circuits*, John Wiley & Sons, Inc., New York, 1957.
17. Terman, F. E., *Radio Engineers' Handbook*, McGraw-Hill Book Co., Inc., New York, 1943.
18. Tuttle, D. F., Jr., *Network Synthesis*, Vol. I, John Wiley & Sons, Inc., New York, 1958.
19. Van Valkenburg, M. E., *Network Analysis*, Prentice-Hall, Inc., Englewood Cliffs, N.J., 1955.
20. Ware, L. A., and Town, G. R., *Electrical Transients*, The Macmillan Co., New York, 1954.
21. Institute of Radio Engineers, "Standards on Circuits: Definitions of Terms in Network Topology, 1950," *Proc.* IRE, Vol. 39, pp. 27–29 (1951).
22. Institute of Radio Engineers, "IRE Standards on Circuits: Definitions of Terms for Linear Passive Reciprocal Time Invariant Networks, 1960," *Proc.* IRE, Vol. 48, pp. 1608–10 (Sept. 1960).

Chapter 6

NETWORK THEOREMS

The methods of loop and node analysis developed in Chapter 5 are entirely general. Either method may be used to set up the equations for a linear active or linear passive circuit regardless of whether a general problem or a problem involving only the sinusoidal steady state is involved. Because of the general nature of loop and node analysis, we can solve a whole class of network problems, obtaining the solution in the form of a theorem. Such network theorems, in turn, often simplify the analysis of specific circuits, and clarify their physical interpretation.

In the present chapter we shall derive and state network theorems in terms of Laplace transforms of voltages and currents. The use of transforms will make the effect of initial conditions immediately evident, while a simple redefinition of symbols will lead to conclusions for the sinusoidal steady state. The distinction drawn in Chapter 5 between the equations for linear passive circuits consisting of bilateral elements and those for linear active circuits will yield a proper interpretation of each theorem for these two cases.

6-1 Equations of the General Network

The equations of loop analysis, developed in Section 5–2 in connection with a 3-loop network, can be written for n loops.

$$\begin{aligned}
E_1 &= Z_{11}I_1 + Z_{12}I_2 + \cdots + Z_{1n}I_n \\
E_2 &= Z_{21}I_1 + Z_{22}I_2 + \cdots + Z_{2n}I_n \\
&\vdots \\
E_n &= Z_{n1}I_1 + Z_{n2}I_2 + \cdots + Z_{nn}I_n
\end{aligned} \qquad (6\text{–}1)$$

where the rth equation ($r = 1, 2, \ldots, n$) represents Kirchhoff's voltage law applied to the loop for which loop current i_r is drawn.

These loop equations and corresponding node equations form the basis of theorems to be derived in the present chapter. The meaning of the symbols in the equations, the role of initial conditions as sources, and the handling of dependent sources (as μe_g in the vacuum-tube equivalent)* were discussed in Chapter 5. It was also shown (Section 5–1) that, while it is not necessary, it is always possible (sometimes with the aid of an artifice or limiting process) to represent all sources as either current sources or as e.m.f. sources. Because of this possibility, *we can, when developing theorems, enjoy the convenience of assuming all sources to be of one type, without in this way limiting the generality of the theorems.*

We now turn to the derivation of several network theorems. Each will be interpreted both for transient analysis and for analysis of the sinusoidal steady state.

6-2 Superposition Theorem

The superposition theorem states in effect that the response to several sources of voltage or current is the sum of the responses to the individual sources, calculated as if each individual source acted alone. Both the theorem and its more precise statement can be obtained from the solution of equations (6–1) in determinant form. We shall show that the solution of these equations consists of a sum of terms each proportional to one of the E's.

Let us suppose that the loop current of interest has been numbered 1, so that we seek the transform I_1; it follows from (6–1) that

$$I_1 = \frac{\begin{vmatrix} E_1 & Z_{12} \cdots Z_{1n} \\ E_2 & Z_{22} \cdots Z_{2n} \\ \cdot & \cdot \quad\quad \cdot \\ \cdot & \cdot \quad\quad \cdot \\ \cdot & \cdot \quad\quad \cdot \\ E_n & Z_{n2} \cdots Z_{nn} \end{vmatrix}}{D} \tag{6–2}$$

where D, the determinant of the equations (6–1), is given by

$$D = \begin{vmatrix} Z_{11} & Z_{12} \cdots Z_{1n} \\ Z_{21} & Z_{22} \cdots Z_{2n} \\ \cdot & \cdot \quad\quad \cdot \\ \cdot & \cdot \quad\quad \cdot \\ \cdot & \cdot \quad\quad \cdot \\ Z_{n1} & Z_{n2} \cdots Z_{nn} \end{vmatrix}$$

* Where an alternative way of handling dependent sources can be used, this will be pointed out.

Expanding the numerator of (6–2) by cofactors of the first column leads to

$$I_1 = \frac{A_{11}}{D}E_1 + \frac{A_{21}}{D}E_2 + \cdots + \frac{A_{n1}}{D}E_n \tag{6–3}$$

Now since neither the cofactors $A_{11}, \ldots, A_{n1}$ nor the determinant D depend on the E's, we see that equation (6–3) is effectively a statement of the superposition theorem, for each term is the value to which I_1 reduces when the E's in all the other terms are zero. Hence I_1 is a sum of values individually calculated on the assumption that each E acts alone.

Two corollaries follow immediately from equation (6–3):

First, if one or more of the E's consists of several terms, the nature of (6–3) remains unaltered. Let us say that E_1 is a sum of two terms, one due to an initial condition, the other due to an applied e.m.f. Then $E_1 = E_1' + E_1''$, and $(A_{11}/D)E_1 = (A_{11}/D)E_1' + (A_{11}/D)E_1''$. Hence (6–3) will contain $n+1$ instead of n terms, but each is still the value to which I_1 reduces when the E's in all the other terms are zero.

Second, the theorem, although derived in terms of loop-current transforms, also applies to branch-current transforms. Suppose, for example, that a branch-current transform I_A is given by the relation

$$I_A = I_1 - I_2 + I_3$$

where I_1, I_2, and I_3 are loop-current transforms. Now I_1, I_2, and I_3 are each given by a sum of the form (6–3), i.e., a sum of terms each having an E multiplied by a constant. Clearly, then, I_A is also a sum of terms, each term having one of the E's as a factor, so that the superposition theorem applies again.

We may now put the theorem into words both for the general case and for the special case of the sinusoidal steady state.

> SUPERPOSITION THEOREM—GENERAL. The value of the Laplace transform of a current in a linear electric network may be obtained by adding the individual contributions calculated from each applied e.m.f. or current-source transform taken alone.

> SUPERPOSITION THEOREM—SINUSOIDAL STEADY STATE. The value of a complex current in a linear electric network may be obtained by adding the individual contributions calculated from each complex e.m.f. or current source taken alone.

Application of the Superposition Theorem to Electronic Circuits

The equations (6–1) are valid both for linear passive circuits consisting of bilateral elements, and for linear active circuits; the only difference between these cases is that the symmetrically placed off-diagonal coefficients need not all be equal in the electronic (active) circuit (for example, we may have $Z_{13} \neq Z_{31}$). Nothing in the derivation of the superposition theorem made reference to the equality or inequality of these coefficients, so that the result must apply to both types of circuit.

It is important to note, however, that when the loop equations were developed in Section 5–2, a distinction was made between *independent sources* and *dependent sources*. The latter are sources such as μe_g in the vacuum-tube equivalent circuit, whose transforms are determined when the transforms of the independent sources ($E_1, \ldots, E_n$ in equations (6–1)) are specified. Basically, then, an n-loop network containing linear vacuum-tube or transistor equivalent circuits requires more than n equations, for there are n unknown loop current transforms and, in addition, a number of unknown dependent sources. However, when each dependent source is expressed in terms of one or more of the applied E's and/or IZ terms,* the number of equations in the set (6–1) is equal to the number of unknowns. Hence the superposition theorem *as derived* from (6–1) refers to superposition of the effects of applied sources.

An alternative approach is possible. The loop equations can be written as if the value of each dependent source were known. Formal solution of these equations will then yield a sum of terms, indicating that superposition applies to dependent sources as well as to others. However, the result is only temporary, since the final solution to a specific problem is obtained when each dependent source has been eliminated by substitution.

Examples of the Superposition Theorem: (a) *Output Voltage of a Difference Amplifier*[12]

The amplifier whose circuit and small-signal equivalent circuit are shown in Fig. 6–1(a) and (b) produces an output voltage proportional to the difference between two signal voltages. The signals e_1 and e_2 are applied to the grids G_1 and G_2 of tubes 1 and 2 respectively. The tube coefficients are equal, as are the plate load resistors shown as R_L. The output voltage we seek is $e_{p1} - e_{p2}$, i.e., the potential difference between the points P_1 and P_2, in the small-signal equivalent circuit of Fig. 6–1(b).

We shall assume that the frequency content of the applied signals is sufficiently low so that capacitance can be omitted from the equivalent circuit. With the resulting purely resistive circuit, there is, of course, no difficulty in writing and solving the circuit equations directly in terms of

* In some developments we require that dependent sources be expressed in terms of response alone, in the general circuit.

instantaneous values of voltage and current. However, for consistency with our general method, the circuit equations will be written in terms of voltage and current transforms.

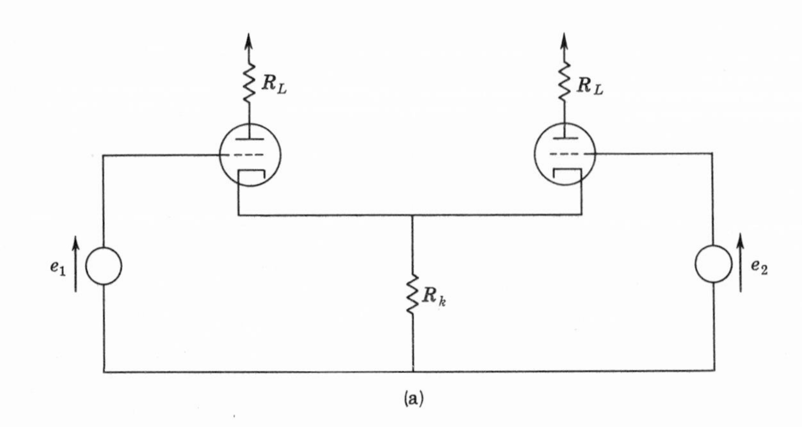

(a)

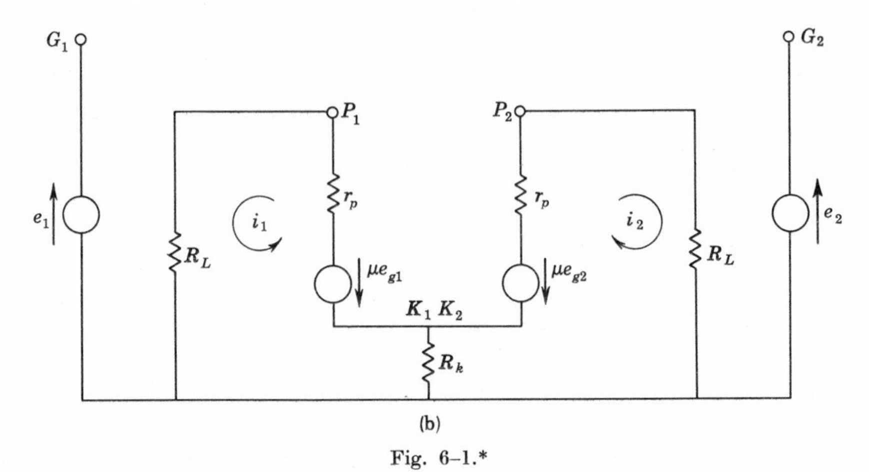

(b)

Fig. 6–1.*

In order to solve with the aid of the superposition theorem, we first assume $e_2 = 0$ and write the equations for the loop current transforms as

$$-\mu E_{g1} = (R_L + r_p + R_k)I_1 + R_k I_2 \tag{6–4}$$

$$-\mu E_{g2} = R_k I_1 + (R_L + r_p + R_k)I_2 \tag{6–5}$$

The dependent quantities E_{g1} and E_{g2} may be expressed by the equations:

* Fig. 6–1 follows, with slight modification, Fig. 6–20 of Seely,[12] by permission of McGraw-Hill Book Company, Inc.

$$E_{g1} = E_1 + (I_1 + I_2)R_k \tag{6-6}$$

$$E_{g2} = (I_1 + I_2)R_k \tag{6-7}$$

Equation (6–7) is based on the assumption $e_2 = 0$.

Substituting (6–6 and 7) into (6–4 and 5) yields

$$-\mu E_1 = [R_L + r_p + (1+\mu)R_k]I_1 + (1+\mu)R_k I_2 \tag{6-8}$$

$$0 = (1+\mu)R_k I_1 + [R_L + r_p + (1+\mu)R_k]I_2 \tag{6-9}$$

The equality of the off-diagonal coefficients $(1+\mu)R_k$ is a result of the symmetry of the particular circuit and not a general network property as in the case of passive circuits consisting of bilateral elements.

Now in order to denote the Laplace transforms of the voltages across the resistors R_L in Fig. 6–1(b), we shall use a double subscript notation, thus: E_{p11}, E_{p21}, E_{p12}, and E_{p22} = the transforms of the voltages across R_L connected to tube 1 when only e_1 acts, to tube 2 when only e_1 acts, to tube 1 when only e_2 acts, and to tube 2 when only e_2 acts, respectively. Hence

$$E_{p11} = I_1 R_L \tag{6-10}$$

$$E_{p21} = I_2 R_L \tag{6-11}$$

where I_1 and I_2 are solutions of equations (6–8) and (6–9). We then obtain directly

$$E_{p11} = \frac{-\mu E_1 R_L[R_L + r_p + (1+\mu)R_k]}{D} \tag{6-12}$$

and

$$E_{p21} = \frac{\mu E_1(1+\mu)R_k R_L}{D} \tag{6-13}$$

where

$$D = \begin{vmatrix} R_L + r_p + (1+\mu)R_k & (1+\mu)R_k \\ (1+\mu)R_k & R_L + r_p + (1+\mu)R_k \end{vmatrix}$$

and is the determinant of equations (6–8) and (6–9). The transform of the potential difference across the points P_1 and P_2 is, under the assumption $e_2 = 0$, given by

$$E_{p11} - E_{p21} = \frac{-\mu E_1 R_L[R_L + r_p + 2(1+\mu)R_k]}{D} \tag{6-14}$$

Now if the signal e_2 acts and $e_1 = 0$, it is evident from the symmetry of the circuit that the same result will be obtained, save for the fact that the subscripts 1 and 2 must be interchanged wherever they appear. Hence we have at once

$$E_{p22}-E_{p12} = \frac{-\mu E_2 R_L[R_L+r_p+2(1+\mu)R_k]}{D} \tag{6–15}$$

where E_{p22} and E_{p12} are the voltage transforms across the right- and left-hand load resistors, respectively, and e_1 is assumed to be zero. Now employing the superposition principle, we know that when both signals, e_1 and e_2, act, we have $E_{p1} = E_{p11}+E_{p12}$ and $E_{p2} = E_{p21}+E_{p22}$. Hence $E_{p1}-E_{p2}$ is obtained by subtracting (6–15) from (6–14) with the result

$$E_{p1}-E_{p2} = \frac{-\mu R_L[R_L+r_p+2(1+\mu)R_k](E_1-E_2)}{D} \tag{6–16}$$

Expanding the determinant D leads to the simpler expression

$$E_{p1}-E_{p2} = \frac{-\mu R_L}{R_L+r_p}(E_1-E_2) \tag{6–17}$$

Taking inverse transforms, we see that, at any instant,

$$e_{p1}-e_{p2} = \frac{-\mu R_L}{R_L+r_p}(e_1-e_2) \tag{6–18}$$

The sinusoidal steady-state solution in terms of complex voltages is also given by (6–17) if the E's are interpreted as complex voltages.

Examples of the Superposition Theorem: (b) *Circuit with an Initial Condition*

Since the e.m.f. transforms $E_1, \ldots, E_n$ in equations (6–1) may include terms representing initial conditions, it is evident that the effects of initial currents in inductances and voltages across capacitances can be obtained by superposition. As a simple illustration of this procedure, let us find the Laplace transform of the current in the resistor R_2 of the circuit of Fig. 6–2. Using the superposition theorem, we first ignore the initial current in the inductance. The equations for the current transforms then become

$$\frac{V}{s} = (R_1+R_3+Ls)I_1'-(R_3+Ls)I_2' \tag{6–19}$$

$$0 = -(R_3+Ls)I_1'+(R_2+R_3+Ls)I_2' \tag{6–20}$$

Now ignoring the source voltage, but considering the initial condition, we obtain

$$Li_0 = (R_1+R_3+Ls)I_1'' - (R_3+Ls)I_2'' \tag{6–21}$$

$$-Li_0 = -(R_3+Ls)I_1'' + (R_2+R_3+Ls)I_2'' \tag{6–22}$$

where $i_0 = V/(R_1+R_3)$. Writing D for the network determinant, which, of course, is the same for the pair of equations (6–19) and (6–20) as for the pair (6–21) and (6–22), we find

$$I_2' = \frac{V}{D}\left(\frac{R_3}{s}+L\right) \tag{6–23}$$

$$I_2'' = -\frac{R_1 L i_0}{D} \tag{6–24}$$

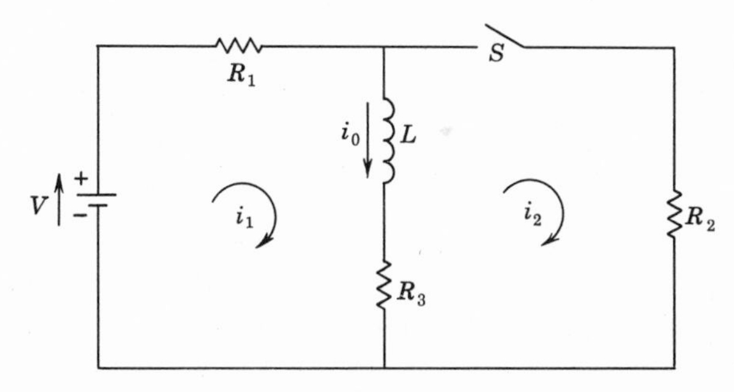

Fig. 6–2. S closes at $t = 0$. Steady state established prior to closing S.

The Laplace transform of the current in R_2 is, by the superposition principle, $I_2 = I_2' + I_2''$ so that

$$I_2 = VR_3\left(\frac{1}{s} + \frac{L}{R_1+R_3}\right)\frac{1}{D} \tag{6–25}$$

where i_0 has been replaced by $V/(R_1+R_3)$. The expansion of the network determinant yields

$$D = L(R_1+R_2)s + R_1R_2 + R_2R_3 + R_3R_1$$

The expression for the instantaneous current is easily obtained by the residue method developed in Chapter 3 and illustrated in Chapter 4. Alternatively, the transform may first be split into its simplest terms by the partial fraction expansion of Chapter 3. For either procedure, we note that simple poles occur at $s = 0$ and at

$$s = -(R_1R_2 + R_2R_3 + R_3R_1)/L(R_1+R_2)$$

Hence the expression for i_2 is directly determined as

$$i_2 = VR_3\left[\frac{1}{R_1R_2+R_2R_3+R_3R_1}(1-e^{-\alpha t})+\frac{1}{(R_1+R_3)(R_1+R_2)}e^{-\alpha t}\right] \quad (6\text{–}26)$$

where $\alpha = (R_1R_2+R_2R_3+R_3R_1)/L(R_1+R_2)$.

It is of interest to note that the loop current i_2 jumps from the value zero to the value $VR_3/(R_1+R_3)(R_1+R_2)$ at the instant of switching. Since the current in the inductance is continuous, the loop current i_1 also suffers a discontinuity at $t = 0$, so that

$$\lim_{t\to 0}(i_1-i_2) = i_0$$

where the limit is taken as t reduces to zero through positive values.

Comment on the Use of the Superposition Principle in Circuit Problems

The principle of superposition is, of course, interesting, and adds to the understanding of linear electric network behavior. While many problems are solved more speedily by direct application of the loop and node equations, the superposition theorem will have certain uses. It will be of help in the recognition of erroneous results, since an answer to a linear electric network problem must be consistent with the superposition principle. It will also prove useful where one already has the solution to a linear electric network problem, and wishes to find the effect of an added voltage or initial condition.

6-3 Reciprocity Theorem

The reciprocity theorem, valid for passive circuits consisting of bilateral elements, states in effect that if we interchange the location of an ideal e.m.f., in a circuit free of other sources, with the location of an impedanceless ammeter, the reading of the latter will remain unchanged. This theorem highlights the major distinction between the linear passive circuit consisting of bilateral elements and circuits with nonbilateral elements. It will be derived directly from the equations of an n-loop network given in (6–1), and will be stated and interpreted in the light of the meanings attached to the symbols used in those equations.

In equations (6–1), we can consider the case where

$$E_2 = E_3 = \cdots = E_n = 0$$

and $E_1 = E \neq 0$. We then have as network equations

$$\begin{aligned} E &= Z_{11}I_1 + Z_{12}I_2 + \cdots + Z_{1n}I_n \\ 0 &= Z_{21}I_1 + Z_{22}I_2 + \cdots + Z_{2n}I_n \\ &\vdots \\ 0 &= Z_{n1}I_1 + Z_{n2}I_2 + \cdots + Z_{nn}I_n \end{aligned} \tag{6–1a}$$

Solving (6–1a) for I_2 yields directly

$$I_2 = \frac{\begin{vmatrix} Z_{11} & E \cdots Z_{1n} \\ Z_{21} & 0 \cdots Z_{2n} \\ \vdots & \vdots \quad \vdots \\ Z_{n1} & 0 \cdots Z_{nn} \end{vmatrix}}{D} = \frac{EA_{12}}{D} \tag{6–27}$$

where the cofactor A_{12} equals the negative of the minor of the determinant D obtained by striking out the first row and second column. D is the determinant of the equations and does not depend either on E or on the particular current transform which is sought. Now if E appears in loop 2 and we solve for I_1, equations (6–1) become

$$\begin{aligned} 0 &= Z_{11}I_1 + Z_{12}I_2 + \cdots + Z_{1n}I_n \\ E &= Z_{21}I_1 + Z_{22}I_2 + \cdots + Z_{2n}I_n \\ &\vdots \\ 0 &= Z_{n1}I_1 + Z_{n2}I_2 + \cdots + Z_{nn}I_n \end{aligned} \tag{6–1b}$$

and

$$I_1 = \frac{\begin{vmatrix} 0 & Z_{12} \cdots Z_{1n} \\ E & Z_{22} \cdots Z_{2n} \\ \vdots & \vdots \quad \vdots \\ 0 & Z_{n2} \cdots Z_{nn} \end{vmatrix}}{D} = \frac{EA_{21}}{D} \tag{6–28}$$

where A_{21} equals the negative of the minor of the determinant D obtained by striking out the second row and first column. Now let us suppose that the coefficients Z are characterized by the relationship

$$Z_{rs} = Z_{sr} \tag{6–29}$$

where $r = 1, \ldots, n$ and $s = 1, \ldots, n$. *This relationship is characteristic of equations* (6–1) *when they are written for passive circuits consisting of bilateral elements.*

We can easily demonstrate that if (6–29) is true, the cofactor A_{21} in (6–28) is equal to the cofactor A_{12} in (6–27) thus

$$A_{21} = -\begin{vmatrix} Z_{12} & Z_{13} \cdots Z_{1n} \\ Z_{32} & Z_{33} \cdots Z_{3n} \\ \cdot & \cdot \quad\quad \cdot \\ \cdot & \cdot \quad\quad \cdot \\ \cdot & \cdot \quad\quad \cdot \\ Z_{n2} & Z_{n3} \cdots Z_{nn} \end{vmatrix} = -\begin{vmatrix} Z_{21} & Z_{31} \cdots Z_{n1} \\ Z_{23} & Z_{33} \cdots Z_{n3} \\ \cdot & \cdot \quad\quad \cdot \\ \cdot & \cdot \quad\quad \cdot \\ \cdot & \cdot \quad\quad \cdot \\ Z_{2n} & Z_{3n} \cdots Z_{nn} \end{vmatrix} \tag{6–30}$$

where the interchange of subscripts for each Z makes no change when (6–29) holds. Since the value of a determinant is unaltered if we interchange rows and columns,(6) we have

$$A_{21} = -\begin{vmatrix} Z_{21} & Z_{23} \cdots Z_{2n} \\ Z_{31} & Z_{33} \cdots Z_{3n} \\ \cdot & \cdot \quad\quad \cdot \\ \cdot & \cdot \quad\quad \cdot \\ \cdot & \cdot \quad\quad \cdot \\ Z_{n1} & Z_{n3} \cdots Z_{nn} \end{vmatrix} = A_{12} \tag{6–31}$$

It now follows from equations (6–27) and (6–28) that, if the symmetry property $Z_{rs} = Z_{sr}$ is valid, the value of I_1 when E appears in the second equation equals the value of I_2 when E appears in the first equation. This reciprocity between the equations leads, after a few minor considerations, to a statement of the reciprocity theorem.

Since the numbering of loops is entirely arbitrary, it is evident that our result applies to the interchange of e.m.f. and current transforms in any two loops of the network. The choice of numbers 1 and 2 is a matter of convenience and does not limit the generality of the final result.

One may wish to apply the theorem to an e.m.f. transform and current transform at any two *branches* of the network. Since E appears in only one of the loop equations—see (6–1a) and (6–1b)—it is implied that the loops are so selected that E is in an independent branch, i.e., a branch not common to two loops, and that we can also draw our loops such that the branch current of interest lies in an independent branch. In that case, the loop current transform I_1 or I_2 equals the branch current transform, and the theorem will apply to e.m.f. and current transforms in two branches of the network.*

The internal impedance of a physical generator must always be regarded as one of the impedances of the network. In applying the principle of

* For the theorem to come out directly in terms of branch current transforms, one may begin with the node equations.

reciprocity, one must think of moving an ideal e.m.f. rather than a physical generator. This means that the reciprocity principle will have its prime use in the general interpretation of circuit properties, rather than in particular problems. Of course, when generator and load impedance are equal, this difficulty is obviated.

When the meanings of the symbols used in (6–1) are recalled, the principle of reciprocity is seen to apply both to Laplace transforms and to the complex quantities of the sinusoidal steady state. We must note that initial conditions are included among applied e.m.f. transforms. However, the fact that all circuit elements cannot exhibit the same initial condition must be considered. For example, if E in our equations equals Li_0, where i_0 is the initial current in a coil, this E, when moved to a new branch, can be proportional to initial current only if the new branch contains an inductance.

The theorem may now be stated both for the general case and for the sinusoidal steady state.

> Reciprocity Theorem—General. In a passive network of bilateral elements with only one applied e.m.f. transform, the position of the e.m.f. transform and any current transform may be interchanged without altering the value of the current transform.*

Note: An e.m.f. transform representing an initial condition at a certain circuit element may be moved only to a circuit element of the same type, if it is to represent an initial condition at the new element.

> Reciprocity Theorem—Sinusoidal Steady State. In a passive network of bilateral elements, with only one applied complex e.m.f., the position of the complex e.m.f. and any complex current may be interchanged without altering the value of the complex current.*

Examples of the Reciprocity Theorem: (a) *Two Simple Circuits—Steady Sinusoidal Voltage Applied*

In Fig. 6–3, the sinusoidal source impedance and load impedance are equal so that we may apply reciprocity between the source and load without separating the e.m.f. from the internal impedance of the source. From the reciprocity theorem we know at once that I_L in Fig. 6–3(a) is equal to I_L' in Fig. 6–3(b), so that the voltage ratio E/I_LR_0 is equal to $E/I_L'R_0$, i.e., the ratio of input to output voltage is the same in either

* Equations (6–1a) and (6–1b) imply that the e.m.f. has the same reference direction as the loop current in each loop (numbered 1 and 2) in which the e.m.f. is placed. Alternatively, if the e.m.f. is placed in loop 2 with its polarity in the opposite sense, the reciprocity theorem applies to the value of the reversed current in loop 1 (see Fig. 6–3).

direction. (The result can, of course, easily be checked by direct computation of the currents in the two figures.)

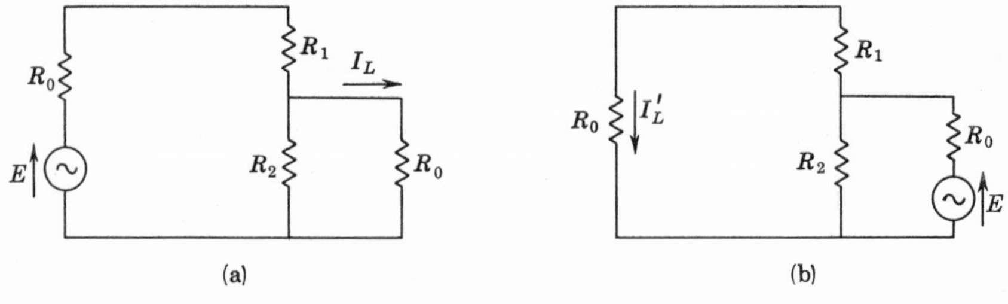

Fig. 6–3.

In the circuit of Fig. 6–4, the same result will apply. For simplicity, let us assume an ideal transformer with a turns ratio of 10:1. The output voltage in the circuit of Fig. 6–4(a) is clearly

$$\frac{E}{R_0 + 100R_0} \cdot 10R_0$$

while that in Fig. 6–4(b) is

$$\frac{E}{R_0 + \dfrac{1}{100}R_0} \cdot \frac{1}{10}R_0$$

These two expressions are equal.

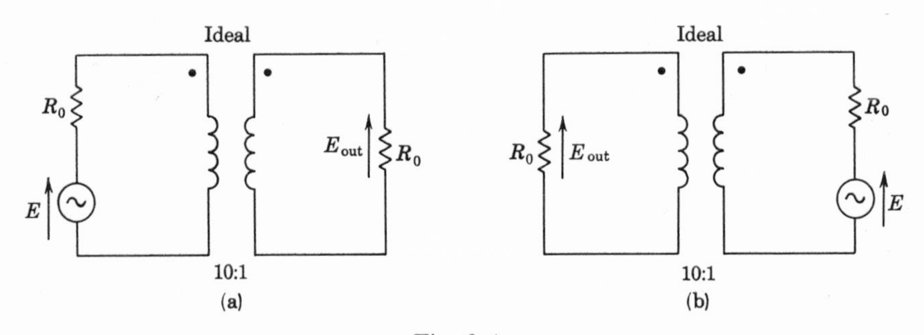

Fig. 6–4.

Examples of the Reciprocity Theorem: (b) *Application of the Reciprocity Theorem in a Transient Problem Involving an Initial Condition*

In the circuit of Fig. 6–5 we apply the reciprocity theorem to an initial charge on a condenser. The initial voltage across the capacitor C_1 is v_{C0} in Fig. 6–5(a) and is presumed to be equal to the initial voltage across C_2 in Fig. 6–5(b). The initial charges are, of course, unequal and in inverse proportion to the capacitances. From the reciprocity theorem we may state at once that the transform I_1' of the loop current i_1' in Fig. 6–5(b) is equal to the transform I_1 of the loop current i_1 in Fig. 6–5(a). If this is true of the transforms, it is also true of the instantaneous currents. It is of interest to verify the result. The circuit of Fig. 6–5(a) leads to the equations

$$\frac{v_{C0}}{s} = \left(R_1 + \frac{1}{C_1 s}\right) I_1 - R_1 I_2 \tag{6–32}$$

$$0 = -R_1 I_1 + \left(R_1 + R_2 + \frac{1}{C_2 s}\right) I_2 \tag{6–33}$$

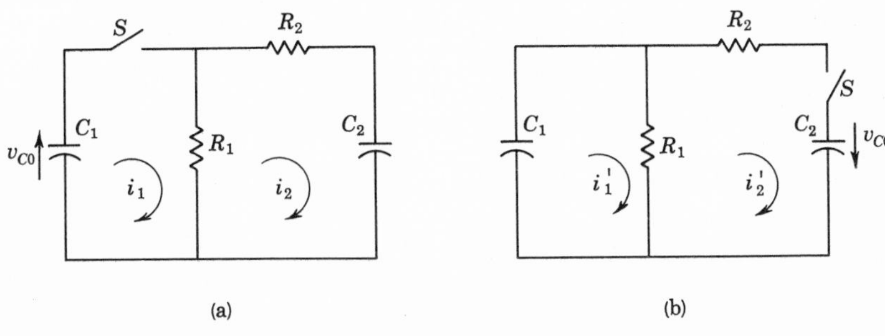

Fig. 6–5.

while the circuit of Fig. 6–5(b) yields the equations

$$0 = \left(R_1 + \frac{1}{C_1 s}\right) I_1' - R_1 I_2' \tag{6–34}$$

$$\frac{v_{C0}}{s} = -R_1 I_1' + \left(R_1 + R_2 + \frac{1}{C_2 s}\right) I_2' \tag{6–35}$$

Solving (6–32) and (6–33) for I_2 yields

$$I_2 = \frac{\begin{vmatrix} R_1 + \dfrac{1}{C_1 s} & \dfrac{v_{C0}}{s} \\ -R_1 & 0 \end{vmatrix}}{D} = \frac{v_{C0} R_1}{sD} \tag{6–36}$$

while solving (6–34) and (6–35) for I_1' results in

$$I_1' = \frac{\begin{vmatrix} 0 & -R_1 \\ \dfrac{v_{C0}}{s} & R_1 + R_2 + \dfrac{1}{C_2 s} \end{vmatrix}}{D} = \frac{v_{C0}\, R_1}{sD} \tag{6–37}$$

The equality of I_2 and I_1' again illustrates the reciprocity theorem.

The Role of the Reciprocity Theorem in Circuit Analysis

The reciprocity theorem, like the superposition principle, adds to general understanding of circuit behavior. In certain special problems, it will serve to save steps of analysis. In the next chapter, dealing with two-port networks, we shall define a ratio of forward to backward gain. The reciprocity theorem will be seen to represent the class of circuits in which this ratio reduces to 1.

6-4 Thévenin's and Norton's Theorems

Thévenin's and Norton's theorems state in effect that a linear network, supplying current to a load, may be replaced by a generator and an internal impedance which are equivalent to the original network for the purpose of calculating load current and voltage. When the equivalent generator consists of an e.m.f. source with internal impedance, the theorem is termed *Thévenin's*. The equivalent current-source representation is known as *Norton's theorem*. A more precise statement of these theorems will follow their derivation.

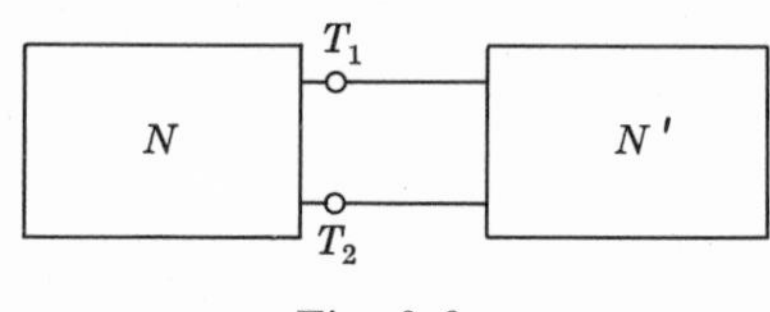

Fig. 6–6.

The terminology to be used in the derivation is simply stated:

(a) A network N has two accessible terminals termed *load terminals* (T_1, T_2 in Fig. 6–6).

(b) A second network N' may be connected to these terminals and is designated as *load*.

(c) The current through the load terminals and the voltage across them are termed *load current* and *voltage* respectively.

The symbols to be used are:

I_L = Laplace transform of load current.
V_L = Laplace transform of load voltage.

$I_{s.c.}$ = Laplace transform of short-circuit current through load terminals, i.e., the value of I_L when $V_L = 0$.

$V_{o.c.}$ = Laplace transform of open-circuit voltage across load terminals, i.e., the value of V_L when $I_L = 0$.

$Z_s = V_{o.c.}/I_{s.c.}$ This impedance is termed the *source impedance.*

$Y_s = 1/Z_s$. This admittance is termed the *source admittance.*

We shall assume that:

(1) The network N (Fig. 6–6) is linear.

(2) The parameters of N remain constant for all values of load current or voltage which occur.

(3) The load current and voltage, as well as all other currents and voltages of N, are Laplace transformable when the load is connected, disconnected, or shorted out.

(4) In sinusoidal steady-state analysis, the load current and voltage are sinusoids at the same frequency as all other currents and voltages of N. (In this case, transforms are, of course, replaced by the usual complex quantities of sinusoidal steady-state analysis.)

Assumption (2) is violated if instability with excessive voltage or current occurs when the load terminals of N are open, shorted, or connected to N'. Assumption (2) is also violated if N' contains a source which creates voltage or current of sufficient magnitude to alter or destroy N. It will be noted that assumption (3) is also a restriction on N' as well as N. Assumption (4), for the sinusoidal steady state, requires that N' be linear. Assumption (3), however, does not require a linear load, for the load voltage and current can each be a Laplace transformable time-function even with a nonlinear load N'.

The node equations are:

$$\begin{aligned} I_1 &= Y_{11}V_1 + Y_{12}V_2 + \cdots + Y_{1n}V_n \\ I_2 &= Y_{21}V_1 + Y_{22}V_2 + \cdots + Y_{2n}V_n \\ &\vdots \\ I_n &= Y_{n1}V_1 + Y_{n2}V_2 + \cdots + Y_{nn}{}^*V_n + I_L \end{aligned} \tag{6–38}$$

where it is to be understood or further assumed that:

(a) The nodes have been so numbered, and the reference node has been so chosen, that the load N' is connected between node n and the reference node.

(b) If the network N contains dependent or controlled sources, each such source has been represented by a summation of the form

$$\sum_{i=1}^{n} Y_i(s)V_i$$

in which each coefficient Y_i has the dimensions of admittance and is unaltered when the load is disconnected or short-circuited. (If r and q represent grid and cathode nodes of a vacuum-tube equivalent circuit, we let $Y_r = -Y_q = g_m$ and $Y_i = 0$ for all $i \neq r$ or q. The summation then reduces to $g_m(V_r - V_q)$.) Our derivation will not apply when controlled sources cannot be represented in the manner stated above.

(c) Y_{nn}^* is the self-admittance of node n when the load N' is disconnected.

(d) The representation of applied sources as current sources does not imply any loss of generality. (See Section 5–1.)

(e) The use of all plus signs in (6–38) means merely that negative signs are included in the Y's where necessary.

(f) The node potential transform V_n is identical with V_L.

In view of (a), (b), and the basic assumption (2), it is evident that the Y coefficients in (6–38) are not dependent on the load parameters and are, therefore, unchanged when the load is connected, shorted, or disconnected. Hence, the equations of the network N with load N' disconnected consist of (6–38) with I_L replaced by zero. When the load is shorted, I_L is replaced by $I_{s.c.}$

The n equations (6–38) contain $n+1$ unknowns, namely

$$V_1, V_2, \ldots, V_n, I_L$$

This is to be expected, since the load is as yet unspecified. We can easily show, however, that V_L and I_L are related as the terminal voltage and current of a generator. The transform I_L is transferred to the left and V_L is then obtained in terms of I_L and the known quantities. We find:

$$V_L = \frac{\begin{vmatrix} Y_{11} & Y_{12} \cdots I_1 \\ Y_{21} & Y_{22} \cdots I_2 \\ \vdots & \vdots \quad \vdots \\ Y_{n1} & Y_{n2} \cdots I_n - I_L \end{vmatrix}}{D^*} \tag{6–39}$$

We note that D^* is the determinant of the node equations (6–38) when the load branch is disconnected, i.e., when $I_L = 0$. When the numerator of (6–39) is expanded in terms of cofactors of the nth column, we find

$$V_L = \frac{N_c - I_L A_{nn}^*}{D^*} \tag{6–40}$$

Here N_c consists of all terms in the cofactor expansion except for $I_L A_{nn}^*$, and A_{nn}^* is equal to the cofactor nn of the determinant D^*.

Since the load branch parameters are not included in the admittances Y_{rs} of equation (6–38), the quantities N_c, A_{nn}^*, and D^* are independent of I_L.

Now, when $I_L = 0$, we have $V_L = V_{o.c.}$ and (6–40) becomes

$$V_{o.c.} = \frac{N_c}{D^*} \tag{6–41}$$

Further, when $V_L = 0$, we have $I_L = I_{s.c.}$ and (6–40) yields

$$I_{s.c.} = \frac{N_c}{A_{nn}^*} \tag{6–42}$$

The source impedance Z_s, defined as $V_{o.c.}/I_{s.c.}$, is, therefore, given by

$$Z_s = \frac{A_{nn}^*}{D^*} \tag{6–43}$$

Hence we find that (6–40) can be written

$$V_L = V_{o.c.} - Z_s I_L \tag{6–44}$$

in which the load voltage transform is related to the load current transform as if the load were connected to a generator of e.m.f. transform $V_{o.c.}$ and internal series impedance Z_s, i.e., we have *Thévenin's theorem.* Division of both sides of equation (6–44) by Z_s and solution for I_L yield

$$I_L = I_{s.c.} - Y_s V_L \tag{6–45}$$

in which the load current transform is related to the load voltage transform as if the load were connected to a current generator with source current transform $I_{s.c.}$ and internal shunt admittance Y_s, i.e., we have *Norton's theorem.*

Since each of the previous equations, (6–44) and (6–45), has two unknowns, namely V_L and I_L, further information is required in order to apply these theorems. Specifically, an additional relationship between V_L and I_L is required. We, therefore, consider the load network N'. Two special cases are of interest:

CASE 1: *The load N' is a linear network*

We assume now that N' satisfies the requirements we have placed on N in the preceding derivation. Thus Thévenin's theorem applies to N' as well as to N, and we have at once

$$V_L' = V_{o.c.}' - Z_s' I_L' \tag{6–46}$$

where the primed quantities refer to the network N'. The load terminals of N and of N' are the same terminal pair, so that

$$V_L = V_L' \tag{6–47}$$

and

$$I_L = -I_L' \tag{6–48}$$

Now using these relationships and combining (6–44) and (6–46), we obtain

$$I_L = \frac{V_{o.c.} - V_{o.c.}'}{Z_s + Z_s'} \tag{6–49}$$

Thus the current to the network N', designated as load, may be calculated by replacing each network by its Thévenin generator. These two generators oppose each other.

Application of Norton's theorem to N' yields

$$I_L' = I_{s.c.}' - Y_s' V_L' \tag{6–50}$$

With the relationships (6–47) and (6–48), we find on combining (6–45) and (6–50) that

$$V_L = \frac{I_{s.c.} + I_{s.c.}'}{Y_s + Y_s'} \tag{6–51}$$

Thus the voltage across the load terminals may be calculated by replacing each network by its Norton equivalent current generator.

CASE 2: *The load N' is linear and is an impedance Z_L.*

When the load N' can be represented as an impedance Z_L, we have $V_L = Z_L I_L$, so that (6–44) yields at once

$$I_L = \frac{V_{o.c.}}{Z_s + Z_L} \tag{6–52}$$

that is, Thévenin's theorem for this case. We also note that (6–49) reduces to (6–52) if $V_{o.c.}' = 0$ and $Z_s' = Z_L$. The latter of these two equalities is justified by the alternative definition of source impedance presented in the next subsection.

If I_L is replaced by $V_L Y_L$ where $Y_L = 1/Z_L$, the general form of Norton's theorem (6–45) yields

$$V_L = \frac{I_{s.c.}}{Y_s + Y_L} \tag{6–53}$$

The forms (6–44) and (6–45) apply to the sinusoidal steady state when the load N' is linear (see basic assumption (4)). Hence the special cases 1 and 2 can be applied to the sinusoidal steady state as well as to a Laplace transform analysis.

An Alternative Definition of Source Impedance and Admittance

We wish to arrive at another commonly used and often more convenient definition of the source impedance Z_s. We have established Thévenin's theorem in the general form

$$V_L = V_{o.c.} - Z_s I_L \tag{6–44}$$

where $Z_s = V_{o.c.}/I_{s.c.}$.

We now let the load branch N' be an ideal source of e.m.f., $e(t)$, for which $\mathcal{L}e = E$. Then $V_L = E$. Also, let all independent sources in the network N have the value zero so that N_c in equation (6–41) is zero, whence $V_{o.c.} = 0$. It is evident from (6–41) and (6–42), or from (6–43), that Z_s remains constant when $V_{o.c.}$ is reduced to zero in this manner. Equation (6–44), therefore, reduces to

$$E = -Z_s I_L \tag{6–54}$$

Now, $-I_L$ is the transform of the current flowing into node n and out of the e.m.f. source which we have connected to the load terminals. Hence Z_s equals the impedance "looking into" the load terminals when all independent sources are set equal to zero. Dependent or controlled sources such as μE_g in the vacuum-tube equivalent circuit must be given values consistent with the specified conditions under which Z_s is calculated.

We can equally well apply an ideal current source to the load terminals, set all independent sources in N equal to zero, and show that Norton's form (6–45) yields Y_s as I/V_L where I is the Laplace transform of the current i driven into the load terminals by the ideal current source, and V_L is the Laplace transform of the terminal voltage when i is applied.

Comments

The expressions for $V_{o.c.}$ and $I_{s.c.}$, (6–41) and (6–42), were obtained from (6–38). In these equations, I_L appeared only once and was not multiplied by a factor. In a loop analysis, the load voltage V_L would appear in a corresponding or dual role. A difficulty would occur, however. Frequently the dependent source μE_g in a vacuum-tube equivalent circuit is expressed in terms of load voltage as $(1+\mu)Z_k I_L$ or $(1+\mu)V_L$. Thus V_L is multiplied by a factor and may appear in more than one loop equation. This would complicate the expressions for $V_{o.c.}$ and $I_{s.c.}$ In order to avoid this situation, the equally general node equations were chosen as the basis of our derivation.

A derivation based on loop analysis can also be carried out simply if one assumes that each dependent source is expressed in terms of loop currents, in such a way that V_L occurs but once in the loop equations and is not multiplied by a factor. Thus if an impedance, Z_{gk}, between grid and cathode is included in a vacuum-tube circuit, E_g may be expressed as $Z_{gk}I$, where I is the transform of the current in this impedance. Basically we would require that each dependent source be expressed as

$$\sum_{i=1}^{n} Z_i I_i$$

where each Z_i is unaltered when the load is disconnected or short-circuited.*

We note further that the expressions (6–41) and (6–42) for $V_{o.c.}$, $I_{s.c.}$, and Z_s in terms of the determinant D^* and its cofactors are not needed when Thévenin's and Norton's theorems are applied to circuit problems (see Section 6–5, Applications). To use these expressions would be to solve by node analysis, with perhaps the advantage of greater formalization of the algebraic steps. The expressions for $V_{o.c.}$, $I_{s.c.}$, and Z_s were obtained to demonstrate the theorems. The advantage of the theorems lies in the fact that these quantities are often easily obtained on direct examination of the circuit.

Statement of Thévenin's and Norton's Theorems

We now formally state Thévenin's and Norton's theorems, both for the general case and for the case of the sinusoidal steady state.

THÉVENIN'S AND NORTON'S THEOREMS—GENERAL CASE. If a linear network N has two available terminals (named load terminals) to which may be connected a second network N', the voltage across and the current through these terminals are related as the terminal voltage and current of a generator. This generator may be represented as an e.m.f. in series with impedance (*Thévenin representation*), or as a current source shunted by admittance (*Norton representation*). When N' is disconnected, the Laplace transform of the voltage across the

* If Z_{gk} were chosen as load, the loop derivation would present a difficulty: we could not treat μZ_{gk} as a factor which would remain unaltered when the load is disconnected or short-circuited. The node equations present no difficulty in this case.

For similar reasons, (b) following equation (6–38) implies that the elements of the transistor equivalent circuit (such as Z_ϵ) have not been designated as load in our derivation of the theorem.

load terminals, called the open-circuit voltage transform, is equal to the transform of the e.m.f. in the Thévenin representation. When the load terminals are short-circuited, the Laplace transform of the current through the load terminals, called the short-circuit current transform, is equal to the transform of the source current in the Norton representation. The series impedance in the Thévenin representation and the shunting admittance in the Norton representation are reciprocals of each other, the former being the ratio of the open-circuit voltage transform to the short-circuit current transform. The source impedance can alternatively be found as the impedance "looking into" the load terminals of N when all independent sources in N have zero value.

The foregoing statement can be converted directly into a statement which applies to sinusoidal steady-state analysis. Each voltage and current transform is now replaced by the corresponding complex voltage or current. The source impedance Z_s becomes $Z_s(j\omega)$. Since all voltages and currents are sinusoids at the same frequency, we require that N' as well as N be linear. A formal statement follows:

THÉVENIN'S AND NORTON'S THEOREMS—SINUSOIDAL STEADY STATE. If a linear network N has two available terminals (named load terminals) to which may be connected a second linear network N', the voltage across and the current through these terminals are related as the terminal voltage and current of a generator. This generator may be represented as an e.m.f. in series with impedance (*Thévenin representation*) or as a current source shunted by admittance (*Norton representation*). When N' is disconnected, the complex voltage across the load terminals is equal to the complex e.m.f. in the Thévenin representation. When the load terminals are short-circuited, the complex current through the load terminals is equal to the complex source current in the Norton representation. The series impedance in the Thévenin representation and the shunting admittance in the Norton representation are reciprocals of each other, the former being the ratio of the complex open-circuit voltage to the complex short-circuit current. The source impedance can alternatively be found as the impedance "looking into" the load terminals of N when all independent sources in N have zero value.

6-5 Applications of Thévenin's and Norton's Theorems

(a) *Passive Circuit Initially at Rest*

In the circuit shown in Fig. 6–7, we seek the transform of the current flowing down the center leg. For the boxes A, B, and C, the ratio of voltage transform to current transform is given by the impedances Z_A, Z_B, and Z_C, respectively. The dotted line separates the figure into two networks connected as in the statement of the theorem. The transform of the open-circuit voltage at the terminals aa' of the network within the dotted lines is E_C. The open-circuit voltage transform at the terminals bb' of the network outside the dotted lines is

$$(E_AZ_B+E_BZ_A)/(Z_A+Z_B)$$

where E_A and E_B are the transforms of e_A and e_B respectively. The source impedance of the dotted box is simply Z_C, while that of the

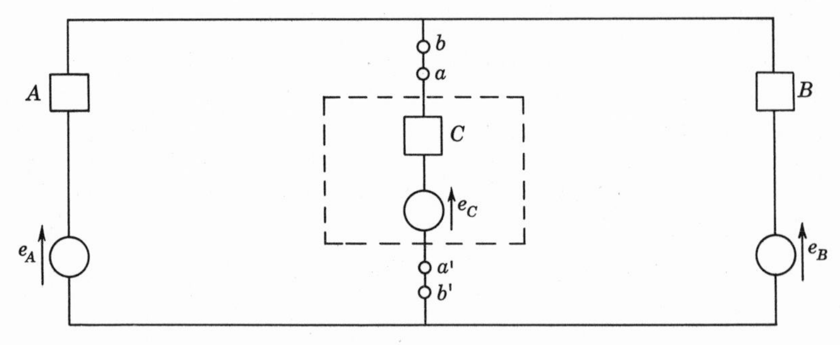

Fig. 6–7.

external circuit with output terminals bb' is $Z_AZ_B/(Z_A+Z_B)$. Hence the transform of the current down the center leg is, with reference to (6–49),

$$I = \frac{\dfrac{E_AZ_B+E_BZ_A}{Z_A+Z_B} - E_C}{\dfrac{Z_AZ_B}{Z_A+Z_B} + Z_C} \tag{6–55}$$

The dotted line can, of course, be drawn around the box C alone. The open-circuit voltage transform at the terminals of C will then be zero, while E_C will contribute to the open-circuit voltage transform at the output terminals of the circuit consisting of e_A, e_B, e_C, A, and B. The end result will be the same.

(b) *Linear Electronic Circuits*

Thévenin's and Norton's theorems will be applied to a number of vacuum-tube circuits. In each case, $V_{o.c.}$ and $I_{s.c.}$ will represent the open-circuit voltage and short-circuit current at the load terminals of the linear equivalent circuit. We note that opening or shorting these terminals or applying a current or voltage source to them can be done on paper in the linear equivalent circuit for the purpose of calculation, whether or not such a step is feasible in the physical circuit.

(1) CATHODE FOLLOWER:[2] FIG. 6–8(a). For simplicity of detail, we shall assume the sinusoidal steady state, the signal frequency being such that tube capacitance can be neglected. We refer only to the equivalent

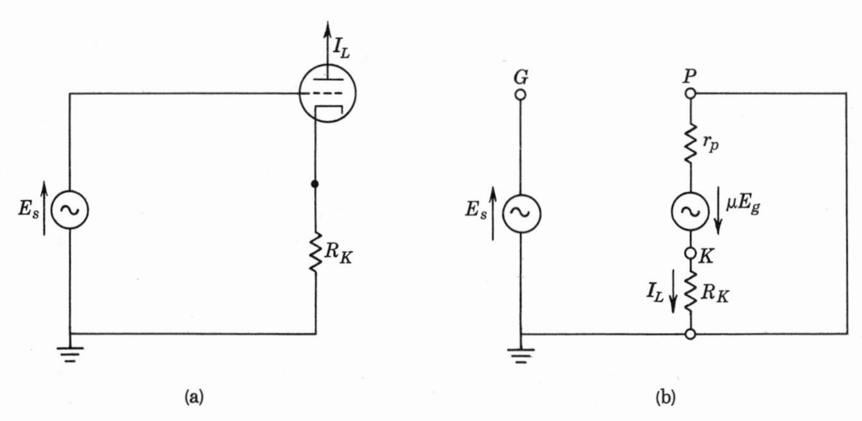

Fig. 6–8.

circuit illustrated in Fig. 6–8(b). The open-circuit voltage $V_{o.c.}$ across the terminals K and P is

$$V_{o.c.} = \mu E_{g_{o.c.}} \tag{6–56}$$

where $E_{g_{o.c.}}$ is the value of E_g when R_K is replaced by an open circuit. Then

$$E_s = V_{o.c.} + E_{g_{o.c.}} \tag{6–57}$$

Combining (6–56) and (6–57), we find

$$V_{o.c.} = \frac{\mu E_s}{\mu + 1} \tag{6–58}$$

The source impedance Z_s is easily found. The short-circuit current $I_{s.c.}$ is

$$I_{s.c.} = \frac{\mu E_{g_{s.c.}}}{r_p} = \frac{\mu E_s}{r_p} \tag{6–59}$$

where $E_{g_{s.c.}}$, the value of E_g with R_K shorted, is identical with E_s and the reference direction of $I_{s.c.}$ is downward. Then combining (6–58) and (6–59),

$$Z_s = = \frac{r_p}{\mu+1} \tag{6–60}$$

Applying Thévenin's theorem with (6–58) and (6–60), we have the familiar result

$$I_L = \frac{\dfrac{\mu E_s}{\mu+1}}{\dfrac{r_p}{\mu+1} + R_K} \equiv \frac{\mu E_s}{r_p + (\mu+1)R_K} \tag{6–61}$$

The derivation of (6–61) by Thévenin's theorem illustrates the role of the equivalent generator μE_g as a response rather than a source. It cannot arbitrarily be replaced by zero, and its presence results in a source impedance Z_s which depends on μ. If we wish to determine Z_s as the impedance "looking back" from the load terminals, we must again consider the response μE_g. Thus in Fig. 6–9(a), a generator E has been applied to the load terminals of the equivalent circuit, and E_s has been replaced by zero. The equivalent generator μE_g is not replaced by zero. It takes on the value $-\mu E$ since $E_s = 0 = E + E_g$. The source impedance, as seen from the output terminals of E, is E/I.

$$I = \frac{E - \mu E_g}{r_p} = \frac{E(1+\mu)}{r_p} \tag{6–62}$$

whence

$$Z_s = \frac{E}{I} = \frac{r_p}{1+\mu} \tag{6–63}$$

which is the same as the value obtained from the ratio $V_{o.c.}/I_{s.c.}$.

We may also obtain Z_s as the impedance "looking back" by applying a current source to the load terminals of the equivalent circuit. In Fig. 6–9(b), the current through r_p must be $I + g_m E_g$, so that

$$V = Ir_p + g_m r_p E_g$$

$E_g = -V$, and $g_m r_p = \mu$ so that $V = Ir_p - \mu V$, and $(V/I) = r_p/(1+\mu)$ as before.

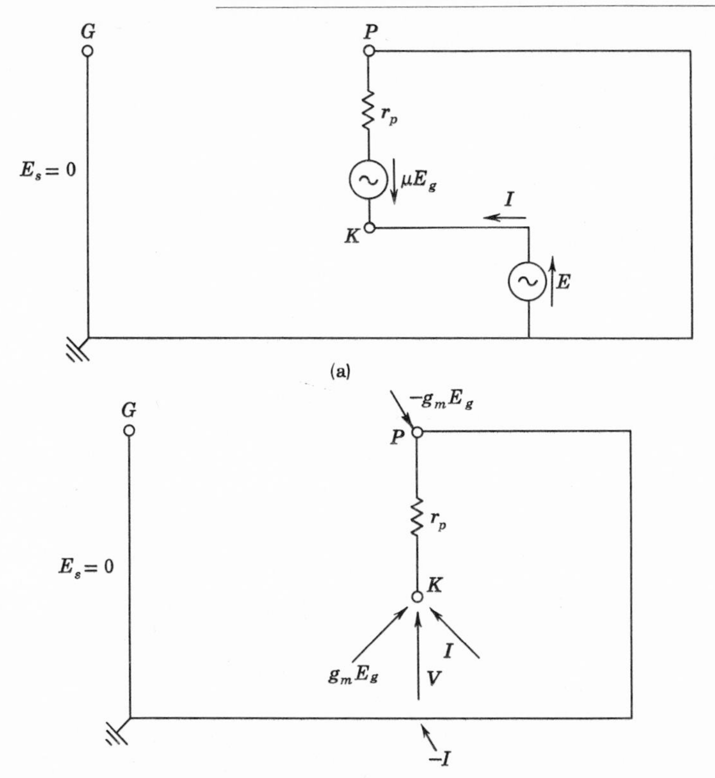

(Current source I applied between K and reference node adds to $g_m E_g$)

(b)

Fig. 6–9.

(2) VOLTAGE FEEDBACK CIRCUIT. As a further illustration of the application of Thévenin's theorem to an electronic circuit, we shall consider the voltage feedback circuit and its small-signal equivalent shown in Fig. 6–10. Our result will be valid for a problem involving only the sinusoidal steady state provided that our symbols are interpreted as complex voltages, and provided that the signal frequency permits neglecting the effect of interelectrode capacitance and blocking capacitor. We consider only the equivalent circuit of Fig. 6–10(b) in the equations given below.

The open-circuit voltage, with Z_L disconnected, may be expressed as

$$V_{o.c.} = \frac{-\mu E_{g_{o.c.}}}{r_p + R_1 + R_2}(R_1 + R_2) \tag{6–64}$$

where $E_{g_{o.c.}}$ is the value of E_g when Z_L is disconnected. The value of $E_{g_{o.c.}}$ is seen from Fig. 6–10(b) to satisfy the equation

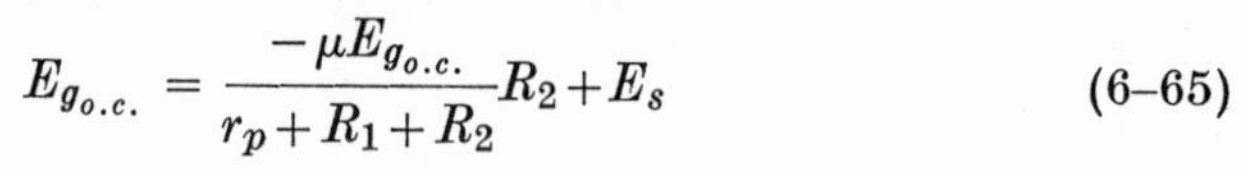

$$E_{g_{o.c.}} = \frac{-\mu E_{g_{o.c.}}}{r_p + R_1 + R_2} R_2 + E_s \tag{6–65}$$

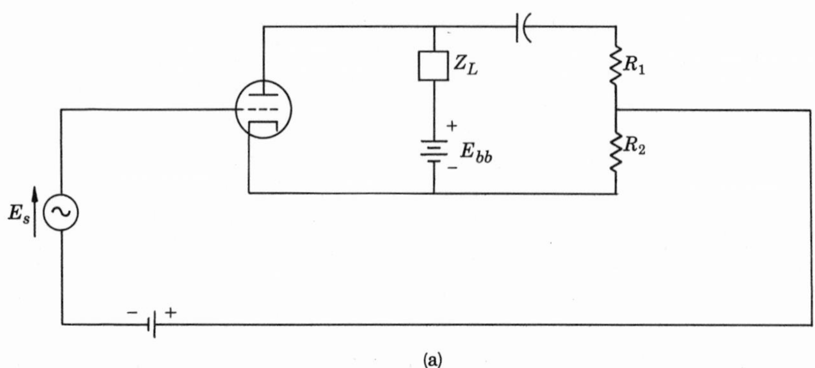

(a)

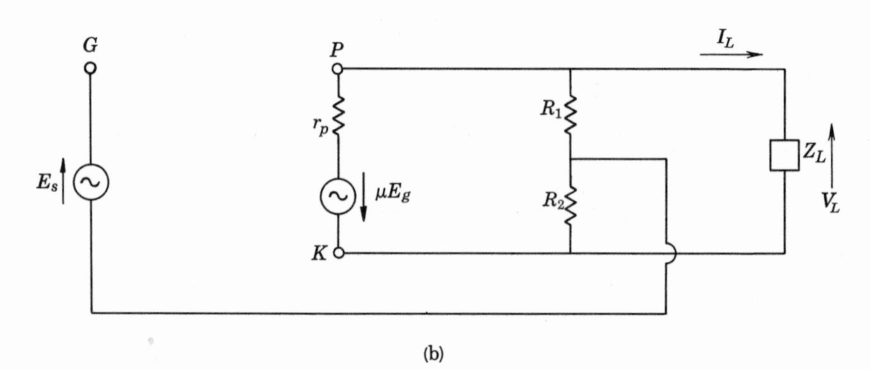

(b)

Fig. 6–10.*

Substituting the expression for $E_{g_{o.c.}}$ obtained from (6–65) into (6–64) yields

$$V_{o.c.} = \frac{-\mu(R_1 + R_2)E_s}{r_p + R_1 + R_2 + \mu R_2} \tag{6–66}$$

When Z_L is short-circuited, there can be no voltage across R_2, so that $E_{g_{s.c.}} = E_s$ and

$$I_{s.c.} = \frac{-\mu E_s}{r_p} \tag{6–67}$$

* Fig. 6–10(a) follows, with slight modification, Fig. 5–19 of Seely,(12) by permission of McGraw-Hill Book Company, Inc.

whence

$$Z_s = \frac{V_{o.c.}}{I_{s.c.}} = \frac{r_p(R_1+R_2)}{r_p+R_1+R_2+\mu R_2} \tag{6-68}$$

Now applying Thévenin's theorem, we have

$$V_L = I_L Z_L = \frac{-\mu(R_1+R_2)E_s}{r_p+R_1+R_2+\mu R_2} \cdot \frac{Z_L}{\dfrac{r_p(R_1+R_2)}{r_p+R_1+R_2+\mu R_2} + Z_L} \tag{6-69}$$

or more simply

$$V_L = \frac{-\mu(R_1+R_2)Z_L}{r_p(R_1+R_2)+(r_p+R_1+R_2+\mu R_2)Z_L} E_s \tag{6-69a}$$

It is also of interest, as in the preceding example, to find Z_s as the impedance "looking back" from the output terminals. Fig. 6–11(a) shows the application of a generator of zero internal impedance to the output terminals of the equivalent circuit. The signal voltage is replaced by zero as illustrated. The current I is easily expressed as

$$I = \frac{E}{R_1+R_2} + \frac{E+\mu E_g}{r_p} \tag{6-70}$$

With E_s replaced by zero, the value of E_g is

$$E_g = \frac{E}{R_1+R_2} R_2 \tag{6-71}$$

Putting (6–71) into (6–70) and solving for E/I, i.e., for Z_s, we find at once

$$Z_s = \frac{r_p(R_1+R_2)}{r_p+R_1+R_2+\mu R_2} \tag{6-68}$$

precisely the result found from the definition of Z_s as $V_{o.c.}/I_{s.c.}$.

Application of a current source to the load terminals of the equivalent circuit as shown in Fig. 6–11(b) also leads to the expression for Z_s. With K as reference node (since it is one of the load terminals), we find

$$I - g_m E_g = V(r_p+R_1+R_2)/r_p(R_1+R_2)$$

Under this condition E_g is simply $VR_2/(R_1+R_2)$ and the result given by equation (6–68) is obtained on solving for V/I and using $g_m r_p = \mu$.

(3) AN INTERSTAGE NETWORK.[11] As an illustration of Norton's theorem, we shall, assuming the sinusoidal steady state, obtain the

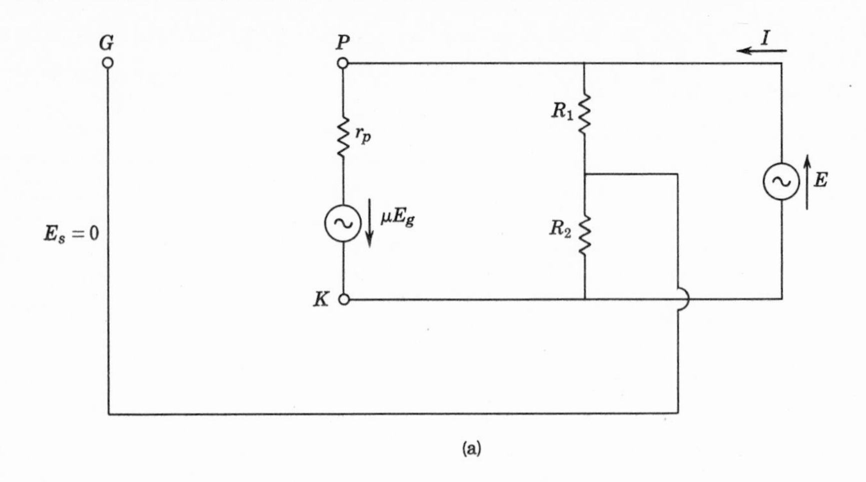

(a)

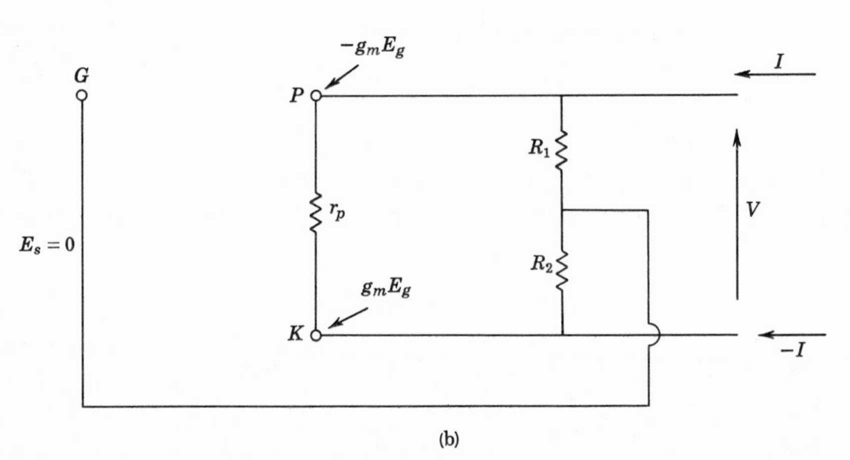

(b)

Fig. 6–11.

complex output voltage E_o of the interstage circuit shown in Fig. 6–12. For convenience of notation, we define

$$Y_1 = C_1 s + \frac{1}{R_1} + \frac{1}{L_1 s}$$

$$Y_3 = \frac{1}{L_3 s + \dfrac{1}{C_3 s}} = \frac{C_3 s}{1 + L_3 C_3 s^2} \quad \text{with } s = j\omega$$

The plate resistance r_p of the vacuum-tube equivalent circuit is included in R_1. The voltage we seek is across the parallel combination of R_2, L_2, and C_2. For ease of application of the theorem, we regard this parallel combination as the load admittance $Y_L = C_2s + (1/R_2) + (1/L_2s)$. The current source representing the generator in the equivalent plate circuit is indicated by arrows at the node points P and K. Now $I_{s.c.}$ is the transform of the current through a short circuit across Y_L. Since there is no feedback, the current source whose transform is $-g_mE_g$ is identical

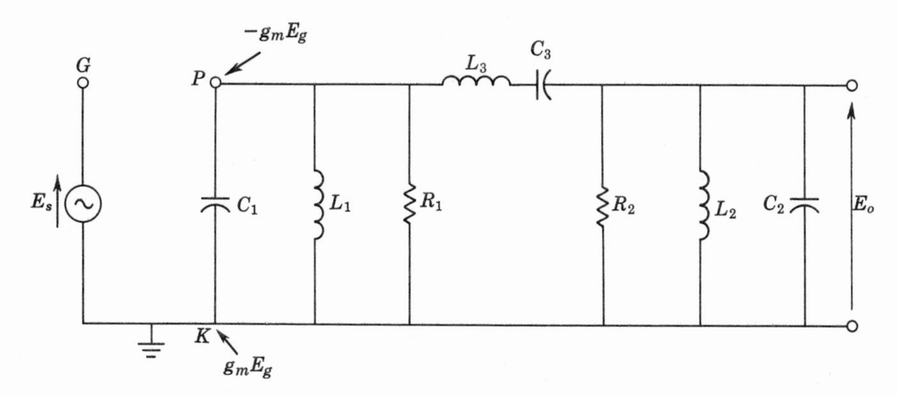

Fig. 6–12.

with $-g_mE_s$ and independent of the load admittance. Hence we can write on inspection

$$I_{s.c.} = \frac{-g_mE_sY_3}{Y_1 + Y_3} \tag{6–72}$$

The admittance Y_s is the admittance "looking in" from the output terminals with all independent sources eliminated. Since feedback is absent, replacement of the independent source e_s by zero automatically reduces the current source $-g_me_g$ to zero. Hence the admittance "looking back" from the output terminals is seen on inspection to be the admittance of Y_3 and Y_1 in series, i.e.,

$$Y_s = \frac{Y_1Y_3}{Y_1 + Y_3} \tag{6–73}$$

Norton's theorem yields directly, with reference to (6–53),

$$E_o = \frac{-g_mE_sY_s}{Y_1 + Y_3} \cdot \frac{1}{\dfrac{Y_1Y_3}{Y_1 + Y_3} + Y_L} \tag{6–74}$$

or more simply

$$E_o = \frac{-g_m E_s Y_s}{Y_1 Y_3 + Y_3 Y_L + Y_L Y_1} \tag{6–75}$$

as the complex voltage across Y_L.

(4) NORTON'S THEOREM APPLIED TO A CIRCUIT WITH FEEDBACK. The illustration given above was chosen partly to demonstrate that, with feedback absent, the analysis of an electronic circuit in terms of Norton's (and also Thévenin's) theorem is entirely similar to the analysis of a passive circuit. This, of course, results from the fact that, without feedback, μe_g is directly proportional to the signal voltage e_s, regardless of the load conditions. It is of interest, now, to apply Norton's theorem to a circuit where feedback is present. We shall obtain the output voltage for the vacuum-tube circuit[9] illustrated in Fig. 6–13(a). The equivalent circuit, Fig. 6–13(b), omits the capacitance C, the resistance R_{k1}, as well as tube capacitances. Our solution will, therefore, be valid for the complex quantities of the sinusoidal steady state at a frequency where the reactance of C and the susceptance of the tube capacitances may be neglected. R_{k1}, neglected here, can also be by-passed by a capacitor.† All resistances in the equivalent circuit are labeled as conductances with $g_p = 1/r_p$. When the node K is shorted to ground, E_s (the signal voltage) becomes identical with $E_{g_{s.c.}}$, i.e., the voltage between grid and cathode with G_k shorted out. It follows then that the current through the short circuit across G_k is

$$I_{s.c.} = E_s(G_G + g_m) \tag{6–76}$$

The admittance Y_s "looking in" from the terminals K and ground can be obtained by applying a pure current source to these points and setting $E_s = 0$. From Fig. 6–13(c), we see that the complex cathode potential E_k is, under this condition,

$$E_k = \frac{I + g_m E_g}{G_G + g_p} \tag{6–77}$$

Now when $E_s = 0$, $E_g = -E_k$ so that equation (6–77) may be solved, yielding

$$Y_s = \frac{I}{E_k} = G_G + g_p + g_m \tag{6–78}$$

† See Ryder,[9] 2nd ed., Fig. 8–40.

Direct substitution into Norton's theorem yields

$$E_o = \frac{E_s(G_G + g_m)}{G_G + g_m + g_p + G_k} \tag{6-79}$$

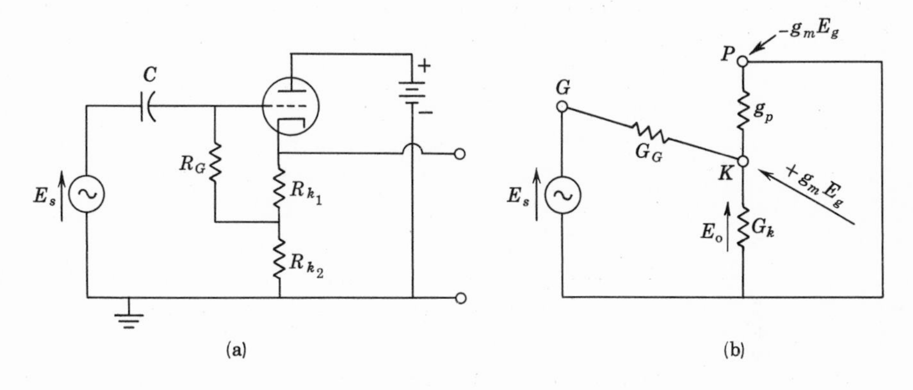

(a) (b)

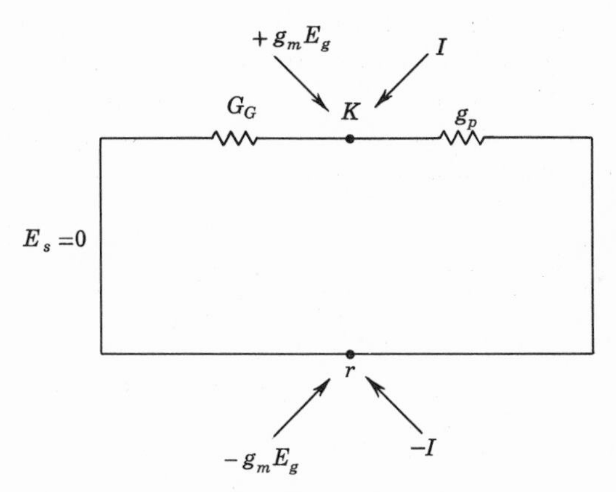

Circuit for computing Y_S

(c)

Fig. 6–13.

Fig. 6–13(a) and (b) follow, with slight modifications, Fig. 9–17 of John D. Ryder, *Electronic Fundamentals and Applications*, Copyright 1954, Prentice-Hall, Inc., by permission.

or

$$\frac{E_o}{E_s} = \frac{1}{1 + \dfrac{g_p + G_k}{G_G + g_m}} \tag{6-80}$$

(c) *Transient Problems with Non-Zero Initial Conditions*

Since the E's in our basic loop equations (6–1) or the I's in the node equations (6–38) may include transforms arising from initial conditions, we must expect that Thévenin's theorem can be applied to such problems, the initial conditions being expressed as e.m.f. or current transforms. Consider for example the circuit of Fig. 6–14. It is desired to find the

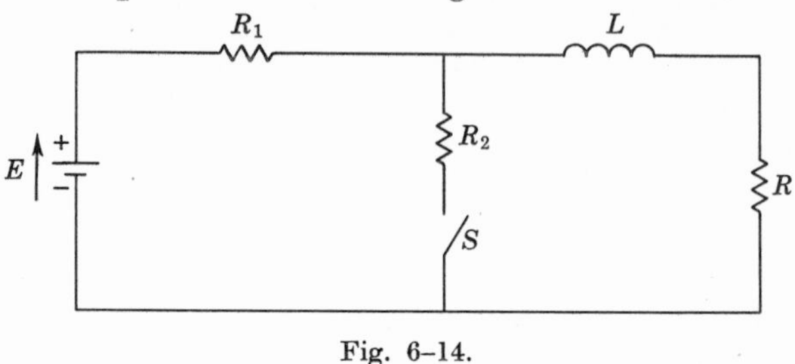

Fig. 6–14.

current in the load resistor R after the switch S closes at a time designated as $t = 0$. Since the chief purpose of using Thévenin's theorem is to avoid or simplify the writing of loop equations, and to reason as much as possible directly from the circuit, it will be convenient to represent our transform quantities directly on a circuit diagram as in Fig. 6–14(a). Such a diagram is termed a *transform circuit*.

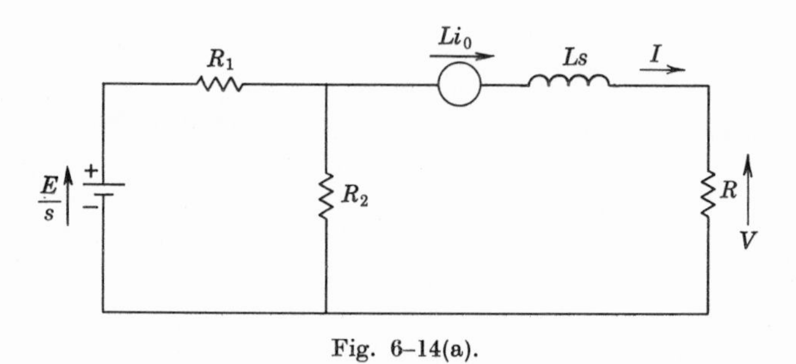

Fig. 6–14(a).

The generator symbol for Li_0 results from the fact that the effect of the initial current, i_0, in the coil is expressed by an e.m.f. transform in the loop equations. Now, for the purpose of calculation, we consider R disconnected (ignoring the arcing which would occur if the circuit were actually opened). We find

$$V_{o.c.} = \frac{E}{s} \cdot \frac{R_2}{R_1 + R_2} + Li_0 \tag{6–81}$$

where we note that Li_0 is the transform of a voltage impulse.

The source impedance as seen from the output terminals with E/s and Li_0 replaced by zero is

$$Z_s = Ls + \frac{R_1R_2}{R_1+R_2} \tag{6-82}$$

Hence, by substitution in Thévenin's theorem, the Laplace transform of the load current becomes

$$I = \frac{\dfrac{E}{s} \cdot \dfrac{R_2}{R_1+R_2} + Li_0}{Ls + \dfrac{R_1R_2}{R_1+R_2} + R} \tag{6-83}$$

Simplifying equation (6–83) yields

$$I = \frac{ER_2}{(R_1+R_2)L} \cdot \frac{1}{s\left(s + \dfrac{r}{L}\right)} + \frac{i_0}{s + \dfrac{r}{L}} \tag{6-84}$$

where $r = R + [R_1R_2/(R_1+R_2)]$ and $i_0 = E/(R_1+R)$, the latter being evident on inspection of Fig. 6–14. The instantaneous current $i(t)$ can be obtained by the residue method developed in Chapter 3 and illustrated in Chapter 4. The first term contains simple poles at $s = 0$ and $s = -r/L$, while the second term has a simple pole at $s = -r/L$. Hence

$$i = \frac{ER_2}{(R_1+R_2)R + R_1R_2}(1 - e^{-(r/L)t}) + i_0e^{-(r/L)t} \tag{6-85}$$

The same result is, of course, obtained if the first term of (6–84) is expressed as a sum of two transforms with the aid of the partial fraction theorem developed in Chapter 3.

A second circuit is illustrated in Fig. 6–15. The switch is presumed to close at a time after the steady state is established in the first loop. The instant at which S closes is designated as $t = 0$ and we seek the transform of the subsequent current in R. Again the application of Thévenin's theorem to the circuit proceeds easily if we first draw the transforms on a circuit as in Fig. 6–15(a). By inspection

$$V_{o.c.} = \frac{\dfrac{E}{s} - \dfrac{v_{C0}}{s}}{R_1 + \dfrac{1}{Cs}} \cdot \frac{1}{Cs} + \frac{v_{C0}}{s} \tag{6-86}$$

where v_{C0}/s and E/s have been regarded as generators (precisely their role in the basic equations 6–1). The source impedance is found with all e.m.f. transforms replaced by zero. It is then given by the expression

$$Z_s = Ls + \frac{R_1 \dfrac{1}{Cs}}{R_1 + \dfrac{1}{Cs}} \tag{6–87}$$

Fig. 6–15.

Hence we have at once

$$I = \frac{\dfrac{E - v_{C0}}{1 + R_1 Cs} \cdot \dfrac{1}{s} + \dfrac{v_{C0}}{s}}{Ls + \dfrac{R_1}{1 + R_1 Cs} + R} \tag{6–88}$$

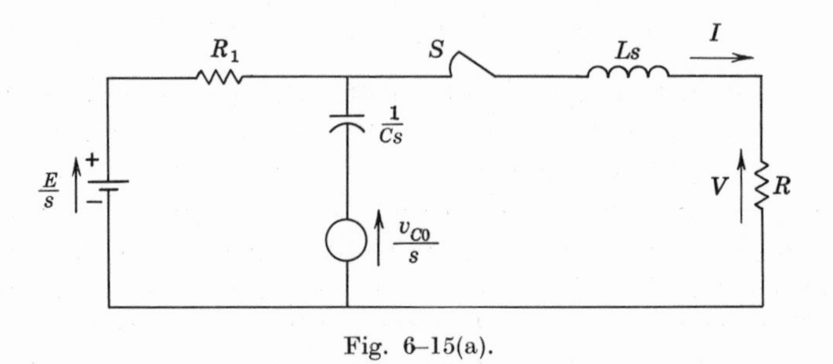

Fig. 6–15(a).

where I is the Laplace transform of the desired current. Simplifying (6–88) yields

$$I = \frac{E + R_1 C v_{C0} s}{R_1 LCs\left[s^2 + \left(\dfrac{R}{L} + \dfrac{1}{R_1 C}\right)s + \dfrac{R_1 + R}{R_1 LC}\right]} \tag{6–89}$$

where $v_{C0} = E$, as is evident upon inspection of the circuit of Fig. 6–15.

The instantaneous current i can be obtained after the denominator of equation (6–89) is factored in terms of its roots. We may then apply the partial fraction theorem to obtain simpler transforms, or we may directly evaluate the sum of the residues of Ie^{st} at its poles. The form of the solution will, of course, depend on the location and nature of these poles.

The procedure of these two examples illustrates the basic principle developed in Chapter 4, where it was demonstrated that Kirchhoff's laws apply directly to voltage and current transforms, provided that transforms arising from initial conditions are treated as e.m.f. or current transforms.

6-6 Vratsanos' Theorem

According to a recent theorem, published by Vratsanos,[14]

$$\left(\frac{I_b}{I}\right)^2 = \frac{\partial Z}{\partial Z_b} \tag{6–90}$$

where I_b is the current (complex a-c) through a branch of impedance Z_b, and I and Z are the input current (complex a-c) and input impedance of a passive network consisting of bilateral elements. The proof of this theorem can be shortened considerably[1] with the aid of two-port network theory to be taken up in the next chapter. The proof is, therefore, reserved for Section 7–10, where we shall also obtain a more general theorem of which (6–90) is a special case. The more general result will apply to linear active circuits as well as to linear passive circuits consisting of bilateral (or even nonbilateral) elements. Since the proof will be written in terms of transforms, we shall find that the theorem applies to transient problems (when the circuit is initially at rest).

6-7 Summary

Several common network theorems—superposition, reciprocity, Thévenin's, and Norton's—were developed in this chapter. The more recent Vratsanos theorem was stated, but its proof and generalization are deferred to Chapter 7. Each derived theorem was stated in terms of Laplace transforms of current and voltage. In each case, a statement was also given in terms of the complex voltages and currents of sinusoidal steady-state analysis. In general problems (that is, those including transients), the Laplace transform of each desired voltage or current was obtained. Initial voltages across capacitors and initial currents in coils were regarded as sources of energy applied to the circuit, and the transforms arising from these conditions were then treated as e.m.f. transforms. In problems where the sinusoidal steady-state solution, alone, was desired, the theorems were applicable to the complex voltages and currents of a-c analysis, since these also satisfy the loop and node equations.

The theorems of this chapter, with the exception of the reciprocity principle, were applied to linear vacuum-tube circuits as well as to linear passive circuits. In these applications, e_g was always given a value consistent with the assumed load conditions, since the equivalent plate-circuit generator μe_g is a response rather than an applied source.

Problems

6-1. In the circuit in the figure, $R_1 = 500\ \Omega$, $R_2 = 1000\ \Omega$, $R_3 = 2000\ \Omega$, $R_4 = 1000\ \Omega$, $R_5 = 5000\ \Omega$, $E_0 = 25$ volts, $E_1 = 1$ volt. Find the current in R_5, using at least one of the theorems derived in this chapter.

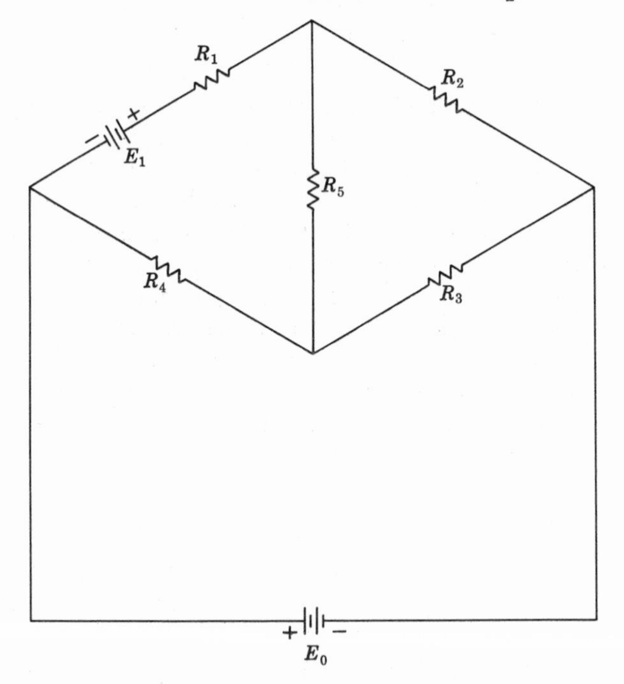

Problem 6-1.

6-2. The circuit in the figure is at rest when the sinusoidal voltage e_s is applied. The switch S remains open until a sinusoidal steady state is established. Then at an instant when e_s is at a peak value, S closes. If $t = 0$ at this instant, show that the current in the resistance R/k is zero for $t > 0$. HINT: Use Thévenin's theorem but do not select R/k as load.

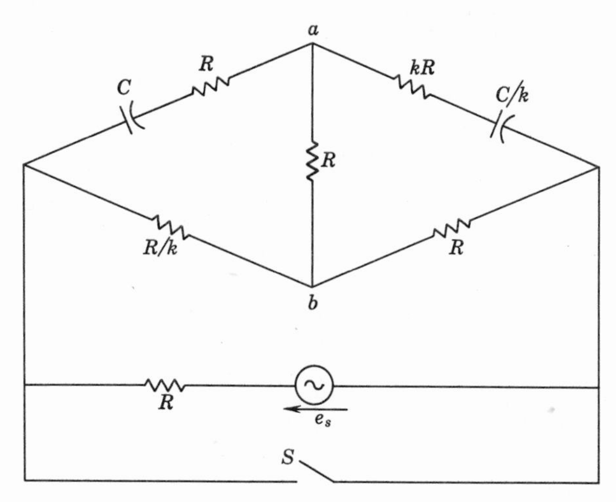

Problem 6–2.

6-3. The currents i_1 and i_2 are shown in the figure. With the e.m.f. source $e(t)$ and with the initial values shown in the figure, we find $\mathfrak{L}i_2 = F(s) + G(s)v_{C0}$ where $F(s)$ is independent of v_{C0}. Now state a new set of values for $e(t)$ and for initial conditions which will yield $\mathfrak{L}i_1 = G(s)\ v_{C0}$.

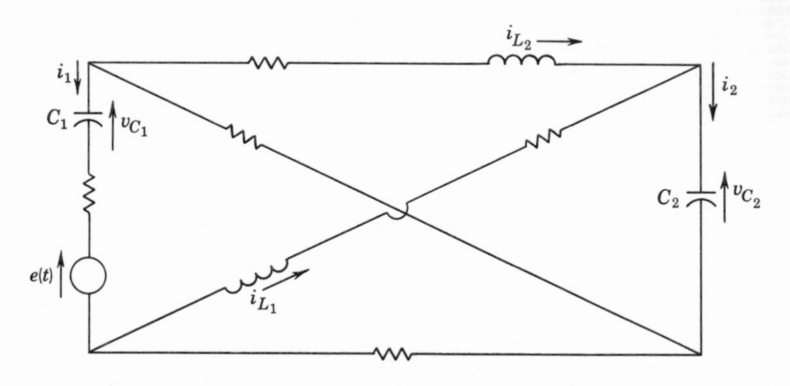

At $t = 0+$, $v_{C_1} = v_{C0}$, $i_{L_1} = i_{L0}$, $i_{L_2} = 0$, $v_{C_2} = 0$

Problem 6–3.

6-4. A small signal e.m.f., e_s, in series with a resistance R_g is applied to the input terminals of a grounded-grid triode. The latter is connected to a load resistance R_L. Draw and label the Thévenin equivalent generator connected to R_L. (Assume, here, low frequency sinusoidal steady state.)

6-5. Repeat Problem 6-4 for a cathode follower circuit. Include capacitances and let R_K be the load.

6-6. Repeat Problem 6-4 for the linear transistor equivalent circuit[8] shown in the figure. Upper case E's and I's represent complex quantities of sinusoidal analysis. (We assume a frequency at which this resistive circuit is valid.)

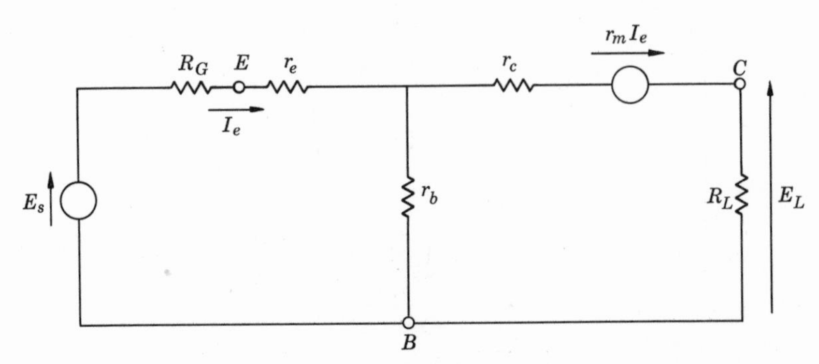

Problem 6-6.

6-7. Repeat Problem 6-4 for the circuit of Fig. 5-4 in Chapter 5 with Z_L as load.

6-8. Solve Problem 5-4 (Chapter 5) with the aid of Norton's theorem.

6-9. Find the ratio I_b/I_0 for the circuit in the figure with the aid of the Vratsanos theorem. Verify the result.

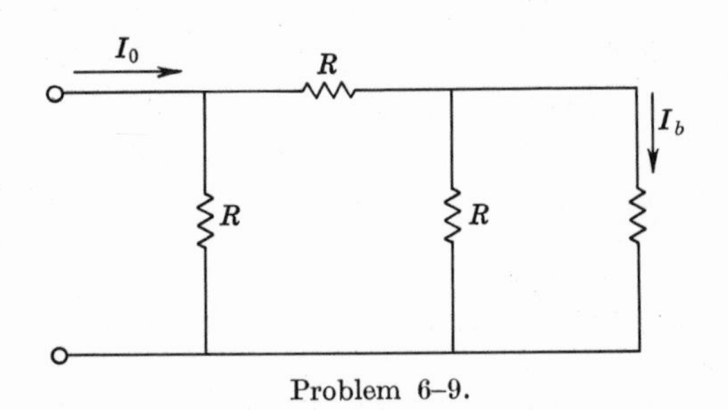

Problem 6-9.

6-10. The impedances of a circuit contain reactive components. Does the Vratsanos theorem yield a means of determining the frequency dependence of the ratio I_b/I in the sinusoidal case? Justify your answer and note that the proof of the theorem is not needed to answer this question.

References for Chapter 6

1. Ansell, H. G., "Vratsanos' Theorem," IRE *Trans. Circuit Theory*, Vol. CT-5, p. 143 (June 1958).
2. Arguimbau, L. B., *Vacuum-Tube Circuits*, John Wiley & Sons, Inc., New York, 1948; *Vacuum-Tube Circuits and Transistors*, John Wiley & Sons, Inc., New York, 1956 (with transistor contributions by R. B. Adler).
3. Bode, Hendrik, W., *Network Analysis and Feedback Amplifier Design*, D. Van Nostrand Co., Inc., New York, 1945.
4. Carslaw, H. S., and Jaeger, J. C., *Operational Methods in Applied Mathematics*, 2nd ed., Oxford University Press, New York, 1949.
5. Carson, J. R., *Electric Circuit Theory and the Operational Calculus*, 1st ed., McGraw-Hill Book Co., Inc., New York, 1926; 2nd ed., Chelsea Publishing Company, New York, 1953.
6. Guillemin, E. A., *The Mathematics of Circuit Analysis*, John Wiley & Sons, Inc., New York, 1949.
7. LePage, W. R., and Seely, S., *General Network Analysis*, McGraw-Hill Book Co., Inc., New York, 1952.
8. Millman, J., *Vacuum-Tube and Semiconductor Electronics*, McGraw-Hill Book Company, Inc., New York, 1958.
9. Ryder, J. D., *Electronic Fundamentals and Applications*, Prentice-Hall, Inc., New York, 1954: 2nd ed., 1959.
10. Ryder, J. D., *Networks, Lines, and Fields*, Prentice-Hall, Inc., New York, 1949; 2nd ed., 1955.
11. Sarbacher, R. I., and Edson, W. A., *Hyper and Ultrahigh Frequency Engineering*, John Wiley & Sons, Inc., New York, 1943.
12. Seely, S., *Electron-Tube Circuits*, McGraw-Hill Book Co., Inc., New York, 1950; 2nd ed., 1958.
13. Valley, G. E., Jr., and Wallman, H., *Vacuum Tube Amplifiers*, McGraw-Hill Book Co., Inc., New York, 1948.
14. Vratsanos, J. : "Calculation of Current Distribution in a Linear Network," *Arch. elekt. Übertr.*, Vol. 11, pp. 76–80 (Feb. 1957).
15. Ware, L. A., and Reed, H. R., *Communication Circuits*, 3rd ed., John Wiley & Sons, Inc., New York, 1949.

Chapter 7

TWO-PORT NETWORK ANALYSIS

Electric networks will now be analyzed from a different viewpoint. Instead of looking at loops containing impedances, or at nodes from which admittances radiate, we shall find that it is often useful to regard a network as constituted of interconnected boxes, each with two input and two output terminals. Such a box is called a *two-terminal pair*,(16) *four-pole*,(16) or *twoport*.(17) The term *twoport*, or *two-port network*,* is the

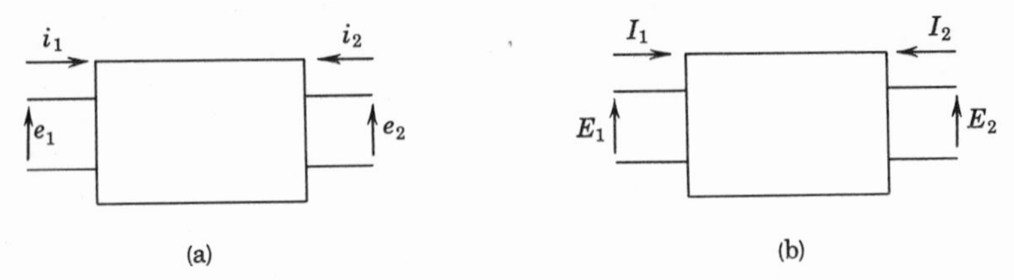

Fig. 7–1.

most recent of these. Any two terminals designated as a pair may be termed a *port*,(18) so that if $2n$ terminals are associated in n pairs, we have an *n-port network*. The terms *two-terminal pair network*, *four-pole*, and *two-port network* are preferable to the phrase *four-terminal network*, which does not imply a separation of terminals into an input and an output pair.

A twoport is represented in Fig. 7–1, where the usual sign conventions have been adopted.(4,10) In part (a) of this figure, the lower-case letters represent instantaneous voltage and current. In part (b), the letters E_1, E_2, I_1, and I_2 represent voltage and current transforms or the complex numbers of sinusoidal steady-state analysis, depending on the application of interest.

* The use of *twoport* as an unhyphenated noun has been adopted by the Institute of Radio Engineers,(17, 18) as has been the use of *two-port* as a hyphenated adjective.(17, 18).

Since each twoport is to be analyzed in terms of certain coefficients, independent of external conditions, there will be some limitation on the range of applicability of the methods to be developed. Basically we are limited by the fact that the individual twoport must not contain an independent source of energy. In particular, the box in Fig. 7–1 must not contain an applied e.m.f. or current source; and in problems concerned with transients, a further limitation is that the box must not contain initially charged capacitance or inductance with initial current. The theory will apply, however, whether the twoport of constant elements is active or passive, provided, of course, that in the active case we have small signals, resulting in linear operation. In problems involving transient response, we shall obtain the Laplace transforms of voltage and current. When problems involve only the sinusoidal steady state, the theory will yield the usual complex voltages and currents.

7-1 General Derivation of Two-Port Network Coefficients[4]

The basis of our analysis may be, as before, the loop or node equations of a general network. For convenience we refer to the n loop equations (6–1) of Chapter 6. We note that in the equations (6–1):

(a) The voltage and current symbols are to be interpreted as transforms or as complex voltages and currents, depending upon whether a transient problem or a problem involving only the sinusoidal steady state is at hand.

(b) The impedance coefficients Z_{qr} are functions of s when transforms are sought, and are identical functions of $j\omega$ in problems involving only the sinusoidal steady state.

(c) E.m.f. transforms of equivalent generators of active circuits* (as μE_g) are expressed in such manner that they alter the coefficients Z_{qr}, but are not included among the known E's on the left-hand side of (6–1).

(d) If initial conditions are present, the transforms representing them must be treated as transforms of applied e.m.f.'s, i.e., included with $E_1, E_2, \ldots, E_n$ in the equations (6–1).

Referring to Fig. 7—1, let us number the loop closed by E_1, number 1, and that closed by E_2, number 2. We now limit our consideration to problems for which $E_3, \ldots, E_n$ are all zero. In terms of the statements (a), (b), (c), (d), this means that transient problems in which the circuit within the box is not initially at rest are *excluded*. On the other hand,

* The vacuum-tube and transistor circuits referred to in this chapter are subject to the limitations mentioned in Section 1–4 (subsection Linear Devices with Active Response). For a more general treatment of the vacuum-tube twoport, see L. C. Peterson, *Equivalent Circuits of Linear Active Four-terminal Networks*.[7]

we do include the possibility of linear active as well as linear passive circuits within the box.

Under these assumptions the equations (6–1) reduce to the form

$$\begin{aligned} E_1 &= Z_{11}I_1 + Z_{12}I_2 + Z_{13}I_3 + \cdots + Z_{1n}I_n \\ E_2 &= Z_{21}I_1 + Z_{22}I_2 + Z_{23}I_3 + \cdots + Z_{2n}I_n \\ 0 &= Z_{31}I_1 + Z_{32}I_2 + Z_{33}I_3 + \cdots + Z_{3n}I_n \\ &\vdots \\ 0 &= Z_{n1}I_1 + Z_{n2}I_2 + Z_{n3}I_3 + \cdots + Z_{nn}I_n \end{aligned} \tag{7-1}$$

In the case of vacuum-tube circuits, we assume that E_g is expressed as $I(1/sC_{gk})$, where I is the transform of the current through the grid-cathode capacitance, C_{gk}. The form (7–1), with only E_1 on the left of the first equation and only E_2 on the left of the second, can, then, be obtained easily. When tube capacitance is neglected, the expression for E_g may involve both E_1 and E_2, with the result that E_1 may not be confined to the first equation nor E_2 to the second. For this reason, it is preferable in a general development to assume that this capacitance has been included and that each E_g has been expressed as $I(1/sC_{gk})$. Circuits in which C_{gk} is to be neglected can be regarded as limiting cases. It is important to note, however, that this limiting process need not be carried out in individual problems. Our general development will show that each twoport can be characterized by certain coefficients. The coefficients, once their existence is established, can be found by any of a number of methods without resort to equations (7–1).*

Equations (7–1) are easily solved for I_1 and I_2. We find

$$I_1 = \frac{\Delta_{11}}{\Delta}E_1 - \frac{\Delta_{21}}{\Delta}E_2 \tag{7-2}$$

and

$$I_2 = -\frac{\Delta_{12}}{\Delta}E_1 + \frac{\Delta_{22}}{\Delta}E_2 \tag{7-3}$$

where Δ is the determinant of the equations (7–1), and Δ_{qr} (with q and r each equal to 1 or 2) is the minor obtained by striking out row q and column r of the determinant Δ. Both this determinant and its minors depend on the Z coefficients in the equations (7–1) and are clearly independent of E_1, E_2, I_1, and I_2. We see, then, that the equations (7–2) and (7–3) express I_1 and I_2 in terms of E_1 and E_2, and the coefficients (Δ_{11}/Δ, $-\Delta_{21}/\Delta$, etc.) which characterize the circuit within the box. Since these

* More generally, each E_g may be expressed as IZ_{gk} where Z_{gk} is an impedance from grid to cathode.

coefficients have the dimensions of admittance, it is customary to write equations (7–2) and (7–3) in the form

$$I_1 = y_{11}E_1 + y_{12}E_2 \tag{7–4}$$

$$I_2 = y_{21}E_1 + y_{22}E_2 \tag{7–5}$$

where

$$y_{11} = \frac{\Delta_{11}}{\Delta}$$

$$y_{22} = \frac{\Delta_{22}}{\Delta}$$

$$y_{12} = -\frac{\Delta_{21}}{\Delta}$$

$$y_{21} = -\frac{\Delta_{12}}{\Delta}$$

For convenience, we define the constant[2]

$$\eta = \frac{y_{12}}{y_{21}} \tag{7–6}$$

We now define a *reciprocal twoport** as one for which

$$\eta = 1 \tag{7–7}$$

* A conflict in usage surrounds the terms *reciprocal* and *bilateral*. Since the reciprocity theorem (Chapter 6) applies to networks of bilateral elements (see Chapter 1 for definition of *bilateral element*), two terms describing such networks arise in the literature: namely, *bilateral network* and *reciprocal network*. Since each of these terms has also a second meaning, it is perhaps true to say that they are equally bad rather than equally good. One finds, for example, a pair of networks having the relationship between driving-point impedances $Z_1Z_2 = 1\Omega^2$ referred to and indexed as *reciprocal networks*[5, 12, 20] (see also Section 5–8). This relationship is not a consequence of the reciprocity theroem. Again one finds the term *bilateral transducer*[15] defined as a transducer capable of simultaneous transmission in both directions between specified pairs of terminals (ports). This broad property is likewise not a consequence of the reciprocity theorem. (Recent standards[19] accepting this definition prefer the term *bidirectional* to *bilateral* here.)

The term *reciprocal twoport* is used in this text for a twoport which satisfies the reciprocity theorem, because:

(a) IRE standards[15] and AIEE standards[19] define a *reciprocal transducer* as one which satisfies the reciprocity theorem.

(b) The word *reciprocal* applied to a single twoport cannot be confused with the use of *reciprocal* to specify two networks whose driving-point impedances are related by $Z_1Z_2 = 1\Omega^2$.

The term *bilateral transducer* or *bilateral twoport* will not be used in this text, since the wide usage of *bilateral* as an adjective descriptive of a network which obeys the reciprocity theorem is in conflict with the definition in the transducer standards referred to above.[15] We retain, of course, the term *bilateral element* as defined in Chapter 1.

From the definition of the y's, it is evident that a twoport consisting of passive bilateral two-terminal circuit elements (and/or ideal transformers), will be reciprocal. (See proof of reciprocity theorem, Chapter 6, and definition of *bilateral two-terminal circuit element*, Section 1–4). An active twoport, on the other hand, contains dependent or controlled sources of voltage or current. Since a current or voltage source has an associated direction, it is not a bilateral element, and active twoports are non-reciprocal (see treatment of active networks by loop and node analysis in Chapter 5). (If a particular circuit arrangement and selected values of tube parameters should happen to lead to $\eta = 1$, this result would be a property of that special case and not part of a general characteristic of active circuits.)

7-2 The Number of Parameters Necessary to Characterize a Two-Port Network

Equations (7–4) and (7–5) indicate that four parameters or measurements will be needed to characterize a two-port network. We shall find, however, that the number of independent parameters will be reduced for many classes of these networks.

The first and most obvious reduction occurs for reciprocal twoports. Equation (7–7) equates y_{12} and y_{21}, so that only three independent parameters remain. A further limitation occurs when a twoport is both reciprocal and symmetrical. *Symmetry* means that reversing the orientation of the twoport has no measurable effect, i.e., end 1 and end 2 are electrically indistinguishable. Hence the subscripts 1 and 2 must be interchangeable, and $y_{11} = y_{22}$ as well as $y_{12} = y_{21}$ for a reciprocal symmetrical twoport.

These properties may be illustrated in terms of the passive Π section of Fig. 7–2. With loops chosen as indicated, the equations (7–1) become for this circuit

$$\begin{aligned} E_1 &= Z_a I_1 + 0 I_2 - Z_a I_3 \\ E_2 &= 0 I_1 + Z_b I_2 + Z_b I_3 \\ 0 &= -Z_a I_1 + Z_b I_2 + (Z_a + Z_b + Z_c) I_3 \end{aligned} \qquad (7\text{–}8)$$

Evaluating the network determinant and its minors, we find

$$\Delta = Z_a Z_b Z_c \qquad (7\text{–}9)$$

$$\Delta_{11} = Z_b(Z_a + Z_c) \qquad (7\text{–}10)$$

$$\Delta_{22} = Z_a(Z_b + Z_c) \qquad (7\text{–}11)$$

$$\Delta_{12} = \Delta_{21} = Z_a Z_b \qquad (7\text{–}12)$$

whence

$$y_{11} = \frac{Z_a + Z_c}{Z_a Z_c} \tag{7-13}$$

$$y_{22} = \frac{Z_b + Z_c}{Z_b Z_c} \tag{7-14}$$

$$y_{12} = y_{21} = -\frac{1}{Z_c} \tag{7-15}$$

While this is not the easiest way to find the y coefficients, we have used it to illustrate the theory from which they derive. Equations (7-13),

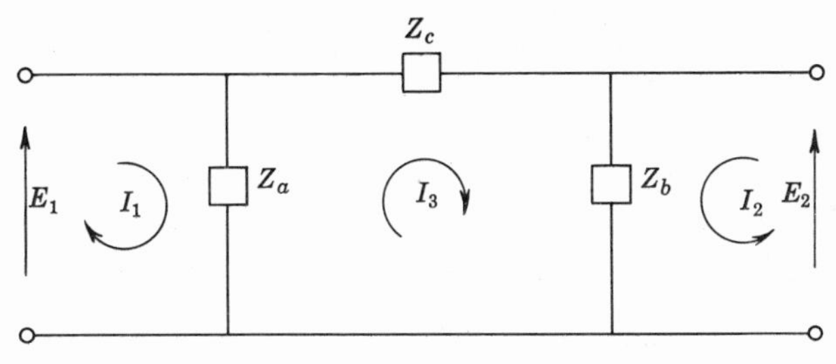

Fig. 7-2.

(7-14), and (7-15) illustrate the fact that for a reciprocal twoport there are but three independent parameters, y_{11}, y_{22}, and y_{12}.

Now let the Π structure be symmetrical, i.e., $Z_b = Z_a$. Equations (7-13), (7-14), and (7-15) yield

$$y_{11} = y_{22} = \frac{Z_a + Z_c}{Z_a Z_c} \tag{7-16}$$

and

$$y_{12} = y_{21} = -\frac{1}{Z_c} \tag{7-15}$$

Thus only two parameters, y_{11} and y_{12}, are sufficient to characterize the reciprocal symmetrical Π structure.

Still another class of two-port networks can be characterized by less than four independent parameters. The *unilateral twoport* is a twoport whose input voltage and current are entirely unaffected by a signal applied to the output terminals. (The unilateral twoport, as defined here, is an example of a *unilateral transducer* as defined by the IRE Standards Committee.[15]) Consider again the equation

$$I_1 = y_{11}E_1 + y_{12}E_2 \tag{7-4}$$

Now apply an additional signal to the output terminals of the circuit so that E_2 becomes $E_2+\Delta E_2$. Then, if the circuit is unilateral, E_1 and I_1 must remain unchanged. Equation (7–4) now becomes

$$I_1 = y_{11}E_1+y_{12}E_2+y_{12}\Delta E_2 \tag{7–17}$$

Subtracting equation (7–4) from (7–17), we find $0 = y_{12}\Delta E_2$, whence

$$y_{12} = 0 \tag{7–18}$$

This characterizes the unilateral twoport. From equations (7–6 and 18),

$$\eta = 0 \tag{7–19}$$

The unilateral twoport will be characterized, then, by three, rather than four, coefficients.

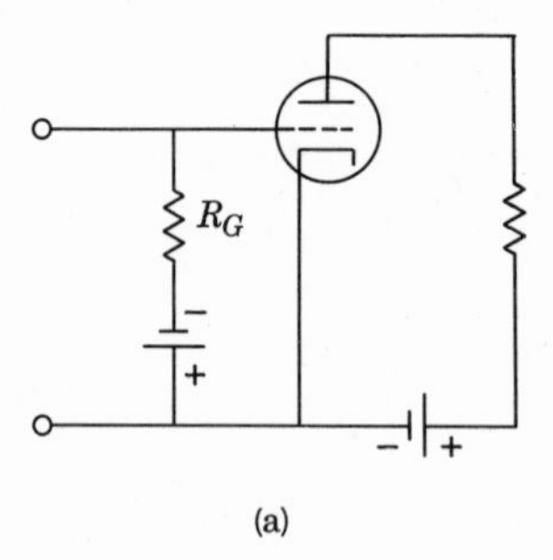

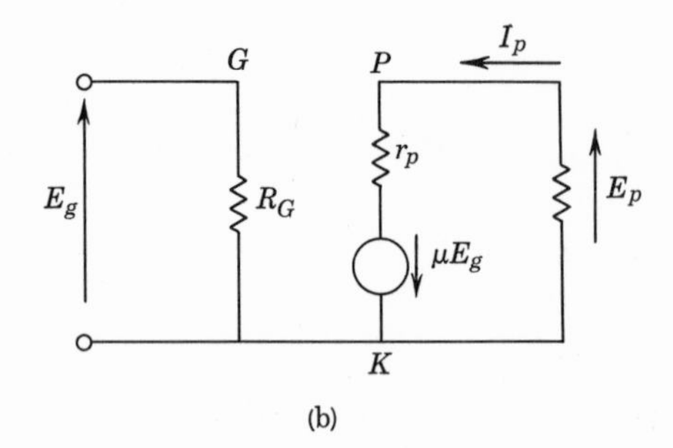

Fig. 7–3.

A simple illustration of this situation is provided by a grounded-cathode tube under an a-c signal at a sufficiently low frequency so that interelectrode capacitance can be ignored. The circuit is shown in Fig. 7–3. The equivalent plate-circuit yields at once

$$\mu E_g = r_p I_p - E_p \tag{7–20}$$

Since $E_p = E_2$, $I_p = I_2$, and $E_g = E_1$, we have at once from (7–20) and the figure

$$I_1 = \frac{1}{R_G}E_1+0E_2 \tag{7–21}$$

and

$$I_2 = g_m E_1 + \frac{1}{r_p}E_2 \tag{7–22}$$

whence $y_{11} = 1/R_G$, $y_{12} = 0$, $y_{21} = g_m$, $y_{22} = 1/r_p$, and $\eta = 0$.

Table 7–1 summarizes the findings of this section:

TABLE 7–1

Type of Two-Port Network	y Coefficient Relationship	No. of Independent Parameters Required to Characterize the Two-Port Network
General	None	4
Reciprocal	$y_{12} = y_{21}$	3
Reciprocal symmetrical	$y_{12} = y_{21}$, $y_{11} = y_{22}$	2
Unilateral	$y_{12} = 0$	3

One point should be kept in mind in connection with the term *unilateral.* As defined earlier (see definition of *unilateral twoport* above, based on IRE Standards on Transducers(15)), this term implies an idealized circuit. A vacuum-tube circuit, although not ideal, may be approximately unilateral at low frequencies. At higher frequencies such a circuit loses its unilateral property, since interelectrode capacitance is then not negligible and provides a backward transmission path. Now we have seen in Chapter 2 on Fourier analysis that a large frequency range is generally needed to represent non-sinusoidal voltage or current; with a non-sinusoidal signal, then, the vacuum-tube circuit will generally not be unilateral. Usually, therefore, an approximation to the unilateral circuit as defined is given by the vacuum-tube circuit only in the low-frequency sinusoidal steady state.

7-3 Additional Parameters for the Characterization of Two-Port Networks(2,4)

When, for the purpose of analysis, a more complicated network is regarded as consisting of twoport units, coefficients other than the y's are often needed to describe the individual twoports. For example, one of the most common arrangements is the cascade illustrated in Fig. 7–4. Here it is evident that we shall seek the output voltage and current of each unit in terms of the input voltage and current. In doing so, we arrive at the all-important **A**, **B**, **C**, **D** coefficients of two-port networks. The method of combining the results for each unit into the result for the entire cascade is reserved for later.

Solving equation (7–5) for E_1 and using the resulting expression in (7–4), we find

$$E_1 = -\frac{y_{22}}{y_{21}}E_2 + \frac{1}{y_{21}}I_2 \tag{7–23}$$

and

$$I_1 = \frac{y_{12}y_{21} - y_{11}y_{22}}{y_{21}}E_2 + \frac{y_{11}}{y_{21}}I_2 \tag{7–24}$$

These are generally written

$$E_1 = \mathbf{A}E_2 - \mathbf{B}I_2 \tag{7–25}$$

$$I_1 = \mathbf{C}E_2 - \mathbf{D}I_2 \tag{7–26}$$

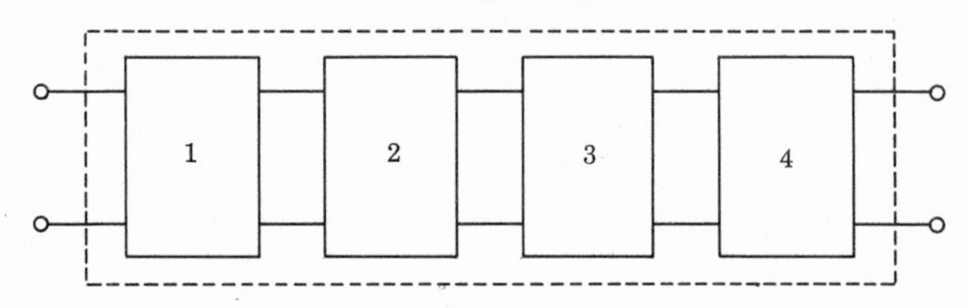

Fig. 7–4.

with the definitions

$$\mathbf{A} = -\frac{y_{22}}{y_{21}}$$

$$\mathbf{B} = -\frac{1}{y_{21}}$$

$$\mathbf{C} = -\frac{y_{11}y_{22} - y_{12}y_{21}}{y_{21}}^{*}$$

$$\mathbf{D} = -\frac{y_{11}}{y_{21}}$$

As seen in the last section, four independent quantities are not always needed to characterize a twoport. By direct substitution of the definitions following (7–26), we find

$$\mathbf{AD} - \mathbf{BC} = \frac{y_{12}}{y_{21}} = \eta \tag{7–27}$$

Hence for a reciprocal twoport

$$\mathbf{AD} - \mathbf{BC} = 1 \tag{7–28}$$

* The numerator of this fraction is the determinant of equations (7–4) and (7–5) and is often represented as $|y|$.

and for a unilateral twoport (see definition in Section 7–2)

$$\mathbf{AD}-\mathbf{BC} = 0 \qquad (7\text{–}29)$$

Further, we have seen that for a twoport which is symmetrical as well as reciprocal $y_{11} = y_{22}$ as well as $y_{12} = y_{21}$, so that

$$\mathbf{A} = \mathbf{D} \qquad (7\text{–}30)$$

in addition to the relation (7–28).

The solution of (7–25) and (7–26) yields E_2 and I_2 in terms of E_1 and I_1. Noting from (7–27) that η is the negative of the determinant of equations (7–25) and (7–26), we find

$$E_2 = \frac{\mathbf{D}}{\eta}E_1 - \frac{\mathbf{B}}{\eta}I_1 \qquad (7\text{–}31)$$

$$I_2 = \frac{\mathbf{C}}{\eta}E_1 - \frac{\mathbf{A}}{\eta}I_1 \qquad (7\text{–}32)$$

provided that $\eta \neq 0$.*

* The quantity η may be regarded as a ratio of backward to forward gain.(2) In order to demonstrate this, we require a definition of each gain. Since the gain of a circuit is devoid of meaning unless the terminating impedance is specified, we shall define forward gain as $G_F = E_2/E$ in Fig. 7–A, and backward gain as $G_B = E_1'/E'$ in Fig. 7–B. The twoport and terminating impedances Z are the same in each figure. (See p. 314 for the figures.)

From Fig. 7–A,

$$E - I_1Z = E_1 \qquad (a)$$

$$-I_2Z = E_2 \qquad (b)$$

Substitution of equations (7–25) and (7–26) into (a) and (b) yields

$$E = \mathbf{A}E_2 - \mathbf{B}I_2 + Z\mathbf{C}E_2 - Z\mathbf{D}I_2 \qquad (c)$$

and

$$\frac{1}{G_F} = (\mathbf{A}+\mathbf{D}) + Z\mathbf{C} + \frac{1}{Z}\mathbf{B} \qquad (d)$$

where we have used $Z = E_2/(-I_2)$.

Now Fig. 7–B yields

$$E' - I_2'Z = E_2' \qquad (e)$$

$$-I_1'Z = E_1' \qquad (f)$$

On substitution of these into (7–31) and (7–32), we find

$$E' = \frac{\mathbf{D}}{\eta}E_1' - \frac{\mathbf{B}}{\eta}I_1' + Z\frac{\mathbf{C}}{\eta}E_1' - Z\frac{\mathbf{A}}{\eta}I_1' \qquad (g)$$

and

$$\frac{1}{G_B} = \frac{1}{\eta}\left[(\mathbf{D}+\mathbf{A}) + Z\mathbf{C} + \frac{1}{Z}\mathbf{B}\right] \qquad (h)$$

whence

$$\eta = \frac{G_B}{G_F} \qquad (i)$$

For a reciprocal twoport, $\eta = 1$, and therefore $G_B = G_F$. This is now another statement of the reciprocity theorem. Although $\eta \neq 0$ is assumed in (7–31) and (7–32), the limit of equation (i) is reasonable for $\eta = 0$, i.e., $\eta = 0$ corresponds to $G_B = 0$, and the network is unilateral.

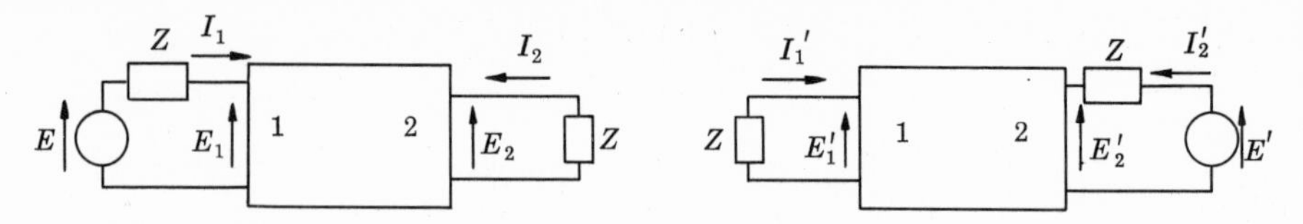

Fig. 7–A (for footnote, p. 313). Fig. 7–B (for footnote, p. 313).

There are a number of other pairs of equations relating E_1, E_2, I_1, and I_2. Since they are easily obtained from the pairs already found, they need merely be listed:

$$E_1 = z_{11}I_1 + z_{12}I_2 \tag{7–33}$$

$$E_2 = z_{21}I_1 + z_{22}I_2 \tag{7–34}$$

and

$$I_1 = g_{11}E_1 + g_{12}I_2 \tag{7–35}$$

$$E_2 = g_{21}E_1 + g_{22}I_2 \tag{7–36}$$

and finally

$$E_1 = h_{11}I_1 + h_{12}E_2 \tag{7–37}$$

$$I_2 = h_{21}I_1 + h_{22}E_2 \tag{7–38}$$

where the z, g, and h coefficients are additional parameters for the characterization of twoports.

Relationships between the parameters of twoports have been tabulated by Brown and Bennett[(2)] in Table 7–2. In this table, A, B, C, and D correspond to our **A**, **B**, **C**, and **D**.

TABLE 7–2*

$A =$	$A =$	$\dfrac{z_{11}}{z_{21}} =$	$-\dfrac{y_{22}}{y_{21}} =$	$\dfrac{1}{g_{21}} =$	$-\dfrac{\lvert h\rvert}{h_{21}}$
$B =$	$B =$	$\dfrac{\lvert z\rvert}{z_{21}} =$	$-\dfrac{1}{y_{21}} =$	$\dfrac{g_{22}}{g_{21}} =$	$-\dfrac{h_{11}}{h_{21}}$
$C =$	$C =$	$\dfrac{1}{z_{21}} =$	$-\dfrac{\lvert y\rvert}{y_{21}} =$	$\dfrac{g_{11}}{g_{21}} =$	$-\dfrac{h_{22}}{h_{21}}$

* Reproduced, by permission of the *Proceedings of the IRE*, from the paper by J. S. Brown and F. D. Bennett, "The Application of Matrices to Vacuum-Tube Circuits," *Proc.* IRE, Vol. 36, pp. 844–52, 1948. Our Table 7–2 is a slightly abridged form of Appendix I of that paper.

TABLE 7–2 (continued)

$$D = D = \frac{z_{22}}{z_{21}} = -\frac{y_{11}}{y_{21}} = \frac{|g|}{g_{21}} = -\frac{1}{h_{21}}$$

$$z_{11} = \frac{A}{C} = z_{11} = \frac{y_{22}}{|y|} = \frac{1}{g_{11}} = \frac{|h|}{h_{22}}$$

$$z_{12} = \frac{\eta}{C} = \eta z_{21} = -\frac{\eta y_{21}}{|y|} = \frac{\eta g_{21}}{g_{11}} = -\frac{\eta h_{21}}{h_{22}}$$

$$z_{21} = \frac{1}{C} = z_{21} = -\frac{y_{21}}{|y|} = \frac{g_{21}}{g_{11}} = -\frac{h_{21}}{h_{22}}$$

$$z_{22} = \frac{D}{C} = z_{22} = \frac{y_{11}}{|y|} = \frac{|g|}{g_{11}} = \frac{1}{h_{22}}$$

$$y_{11} = \frac{D}{B} = \frac{z_{22}}{|z|} = y_{11} = \frac{|g|}{g_{22}} = \frac{1}{h_{11}}$$

$$y_{12} = -\frac{\eta}{B} = -\frac{\eta z_{21}}{|z|} = \eta y_{21} = -\frac{\eta g_{21}}{g_{22}} = \frac{\eta h_{21}}{h_{11}}$$

$$y_{21} = -\frac{1}{B} = -\frac{z_{21}}{|z|} = y_{21} = -\frac{g_{21}}{g_{22}} = \frac{h_{21}}{h_{11}}$$

$$y_{22} = \frac{A}{B} = \frac{z_{11}}{|z|} = y_{22} = \frac{1}{g_{22}} = \frac{|h|}{h_{11}}$$

$$g_{11} = \frac{C}{A} = \frac{1}{z_{11}} = \frac{|y|}{y_{22}} = g_{11} = \frac{h_{22}}{|h|}$$

$$g_{12} = -\frac{\eta}{A} = -\frac{\eta z_{21}}{z_{11}} = \frac{\eta y_{21}}{y_{22}} = -\eta g_{21} = \frac{\eta h_{21}}{|h|}$$

$$g_{21} = \frac{1}{A} = \frac{z_{21}}{z_{11}} = -\frac{y_{21}}{y_{22}} = g_{21} = -\frac{h_{21}}{|h|}$$

$$g_{22} = \frac{B}{A} = \frac{|z|}{z_{11}} = \frac{1}{y_{22}} = g_{22} = \frac{h_{11}}{|h|}$$

$$h_{11} = \frac{B}{D} = \frac{|z|}{z_{22}} = \frac{1}{y_{11}} = \frac{g_{22}}{|g|} = h_{11}$$

$$h_{12} = \frac{\eta}{D} = \frac{\eta z_{21}}{z_{22}} = -\frac{\eta y_{21}}{y_{11}} = \frac{\eta g_{21}}{|g|} = -\eta h_{21}$$

TABLE 7-2 (continued)

$$h_{21} = -\frac{1}{D} = -\frac{z_{21}}{z_{22}} = \frac{y_{21}}{y_{11}} = -\frac{g_{21}}{|g|} = h_{21}$$

$$h_{22} = \frac{C}{D} = \frac{1}{z_{22}} = \frac{|y|}{y_{11}} = \frac{g_{11}}{|g|} = h_{22}$$

where

$$|z| = z_{11}z_{22}-\eta(z_{21})^2$$
$$|y| = y_{11}y_{22}-\eta(y_{21})^2$$
$$|g| = g_{11}g_{22}+\eta(g_{21})^2$$
$$|h| = h_{11}h_{22}+\eta(h_{21})^2$$
$$|z| = |y|^{-1}$$
$$|g| = |h|^{-1}$$
$$\eta = AD-BC.$$

7-4 Direct Methods of Computing Two-Port Network Parameters

Basically, the coefficients appearing in the various pairs of equations are defined in terms of the network determinant Δ and its minors Δ_{11}, Δ_{22}, Δ_{12}, Δ_{21}. At this point, however, the reader may ask: What is the advantage over loop analysis, if the loop equations must be written and their determinant and minors evaluated? The answer to this objection lies in the fact that the loop equations were necessary to prove the existence of four characteristic parameters. Now that we know that the parameters exist, easier means can be used for their determination. These parameters will be evaluated in terms of simple hypothetical or actual measurements. With simple circuits the determination will be easy. More complicated networks will be regarded as composed of simpler twoports. In later sections we shall develop the means of finding the coefficients of a network in terms of those of the elementary twoports of which it is constituted.

Direct Computation of y Coefficients

Let us consider the y coefficients of equations (7–4) and (7–5). With a short circuit across the output terminals of the structure of Fig. 7–1, the instantaneous voltage $e_2 = 0$. Therefore in a problem involving only the sinusoidal steady state, the complex voltage $E_2 = 0$. In other problems,

E_2 represents the Laplace transform of e_2, and since $\mathcal{L}0 = 0$, we have again $E_2 = 0$. Hence, in any case, a short circuit across the output terminals reduces equations (7–4) and (7–5) to

$$I_1 = y_{11}E_1 \tag{7–39}$$

$$I_2 = y_{21}E_1 \tag{7–39a}$$

Clearly, then y_{11} is the admittance calculated (or measured) at the input with the output shorted. The coefficient y_{21} is a transfer admittance equal to the ratio of I_2 to E_1 when the output terminals are shorted. In a similar manner, we can find means of calculating (or measuring) y_{22} and y_{12} as the ratios I_2/E_2 and I_1/E_2 respectively when $E_1 = 0$.

Direct Computation of z Coefficients

If we seek the z coefficients of equations (7–33) and (7–34), we can use an analogous (or dual) procedure. With end 2 of the twoport of Fig. 7–1 open-circuited, $i_2 = 0$. Whether I_2 represents complex current of a-c analysis or the Laplace transform of i_2, $I_2 = 0$ in equations (7–33) and (7–34), so that

$$E_1 = z_{11}I_1 \tag{7–40}$$

$$E_2 = z_{21}I_1 \tag{7–41}$$

Clearly z_{11} is the input impedance to the network with end 2 open-circuited, while z_{21} is a transfer impedance equal to the ratio of E_2 to I_1 when the output terminals are open. As in the preceding illustration, the coefficients z_{22} and z_{12} are determined respectively as the ratios E_2/I_2 and E_1/I_2 when $I_1 = 0$, i.e., with end 1 open-circuited.

Direct Computation of **A B C D** *Coefficients*

A similar procedure may be used to obtain the **A B C D** coefficients of a two-port network. With end 2 of the circuit open, $I_2 = 0$ as before, and (7–25) and (7–26) become

$$E_1 = \mathbf{A}E_2 \tag{7–42}$$

$$I_1 = \mathbf{C}E_2 \tag{7–43}$$

Here **A** is seen to be the reciprocal of the gain when the output is open-circuited. Dividing (7–42) by (7–43) we find that **A**/**C** is the input impedance with the output terminals open. With end 2 short-circuited, $E_2 = 0$, and (7–25) and (7–26) become

$$E_1 = -\mathbf{B}I_2 \tag{7–44}$$

$$I_1 = -\mathbf{D}I_2 \tag{7–45}$$

Division of (7–44) by (7–45) yields **B**/**D** as the input impedance to the circuit with the output shorted. The coefficients **B** and **D** can then be calculated by inspection of the circuit and equation (7–44) or (7–45), whichever is easier. One should bear in mind that, with reciprocal or with unilateral twoports, at most three of these coefficients need be separately determined. When the twoport is reciprocal the remaining coefficient can be obtained from (7–28). When the twoport is unilateral the remaining coefficient will be found from (7–29).

Parameters of a Symmetrical Π *Section*

As an illustration of the foregoing methods, let us find the parameters of the symmetrical Π section illustrated in Fig. 7–5, in which Z_a is the impedance of the series branch and $Y_b/2$ the admittance of each shunt branch.

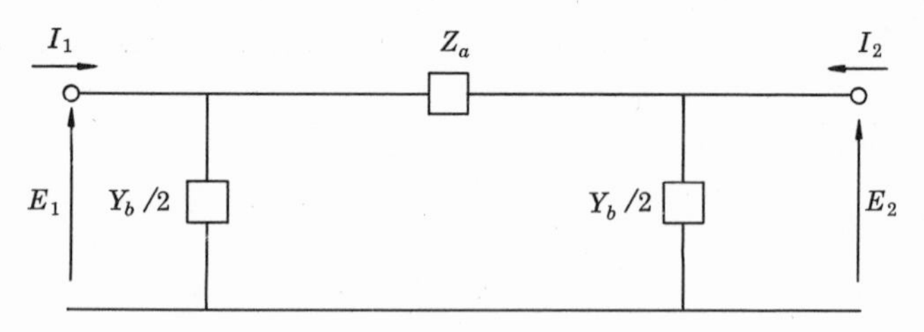

Fig. 7–5.

With the output terminals short-circuited, equations (7–25) and (7–26) reduce to (7–44) and (7–45). From the figure it is evident that

$$-I_2 = \frac{\dfrac{2}{Y_b}}{Z_a + \dfrac{2}{Y_b}} I_1 \tag{7–46}$$

On comparison with (7–45), this relation easily yields

$$\mathbf{D} = 1 + \frac{Z_a Y_b}{2} \tag{7–47}$$

Since the Π structure of interest is symmetrical, we have at once

$$\mathbf{A} = 1 + \frac{Z_a Y_b}{2} \tag{7–48}$$

Since $\mathbf{B}/\mathbf{D}$ is the input impedance when the output terminals are short-circuited, we find

$$\mathbf{B} = Z_a \tag{7-49}$$

Finally, since the circuit consists of passive bilateral two-terminal elements, it is a reciprocal twoport. Therefore $\mathbf{C}$ may be obtained from (7–28):

$$\mathbf{C} = Y_b\left(1 + \frac{Z_a Y_b}{4}\right) \tag{7-50}$$

Two Illustrative Problems

Let us consider a voltage, e_1, applied to the input terminals of the circuit of Fig. 7–6 at the instant $t = 0$. Let the voltage source be ideal,

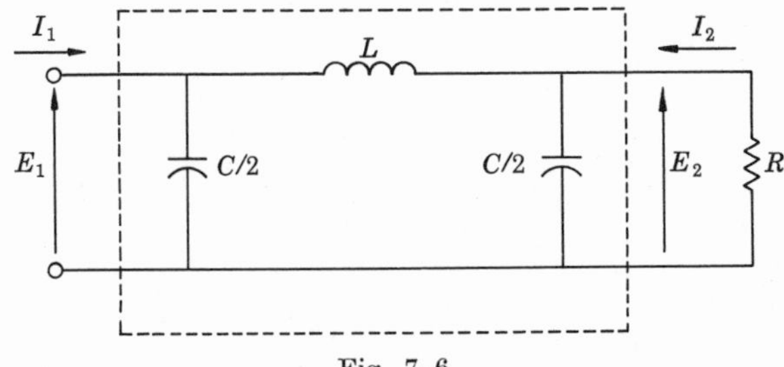

Fig. 7–6.

i.e., have negligible internal impedance. We seek the voltage across the resistor R. With the source ideal, the left-hand capacitance cannot affect the solution for the output voltage, e_2. Retaining this capacitance in the circuit diagram, however, we may use the parameters which have just been derived for the symmetrical Π structure.

The Laplace transform of the desired voltage is the E_2 of twoport theory, and the Laplace transform of the applied voltage, e_1, is E_1. If the circuit is initially at rest,* our twoport theory applies and we may use the coefficients of the symmetrical Π structure within the dotted lines of Fig. 7–6. Since the applied voltage transform is given, while the output voltage transform is sought, we shall find the **A B C D** coefficients most convenient. In fact, only two of these will be necessary. With our usual

* Since the circuit is regarded as initially at rest, the current i_1, equal to $\mathfrak{L}^{-1}I_1$, must have an impulse term, which will express the instantaneous charging of the left-hand capacitance by the idealized voltage source. The voltage e_2 does not contain an impulse term.

sign convention, we have $-I_2 = E_2/R$. Substituting into (7–25), i.e., into $E_1 = \mathbf{A}E_2 - \mathbf{B}I_2$, yields

$$E_1 = \left(\mathbf{A} + \frac{\mathbf{B}}{R}\right)E_2 \tag{7–51}$$

Thus E_2 and E_1 are directly related without a loop analysis of this circuit. Actually, the loop analysis was done in advance when the existence of two-port network coefficients was proved. Now Fig. 7–6 and equations (7–48) and (7–49) yield at once

$$\mathbf{A} = 1 + \frac{s^2LC}{2} \tag{7–52}$$

$$\mathbf{B} = sL \tag{7–53}$$

where sL is substituted for Z and sC for Y. Solving equation (7–51) for E_2, we have, with the aid of (7–52) and (7–53),

$$E_2 = E_1 \frac{2}{LC} \frac{1}{s^2 + \dfrac{2}{RC}s + \dfrac{2}{LC}} \tag{7–54}$$

If now the applied voltage is a direct voltage, V, we have E_1 equal to V/s. Inserting V/s for E_1, we obtain

$$E_2 = \frac{V}{s} \frac{2}{LC} \frac{1}{s^2 + \dfrac{2}{RC}s + \dfrac{2}{LC}} \tag{7–55}$$

There will be, of course, three types of solution to this problem depending on the relative magnitudes of $1/(RC)^2$ and $2/LC$. For concreteness, let us suppose $R = \sqrt{L/C}$ (as it might well be in a filter circuit). Then $E_2\, e^{st}$ will have three simple poles occurring at

$$\begin{aligned} s &= 0 \\ s &= -\frac{1}{\sqrt{LC}} + j\frac{1}{\sqrt{LC}} \\ s &= -\frac{1}{\sqrt{LC}} - j\frac{1}{\sqrt{LC}} \end{aligned} \tag{7–56}$$

The time-function can now be obtained either with the aid of the partial fraction expansion (Section 3–17) or directly by the residue method (developed in Chapter 3 and illustrated in Chapter 4). Bearing in mind that two of these poles are complex conjugates, we can easily find the residues at the poles of $E_2 e^{st}$. Adding the residues yields the output voltage

$$e_2 = V + \sqrt{2}\, V e^{-t/\sqrt{LC}} \cos\left(\frac{1}{\sqrt{LC}} t - \frac{5\pi}{4}\right) \tag{7-57}$$

when $R = \sqrt{L/C}$. It is of interest to note that, since the inductance prevents instantaneous charging of the right-hand capacitance, the initial value of e_2 is zero. The final value of e_2 is, of course, V, since the inductance is merely a short circuit in the d-c steady state.

We shall now solve a second problem. Let a sinusoidal voltage be applied to the input terminals of the circuit of Fig. 7–6. We seek the steady-state output voltage, the input voltage being taken as a phase reference. The Π structure coefficients are now unchanged, except that we write $j\omega$ in place of s. Hence $\mathbf{A} = 1 - (\omega^2 LC/2)$ and $\mathbf{B} = j\omega L$. Equation (7–54) is still valid provided that we interpret E_1 and E_2 as complex voltages rather than transforms, and provided that we replace s by $j\omega$. The complex voltage E_2 is then given by

$$E_2 = E_1 \frac{2}{LC} \cdot \frac{1}{-\omega^2 + \frac{2}{RC} j\omega + \frac{2}{LC}} \tag{7-58}$$

Whence the ratio of the magnitude of input to output voltage is given by

$$\frac{|E_1|}{|E_2|} = \left[\left(1 - \frac{\omega^2 LC}{2}\right)^2 + \left(\frac{\omega L}{R}\right)^2\right]^{1/2} \tag{7-59}$$

The phase shift through the network follows from (7–58) and is

$$\underline{/E_1} - \underline{/E_2} = \tan^{-1} \frac{\frac{\omega L}{R}}{1 - \frac{\omega^2 LC}{2}} \tag{7-60}$$

7-5 Matrix Notation and Elements of Matrix Algebra[1,4,6]

As mentioned earlier, it is often convenient to consider a network as made up of elementary twoports. In Fig. 7–4, each box is such a unit, while the dotted lines bound the over-all network, which also is seen to have a pair of input and a pair of output terminals. We shall often seek the coefficients of such an over-all network in terms of those of its simpler components.

Another illustration of this approach to network analysis is shown in Fig. 7–7. Box 1 contains the equivalent circuit of a vacuum tube, the Π section in box 2 consists of the interelectrode capacitances of the tube, and, finally, box 3 contains the load resistor. The over-all network bounded by the dotted lines is open-circuited. Hence in a problem involving the sinusoidal steady state, the over-all network's **A** coefficient, as a function of $j\omega$, is the reciprocal of the complex gain of the amplifier. In a general problem, **A**, as a function of s, yields the ratio of input voltage transform to output voltage transform. The problem then reduces to that of finding the **A** coefficient of the over-all network in terms of the

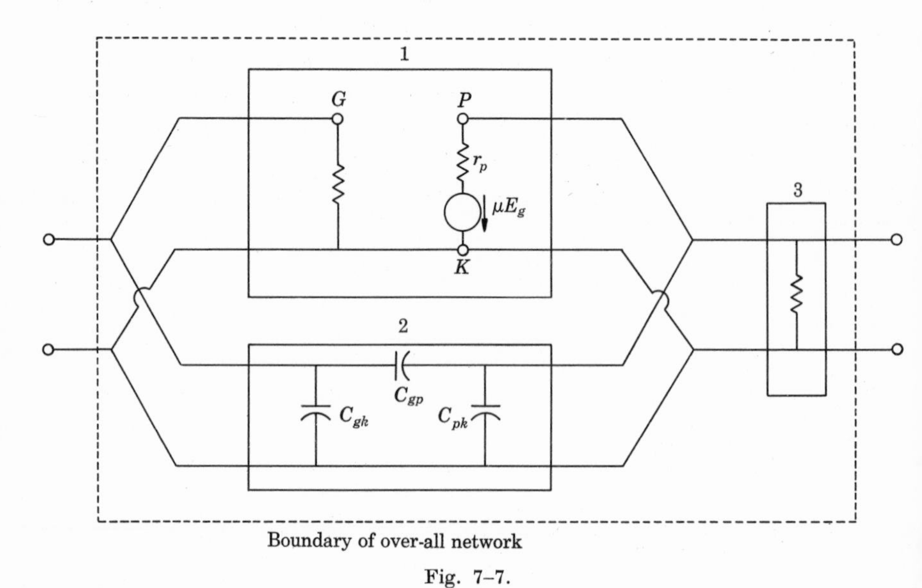

Fig. 7–7.

coefficients of the individual twoports 1, 2, and 3. This will be easy with the techniques of matrix algebra.

Definition of a Matrix

A matrix is a rectangular array of numbers as

$$\begin{Vmatrix} a_{11} & a_{12} & a_{13} \\ a_{21} & a_{22} & a_{23} \end{Vmatrix}$$

where the first subscript of each element is the number of the row (horizontal) and the second is the number of the column (vertical). Often the matrix will be the list of coefficients in a set of simultaneous equations. Thus the square matrix

$$\begin{Vmatrix} \mathbf{A} & \mathbf{B} \\ \mathbf{C} & \mathbf{D} \end{Vmatrix}$$

will be referred to as the matrix of equations (7–25) and (7–26).* As such, it must be distinguished from a determinant. The latter has a value, while the matrix is simply a list of coefficients arranged in a certain order.

Definition of Equality of Matrices

Two matrices are said to be equal provided that correspondingly placed coefficients in each are equal. Thus

$$\begin{Vmatrix} a_{11} & a_{12} & a_{13} \\ a_{21} & a_{22} & a_{23} \end{Vmatrix} = \begin{Vmatrix} b_{11} & b_{12} & b_{13} \\ b_{21} & b_{22} & b_{23} \end{Vmatrix} \tag{7–61}$$

provided that $a_{11} = b_{11}$, $a_{12} = b_{12}$, $a_{13} = b_{13}$, $a_{21} = b_{21}$, $a_{22} = b_{22}$, and $a_{23} = b_{23}$. We know that if two twoports are equivalent as viewed from their input and output terminals, their coefficients will be equal, i.e., we shall have $\mathbf{A} = \mathbf{A}'$, $\mathbf{B} = \mathbf{B}'$, $\mathbf{C} = \mathbf{C}'$, and $\mathbf{D} = \mathbf{D}'$ Hence for networks equivalent in this sense,

$$\begin{Vmatrix} \mathbf{A} & \mathbf{B} \\ \mathbf{C} & \mathbf{D} \end{Vmatrix} = \begin{Vmatrix} \mathbf{A}' & \mathbf{B}' \\ \mathbf{C}' & \mathbf{D}' \end{Vmatrix} \tag{7–62}$$

The same will, of course, be true of the matrices of the z, y, g, and h coefficients.

Definition of Addition of Matrices

Addition is a procedure for forming a new matrix as follows:

$$\begin{Vmatrix} a_{11} & a_{12} & a_{13} \\ a_{21} & a_{22} & a_{23} \end{Vmatrix} + \begin{Vmatrix} b_{11} & b_{12} & b_{13} \\ b_{21} & b_{22} & b_{23} \end{Vmatrix}$$
$$= \begin{Vmatrix} a_{11}+b_{11} & a_{12}+b_{12} & a_{13}+b_{13} \\ a_{21}+b_{21} & a_{22}+b_{22} & a_{23}+b_{23} \end{Vmatrix} \tag{7–63}$$

Each element in the matrix after the equal sign is obtained by adding corresponding elements of the matrices preceding the equal sign.

* When the matrix is written in this way, the equations are regarded as $E_1 = \mathbf{A}E_2 + \mathbf{B}(-I_2)$ and $I_1 = \mathbf{C}E_2 + \mathbf{D}(-I_2)$, i.e., **A**, **B**, **C**, and **D** are the coefficients, and E_2 and $-I_2$ are the variables on the right-hand side.

As an indication of the manner in which matrix addition will be applied, let us suppose

$$\begin{Vmatrix} y_{11} & y_{12} \\ y_{21} & y_{22} \end{Vmatrix}$$

to be the matrix of the y coefficients of the tube circuit in box 1 in Fig. 7–7, p. 322. Let

$$\begin{Vmatrix} y_{11}' & y_{12}' \\ y_{21}' & y_{22}' \end{Vmatrix}$$

be the matrix of the Π section of interelectrode capacitances in box 2 of the same figure. From later theory it will be clear that the y coefficients of the twoport consisting of the tube and of the interelectrode capacitances are obtained by addition of these matrices.

Definition of Subtraction of Matrices

Replacement of the plus signs by minus signs in (7–63) yields an illustration of the rule for subtraction of matrices. Thus a new matrix is formed by subtracting corresponding elements.

Definition of a Matrix Equal to Zero

A matrix is said to be zero if *every* element is zero. Thus a matrix subtracted from itself yields a matrix equal to zero. One should observe the sharp difference here between a matrix and a determinant. For the latter to be zero, it is not necessary that any of its elements be zero.

Definition of Multiplication of a Matrix by a Scalar

By a scalar here we mean a number, real or complex, as opposed to a matrix. Multiplication of a matrix by a scalar means multiplication of every element of the matrix by that scalar. Thus

$$s \begin{Vmatrix} a_{11} & a_{12} & a_{13} \\ a_{21} & a_{22} & a_{23} \end{Vmatrix} = \begin{Vmatrix} sa_{11} & sa_{12} & sa_{13} \\ sa_{21} & sa_{22} & sa_{23} \end{Vmatrix} \qquad (7\text{–}64)$$

(Here again the rule differs sharply from that for a determinant.) It will be observed that addition of, say, 5 equal matrices will yield a result equivalent to multiplication by the scalar $s = 5$.

Definition of Multiplication of a Matrix by a Matrix

Matrix multiplication will yield a direct method for determining the coefficients of an over-all network consisting of a cascade of twoports such as that illustrated in Fig. 7–4. The definition of matrix multiplication requires that the number of columns of the first matrix equal the number of rows in the second one. Unless the matrices to be multiplied meet this condition, their multiplication is impossible. Before defining matrix multiplication in general, let us suppose that we have a 3-column matrix as the first "factor" and a 3-row matrix as a second one. We shall illustrate the procedure for obtaining a typical element, say c_{23}, of the product matrix. In the equation (7–65), below, only the elements entering c_{23} are shown. All other elements are indicated by a dash. The dots are used to indicate that the number of rows in the first matrix and the number of columns in the second need not be specified.

$$\begin{Vmatrix} — & — & — \\ a_{21} & a_{22} & a_{23} \\ \cdot & \cdot & \cdot \\ \cdot & \cdot & \cdot \\ \cdot & \cdot & \cdot \\ — & — & — \end{Vmatrix} \times \begin{Vmatrix} — & — & b_{13} & \cdots & — \\ — & — & b_{23} & \cdots & — \\ — & — & b_{33} & \cdots & — \end{Vmatrix} = \|c\| \qquad (7\text{–}65)$$

The element c_{23} of the product matrix $\|c\|$ is given by:

$$c_{23} = a_{21}b_{13} + a_{22}b_{23} + a_{23}b_{33} \qquad (7\text{–}65a)$$

This procedure (which appears arbitrary but will be seen to be useful) suggests the general definition of a product of matrices. If $\|a\|$ and $\|b\|$ represent two matrices, $\|a\|$ having n columns and $\|b\|$ having n rows, a typical element c_{ij} of their product matrix $\|c\| = \|a\| \times \|b\|$ is given by

$$c_{ij} = \sum_{k=1}^{n} a_{ik}b_{kj} \qquad (7\text{–}66)$$

A little consideration shows that, with certain exceptions,

$$\|a\| \times \|b\| \neq \|b\| \times \|a\| \qquad (7\text{–}67)$$

A simple and important illustration will clarify the process of matrix multiplication. Namely:

$$\begin{Vmatrix} \mathbf{A}_1 & \mathbf{B}_1 \\ \mathbf{C}_1 & \mathbf{D}_1 \end{Vmatrix} \times \begin{Vmatrix} \mathbf{A}_2 & \mathbf{B}_2 \\ \mathbf{C}_2 & \mathbf{D}_2 \end{Vmatrix} = \begin{Vmatrix} \mathbf{A}_1\mathbf{A}_2 + \mathbf{B}_1\mathbf{C}_2 & \mathbf{A}_1\mathbf{B}_2 + \mathbf{B}_1\mathbf{D}_2 \\ \mathbf{C}_1\mathbf{A}_2 + \mathbf{D}_1\mathbf{C}_2 & \mathbf{C}_1\mathbf{B}_2 + \mathbf{D}_1\mathbf{D}_2 \end{Vmatrix} \qquad (7\text{–}68)$$

On the other hand if we interchange the order of multiplication

$$\begin{Vmatrix} \mathbf{A}_2 & \mathbf{B}_2 \\ \mathbf{C}_2 & \mathbf{D}_2 \end{Vmatrix} \times \begin{Vmatrix} \mathbf{A}_1 & \mathbf{B}_1 \\ \mathbf{C}_1 & \mathbf{D}_1 \end{Vmatrix} = \begin{Vmatrix} \mathbf{A}_2\mathbf{A}_1 + \mathbf{B}_2\mathbf{C}_1 & \mathbf{A}_2\mathbf{B}_1 + \mathbf{B}_2\mathbf{D}_1 \\ \mathbf{C}_2\mathbf{A}_1 + \mathbf{D}_2\mathbf{C}_1 & \mathbf{C}_2\mathbf{B}_1 + \mathbf{D}_2\mathbf{D}_1 \end{Vmatrix} \qquad (7\text{–}69)$$

Matrices are unequal unless all corresponding elements are equal. We see at once that if $\mathbf{B}_2\mathbf{C}_1 \neq \mathbf{B}_1\mathbf{C}_2$, then $\mathbf{A}_1\mathbf{A}_2+\mathbf{B}_1\mathbf{C}_2 \neq \mathbf{A}_2\mathbf{A}_1+\mathbf{B}_2\mathbf{C}_1$. (Other correspondingly placed coefficients are, of course, also unequal.) Hence the right-hand sides of (7–68) and (7–69) are unequal matrices. It will be interesting to observe later that the non-commutative property of matrix multiplication (i.e., $||a|| \times ||b|| \neq ||b|| \times ||a||$) will describe the parallel fact of network theory that the two circuit arrangements shown in Fig. 7–8 are not equivalent.

A few further facts should be pointed out as cautions in dealing with matrix products. Two non-zero matrices may have a matrix equal to zero as their product. Hence one cannot set either factor equal to zero simply because the product is zero. Matrix division is undefined, and cancellation of factors from both sides of an equation will generally lead to error.*

Representation of Sets of Simultaneous Equations by Matrices

Let us consider the matrix product

$$\begin{Vmatrix} y_{11} & y_{12} \\ y_{21} & y_{22} \end{Vmatrix} \times \begin{Vmatrix} E_1 \\ E_2 \end{Vmatrix} = \begin{Vmatrix} y_{11}E_1+y_{12}E_2 \\ y_{21}E_1+y_{22}E_2 \end{Vmatrix} \tag{7–70}$$

Here a matrix of two columns multiplies a matrix of two rows to yield the single-column matrix on the right-hand side. The elements of this product matrix are seen to be the right-hand sides of equations (7–4) and (7–5), and may therefore be replaced by I_1 and I_2, respectively. We observe, then, that the simultaneous equations (7–4) and (7–5) become the matrix equation

$$\begin{Vmatrix} I_1 \\ I_2 \end{Vmatrix} = \begin{Vmatrix} y_{11} & y_{12} \\ y_{21} & y_{22} \end{Vmatrix} \times \begin{Vmatrix} E_1 \\ E_2 \end{Vmatrix} \tag{7–71}$$

* A simple example will be of interest. It is easy to verify that

$$\begin{Vmatrix} a & a \\ a & a \end{Vmatrix} \times \begin{Vmatrix} b & b \\ b & b \end{Vmatrix} = \begin{Vmatrix} a & a \\ a & a \end{Vmatrix} \times \begin{Vmatrix} \frac{b}{2} & \frac{3b}{2} \\ \frac{3b}{2} & \frac{b}{2} \end{Vmatrix}$$

However:

$$\begin{Vmatrix} b & b \\ b & b \end{Vmatrix} \neq \begin{Vmatrix} \frac{b}{2} & \frac{3b}{2} \\ \frac{3b}{2} & \frac{b}{2} \end{Vmatrix}$$

so that cancellation of the first matrix on each side of the equation is clearly an error.

This means that we shall be able to treat a set of simultaneous equations as a unit, i.e., as a single matrix equation.

In a similar manner, the pair (7–25) and (7–26) becomes the matrix equation

$$\begin{Vmatrix} E_1 \\ I_1 \end{Vmatrix} = \begin{Vmatrix} \mathbf{A} & \mathbf{B} \\ \mathbf{C} & \mathbf{D} \end{Vmatrix} \times \begin{Vmatrix} E_2 \\ -I_2 \end{Vmatrix} \tag{7–72}$$

and again the pair (7–35) and (7–36) becomes

$$\begin{Vmatrix} I_1 \\ E_2 \end{Vmatrix} = \begin{Vmatrix} g_{11} & g_{12} \\ g_{21} & g_{22} \end{Vmatrix} \times \begin{Vmatrix} E_1 \\ I_2 \end{Vmatrix} \tag{7–73}$$

The Determinant and the Inverse of a Matrix

The determinant of a matrix is simply the determinant formed by its elements. Clearly, only a square matrix has a determinant. For simplicity, let us use here the notation $\|a\|$ for the square matrix

$$\begin{Vmatrix} a_{11} & \cdots & a_{1n} \\ \cdot & & \cdot \\ \cdot & & \cdot \\ \cdot & & \cdot \\ a_{n1} & \cdots & a_{nn} \end{Vmatrix}$$

and the notation $|a|$ for the determinant of the matrix $\|a\|$.

Let us suppose that the simultaneous equations (7–4) and (7–5) are solved for E_1 and E_2 in terms of I_1 and I_2 (see equations 7–33 and 7–34). The resulting equations, still in terms of the y coefficients, will be

$$E_1 = \frac{y_{22}}{|y|} I_1 - \frac{y_{12}}{|y|} I_2 \tag{7–74}$$

$$E_2 = -\frac{y_{21}}{|y|} I_1 + \frac{y_{11}}{|y|} I_2 \tag{7–75}$$

In matrix form, (7–74) and (7–75) are written

$$\begin{Vmatrix} E_1 \\ E_2 \end{Vmatrix} = \frac{1}{|y|} \begin{Vmatrix} y_{22} & -y_{12} \\ -y_{21} & y_{11} \end{Vmatrix} \times \begin{Vmatrix} I_1 \\ I_2 \end{Vmatrix} \tag{7–76}$$

where the definition of multiplication of a matrix by a scalar justifies taking out $1/|y|$. The matrix

$$\frac{1}{|y|}\begin{Vmatrix} y_{22} & -y_{12} \\ -y_{21} & y_{11} \end{Vmatrix}$$

is termed the inverse of the $\|y\|$ matrix and is denoted $\|y\|^{-1}$. Comparison of (7–74) and (7–75) with (7–33) and (7–34) shows that $y_{22}/|y| = z_{11}$, $-y_{12}/|y| = z_{12}$, $-y_{21}/|y| = z_{21}$, and $y_{11}/|y| = z_{22}$. We may, therefore, express (7–33) and (7–34) as

$$\begin{Vmatrix} E_1 \\ E_2 \end{Vmatrix} = \begin{Vmatrix} y_{11} & y_{12} \\ y_{21} & y_{22} \end{Vmatrix}^{-1} \times \begin{Vmatrix} I_1 \\ I_2 \end{Vmatrix} \tag{7–77}$$

provided that $|y| \neq 0$. Thus the matrix of z coefficients is the inverse of the matrix of y coefficients when the determinant of the y's is not zero.

In a similar manner, (7–31) and (7–32) become

$$\begin{Vmatrix} E_1 \\ -I_2 \end{Vmatrix} = \begin{Vmatrix} \mathbf{A} & \mathbf{B} \\ \mathbf{C} & \mathbf{D} \end{Vmatrix}^{-1} \times \begin{Vmatrix} E_1 \\ +I_1 \end{Vmatrix} \tag{7–78}$$

provided that $\eta \neq 0$.

Finally, we have from (7–35), (7–36), and (7–73) the conclusion that (7–37) and (7–38) can be represented by

$$\begin{Vmatrix} E_1 \\ I_2 \end{Vmatrix} = \begin{Vmatrix} g_{11} & g_{12} \\ g_{21} & g_{22} \end{Vmatrix}^{-1} \times \begin{Vmatrix} I_1 \\ E_2 \end{Vmatrix} \tag{7–79}$$

provided that $|g| \neq 0$.

The inverse of a matrix will exist only if the determinant of that matrix is not zero. The general form for the inverse matrix is

$$\frac{1}{\Delta}\begin{Vmatrix} A_{11} & A_{21} & \cdots & A_{n1} \\ A_{12} & A_{22} & \cdots & A_{n2} \\ \cdot & \cdot & & \cdot \\ \cdot & \cdot & & \cdot \\ \cdot & \cdot & & \cdot \\ A_{1n} & A_{2n} & \cdots & A_{nn} \end{Vmatrix}$$

where Δ is the determinant of the matrix and the A's are the cofactors of the elements indicated by the subscripts.

For completeness, we add that a matrix times its inverse will yield the unit matrix (or identity matrix) I, a matrix having the property

$$I\|a\| = \|a\|I = \|a\|$$

when $||a||$ is a square matrix having the same number of rows as I. The matrix I is:

$$I = \begin{Vmatrix} 1 & 0 & 0 & \cdot & \cdot & \cdot & 0 \\ 0 & 1 & 0 & \cdot & \cdot & \cdot & 0 \\ 0 & 0 & 1 & \cdot & \cdot & \cdot & 0 \\ \cdot & \cdot & \cdot & & & & \cdot \\ \cdot & \cdot & \cdot & & & & \cdot \\ \cdot & \cdot & \cdot & & & & \cdot \\ 0 & 0 & 0 & \cdot & \cdot & \cdot & 1 \end{Vmatrix} \tag{7-80}$$

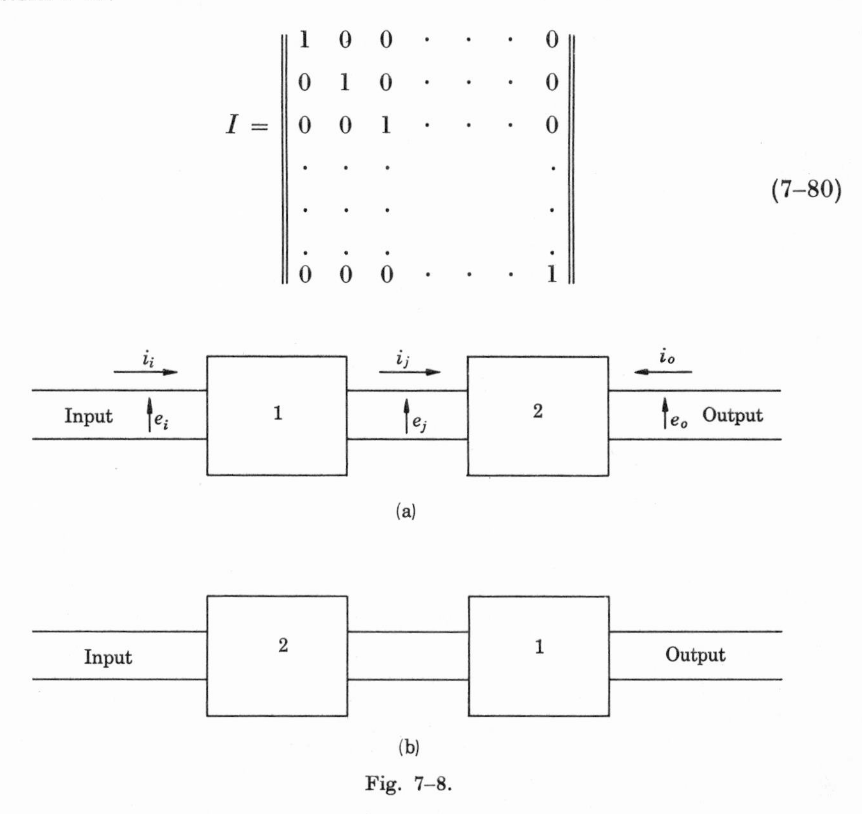

Fig. 7–8.

7-6 Applications of Matrix Multiplication to Network Analysis[4]

In matrix algebra we have a compact means of handling the pairs of equations which represent two-port networks. Perhaps the most frequent application is that of matrix multiplication. Let us consider the cascade of two twoports illustrated in Fig. 7–8(a).

We wish to relate the current and voltage at the input terminals to those at the output terminals of the over-all network. Let the instantaneous voltage and current be denoted at the input terminals by e_i and i_i, at the junction of the two networks by e_j and i_j, and at the output terminals by e_o and i_o. The sign conventions are shown in Fig. 7–8(a). In general problems, then, $E = \mathcal{L}e$ and $I = \mathcal{L}i$ for each voltage and current. When our only concern is a sinusoidal steady-state solution, these capital letters represent complex voltages and currents. Now using (7–72) for box 1, we have

$$\begin{Vmatrix} E_i \\ I_i \end{Vmatrix} = \begin{Vmatrix} \mathbf{A}_1 & \mathbf{B}_1 \\ \mathbf{C}_1 & \mathbf{D}_1 \end{Vmatrix} \times \begin{Vmatrix} E_j \\ I_j \end{Vmatrix} \tag{7–81}$$

where $\mathbf{A}_1$, $\mathbf{B}_1$, $\mathbf{C}_1$, $\mathbf{D}_1$ are the coefficients of the first twoport. The sign of I_j is positive since it is drawn to the right.

For the second twoport, we have at once

$$\begin{Vmatrix} E_j \\ I_j \end{Vmatrix} = \begin{Vmatrix} \mathbf{A}_2 & \mathbf{B}_2 \\ \mathbf{C}_2 & \mathbf{D}_2 \end{Vmatrix} \times \begin{Vmatrix} E_o \\ -I_o \end{Vmatrix} \tag{7–82}$$

Substituting the right-hand side of (7–82) for the matrix

$$\begin{Vmatrix} E_j \\ I_j \end{Vmatrix}$$

in equation (7–81), we find*

$$\begin{Vmatrix} E_i \\ I_i \end{Vmatrix} = \begin{Vmatrix} \mathbf{A}_1 & \mathbf{B}_1 \\ \mathbf{C}_1 & \mathbf{D}_1 \end{Vmatrix} \times \begin{Vmatrix} \mathbf{A}_2 & \mathbf{B}_2 \\ \mathbf{C}_2 & \mathbf{D}_2 \end{Vmatrix} \times \begin{Vmatrix} E_o \\ -I_o \end{Vmatrix} \tag{7–83}$$

The desired matrix with elements which are the coefficients of the over-all network is the product of the two square matrices in (7–83). This product was obtained in equation (7–68) as an illustration of matrix multiplication. If the positions of the two networks are interchanged as as in Fig. 7–8(b), we must interchange the order of multiplication of the matrices. The new over-all network will now have a different set of coefficients given by the matrix on the right-hand side of (7–69). Hence we have here an extremely compact proof that cascades will not, in general, be equivalent if we interchange the relative positions of the separate twoports.

Illustrative Problems

The low-pass filter network of Fig. 7–9 will serve to illustrate the application of matrix multiplication to network analysis. The circuit in that figure is regarded as composed of three sections in cascade. The open-circuit voltage at the output terminals of the *over-all* network is, then, seen to be identical with the voltage across the load resistor. We may easily verify, by substitution of the coefficients into equations

* When (7–82) is substituted into (7–81), we first obtain a product of three matrices with the last two bracketed together. The brackets are omitted from (7–83), however, because of the fact[6] that $\|a\| \times [\|b\| \times \|c\|] = [\|a\| \times \|b\|] \times \|c\|$.

(7–25) and (7–26), that the **A B C D** matrix of the first twoport, consisting, merely, of a series resistor, is

$$\begin{Vmatrix} 1 & R \\ 0 & 1 \end{Vmatrix}$$

We can verify with equal ease that the **A B C D** matrix of the third twoport, consisting, simply, of a shunt resistor, is

$$\begin{Vmatrix} 1 & 0 \\ \dfrac{1}{R} & 1 \end{Vmatrix}$$

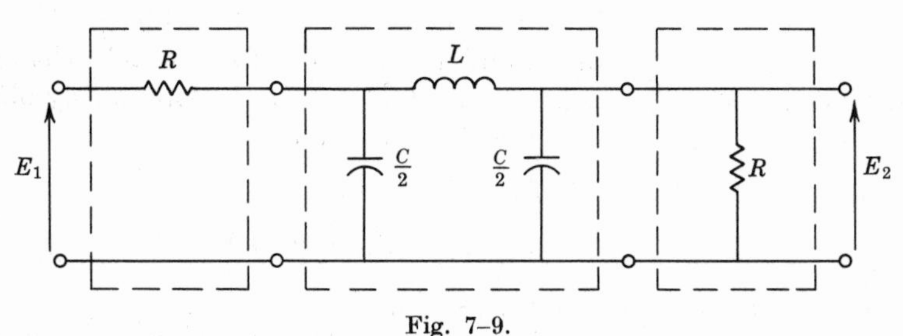

Fig. 7–9.

Hence, with the subscript π to denote the parameters of the Π section, the matrix of the over-all network is given by the product

$$\begin{Vmatrix} 1 & R \\ 0 & 1 \end{Vmatrix} \times \begin{Vmatrix} \mathbf{A}_\pi & \mathbf{B}_\pi \\ \mathbf{C}_\pi & \mathbf{D}_\pi \end{Vmatrix} \times \begin{Vmatrix} 1 & 0 \\ \dfrac{1}{R} & 1 \end{Vmatrix}$$

Let us first multiply the last two matrices *without changing relative positions.* Then,

$$\begin{Vmatrix} \mathbf{A}_\pi & \mathbf{B}_\pi \\ \mathbf{C}_\pi & \mathbf{D}_\pi \end{Vmatrix} \times \begin{Vmatrix} 1 & 0 \\ \dfrac{1}{R} & 1 \end{Vmatrix} = \begin{Vmatrix} \mathbf{A}_\pi + \dfrac{\mathbf{B}_\pi}{R} & - \\ \mathbf{C}_\pi + \dfrac{\mathbf{D}_\pi}{R} & - \end{Vmatrix} \tag{7–84}$$

The second column of the right-hand matrix is indicated by dashes because these elements will not be needed to obtain the **A** coefficient of the over-all network. Only the **A** coefficient is desired, since the output terminals of the over-all network are open-circuited.

With care to avoid interchange in the order of the matrices, the multiplication is completed by

$$\begin{Vmatrix} 1 & R \\ 0 & 1 \end{Vmatrix} \times \begin{Vmatrix} \mathbf{A}_\pi + \dfrac{\mathbf{B}_\pi}{R} & - \\ \mathbf{C}_\pi + \dfrac{\mathbf{D}_\pi}{R} & - \end{Vmatrix} = \begin{Vmatrix} \mathbf{A}_\pi + \dfrac{\mathbf{B}_\pi}{R} + R\mathbf{C}_\pi + \mathbf{D}_\pi & - \\ - & - \end{Vmatrix} \tag{7-85}$$

Equation (7–85) yields at once

$$E_1 = \left[\mathbf{A}_\pi + \frac{\mathbf{B}_\pi}{R} + R\mathbf{C}_\pi + \mathbf{D}_\pi\right] E_2 \tag{7-86}$$

since I_2 must be zero.

Now let $R = \sqrt{L/C}$, that is, the ratio $\sqrt{Z_a/Y_b}$, and let the cutoff frequency of the filter correspond to ω_c equal to $2/\sqrt{LC}$. Using these quantities and the expressions for $\mathbf{A}_\pi$, $\mathbf{B}_\pi$, $\mathbf{C}_\pi$, and $\mathbf{D}_\pi$ previously obtained for a symmetrical II section, Fig. 7–5, we have

$$E_2 = \frac{E_1}{2} \cdot \frac{1}{s_n{}^3 + 2s_n{}^2 + 2s_n + 1} \tag{7-87}$$

where the normalized variable $s_n = s/\omega_c$.

Let us now suppose that E_1 represents the transform of a suddenly applied direct voltage step. Equation (7–87) will be used to determine the output voltage as a function of time. Either by inspection or by one of the longer methods for determining the roots of a cubic equation, we find that $s_n = -1$ is a root of the denominator of (7–87). Division of the denominator polynomial by its factor $(s_n + 1)$, then, yields a quadratic expression as the other factor; the roots of the latter are, of course, directly found. Hence, factoring the denominator in terms of its roots, and inserting $V/\omega_c s_n$ (equal to the transform V/s) for E_1, we find

$$E_2 = \frac{1}{2} \cdot \frac{V}{\omega_c} \cdot \frac{1}{s_n} \cdot \frac{1}{(s_n + 1)(s_n + 0.5 + j\sqrt{0.75})(s_n + 0.5 - j\sqrt{0.75})} \tag{7-88}$$

Now if, in the inverse Laplace transform

$$(1/2\pi j) \int_{c-j\infty}^{c+j\infty} E_2(s) e^{st} ds$$

the change in variable $s_n = s/\omega_c$ be introduced, we find

$$e_2 = \frac{\omega_c}{2\pi j} \int_{(c/\omega_c)-j\infty}^{(c/\omega_c)+j\infty} E_n(s_n) e^{\omega_c s_n t} ds_n \tag{7-89}$$

where $E_n(s_n)$ is the function $E_2(s)$ expressed in terms of s_n. The shifting of the Bromwich contour from c to c/ω_c does not hamper the evaluation of the integral, since the half-plane to the right of c in the s-plane corresponds to the half-plane to the right of c/ω_c in the s_n-plane. Then

$$e_2 = \frac{V}{2} \sum \text{Res} \frac{e^{\omega_c s_n t}}{s_n(s_n+1)(s_n+0.5+j\sqrt{0.75})(s_n+0.5-j\sqrt{0.75})} \tag{7–90}$$

We have four simple poles, two of which are complex conjugates. Evaluating the residues at $s_n = 0$, $s_n = -1$, and $s_n = -0.5+j\sqrt{0.75}$, and taking twice the real part of this last residue, we find

$$e_2 = \frac{V}{2}\left[1 - e^{-\omega_c t} + \frac{1}{\sqrt{0.75}} e^{-0.5\,\omega_c t} \cos\left(0.75\omega_c t - \frac{3\pi}{2}\right)\right] \tag{7–91}$$

Direct evaluation by residues (Chapters 3 and 4) has been used to obtain equation (7–91). The reader may prefer, first, to expand (7–88) by the partial fraction technique developed in Chapter 3.

It is interesting to note that, for large values of time (i.e., $t = \infty$), $e_2 = V/2$, as it must, since the inductance offers no resistance to steady d-c, and the capacitors appear as open circuits. At $t = 0$ we find that $e_2 = 0$; this is consistent with the fact that the filter is initially at rest and current cannot change suddenly in an inductance.

We shall now solve for the steady-state sinusoidal response of the same low-pass filter. The symbols E_1 and E_2 become complex numbers representing the magnitude and phase of the source e.m.f. and output voltage. The necessary matrix analysis is identical with that carried out above for the transient problem. Equation (7–87), therefore, will again be applicable. The variable s, however, must be replaced by $j\omega$. Recalling that $s_n = s/\omega_e$, we shall substitute $j\omega_n$ for s_n in (7–87), defining ω_n as ω/ω_c. Then

$$E_2 = \frac{E_1}{2} \cdot \frac{1}{-j\omega_n^3 - 2\omega_n^2 + 2j\omega_n + 1} \tag{7–92}$$

Putting (7–92) in polar form, we find the relationships

$$|E_2| = \frac{|E_1|}{2} \frac{1}{\sqrt{1+\omega_n^6}} \tag{7–93}$$

and

$$\underline{/E_1} - \underline{/E_2} = \tan^{-1} \frac{\omega_n(2-\omega_n^2)}{1-2\omega_n^2} \tag{7–94}$$

with, again, $\omega_n = \omega/\omega_c$.

The factor 1/2 in (7–93) represents the voltage drop across the source resistance and would be present even if we connected the source to the load as in Fig. 7–10 where the Π section is entirely omitted. The range of frequency corresponding to $0 < \omega_n < 1$ is the transmission band of the filter. It is demonstrated in elementary filter theory that the filter can be terminated in such a way that $|E_2|/|E_1|$ will approximate 1/2 in the transmission range. With our resistive termination, the factor 1/2 is multiplied in (7–93) by $1/\sqrt{1+\omega_n^6}$ which varies from 1 to $1/\sqrt{2}$ in the

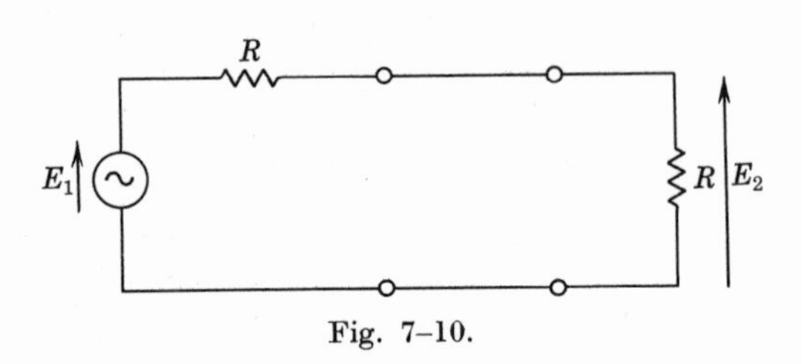

Fig. 7–10.

transmission range. Thus there will be some attenuation in the transmission band. Beyond cutoff, ω_n^6 increases very rapidly, so that ultimately the output voltage falls off as $1/\omega_n^3$.

7-7 Application of Matrix Addition to Network Analysis

In addition to the cascade connection, discussed in Section 7–6, two-port networks may be connected in parallel (Fig. 7–11), in series (Fig. 7–16), in parallel-series (Fig. 7–17), and in series-parallel (Fig. 7–18).

Parallel Connection

We consider the application of matrix algebra to the parallel connection (Fig. 7–11). It will be observed, in that figure, that the input and output terminals of A have been connected in parallel respectively with the input and output terminals of B. We shall seek the coefficients of the circuit enclosed by the dotted lines.

The parameters of a twoport will not always remain valid when a circuit is connected *across* the twoport, i.e., from its input to its output side, as in Fig. 7–11. When these parameters are invalidated, the resulting network must be analyzed as an entirely new circuit, in order to obtain its twoport coefficients. An obvious example is shown in Fig. 7–12, where the two lower terminals of the lattice are short-circuited. In many instances, on the other hand, the parameters of the individual twoports are unaltered by the connection, and we shall be able to obtain the matrix of the over-all network from the matrices of its parts.

Certain simple tests developed by Brune[3] provide an easy means of determining whether or not the parameters of the individual twoports remain valid under a connection such as that shown in Fig. 7–11. We

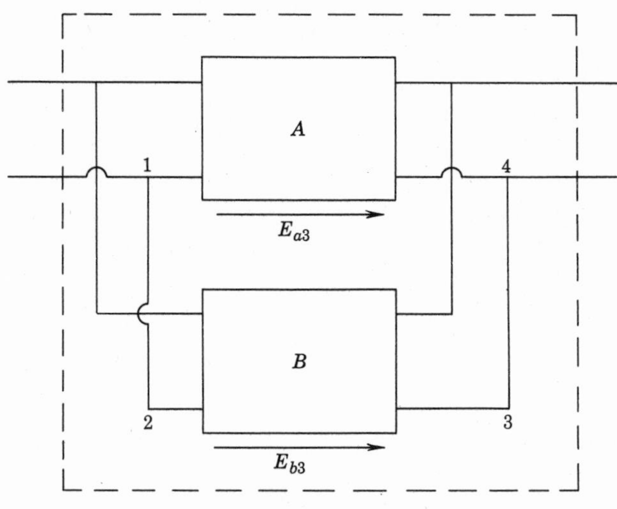

Fig. 7–11.

first consider E_{a3} and E_{b3} of the figure, with the twoports temporarily separated. Recalling the superposition theorem of Chapter 6, we have for each twoport:

$$E_{a3} = \alpha_{a1}E_{a1} + \alpha_{a2}E_{a2} \tag{7-95}$$

$$E_{b3} = \alpha_{b1}E_{b1} + \alpha_{b2}E_{b2} \tag{7-96}$$

where E_{a1} and E_{a2} correspond to the voltages across the input and output terminals, respectively, of network A. For network B, these quantities are designated as E_{b1} and E_{b2}.

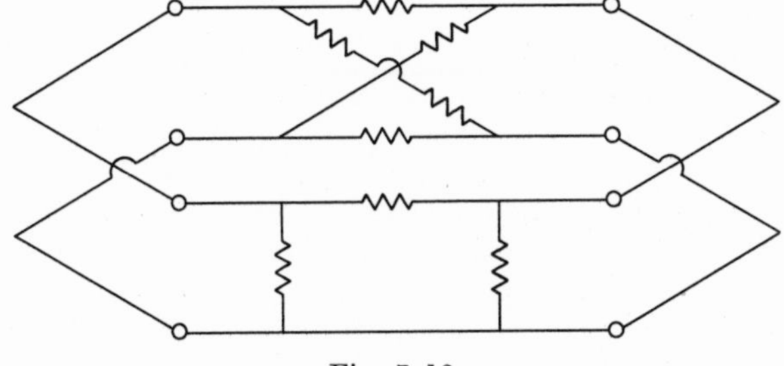

Fig. 7–12.

If $\alpha_{a1} = \alpha_{b1}$ and $\alpha_{a2} = \alpha_{b2}$, the equality of E_{a3} and E_{b3} will be assured by equating the end voltages, i.e., by $E_{a1} = E_{b1}$ and $E_{a2} = E_{b2}$. Since the parallel connection equates these voltages, networks with equal α's may be connected in parallel at both ends without the voltage across the bottom (or top) of either one being disturbed. On the other hand, if $\alpha_{a1} \neq \alpha_{b1}$, or $\alpha_{a2} \neq \alpha_{b2}$, or if both these inequalities occur, equations (7–95) and (7–96) will ordinarily yield $E_{a3} \neq E_{b3}$. (Exceptions occur for particular values of end voltages or a particular relationship between input and output end voltages. Such exceptions, however, are of no importance, since we seek conditions under which the parameters of the twoports will hold for all possible end voltages.) If (7–95) and (7–96) yield $E_{a3} \neq E_{b3}$ even though $E_{a1} = E_{b1}$ and $E_{a2} = E_{b2}$, we note that "something is wrong," for the parallel connection clearly equates E_{a3} and E_{b3}. We conclude, then, that current driven in a path through 1, 2, 3, 4, 1 brings E_{a3} to equality with E_{b3}.* Hence in this case we cannot regard the twoport as entirely specified by its parameters which were determined on the basis of input–output conditions alone.

We find, therefore, that $\alpha_{a1} = \alpha_{a2}$ and $\alpha_{b1} = \alpha_{b2}$ are the conditions under which each twoport in the parallel connection will be specified by its own coefficients. The equality of the α's will easily be checked by Brune's first and second tests as follows:

First: For the parallel connection of Fig. 7–11, suppose the input ends are connected in parallel as in the figure, but the output ends remain separated, and a short circuit is placed across the output terminals of each twoport. The circuit is then examined to see whether there is any potential difference between the short-circuited ends of the two twoports. Now with the output ends individually short-circuited, the instantaneous voltage across each is zero, that is, $e_{a2} = e_{b2} = 0$, whence $E_{a2} = E_{b2} = 0$. With the input ends connected in parallel, the instantaneous voltages across these ends, e_{a1} and e_{b1}, are identical, so that $E_{a1} = E_{b1}$. If we find that there is no potential difference at any instant between the two short-circuited ends, then $E_{a3} = E_{b3}$, since the corresponding instantaneous voltages, e_{a3} and e_{b3}, are equal. Equations (7–95) and (7–96) now lead to the conclusion $\alpha_{a1} = \alpha_{b1}$. *Second*: We must repeat the test from the other end of the network to determine whether or not $\alpha_{a2} = \alpha_{b2}$.

When the corresponding α's are equal, each twoport in the parallel connection is specified by the same coefficients as those derived for it alone. Since equating instantaneous voltages equates their transforms or the corresponding complex voltages of a-c analysis, the conclusions

* Guillemin[4] points out that under these conditions the current entering the upper input (or output) terminal will not equal that leaving the corresponding lower terminal of the same twoport.

of Brune's tests must apply whether we are concerned with Laplace transforms or a steady-state sinusoidal problem.

When it is ascertained that $\alpha_{a1} = \alpha_{b1}$ and $\alpha_{a2} = \alpha_{b2}$, the individual sections connected as in Fig. 7–11 are characterized by the matrix equations

$$\begin{Vmatrix} I_{a1} \\ I_{a2} \end{Vmatrix} = \begin{Vmatrix} y_{a11} & y_{a12} \\ y_{a21} & y_{a22} \end{Vmatrix} \times \begin{Vmatrix} E_1 \\ E_2 \end{Vmatrix} \tag{7–97}$$

and

$$\begin{Vmatrix} I_{b1} \\ I_{b2} \end{Vmatrix} = \begin{Vmatrix} y_{b11} & y_{b12} \\ y_{b21} & y_{b22} \end{Vmatrix} \times \begin{Vmatrix} E_1 \\ E_2 \end{Vmatrix} \tag{7–98}$$

The transforms (or complex voltages) E_1 and E_2 do not carry the subscripts a and b, since the parallel connection makes them identical for both twoports. Adding (7–97) and (7–98) yields

$$\begin{Vmatrix} I_{a1}+I_{b1} \\ I_{a2}+I_{b2} \end{Vmatrix} = \left[\begin{Vmatrix} y_{a11} & y_{a12} \\ y_{a21} & y_{a22} \end{Vmatrix} + \begin{Vmatrix} y_{b11} & y_{b12} \\ y_{b21} & y_{b22} \end{Vmatrix} \right] \times \begin{Vmatrix} E_1 \\ E_2 \end{Vmatrix} \tag{7–99}$$

or

$$\begin{Vmatrix} I_{a1}+I_{b1} \\ I_{a2}+I_{b2} \end{Vmatrix} = \begin{Vmatrix} y_{a11}+y_{b11} & y_{a12}+y_{b12} \\ y_{a21}+y_{b21} & y_{a22}+y_{b22} \end{Vmatrix} \times \begin{Vmatrix} E_1 \\ E_2 \end{Vmatrix} \tag{7–100}$$

The $||y||$ matrix of equation (7–100) is the $||y||$ matrix of the over-all network of Fig. 7–11, provided that Brune's tests for the equality of the α's are satisfied.

Illustrative Problem

As an illustrative problem, let us consider the cathode follower circuit of Fig. 7–13(a).[8,9]* We regard its equivalent circuit as consisting of three twoports, Fig. 7–13(b). The equivalent circuit of the tube itself is a unilateral twoport and its y coefficients may be called y_{T11}, y_{T12}, y_{T21}, and y_{T22}, with $y_{T12} = 0$. The capacitances form a passive Π section and constitute a reciprocal twoport. We shall term its coefficients y_{s11}, y_{s12}, y_{s21}, and y_{s22}, with $y_{s12} = y_{s21}$. There is a direct connection between the low input and low output terminals of the tube twoport. Since this is also true of the twoport formed by the capacitances, Brune's tests are immediately satisfied. The matrix of the twoport

***Fig. 7–13(a) follows, with modifications, Fig. 6–9 of Seely,[9] by permission of McGraw-Hill Book Company, Inc.**

consisting of tube and capacitances is therefore obtained by the addition

$$\begin{Vmatrix} y_{T11} & 0 \\ y_{T21} & y_{T22} \end{Vmatrix} + \begin{Vmatrix} y_{s11} & y_{s21} \\ y_{s21} & y_{s22} \end{Vmatrix} = \begin{Vmatrix} y_{T11}+y_{s11} & y_{s21} \\ y_{T21}+y_{s21} & y_{T22}+y_{s22} \end{Vmatrix} \quad (7\text{–}101)$$

Corresponding to the y coefficients of the twoport containing both tube and capacitances, we have the parameters $\mathbf{A}_{Ts}$, $\mathbf{B}_{Ts}$, $\mathbf{C}_{Ts}$, and

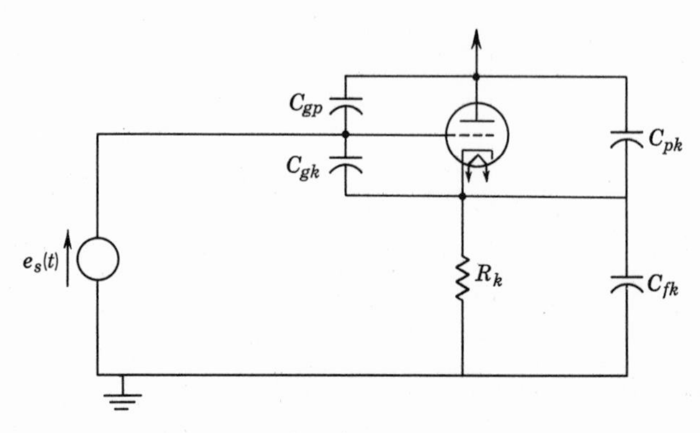

Fig. 7–13(a).

$\mathbf{D}_{Ts}$ related to the y's as in Table 7–2. Regarding the load resistance R as a twoport, we may obtain the ratio of input and output voltages by using only the coefficients $\mathbf{A}_{Ts}$ and $\mathbf{B}_{Ts}$, thus:

$$\begin{Vmatrix} \mathbf{A}_{Ts} & \mathbf{B}_{Ts} \\ - & - \end{Vmatrix} \times \begin{Vmatrix} 1 & 0 \\ \dfrac{1}{R} & 1 \end{Vmatrix} = \begin{Vmatrix} \mathbf{A}_{Ts} + \dfrac{\mathbf{B}_{Ts}}{R} & - \\ - & - \end{Vmatrix} \quad (7\text{–}102)$$

where the dashes represent coefficients which we shall not need.

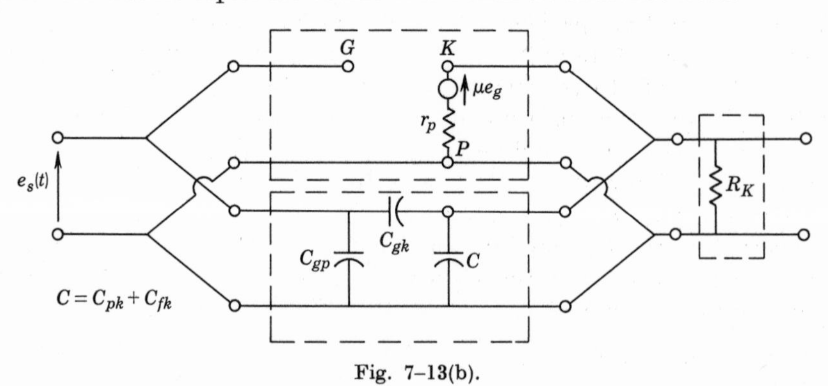

Fig. 7–13(b).

Equations (7–101) and (7–102) illustrate the structure of the method. The y coefficients of the tube and Π circuits will generally be available. For the present, however, it will be well to derive them. From the equivalent circuit of the tube alone (Fig. 7–14), we have

$$E_2 = \mu E_g + r_p I_2 \tag{7–103}$$

where

$$E_g = -E_2 + E_1 \tag{7–104}$$

so that

$$I_2 = \frac{-\mu}{r_p} E_1 + \frac{1+\mu}{r_p} E_2 \tag{7–105}$$

whence $y_{T21} = -\mu/r_p = -g_m$, and $y_{T22} = (1+\mu)/r_p$. Since I_1, in this circuit, is zero regardless of E_1 or E_2, we have $y_{T11} = y_{T12} = 0$.

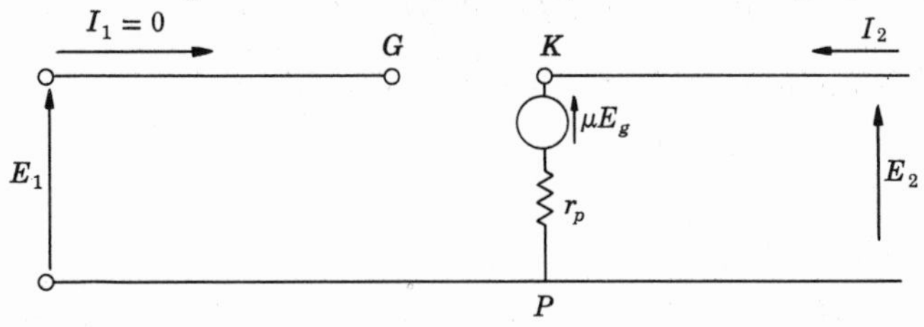

Fig. 7–14.

The grounded-plate tube is, of course, a feedback circuit since the grid voltage E_g is affected by E_2. Regarded as a twoport, it is unilateral since I_1 and E_1 are completely uninfluenced by E_2. This is expressed by $y_{T12} = 0$.

The y coefficients of a Π section (Fig. 7–15) are easily determined (see Section 7–4). First, short-circuiting the output terminals yields

$$y_{s11} = s(C_{gp} + C_{gk}) \tag{7–106}$$

$$y_{s12} = y_{s21} = -sC_{gk} \tag{7–107}$$

Now moving the short circuit to the input terminals yields

$$y_{s22} = s(C + C_{gk}) \tag{7–108}$$

Using Table 7–2, we have at once

$$\mathbf{A}_{Ts} = -\frac{y_{T22} + y_{s22}}{y_{T21} + y_{s21}} = \frac{\dfrac{1+\mu}{r_p} + s(C + C_{gk})}{g_m + sC_{gk}} \tag{7–109}$$

and

$$\frac{\mathbf{B}_{Ts}}{R} = \frac{-1}{R(y_{T21}+y_{s21})} = \frac{1}{R(g_m+sC_{gk})} \tag{7-110}$$

The reciprocal of the **A** coefficient of the complete network (tube, capacitances, and load resistor) yields the ratio of output to input voltage transforms. We therefore find

$$\frac{E_2}{E_1} = \frac{1}{\mathbf{A}_{Ts} + \dfrac{\mathbf{B}_{Ts}}{R}} \tag{7-111}$$

i.e.,

$$\frac{E_2}{E_1} = \frac{(\mu+sC_{gk}r_p)R}{(1+\mu)R+Rr_p(C+C_{gk})s+r_p} \tag{7-112}$$

After slight simplification, the result (7–112) will be seen to be the same

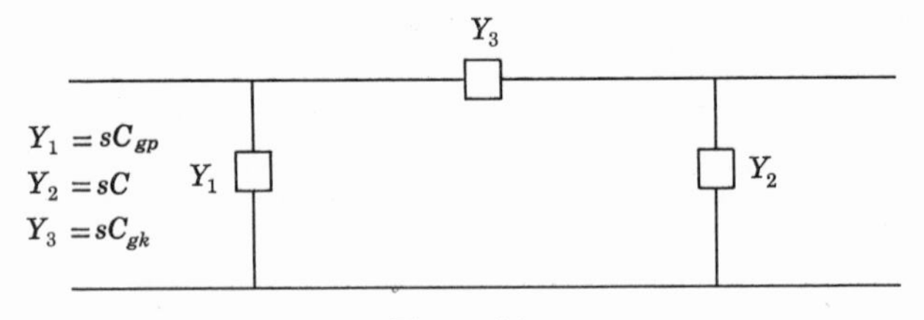

Fig. 7–15.

as equations (5–22) and (5–39) where this circuit was solved by loop and node analysis. Here, as there, we can interpret E_1/E_2 as a ratio of transforms and solve a general problem, or we can replace s by $j\omega$, regard E_1/E_2 as a ratio of complex voltages, and thus have a steady-state sinusoidal solution.

When comparing the matrix method with earlier methods of solution, it is well to bear in mind that the parameters of commonly used two-port networks will generally be available, or easy to determine. With these data at hand, the necessary matrix analysis consists of a few simple routine steps.

Series, Parallel-Series, and Series-Parallel Connections

Having discussed the important cascade and parallel connections of twoports, we now turn to the remaining three ways in which twoport units may be joined.

The input and output terminals of A may be connected in series respectively with the input and output terminals of B, as illustrated in Fig. 7–16. In Fig. 7–17, the input terminals are connected in parallel and the output ones in series. Fig. 7–18 illustrates the reversal of Fig. 7–17, in that the input terminals have been connected in series and the output ones in parallel. In each of these connections, we see one thing in common with the parallel connection discussed at the beginning of this section: either one of the twoports constitutes a path from the input to the output side of the other one. Hence, before combining matrices of the individual sections, we must ascertain whether or not the parameters of each twoport remain valid when the connection has been made.

In the *series* case, (Fig. 7–16), we note that $E_{a3} = E_{b3}$. There is, however, the possibility that this equality requires unequal currents through the

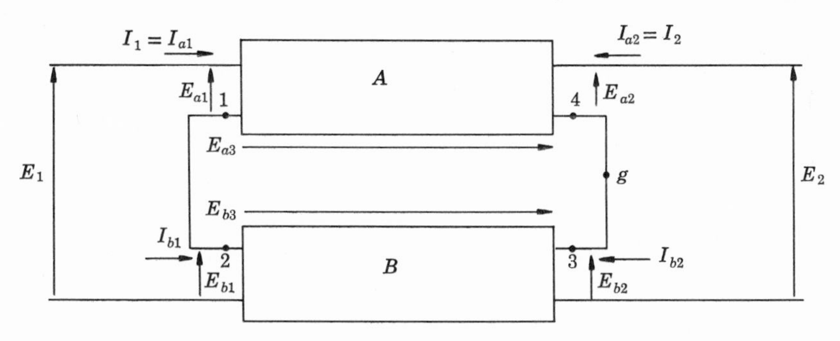

Fig. 7–16.

upper and lower terminals at the ends of each twoport. In order to investigate this, Brune used the equations

$$E_{a3} = \beta_{a1}I_{a1} + \beta_{a2}I_{a2} \tag{7–113}$$

$$E_{b3} = \beta_{b1}I_{b1} + \beta_{b2}I_{b2} \tag{7–114}$$

These equations are, of course, valid for each twoport alone. Temporarily let us assume an e.m.f. source at g (Fig. 7–16). Let this source be of such magnitude that $I_{a2} = I_{b2}$. It is easy to show that if $I_{a2} = I_{b2}$, then $I_{a1} = I_{b1}$ (for the sum of the currents entering the upper twoport is zero). Thus with the generator at g, the currents into the upper terminal and out of the lower terminal are equated at each end of each twoport, and equations (7–113) and (7–114) may be used. Now if $\beta_{a1} = \beta_{b1}$ and $\beta_{a2} = \beta_{b2}$, these equations yield $E_{a3} = E_{b3}$. But if $E_{a3} = E_{b3}$, the e.m.f. of the generator at g equals *zero*, i.e., we have the original series connection with $I_{a1} = I_{b1}$, $I_{a2} = I_{b2}$, and $E_{a3} = E_{b3}$, so that each twoport is characterized by its own coefficients. If, on the other hand, the β's are unequal,

(7–113) and (7–114) yield $E_{a3} \neq E_{b3}$ except for special values of currents I_{a1}, I_{a2}. (These special values are of no importance, since we seek criteria for analyzing the series connection, which hold for all external current values.) Now with the β's unequal, it is evident that the source g is not zero if it maintains the equalities $I_{a1} = I_{b1}$, $I_{a2} = I_{b2}$. Hence when the β's are unequal, the twoports in the series connection cannot be characterized by their individual coefficients.

Brune's tests for the equality of the β coefficients consist of two steps: *First*, suppose that the input terminals are connected in series while the output terminals of each twoport remain open. We then have $I_{a2} = I_{b2} = 0$, and $I_{a1} = I_{b1}$. Now if there is no potential difference, at any instant, between the output terminals which will ultimately be put

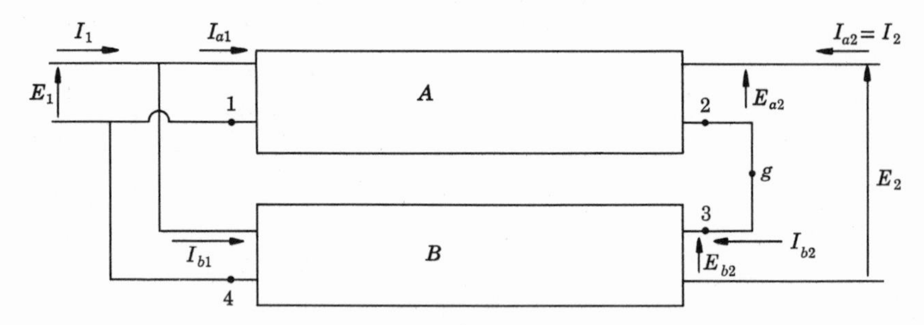

Fig. 7–17.

in series, $E_{a3} = E_{b3}$, and $\beta_{a1} = \beta_{b1}$. *Second*, the network is reversed (i.e., the words "input" and "output" are interchanged above) and the test repeated to determine whether $\beta_{a2} = \beta_{b2}$. If both tests are successful, the matrices of the individual twoports remain valid when the series connection is made at both ends.

The *parallel-series* and *series-parallel* circuits of Figs. 7–17 and 18 are essentially the same circuit with input and output ends reversed. The voltages E_{a3} and E_{b3} will in each case be drawn from a point common to both networks on the input side to a similar common point on the output side. Thus in Fig. 7–17, E_{a3} may be drawn from point 1 to point 2, and E_{b3} from point 4 to point 3. We may, as in the series case, temporarily insert an e.m.f. source at g in order to have equality of currents, and thus arrive at the criteria under which the twoports in these connections are characterized by their individual parameters. Again we shall require that parameters (similar to the β's) be equated, and again Brune's tests will determine when these conditions are met. Rather than describe these tests separately for the parallel-series and series-parallel cases, we can now summarize Brune's tests in a form applicable to all four connections considered in this section, namely parallel, series, parallel-series, and series-parallel:

In Brune's *first test*, in each of these cases, we consider that the desired connection, parallel or series, is made at the input side, and:

(a) when, in the desired connection, the output ends are to be connected in parallel, each twoport is short-circuited at its output end: or

(b) when, in the desired connection, the output ends are to be put in series, each twoport is open-circuited at its output end.

If no potential difference exists between the terminals which we desire to connect at the output end, the first of Brune's tests has yielded a favorable result.

Brune's *second test* may be described identically, save that we must interchange the words *input* and *output*.

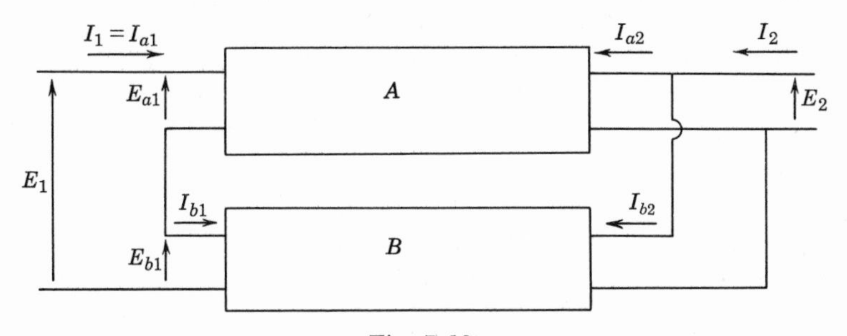

Fig. 7–18.

When Brune's tests, in each direction, yield a favorable result, we may combine matrices for the individual sections in order to obtain a single matrix for the resulting over-all two-port network. Let us first consider the series-connected networks of Fig. 7–16, under the assumption that Brune's tests have given a favorable result. The input and output currents for the over-all network are respectively equal to those of the individual twoports. The input voltages of the individual twoports must be added to obtain the input voltage of the over-all network. The same is true for the voltages at the output side. Since these relationships, which characterize the series connection, must hold at every instant, they are true for the Laplace transforms of voltage and current, and also for the complex voltages and currents used in analysis of the sinusoidal steady-state. The current–voltage relationships of the series connection are most easily expressed through the z-matrix. Hence writing

$$\begin{Vmatrix} E_{a1} \\ E_{a2} \end{Vmatrix} = \begin{Vmatrix} z_{a11} & z_{a12} \\ z_{a21} & z_{a22} \end{Vmatrix} \times \begin{Vmatrix} I_1 \\ I_2 \end{Vmatrix} \tag{7–115}$$

and

$$\begin{Vmatrix} E_{b1} \\ E_{b2} \end{Vmatrix} = \begin{Vmatrix} z_{b11} & z_{b12} \\ z_{b21} & z_{b22} \end{Vmatrix} \times \begin{Vmatrix} I_1 \\ I_2 \end{Vmatrix} \tag{7-116}$$

we find, on adding, that

$$\begin{Vmatrix} E_{a1}+E_{b1} \\ E_{a2}+E_{b2} \end{Vmatrix} = \begin{Vmatrix} z_{a11}+z_{b11} & z_{a12}+z_{b12} \\ z_{a21}+z_{b21} & z_{a22}+z_{b22} \end{Vmatrix} \times \begin{Vmatrix} I_1 \\ I_2 \end{Vmatrix} \tag{7-117}$$

where I_1 and I_2 do not require letter subscripts as they are the same for both networks and for the over-all network.

When Brune's tests yield a satisfactory result, the matrix addition of g coefficients can be applied to the parallel–series connection of Fig. 7–17. The individual twoports are then described by

$$\begin{Vmatrix} I_{a1} \\ E_{a2} \end{Vmatrix} = \begin{Vmatrix} g_{a11} & g_{a12} \\ g_{a21} & g_{a22} \end{Vmatrix} \times \begin{Vmatrix} E_1 \\ I_2 \end{Vmatrix} \tag{7-118}$$

and

$$\begin{Vmatrix} I_{b1} \\ E_{b2} \end{Vmatrix} = \begin{Vmatrix} g_{b11} & g_{b12} \\ g_{b21} & g_{b22} \end{Vmatrix} \times \begin{Vmatrix} E_1 \\ I_2 \end{Vmatrix} \tag{7-119}$$

Here E_1 and I_2 are not distinguished by subscripts a and b, as they must be identical for the two networks in this connection. Adding (7–118) and (7–119) yields the matrix equation for the over-all network

$$\begin{Vmatrix} I_{a1}+I_{b1} \\ E_{a2}+E_{b2} \end{Vmatrix} = \begin{Vmatrix} g_{a11}+g_{b11} & g_{a12}+g_{b12} \\ g_{a21}+g_{b21} & g_{a22}+g_{b22} \end{Vmatrix} \times \begin{Vmatrix} E_1 \\ I_2 \end{Vmatrix} \tag{7-120}$$

With entirely similar reasoning, the series–parallel connection of Fig. 7–18 is described by the matrix equation

$$\begin{Vmatrix} E_{a1}+E_{b1} \\ I_{a2}+I_{b2} \end{Vmatrix} = \begin{Vmatrix} h_{a11}+h_{b11} & h_{a12}+h_{b12} \\ h_{a21}+h_{b21} & h_{a22}+h_{b22} \end{Vmatrix} \times \begin{Vmatrix} I_1 \\ E_2 \end{Vmatrix} \tag{7-121}$$

provided that Brune's tests yield a favorable result.

7-8 Matrices of Vacuum-Tube Circuits in Compact Form

The earlier sections of this chapter have shown that matrix algebra is easy to apply to problems of network analysis, provided that the parameters of basic structures are available. This proviso is particularly true of vacuum-tube circuits, where the presence of the e.m.f., μe_g, and of tube capacitances make the matter of obtaining the coefficients a small problem in itself. We therefore turn to a means* of obtaining and summarizing the parameters of vacuum-tube circuits. The summary will appear as a single matrix equation and a brief associated table defining the symbols in the equation. (See also alternative treatment by Weber[14].)

A useful theorem of matrices will first be obtained. On inspection it is clear that the over-all networks of Fig. 7–19(a) and (b) are identical.

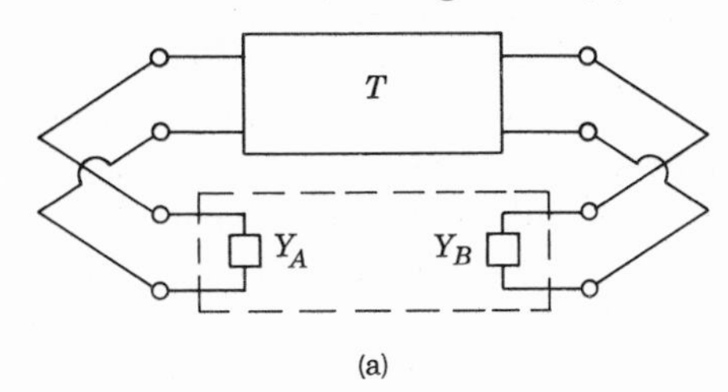

(a)

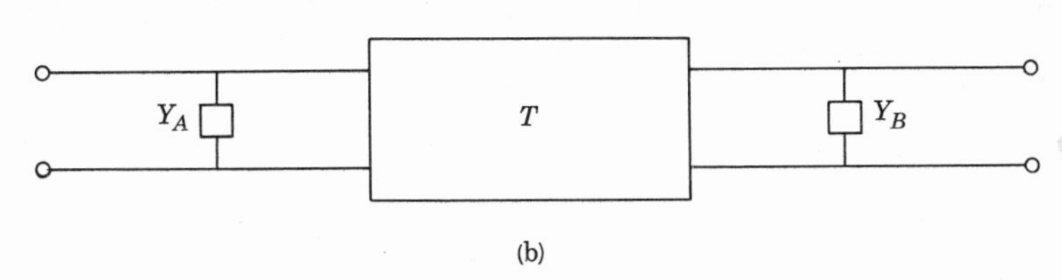

(b)

Fig. 7–19.

The $\|y\|$ matrix of the over-all network, Fig. 7–19(a), can be obtained by the addition of the $\|y\|$ matrices of each twoport in that figure.† Thus

$$\begin{Vmatrix} Y_A & 0 \\ 0 & Y_B \end{Vmatrix} + \begin{Vmatrix} y_{T11} & y_{T12} \\ y_{T21} & y_{T22} \end{Vmatrix} = \begin{Vmatrix} Y_A + y_{T11} & y_{T12} \\ y_{T21} & y_{T22} + Y_B \end{Vmatrix} \qquad (7\text{–}122)$$

From Fig. 7–19(b), we find the **A B C D** matrix of this over-all network as

$$\begin{Vmatrix} \mathbf{A} & \mathbf{B} \\ \mathbf{C} & \mathbf{D} \end{Vmatrix} = \begin{Vmatrix} 1 & 0 \\ Y_A & 1 \end{Vmatrix}$$

$$\times \begin{Vmatrix} y_{T22} & 1 \\ y_{T11}y_{T22} - y_{T12}y_{T21} & y_{T11} \end{Vmatrix} \times \begin{Vmatrix} 1 & 0 \\ Y_B & 1 \end{Vmatrix} \left(-\frac{1}{y_{T21}} \right) \qquad (7\text{–}123)$$

* The method to be followed in this section was developed by V. W. Wall as part of his work in the course "Special Problems in Electrical Engineering" at the Graduate School of Stevens Institute of Technology under the author's supervision (1951).

† The voltage across the bottom of the lower twoport (when alone), Fig. 7–19(a), is indeterminate. However, Brune's tests are not necessary here since a new current loop clearly is not added when the parallel connections are made at each end.

On the right-hand side of the equation, the first and third matrices, respectively, constitute the **A B C D** matrices of Y_A and of Y_B when each is regarded as a single twoport. The center matrix, when multiplied by the scalar $(-1/y_{T21})$, constitutes the **A B C D** matrix of the network in the box T. The position of the scalar in the matrix product is of no consequence.

Now, comparison of (7–122) and (7–123) suggests that admittances included in y_{11} and y_{22} can be removed from the network and regarded instead as cascaded on either side of the remaining network. However, this procedure seems to require that Y_A and Y_B be actual shunt admittances and the network T an actual circuit. Since we may wish to use admittances such as the g_m of a tube for Y_A, it becomes necessary to have our result on a more general, if abstract, basis. This is easily done.

Let the right-hand side of (7–122) be the admittance matrix of a network, where, for convenience, the upper left- and lower right-hand coefficients have been expressed as a sum of two terms. Now using the definitions following equations (7–25) and (7–26), we find the **A B C D** coefficients of the entire network to be

$$\mathbf{A} = -\frac{1}{y_{T21}}(y_{T22}+Y_B) \tag{7–124}$$

$$\mathbf{B} = -\frac{1}{y_{T21}}(1) \tag{7–125}$$

$$\mathbf{C} = -\frac{1}{y_{T21}}(Y_A Y_B+Y_A y_{T22}+Y_B y_{T11}+y_{T11}y_{T22}-y_{T12}y_{T21}) \tag{7–126}$$

$$\mathbf{D} = -\frac{1}{y_{T21}}(Y_A+y_{T11}) \tag{7–127}$$

Multiplication of the three matrices and scalar on the right-hand side of (7–123) yields precisely the same coefficients **A**, **B**, **C**, **D**. Hence if the right-hand side of (7–122) is the $||y||$ matrix of a certain two-port network, the product on the right-hand side of (7–123) yields the **A B C D** matrix of the same network. This result is purely algebraic and its validity does not depend on whether or not Y_A and Y_B are actual circuit elements, or on whether or not taking them out leaves a physically possible circuit as the box T. We shall find that the right-hand side of (7–123) yields a way of describing all three connections of vacuum-tube circuits in one matrix equation.

Grounded-Cathode Connection

The equivalent circuit of the grounded-cathode tube is shown in Fig. 7–20. The equivalent plate-circuit, consisting of a pure e.m.f. μe_g in series with a resistor r_p, has been replaced by an equivalent current source of strength $g_m e_g$ shunted by the admittance g_p, equal to $1/r_p$. The transforms (or the complex a-c quantities) corresponding to e_1, e_2, i_1, and i_2 then satisfy the node equations

$$I_1 = (Y_{gk} + Y_{gp})E_1 - Y_{gp}E_2 \qquad (7\text{–}128)$$

$$I_2 - g_m E_1 = -Y_{gp}E_1 + (Y_{pk} + Y_{gp} + g_p)E_2 \qquad (7\text{–}129)$$

or

$$I_2 = (g_m - Y_{gp})E_1 + (Y_{pk} + Y_{gp} + g_p)E_2 \qquad (7\text{–}130)$$

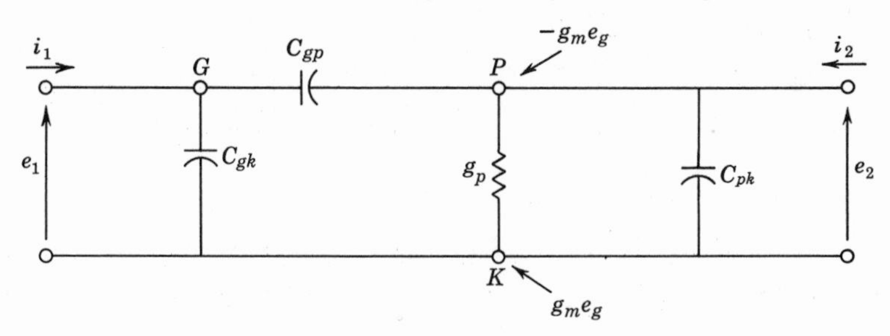

Fig. 7–20.

where

$$Y_{gk} = \frac{1}{sC_{gk}}$$

$$Y_{gp} = \frac{1}{sC_{gp}}$$

and

$$Y_{pk} = \frac{1}{sC_{pk}}$$

The $||y||$ matrix of this four-pole is then

$$||y|| = \begin{Vmatrix} Y_{gk} + Y_{gp} & -Y_{gp} \\ g_m - Y_{gp} & Y_{pk} + Y_{gp} + g_p \end{Vmatrix} \qquad (7\text{–}131)$$

If we regard Y_{gk} and $Y_{pk} + g_p$ as Y_A and Y_B respectively on the right-hand side of (7–122), we find $Y_{gp} = y_{T11} = -y_{T12} = y_{T22}$, and $y_{T21} = g_m - Y_{gp}$. We then have at once $y_{T11}y_{T22} - y_{T12}y_{T21} = Y_{gp}\, g_m$.

Hence for the grounded-cathode tube we find that (7–123) takes the form

$$\begin{Vmatrix} \mathbf{A}_k & \mathbf{B}_k \\ \mathbf{C}_k & \mathbf{D}_k \end{Vmatrix} = \begin{Vmatrix} 1 & 0 \\ Y_{gk} & 1 \end{Vmatrix} \times \begin{Vmatrix} Y_{gp} & 1 \\ Y_{gp}g_m & Y_{gp} \end{Vmatrix} \times \begin{Vmatrix} 1 & 0 \\ Y_{pk}+g_p & 1 \end{Vmatrix} \left(\frac{-1}{g_m - Y_{gp}}\right) \qquad (7\text{–}132)$$

The expression is further simplified if we multiply the center matrix by the scalar Z_{gp} ($= 1/Y_{gp}$), and divide the external scalar by this same quantity.

Then,

$$\begin{Vmatrix} \mathbf{A}_k & \mathbf{B}_k \\ \mathbf{C}_k & \mathbf{D}_k \end{Vmatrix} = \begin{Vmatrix} 1 & 0 \\ Y_{gk} & 1 \end{Vmatrix} \times \begin{Vmatrix} 1 & Z_{gp} \\ g_m & 1 \end{Vmatrix} \times \begin{Vmatrix} 1 & 0 \\ Y_{pk}+g_p & 1 \end{Vmatrix} \left(\frac{1}{1-g_mZ_{gp}}\right) \qquad (7\text{–}133)$$

The Grounded-Plate Connection

The equivalent circuit of the grounded-plate tube and its capacitances is shown in Fig. 7–21.* The node equations relating E_1, E_2, I_1, and I_2

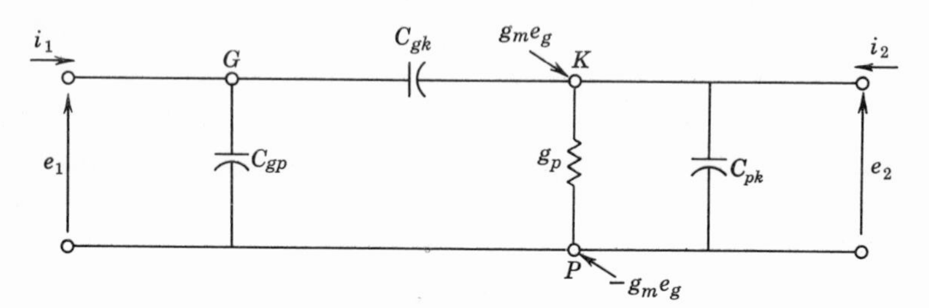

Fig. 7–21.

then are

$$I_1 = (Y_{gp} + Y_{gk})E_1 - Y_{gk}E_2 \qquad (7\text{–}134)$$

$$I_2 + g_mE_g = -Y_{gk}E_1 + (Y_{gk} + g_p + Y_{pk})E_2 \qquad (7\text{–}135)$$

and since $E_g = -E_2 + E_1$, (7–135) becomes

$$I_2 = -(Y_{gk} + g_m)E_1 + (Y_{gk} + g_p + Y_{pk} + g_m)E_2 \qquad (7\text{–}136)$$

* We may add to the interelectrode capacitance C_{pk} any other capacitance between cathode and ground. (In each of the tube connections discussed, in fact, any of the interelectrode capacitances may be augmented when paralleled by other non-negligible capacitance).

where Y_{gp}, Y_{gk}, and Y_{pk} are defined as in the definitions following (7–130).

Hence the $\|y\|$ matrix of this network takes the form

$$\|y\| = \begin{Vmatrix} Y_{gp}+Y_{gk} & -Y_{gk} \\ -(Y_{gk}+g_m) & Y_{gk}+g_p+Y_{pk}+g_m \end{Vmatrix} \tag{7–137}$$

Regarding Y_{gp} as Y_A, and $(Y_{pk}+g_p+g_m)$ as Y_B on the right-hand side of (7–122), we find $Y_{gk} = y_{T11} = -y_{T12} = y_{T22}$, while $y_{T21} = -(Y_{gk}+g_m)$. Hence $y_{T11}y_{T22}-y_{T12}y_{T21} = -Y_{gk}g_m$. Equation (7–123) takes the form

$$\begin{Vmatrix} \mathbf{A}_p & \mathbf{B}_p \\ \mathbf{C}_p & \mathbf{D}_p \end{Vmatrix} = \begin{Vmatrix} 1 & 0 \\ Y_{gp} & 1 \end{Vmatrix} \times \begin{Vmatrix} Y_{gk} & 1 \\ -Y_{gk}g_m & Y_{gk} \end{Vmatrix} \times \begin{Vmatrix} 1 & 0 \\ Y_{pk}+g_p+g_m & 1 \end{Vmatrix} \left(\frac{1}{Y_{gk}+g_m}\right) \tag{7–138}$$

Now multiplying the center matrix after the equals sign by the scalar Z_{gk} (equal to $1/Y_{gk}$) and dividing the scalar on the right by the same quantity, we have

$$\begin{Vmatrix} \mathbf{A}_p & \mathbf{B}_p \\ \mathbf{C}_p & \mathbf{D}_p \end{Vmatrix} = \begin{Vmatrix} 1 & 0 \\ Y_{gp} & 1 \end{Vmatrix} \times \begin{Vmatrix} 1 & Z_{gk} \\ -g_m & 1 \end{Vmatrix} \times \begin{Vmatrix} 1 & 0 \\ Y_{pk}+g_p+g_m & 1 \end{Vmatrix} \left(\frac{1}{1+g_mZ_{gk}}\right) \tag{7–139}$$

as the **A B C D** matrix of the grounded-plate connection when capacitance is included. The resemblance in form of (7–139) and (7–133) should be observed. We shall find a general form applicable to all three connections.

Grounded-Grid Tube

The equivalent circuit of the grounded-grid tube and its capacitances is shown in Fig. 7–22. The node equations relating E_1, E_2, I_1, and I_2 are then

$$I_1+g_m(-E_1) = (g_p+Y_{gk}+Y_{pk})E_1-(g_p+Y_{pk})E_2 \tag{7–140}$$

$$I_2-g_m(-E_1) = -(g_p+Y_{pk})E_1+(g_p+Y_{pk}+Y_{gp})E_2 \tag{7–141}$$

or

$$I_1 = (g_m+g_p+Y_{gk}+Y_{pk})E_1-(g_p+Y_{pk})E_2 \tag{7–142}$$

$$I_2 = -(g_p+g_m+Y_{pk})E_1+(g_p+Y_{pk}+Y_{gp})E_2 \tag{7–143}$$

The $\|y\|$ matrix of the twoport is then

$$\|y\| = \begin{Vmatrix} g_m + Y_{gk} + g_p + Y_{pk} & -(g_p + Y_{pk}) \\ -(g_p + Y_{pk} + g_m) & g_p + Y_{pk} + Y_{gp} \end{Vmatrix} \qquad (7\text{–}144)$$

Noting that $g_p + Y_{pk}$ appears in all four elements, we follow the procedure of the previous cases in regarding $g_m + Y_{gk}$ as Y_A, and Y_{gp} as Y_B in (7–122). We, then, find $g_p + Y_{pk} = y_{T11} = -y_{T12} = y_{T22}$, while $y_{T21} = -(g_p + Y_{pk} + g_m)$. Hence $y_{T11}y_{T22} - y_{T12}y_{T21} = -g_m(g_p + Y_{pk})$. Inserting these quantities in (7–123), we obtain

$$\begin{Vmatrix} \mathbf{A}_g & \mathbf{B}_g \\ \mathbf{C}_g & \mathbf{D}_g \end{Vmatrix} = \begin{Vmatrix} 1 & 0 \\ g_m + Y_{gk} & 1 \end{Vmatrix} \times \begin{Vmatrix} g_p + Y_{pk} & 1 \\ -g_m(g_p + Y_{pk}) & g_p + Y_{pk} \end{Vmatrix} \times \begin{Vmatrix} 1 & 0 \\ Y_{gp} & 1 \end{Vmatrix} \left[\frac{1}{+(g_p + Y_{pk} + g_m)} \right] \qquad (7\text{–}145)$$

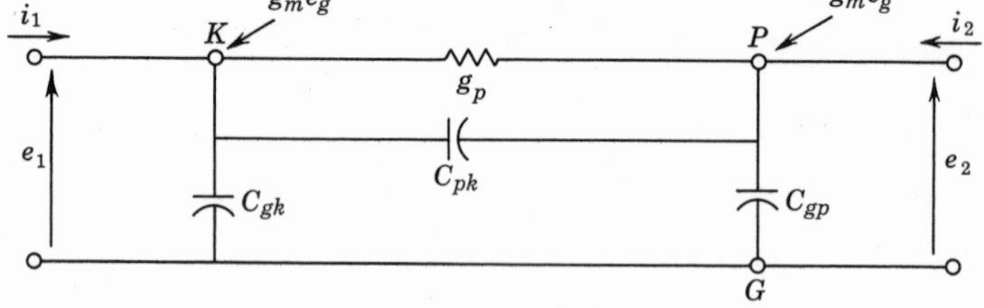

Fig. 7–22.

Letting $Z_{pk}' = 1/(g_p + Y_{pk})$, and multiplying the center matrix by Z_{pk}' while dividing the right-hand scalar by the same quantity, we obtain

$$\begin{Vmatrix} \mathbf{A}_g & \mathbf{B}_g \\ \mathbf{C}_g & \mathbf{D}_g \end{Vmatrix} = \begin{Vmatrix} 1 & 0 \\ g_m + Y_{gk} & 1 \end{Vmatrix} \times \begin{Vmatrix} 1 & Z_{pk}' \\ -g_m & 1 \end{Vmatrix} \times \begin{Vmatrix} 1 & 0 \\ Y_{gp} & 1 \end{Vmatrix} \left(\frac{1}{1 + g_m Z_{pk}'} \right) \qquad (7\text{–}146)$$

A Single-Matrix Expression for the Three Tube Connections

Comparing (7–133), (7–139), and (7–146), we see that all three cases have the same general form as the final matrix product which represents the **A B C D** matrix of the tube. For our general form

let Y_i = the admittance in position 21 of the first matrix
let Z_{FB} = the impedance in position 12 of the center matrix, and
let Y_o = The admittance in position 21 of the third matrix.

Then for any one of the three tube connections we have simply

$$\begin{Vmatrix} \mathbf{A} & \mathbf{B} \\ \mathbf{C} & \mathbf{D} \end{Vmatrix} = \begin{Vmatrix} 1 & 0 \\ Y_i & 1 \end{Vmatrix} \times \begin{Vmatrix} 1 & Z_{FB} \\ \pm g_m & 1 \end{Vmatrix} \times \begin{Vmatrix} 1 & 0 \\ Y_o & 1 \end{Vmatrix} \left(\frac{1}{1 \mp g_m Z_{FB}} \right) \tag{7–147}$$

where the symbols for each case are given in Table 7–3.

TABLE 7–3

	Y_i	Z_{FB}	Y_o	Signs Preceding g_m
Grounded-Cathode	Y_{gk}	$1/Y_{gp}$	$Y_{pk}+g_p$	Upper
Grounded-Plate	Y_{gp}	$1/Y_{gk}$	$Y_{pk}+g_p+g_m$	Lower
Grounded-Grid	g_m+Y_{gk}	$1/(Y_{pk}+g_p)$	Y_{gp}	Lower

Under certain circumstances Z_{FB} will be taken as infinite. This can occur only if capacitance can be neglected in the equivalent circuits of the grounded-cathode and grounded-plate tubes, i.e., in the sinusoidal steady state at sufficiently low frequency. When Z_{FB} is to be infinite, we can first multiply the center matrix on the right-hand side of (7–147) by the scalar on the extreme right of this equation, and then determine the limit, thus:

$$\lim_{Z_{FB}\to\infty} \begin{Vmatrix} \dfrac{1}{1 \mp g_m Z_{FB}} & \dfrac{Z_{FB}}{1 \mp g_m Z_{FB}} \\ \dfrac{\pm g_m}{1 \mp g_m Z_{FB}} & \dfrac{1}{1 \mp g_m Z_{FB}} \end{Vmatrix} = \begin{Vmatrix} 0 & \dfrac{1}{\mp g_m} \\ 0 & 0 \end{Vmatrix} \tag{7–148}$$

Hence when Z_{FB} increases without limit, (7–147) becomes

$$\begin{Vmatrix} \mathbf{A} & \mathbf{B} \\ \mathbf{C} & \mathbf{D} \end{Vmatrix} = \begin{Vmatrix} 1 & 0 \\ Y_i & 1 \end{Vmatrix} \times \begin{Vmatrix} 0 & \dfrac{1}{\mp g_m} \\ 0 & 0 \end{Vmatrix} \times \begin{Vmatrix} 1 & 0 \\ Y_o & 1 \end{Vmatrix} \tag{7–149}$$

It should be borne in mind that (7–149) is applicable only to the grounded-cathode and grounded-plate tubes. It cannot apply to problems in transients or to problems involving high-frequency sinusoidal variation, since capacitance cannot be neglected in either instance.

Another comment regarding (7–147) will be of some interest. If an admittance Y_s be connected across the input terminals of the circuit, the product of the three matrices must be multiplied by

$$\begin{Vmatrix} 1 & 0 \\ Y_s & 1 \end{Vmatrix}$$

so that we have a product of four matrices. However, combining the first two yields

$$\begin{Vmatrix} 1 & 0 \\ Y_s & 1 \end{Vmatrix} \times \begin{Vmatrix} 1 & 0 \\ Y_i & 1 \end{Vmatrix} = \begin{Vmatrix} 1 & 0 \\ Y_s + Y_i & 1 \end{Vmatrix} \tag{7–150}$$

Again, if an admittance Y_L be connected across the output terminals of the tube, its matrix will follow the last matrix of (7–147), so that we shall obtain

$$\begin{Vmatrix} 1 & 0 \\ Y_o & 1 \end{Vmatrix} \times \begin{Vmatrix} 1 & 0 \\ Y_L & 1 \end{Vmatrix} = \begin{Vmatrix} 1 & 0 \\ Y_o + Y_L & 1 \end{Vmatrix} \tag{7–151}$$

Equations (7–150) and (7–151) are each consistent with the picture of Y_s in parallel with Y_i, and Y_L in parallel with Y_o. However, inspection of Table 7–3 shows that Y_i and Y_o may contain tube coefficients as well as actual admittances connected across the tube terminals: the picture of parallel admittances is then somewhat fictitious, the equivalent circuit being represented by the entire matrix product in (7–147) where the first and last matrices may be replaced by the right-hand sides of (7—150) and (7–151), respectively.

7-9 Twoport Parameters of a Transistor Equivalent Circuit

As mentioned in Chapter 5, a number of different equivalent circuits have been developed for transistor representation. The low frequency transistor equivalent circuit of Fig. 5–4 (discussed on pp. 218–19) was analyzed by the loop current method. The h parameters, commonly used to characterize transistor twoports, will now be evaluated for the twoport between the source E_s and the load Z_L of the circuit of Fig. 5–4. Equations (7–37) and (7–38) yield:

$$h_{11} = \left.\frac{E_1}{I_1}\right|_{E_2=0} \tag{7–152}$$

$$h_{21} = \left.\frac{I_2}{I_1}\right|_{E_2=0} \tag{7-153}$$

$$h_{12} = \left.\frac{E_1}{E_2}\right|_{I_1=0} \tag{7-154}$$

$$h_{22} = \left.\frac{I_2}{E_2}\right|_{I_1=0} \tag{7-155}$$

In order to obtain h_{11} and h_{21}, we may use equations (5–25d) and (5–25e) of Chapter 5, *provided* that we replace I_2 of those equations by its negative, E_s by E_1, and Z_L by zero. The equations, then, yield

$$h_{11} = r_b' + \frac{r_e' Z_c}{r_e' + (\alpha' - 1)(\mu_{ec} - 1)Z_c} \tag{7-156}$$

Equation (5–25e), with I_2 replaced by its negative and with $Z_L = 0$, yields

$$h_{21} = -\frac{r_e' + \alpha'(\mu_{ec} - 1)Z_c}{r_e' + (\alpha' - 1)(\mu_{ec} - 1)Z_c} \tag{7-157}$$

In order to find the coefficients h_{12} and h_{22}, we suppose E_s (Fig. 5–4) to be disconnected and Z_L of that figure to be replaced by an ideal source E. Clearly $E = E_2$ in the twoport equations (7–37) and (7–38). Under these conditions we find:

$$E_2 - \alpha' Z_c I_e + \mu_{ec} V_c' = (Z_c + r_e')I_2 \tag{7-158}$$

Since $I_1 = 0$, $I_e = -I_2$, and $V_c' = -Z_c I_2(\alpha' - 1)$, equation (7–158) yields

$$E_2 = [r_e' + (\alpha' - 1)(\mu_{ec} - 1)Z_c]I_2 \tag{7-159}$$

Again using $I_1 = 0$, we find

$$E_1 = [r_e' + \mu_{ec}(\alpha' - 1)Z_c]I_2 \tag{7-160}$$

Equations (7–159) and (7–160) yield

$$h_{12} = \frac{r_e' + \mu_{ec} Z_c(\alpha' - 1)}{r_e' + (\alpha' - 1)(\mu_{ec} - 1)Z_c} \tag{7-161}$$

and

$$h_{22} = \frac{1}{r_e' + (\alpha' - 1)(\mu_{ec} - 1)Z_c} \tag{7-162}$$

7-10 Generalized Vratsanos Theorem

The Vratsanos theorem[13] (Section 6–6) yields the square of the ratio of any branch current transform to the input current transform in a linear network consisting of bilateral elements. A more general theorem which will also include networks containing nonbilateral elements is easily derived. We assume a linear network initially at rest. Let a single e.m.f. source be applied to two terminals designated as input. The terminals of a branch of impedance Z_b are designated as output. The network between the source and Z_b constitutes a twoport for which the theorem

$$\left(\frac{I_b}{I}\right)^2 = \frac{1}{\eta}\frac{\partial Z_{IN}}{\partial Z_b} \tag{7–163}$$

is to be proved. The symbols in (7–163) are defined as follows:

I_b = Laplace transform of current in the branch of impedance Z_b.
I = Laplace transform of input current.
Z_{IN} = input impedance to the twoport.
η = $\mathbf{AD}-\mathbf{BC}$ as obtained in (7–27).

Clearly, if we are concerned with the sinusoidal steady state, the current transforms in (7–163) are replaced by the complex currents of sinusoidal steady-state analysis, and the impedances and η become functions of $j\omega$ rather than s. The proof of the theorem (7–163) follows:

Substituting $I_b = -I_2$ and $I = I_1$ in equations (7–25) and (7–26), we have

$$E_1 = \mathbf{A}E_2+\mathbf{B}I_b \tag{7–164}$$

$$I = \mathbf{C}E_2+\mathbf{D}I_b \tag{7–165}$$

From these we easily obtain

$$\frac{E_1}{I} = \frac{\mathbf{A}\dfrac{E_2}{I_b}+\mathbf{B}}{\mathbf{C}\dfrac{E_2}{I_b}+\mathbf{D}} \tag{7–166}$$

Now $(E_2/I_b) = Z_b$ and $(E_1/I) = Z_{IN}$ so that (7–166) becomes

$$Z_{IN} = \frac{\mathbf{A}Z_b+\mathbf{B}}{\mathbf{C}Z_b+\mathbf{D}} \tag{7–167}$$

Since **A**, **B**, **C**, and **D** are independent of Z_b,

$$\frac{\partial Z_{IN}}{\partial Z_b} = \frac{\mathbf{A}D - \mathbf{B}C}{(\mathbf{C}Z_b + \mathbf{D})^2} = \frac{\eta}{(\mathbf{C}Z_b + \mathbf{D})^2} \tag{7–168}$$

Dividing both sides of (7–165) by I_b and using $(E_2/I_b) = Z_b$, we find

$$\frac{I}{I_b} = \mathbf{C}Z_b + \mathbf{D} \tag{7–169}$$

Inverting and squaring both sides, we find, on comparison with (7–168), the theorem stated in (7–163).

If the twoport is reciprocal, $\eta = 1$ and the original theorem proved by Vratsanos[13] appears as a special case of (7–163).

7-11 Iterative and Image Parameters of a Reciprocal Two-Port Network

The iterative and image parameters, to be defined in the present section, are particularly well suited to certain classes of circuit problems. With these parameters, for example, input and output quantities can be related to each other under actual operating conditions, and long chains of identical networks can be analyzed compactly. In addition, these parameters are closely related to the attenuation and phase shift across a twoport under an applied steady sinusoidal voltage; for this reason, image parameters form the basis, for example, of a number of methods for the design and analysis of electric filter circuits.

Iterative Parameters of a Single Twoport

We have shown in Section 7–2 that three parameters suffice to characterize a reciprocal two-port network. In the present section, we shall confine our attention to networks of this type. The three parameters which we shall now consider are the iterative ones consisting of two characteristic impedances and a propagation constant. They are termed *iterative* because of their applicability to cascades of repeated sections.

The definitions of these quantities will be understood easily with the aid of Fig. 7–23. If the input impedance of a reciprocal twoport equals the impedance connected to its output terminals, that impedance is denoted Z_{01} and is one of the two characteristic impedances of the twoport. When the impedance "looking into" the output end equals that connected to the input end, we have the second characteristic impedance Z_{02}. If the output end of the twoport be terminated in Z_{01}, the propagation constant γ can be defined by the equation

$$\frac{E_1 I_1}{E_2(-I_2)} = e^{2\gamma} \tag{7-170}$$

We shall show presently that γ is independent of the orientation of the twoport. When E_1, E_2, I_1, and I_2 are Laplace transforms of voltage and current, Z_{01}, Z_{02}, and γ will each be a function of s. In sinusoidal steady-state analysis, each becomes a function of $j\omega$.

The iterative impedances and propagation constant may be defined in various consistent ways. One very usual method is to begin with a cascade of n sections and solve the network problem using the method of difference equations. The definitions given above in terms of hypothetical

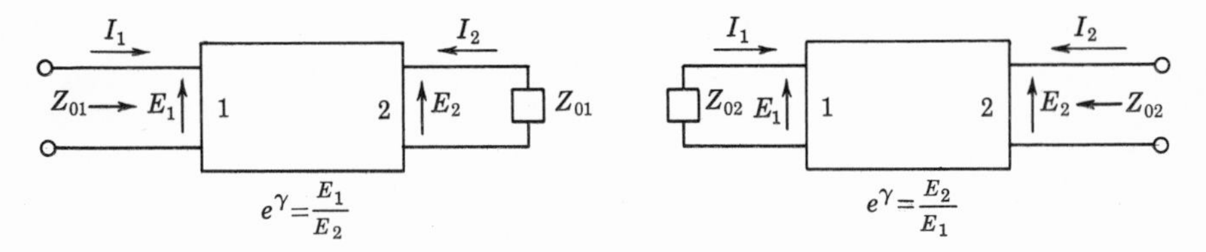

Fig. 7–23.

measurements must be justified by demonstrating that Z_{01}, Z_{02}, and γ are each, indeed, a property of the twoport.

For convenience we repeat

$$E_1 = \mathbf{A}E_2 - \mathbf{B}I_2 \tag{7-25}$$

$$I_1 = \mathbf{C}E_2 - \mathbf{D}I_2 \tag{7-26}$$

whence

$$\frac{E_1}{I_1} = \frac{\mathbf{A}\dfrac{E_2}{-I_2} + \mathbf{B}}{\mathbf{C}\dfrac{E_2}{-I_2} + \mathbf{D}} \tag{7-171}$$

If the network is terminated in Z_{01}, we have by the definition of this quantity,

$$Z_{01} = \frac{\mathbf{A}Z_{01} + \mathbf{B}}{\mathbf{C}Z_{01} + \mathbf{D}} \tag{7-172}$$

Solving for Z_{01} and using the relation $\mathbf{A}\,\mathbf{D} - \mathbf{B}\,\mathbf{C} = 1$, we find

$$Z_{01} = \frac{1}{2\mathbf{C}}[(\mathbf{A} - \mathbf{D}) \pm \sqrt{(\mathbf{A} + \mathbf{D})^2 - 4}] \tag{7-173}$$

We may solve for Z_{02} in the same manner. If **A** and **D** are interchanged, Z_{02} replaces Z_{01} in (7–172), for interchange of **A** and **D** corresponds to reversal of the twoport. We, therefore, find

$$Z_{02} = \frac{1}{2\mathbf{C}}[(\mathbf{D}-\mathbf{A}) \pm \sqrt{(\mathbf{A}+\mathbf{D})^2-4}] \tag{7–174}$$

We see then that Z_{01} and Z_{02} are expressed in terms of parameters of the twoport alone.

The signs preceding the square roots now require consideration. One simplification is immediately evident: The definition of characteristic impedances, stated at the beginning of this subsection, requires that Z_{01} equal Z_{02} for a symmetrical twoport. Consider, first, any unsymmetrical twoport. If we vary its parameters continuously until it becomes symmetrical, Z_{01} and Z_{02} approach equality. It is, therefore, necessary that *the same square root be used in the expressions for Z_{01} and Z_{02}.* With this fact established, we also find that interchange of **A** and **D** always corresponds to interchange of Z_{01} and Z_{02} as well as to reversal of the network.

Since the radicand is not always real and positive, the plus or minus sign before the radical is not too useful in identifying which root is introduced in a particular case.* Because of this, and as a reminder that *the same root must be used in* (7–173) *and* (7–174), these equations are now rewritten:

$$Z_{01} = \frac{1}{2\mathbf{C}}[(\mathbf{A}-\mathbf{D}) + \sqrt{(\mathbf{A}+\mathbf{D})^2-4}] \tag{7–173a}$$

and

$$Z_{02} = \frac{1}{2\mathbf{C}}[(\mathbf{D}-\mathbf{A}) + \sqrt{(\mathbf{A}+\mathbf{D})^2-4}] \tag{7–174a}$$

Two roots are possible, and the choice depends on physical reasoning. We, therefore, turn to an important physical property of characteristic impedances.

* As an example, let x^2 be real and positive and let us seek the "positive" or "first" square root of $(1+x^2\underline{/-\pi})$, i.e., the root obtained by taking half the angle of the radicand. We can write two equally correct statements:

$$+\sqrt{1+x^2\underline{/-\pi}} = +\sqrt{1\underline{/-\pi}(1\underline{/\pi}+x^2)} = -j\sqrt{x^2-1}$$

or

$$+\sqrt{1+x^2\underline{/-\pi}} = +\sqrt{1\underline{/\pi}(1\underline{/-\pi}+x^2\underline{/-2\pi})} = j\sqrt{x^2-1}$$

Both roots are obtained, and the sign preceding the radical fails to identify which is intended.

The student familiar with transmission-line theory will recall that the characteristic impedance of a transmission line is the output impedance to a line of infinite length. That Z_{01} and Z_{02} have a similar significance is seen upon examination of Fig. 7–24, where three sections in an infinite cascade of identical sections have been drawn. While the twoport labeled N is separated from the generator by a finite number of twoports, an infinite cascade extends to the right. The impedance $Z_n = E_n/I_n$ must be identical with the impedance $Z_{n+1} = E_{n+1}/I_{n+1}$, for each is the input impedance to an infinite cascade of sections extending to the right. But if Z_n equals Z_{n+1}, each is Z_{01}, the first characteristic impedance of the box labeled N, in accordance with our definition of Z_{01}. If now each twoport in the infinite chain be reversed (a task easy in concept, if, mechanically difficult), the previous argument will show Z_{02} to be the input impedance to this new infinite line.

If we now postulate that an infinite cascade shall have an input impedance whose properties are consistent with the known properties of

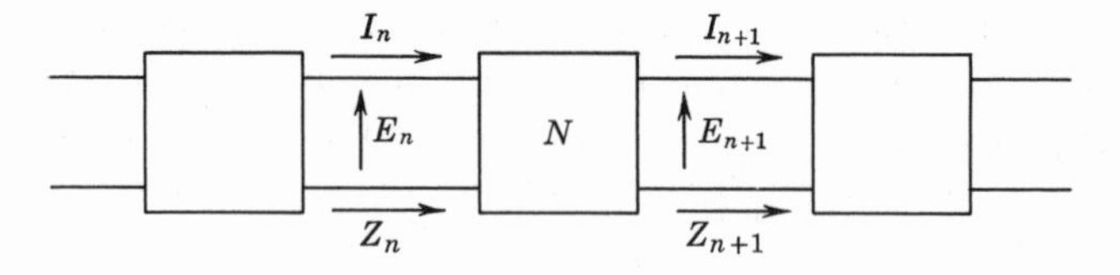

Fig. 7–24.

driving-point impedances of finite passive networks consisting of bilateral elements, we may choose the square root in particular cases. To illustrate this, consider the three twoports of Figs. 7–25, 26, and 27. Figs. 7–25 and 26 both have a constant as the value of Z_{01}, which equals Z_{02} in these cases. Since the resistance of a passive circuit is positive, we choose the positive sign for the square root. Fig. 7–27 is a constant-k high-pass filter circuit. Here the situation is somewhat more involved. The characteristic impedance, calculated for sinusoidal steady-state analysis, is $R\sqrt{1-(\omega_c/\omega)^2}$, where $\omega_c = 1/(2\sqrt{LC})$ and $R = \sqrt{L/C}$. When $\omega_c < \omega < \infty$, the characteristic impedance is real and, therefore, appears as a resistance which varies with frequency. For this reason we select the positive root. On the other hand, when $0 < \omega < \omega_c$, the characteristic impedance is a pure imaginary. It is demonstrable[4] that a purely reactive input impedance jX has a positive slope with increasing frequency, i.e., $(dX/d\omega) > 0$. In order that the characteristic impedance of the filter be consistent with this latter theorem, the negative root should be taken in the range $0 < \omega < \omega_c$.[4]

We now turn to the *propagation constant* γ. When a twoport is terminated in Z_{01}, its input impedance is Z_{01}, so that equation (7–170) may be written

$$\frac{E_1^2}{E_2^2} = e^{2\gamma} \tag{7–175}$$

or

$$\frac{E_1}{E_2} = e^{\gamma} \tag{7–176}$$

The choice of root in this step completes the definition of e^{γ}. Since the ratio E_1/E_2 is to be calculated on the assumption that the twoport is

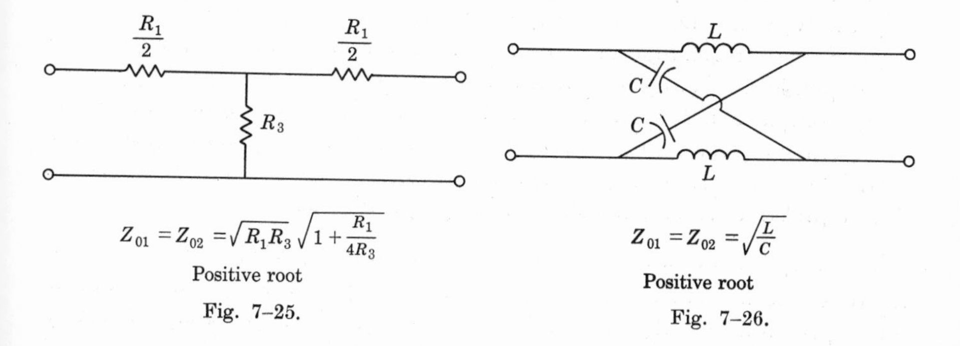

$Z_{01} = Z_{02} = \sqrt{R_1 R_3}\sqrt{1 + \frac{R_1}{4R_3}}$

Positive root

Fig. 7–25.

$Z_{01} = Z_{02} = \sqrt{\frac{L}{C}}$

Positive root

Fig. 7–26.

terminated in Z_{01}, the parameter γ depends on the choice of root for Z_{01}. In order to obtain γ, we may begin with (7–25) which yields

$$\frac{E_1}{E_2} = \mathbf{A} + \mathbf{B}\frac{-I_2}{E_2} \tag{7–177}$$

or

$$\frac{E_1}{E_2} = \mathbf{A} + \mathbf{B}\frac{1}{Z_{01}} \tag{7–178}$$

With the aid of (7–172) this expression can also be written

$$\frac{E_1}{E_2} = \mathbf{C}Z_{01} + \mathbf{D} \tag{7–179}$$

Equations (7–179) and (7–173a) yield

$$e^{\gamma} = \tfrac{1}{2}[(\mathbf{A}+\mathbf{D}) + \sqrt{(\mathbf{A}+\mathbf{D})^2 - 4}] \tag{7–179a}$$

The reciprocal $e^{-\gamma}$ is easily shown to be given by

$$e^{-\gamma} = \tfrac{1}{2}[(\mathbf{A}+\mathbf{D})-\sqrt{(\mathbf{A}+\mathbf{D})^2-4}] \tag{7–179b}$$

Equations (7–179a, b) immediately yield

$$\cosh\gamma = \tfrac{1}{2}(\mathbf{A}+\mathbf{D}) \tag{7–180a}$$

and

$$\sinh\gamma = \tfrac{1}{2}\sqrt{(\mathbf{A}+\mathbf{D})^2-4} \tag{7–180b}$$

Equations (7–179a), (7–179b), (7–180a), and (7–180b) provide important general information:

(a) Since each equation expresses γ in terms of twoport parameters (namely **A** and **D**), γ is a twoport parameter.
(b) Since interchange of **A** and **D** does not alter these equations, γ is independent of twoport orientation.
(c) Comparison of equations (7–179a) and (7–179b) shows that if we arbitrarily interchange square roots, γ is replaced by its negative and the odd function sinh γ is replaced by its negative, so that a decision is required as to choice of root in any specific case.

The proper root can, of course, be chosen directly on physical grounds. However, it is evident that $\sqrt{(A+D)^2-4}$ represents the *same* root in the expressions for Z_{01} and Z_{02} as in the equations (7–179a), (7–179b), and (7–180b). Since, as was shown earlier, the sign preceding the radical does not always identify the root to be taken, we return to (7–178) or (7–179). In these equations, (E_1/E_2) equals e^{γ} and is expressed directly in terms of Z_{01}. Hence, when the root in the expression for Z_{01} has been selected on physical grounds, the expression for e^{γ} follows unambiguously.

An illustration is afforded by the circuit of Fig. 7–27 for which we have found $Z_{01} = R\sqrt{1-(\omega_c/\omega)^2}$ in the range of frequency given by $\omega_c < \omega$, and $Z_{01} = -jR\sqrt{(\omega_c/\omega)^2-1}$ in the range $0 < \omega < \omega_c$. For convenience we write the relations applicable to this circuit:

$$\mathbf{A} = \mathbf{D} = 1-2(\omega_c/\omega)^2$$
$$\mathbf{B} = (2\omega_c R/j\omega)[1-(\omega_c/\omega)^2]$$
$$\mathbf{C} = 2\omega_c/j\omega R$$

where $R = \sqrt{L/C}$ and $\omega_c = 1/(2\sqrt{LC})$. In the range $\omega_c < \omega$, either (7–178) or (7–179) yields

$$e^{\gamma} = 1-2\left(\frac{\omega_c}{\omega}\right)^2 - j2\frac{\omega_c}{\omega}\sqrt{1-\left(\frac{\omega_c}{\omega}\right)^2} \tag{7–180c}$$

where, here, the radical stands for the positive root of the real positive radicand. If we assume termination with Z_{01}, we find $|E_1|/|E_2|$ equal to 1, since $|e^\gamma| = 1$, i.e., we have a filter pass band. With assumed termination Z_{01}, we also find $(d\beta/d\omega) > 0$ where $\beta = \underline{/\gamma} = \underline{/E_1} - \underline{/E_2}$.

This result is necessitated by the concept of $d\beta/d\omega$ as time delay (see Chapter 2 where this concept was derived for straight phase shift characteristics). The slope $(d\beta/d\omega)$ would have the wrong sign if the root chosen in (7–180c) were not that dictated by the choice of root in Z_{01}.

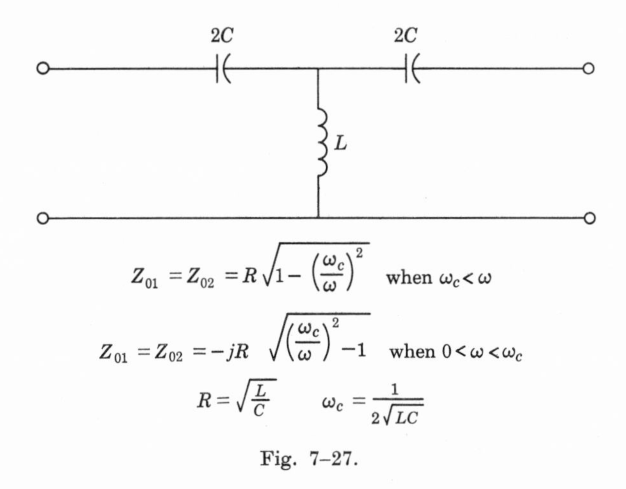

Fig. 7–27.

We now consider the range $0 < \omega < \omega_c$. Again, substitution into either (7–178) or (7–179) yields

$$e^\gamma = 1 - 2\left(\frac{\omega_c}{\omega}\right)^2 - 2\frac{\omega_c}{\omega}\sqrt{\left(\frac{\omega_c}{\omega}\right)^2 - 1} \qquad (7\text{–}180\text{d})$$

where, here as in (7–180c), the radical stands for the positive root of the real positive radicand. We note that $|e^\gamma|$ increases without limit as ω approaches zero, i.e., $(|E_2|/|E_1|)$ approaches zero as ω approaches zero. This result, necessitated by the presence of the series capacitor, is not obtained unless the root chosen is that dictated by Z_{01}.

Image Parameters of a Single Twoport

The image parameters, consisting of two image impedances and an image transfer constant, are so termed because of their applicability to cascades of identical sections connected on the image basis, i.e., with every other twoport reversed. There are, as with the iterative constants, several equivalent ways of defining the image constants of a network. We shall define these in a manner closely tied to our definitions of the iterative constants. Again, our attention is confined to reciprocal two-ports.

In order to define the image impedance Z_{I_1}, let us consider Fig. 7–28(a), which shows two identical twoports cascaded on the image basis. The second twoport contains the same circuit as the first, but has been reversed. The dotted lines enclose the symmetrical over-all network, the *characteristic impedance* of which we shall term Z_{01A}. The subscript A is used to indicate reference to the over-all network. We define the *image impedance* Z_{I_1} of the individual twoport by

$$Z_{I_1} = Z_{01A} \tag{7–181}$$

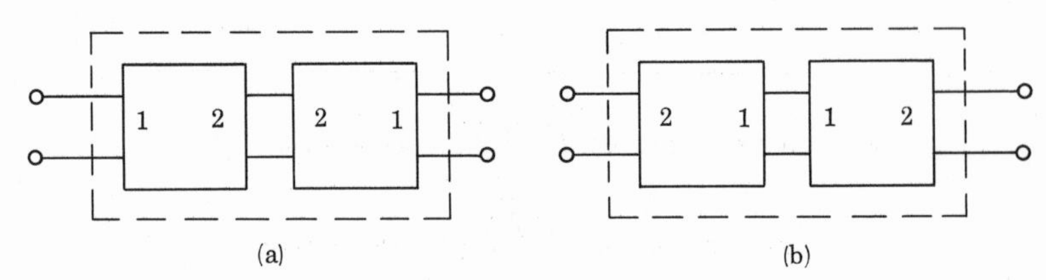

Fig. 7–28.

In a similar manner the characteristic impedance Z_{01B} of the over-all network in Fig. 7–28(b) defines the other image impedance, i.e.,

$$Z_{I_2} = Z_{01B} \tag{7–182}$$

We shall see shortly that these image impedances have interesting as well as valuable properties. The expression for Z_{I_1} will first be obtained. The coefficients of the over-all network, Fig. 7–28(a), are found by matrix multiplication, thus:

$$\begin{Vmatrix} \mathbf{A} & \mathbf{B} \\ \mathbf{C} & \mathbf{D} \end{Vmatrix} \times \begin{Vmatrix} \mathbf{D} & \mathbf{B} \\ \mathbf{C} & \mathbf{A} \end{Vmatrix} = \begin{Vmatrix} \mathbf{AD}+\mathbf{BC} & 2\mathbf{AB} \\ 2\mathbf{CD} & \mathbf{AD}+\mathbf{BC} \end{Vmatrix} \tag{7–183}$$

Substitution into (7–173a), p. 357, yields

$$Z_{01A} = \frac{1}{4\mathbf{CD}}\sqrt{4(\mathbf{AD}+\mathbf{BC})^2-4} \tag{7–184}$$

Since $\mathbf{A}\,\mathbf{D}-\mathbf{B}\,\mathbf{C} = 1$, this expression becomes

$$Z_{I_1} = \sqrt{\frac{\mathbf{AB}}{\mathbf{CD}}} \tag{7–185}$$

In order to obtain the expression for Z_{I_2} let us calculate Z_{01B} for the over-all network of Fig. 7–28(b). Here in place of (7–183) we have

$$\begin{Vmatrix} \mathbf{D} & \mathbf{B} \\ \mathbf{C} & \mathbf{A} \end{Vmatrix} \times \begin{Vmatrix} \mathbf{A} & \mathbf{B} \\ \mathbf{C} & \mathbf{D} \end{Vmatrix} = \begin{Vmatrix} \mathbf{AD}+\mathbf{BC} & 2\mathbf{BD} \\ 2\mathbf{AC} & \mathbf{AD}+\mathbf{BC} \end{Vmatrix} \tag{7–186}$$

Clearly, all we have done is to interchange **A** and **D** so that Z_{I_2} will be given by

$$Z_{I_2} = \sqrt{\frac{\mathbf{DB}}{\mathbf{CA}}} \tag{7–187}$$

Since the impedances Z_{I_1} and Z_{I_2} have been expressed in terms of the parameters **A**, **B**, **C**, **D**, each is a property of the individual twoport.

In order to choose roots for the image impedances in a consistent manner, let us write these as $Z_{I_1} = (1/\mathbf{CD})\sqrt{\mathbf{ABCD}}$ and $Z_{I_2} = (1/\mathbf{CA})\sqrt{\mathbf{ABCD}}$. Since our definition requires that Z_{I_1} become Z_{I_2} on interchange of **A** and **D**, it is evident that $\sqrt{\mathbf{ABCD}}$ represents the same root in each expression. We therefore select the appropriate

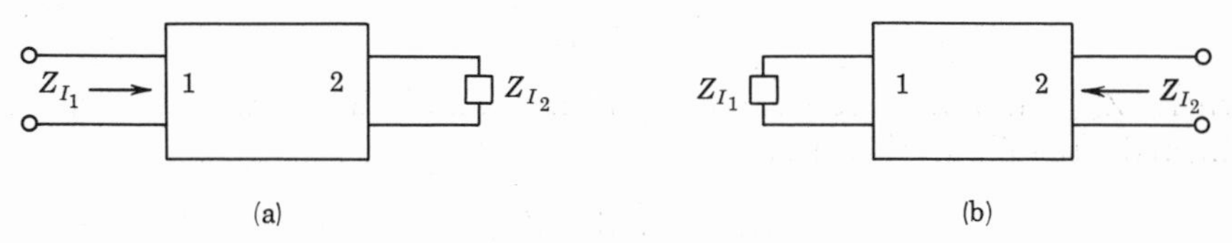

Fig. 7–29.

root for one of the image impedances on physical grounds, and the other image impedance is uniquely determined.

We now consider a basic property of image impedances, illustrated in Fig. 7–29: When the output terminals of a twoport are connected to Z_{I_2}, the input impedance is Z_{I_1}; and when Z_{I_1} is connected to the input terminals, Z_{I_2} will be measured at the output terminals. This image impedance property (which might equally well be taken as definition) will now be derived from the definition used at the beginning of this section.

We suppose, first, that the two-section cascade of Fig. 7–28(a) is terminated with its characteristic impedance. The image impedance Z_{I_1} of each twoport in the cascade has been defined as equal to this characteristic impedance. The input impedance to the cascade is, now, also Z_{I_1}. Temporarily let Z_x be the impedance "looking to the right" at the center junction of the cascade. We observe two facts concerning Z_x: (1) With end 1 of the right-hand twoport terminated in Z_{I_1}, we measure

Z_x at end 2 of the twoport. (2) With end 2 of the left-hand twoport terminated by Z_x, Z_{I_1} is measured at end 1. Now connect Z_x to the output terminals of the cascade of Fig. 7–28(b). From our observations on Fig. 7–28(a), we know that at the center junction, Fig. 28(b), we shall see, "looking to the right", the impedance Z_{I_1}, and that we shall measure Z_x at the input terminals of this cascade. Thus Z_x is the characteristic impedance of the cascade in Fig. 7–28(b). This we have defined as Z_{I_2} of the individual twoport. Hence $Z_x = Z_{I_2}$ and we see that Z_{I_1} and Z_{I_2} obey the property (or definition) of Fig. 7–29.

Image impedances can be calculated directly from open- and short-circuit evaluations. When $I_2 = 0$ in equations (7–25) and (7–26), we find

$$Z_{o.c.} = \frac{\mathbf{A}}{\mathbf{C}} \qquad (7\text{–}188)$$

while when $E_2 = 0$ in those equations, we have

$$Z_{s.c.} = \frac{\mathbf{B}}{\mathbf{D}} \qquad (7\text{–}189)$$

where $Z_{o.c.}$ and $Z_{s.c.}$ represent input impedance with output open or shorted. It follows then that

$$Z_{I_1} = \sqrt{Z_{o.c.}Z_{s.c.}} \qquad (7\text{–}190)$$

where, of course, physical reasoning determines the choice of root. Clearly, Z_{I_2} can be found from the corresponding quantities with the circuit reversed.

The *image transfer constant* θ is defined as we have defined the propagation constant γ, but with an image impedance termination. Referring to Fig. 7–29(a), we write

$$\frac{E_1 I_1}{E_2(-I_2)} = e^{2\theta} \qquad (7\text{–}191)$$

But when the twoport is terminated in Z_{I_2}, its input impedance is Z_{I_1}, so that

$$\frac{Z_{I_2}}{Z_{I_1}}\frac{E_{12}}{E_{22}} = e^{2\theta} \qquad (7\text{–}192)$$

In order to make the definition of e^θ unique, we write

$$e^\theta = \sqrt{\frac{Z_{I_2}}{Z_{I_1}}}\,\frac{E_1}{E_2} \qquad (7\text{–}192a)$$

where the root in (7–192a) is so chosen that if the twoport is made symmetrical (say by varying one or more circuit elements), e^θ becomes E_1/E_2 and not the negative of this ratio.

Now using equations (7–25) and (7–192a) we obtain

$$\sqrt{\frac{Z_{I_2}}{Z_{I_1}}}\left[\mathbf{A}+\mathbf{B}\frac{1}{Z_{I_2}}\right] = e^\theta \tag{7–193}$$

where Z_{I_2} is the assumed termination of the twoport.

Expressing Z_{I_1} and Z_{I_2} in terms of **A**, **B**, **C**, and **D**, and introducing $\mathbf{AD}-\mathbf{BC} = 1$, we easily find

$$e^\theta = \sqrt{\mathbf{AD}}+\sqrt{\mathbf{BC}} \tag{7–194}$$

$$e^{-\theta} = \sqrt{\mathbf{AD}}-\sqrt{\mathbf{BC}} \tag{7–195}$$

$$\cosh\theta = \sqrt{\mathbf{AD}} \tag{7–196}$$

$$\sinh\theta = \sqrt{\mathbf{BC}} \tag{7–196a}$$

Equations (7–194, 195, 196, 196a) show that θ is a two-port network parameter independent of the two-port network orientation, for it is expressed in terms of **A**, **B**, **C**, and **D**, and is unaltered by interchange of **A** and **D**. The square roots in these equations require consideration. The $\sqrt{\mathbf{AD}}$ is uniquely determined, for, according to equation (7–193) it is equal to $\sqrt{Z_{I_2}/Z_{I_1}}\,\mathbf{A}$, and this quantity must reduce to **A**, not $-\mathbf{A}$, when the network is reduced to a symmetrical twoport by varying its parameters. Again according to (7–193), $\sqrt{\mathbf{BC}}$ equals $\sqrt{Z_{I_2}/Z_{I_1}}\mathbf{B}(1/Z_{I_2})$. This expression has either of two values depending on the root chosen for Z_{I_2}, i.e., for $\sqrt{\mathbf{DB}/\mathbf{CA}}$. Now arbitrary replacement of $\sqrt{\mathbf{BC}}$ by its negative replaces θ by its negative—see equations (7–194) and (7–195)—and also replaces the odd function sinh θ by its negative. In order to have correct values, the root for Z_{I_2} can be selected on physical grounds and e^θ calculated from (7–193) where Z_{I_2} appears explicitly. The twoport of Fig. 7–27 affords a useful example which was discussed in connection with iterative parameters. That discussion also applies to the image parameters, since iterative and image parameters become identical for a symmetrical twoport (see next subsection).

Iterative and Image Parameters for a Symmetrical Twoport

The iterative and image parameters become identical when a two-port network has symmetry. A passive reciprocal symmetrical twoport is characterized by the relationships $\mathbf{A} = \mathbf{D}$ and $\mathbf{A}^2 - \mathbf{BC} = 1$. Under these conditions

$$Z_{01} = Z_{02} = Z_{I_1} = Z_{I_2} = \sqrt{Z_{o.c.}Z_{s.c.}} = \sqrt{\frac{\mathbf{B}}{\mathbf{C}}} \tag{7–197}$$

$$\gamma = \theta \tag{7–198}$$

$$\cosh\gamma = \cosh\theta = \mathbf{A} \tag{7–198a}$$

$$\sinh\gamma = \sinh\theta = \sqrt{A^2-1} = \sqrt{\mathbf{BC}} \tag{7–198b}$$

The choice of root in (7–197) is determined by physical reasoning. This choice, when made, determines e^{γ} (or e^{θ}) uniquely, as indicated earlier. The function $\sinh\gamma$ (or $\sinh\theta$) is thus determined without ambiguity. If (7–198b) is used alone, without reference to (7–197), physical reasoning is necessary to determine choice of root for $\sqrt{\mathbf{BC}}$.

7–12 Cascades of Many Sections

The iterative and image impedances provide a means for solving problems involving long chains of repeated sections. With this application in view, we shall first express the **ABCD** coefficients of a two-port network in terms of its iterative and image parameters.

A, B, C, *and* D *in Terms of Iterative Parameters*

In order to express the parameters **A**, **B**, **C**, and **D** in terms of Z_{01}, Z_{02}, and γ, we substitute (7–180b) into (7–173a) and (7–174a). (Since the same root is used in the expressions for Z_{01}, Z_{02}, and $\sinh\gamma$, this step involves no ambiguity.) We find

$$Z_{01} = \frac{\sinh\gamma}{\mathbf{C}} + \frac{\mathbf{A}-\mathbf{D}}{2\mathbf{C}} \tag{7–199}$$

and

$$Z_{02} = \frac{\sinh\gamma}{\mathbf{C}} - \frac{\mathbf{A}-\mathbf{D}}{2\mathbf{C}} \tag{7–200}$$

Addition of these two equations leads almost directly to

$$\mathbf{C} = \frac{2\sinh\gamma}{Z_{01}+Z_{02}} \tag{7–201}$$

Multiplication of (7–173a) and (7–173b) leads, with the aid of

$\mathbf{AD} - \mathbf{BC} = 1$, to the following result (which is independent of the choice of root in the expressions for Z_{01} and Z_{02}):

$$Z_{01}Z_{02} = \frac{\mathbf{B}}{\mathbf{C}} \tag{7–202}$$

whence

$$\mathbf{B} = \frac{2Z_{01}Z_{02}}{Z_{01}+Z_{02}}\sinh\gamma \tag{7–203}$$

Subtracting (7–200) from (7–199) and substituting the left-hand side of (7–201) for $\mathbf{C}$ yield

$$\mathbf{A}-\mathbf{D} = 2\frac{Z_{01}-Z_{02}}{Z_{01}+Z_{02}}\sinh\gamma \tag{7–204}$$

Using (7–204) and (7–180a) we find very simply

$$\mathbf{A} = \cosh\gamma + \frac{Z_{01}-Z_{02}}{Z_{01}+Z_{02}}\sinh\gamma \tag{7–205}$$

and

$$\mathbf{D} = \cosh\gamma + \frac{Z_{02}-Z_{01}}{Z_{01}+Z_{02}}\sinh\gamma \tag{7–206}$$

Although square roots are not seen explicitly in equations (7–201), (7–203), (7–205) and (7–206), $\sinh\gamma$ must be evaluated with the same root as that used for Z_{01} and Z_{02}.

A, B, C, *and* D *in Terms of Image Parameters*

In order to express **A**, **B**, **C**, and **D** in terms of image parameters, we must solve (7–185, 187, and 196). We easily find from (7–185 and 187) that

$$\frac{Z_{I_1}}{Z_{I_2}} = \frac{\mathbf{A}}{\mathbf{D}} \tag{7–207}$$

and that

$$Z_{I_1}Z_{I_2} = \frac{\mathbf{B}}{\mathbf{C}} \tag{7–208}$$

Combining equations (7–207) and (7–196), we have

$$\mathbf{A} = \sqrt{\frac{Z_{I_1}}{Z_{I_2}}}\cosh\theta \tag{7–209}$$

The same equations yield with equal ease

$$\mathbf{D} = \sqrt{\frac{Z_{I_2}}{Z_{I_1}}} \cosh \theta \tag{7-210}$$

Equations (7-208) and (7-196a) combine to give the results

$$\mathbf{B} = \sqrt{Z_{I_1} Z_{I_2}} \sinh \theta \tag{7-211}$$

$$\mathbf{C} = \frac{\sinh \theta}{\sqrt{Z_{I_1} Z_{I_2}}} \tag{7-212}$$

The product or ratio of Z_{I_1} and Z_{I_2} is unaffected by the choice of root in evaluating Z_{I_1} and Z_{I_2}, since the choice of root for one determines this choice for the other. Also sinh θ should be evaluated in a manner consistent with the root chosen for the image impedance (see discussion following equation 7-196a). However, in these equations we still have an apparent ambiguity when we take the roots $\sqrt{Z_{I_1}/Z_{I_2}}$, $\sqrt{Z_{I_2}/Z_{I_1}}$ and $\sqrt{Z_{I_1} Z_{I_2}}$. The choice here may be determined by the physical meaning of **A**, **B**, **C**, and **D**; i.e., $\mathbf{A} = E_1/E_2$ with end 2 open-circuited, $\mathbf{C} = \mathbf{A}/Z_{IN}$ with end 2 open-circuited, etc.

Parameters of an n-Section Iterative Cascade

An iterative cascade consists of a chain of identical twoports, identically oriented as illustrated in Fig. 7-30. We seek the coefficients of the entire

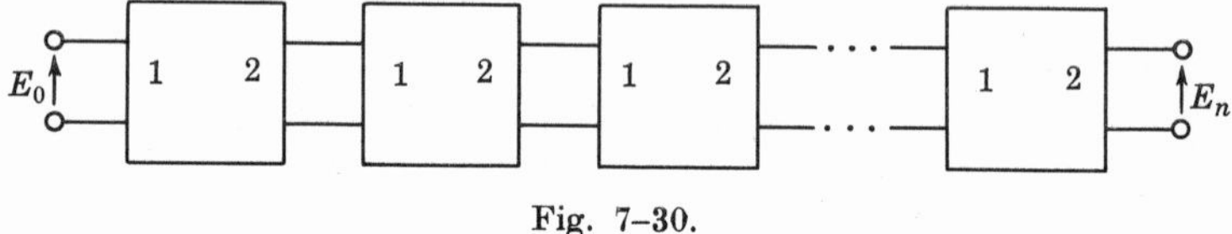

Fig. 7-30.

cascade regarded as a single twoport. Ordinarily this would involve a matrix multiplication of n identical matrices, i.e., raising a matrix to the nth power. With the aid of the characteristic impedances and propagation constants, the result may be arrived at with a little "physical" reasoning.

Let us terminate the cascade with Z_{01}, the first characteristic impedance of one of the twoports in the cascade. Since the last box is terminated in Z_{01}, its input impedance is also Z_{01}. Hence the next-to-last box is terminated in Z_{01} and its input impedance is also Z_{01}. Thus each twoport in the cascade is terminated in Z_{01} and has this characteristic impedance as its input impedance. We now regard the entire cascade as a single twoport. We have terminated it in Z_{01}; we find Z_{01} at its input terminals. Therefore the first characteristic impedance of the entire cascade regarded as a single twoport is Z_{01}. If now Z_{02} be connected across the input end, we shall find in the same manner that Z_{02} is measured at the output end terminals. We conclude then that Z_{01} and Z_{02} are the characteristic impedances of an entire chain of n sections, each of which has Z_{01} and Z_{02} as its characteristic impedances.

We now seek the propagation constant γ. Again we terminate the chain in Z_{01}. Then if γ_n be the propagation constant of the entire chain, we find from (7–176) that

$$\frac{E_0}{E_n} = e^{\gamma_n} \tag{7–213}$$

However we have seen that termination of the cascade in Z_{01} results in termination of each twoport with Z_{01}, so that

$$\begin{aligned} \frac{E_0}{E_1} &= e^{\gamma} \\ \frac{E_1}{E_2} &= e^{\gamma} \\ &\vdots \\ \frac{E_{n-1}}{E_n} &= e^{\gamma} \end{aligned} \tag{7–214}$$

The set of equations (7–214) yields at once

$$\frac{E_0}{E_n} = e^{n\gamma} \tag{7–215}$$

where γ is the propagation constant of the individual twoport. Comparing this equation with (7–213), we find

$$\gamma_n = n\gamma \tag{7–216}$$

We, therefore, conclude that if the individual twoport is characterized by the parameters Z_{01}, Z_{02}, and γ, an iterative cascade of n sections is characterized by the parameters Z_{01}, Z_{02}, and $n\gamma$. From (7–201, 203, 205, 206), we find that

$$\left\| \begin{matrix} \mathbf{A}_n & \mathbf{B}_n \\ \mathbf{C}_n & \mathbf{D}_n \end{matrix} \right\| = \left\| \begin{matrix} \cosh n\gamma + \dfrac{Z_{01} - Z_{02}}{Z_{01} + Z_{02}} \sinh n\gamma & \dfrac{2Z_{01}Z_{02}}{Z_{01} + Z_{02}} \sinh n\gamma \\ \dfrac{2}{Z_{01} + Z_{02}} \sinh n\gamma & \cosh n\gamma + \dfrac{Z_{02} - Z_{01}}{Z_{01} + Z_{02}} \sinh n\gamma \end{matrix} \right\| \tag{7–217}$$

where $\mathbf{A}_n$, $\mathbf{B}_n$, $\mathbf{C}_n$, and $\mathbf{D}_n$ are parameters of the entire cascade of n sections, regarded as a single twoport.

When the individual sections are symmetrical structures, $Z_{01} = Z_{02}$ so that

$$\left\| \begin{matrix} \mathbf{A}_n & \mathbf{B}_n \\ \mathbf{C}_n & \mathbf{D}_n \end{matrix} \right\|_s = \left\| \begin{matrix} \cosh n\gamma & Z_{01} \sinh n\gamma \\ \dfrac{1}{Z_{01}} \sinh n\gamma & \cosh n\gamma \end{matrix} \right\| \tag{7-218}$$

where the subscript s on the left-hand matrix is simply a reminder of the fact that this equation applies only when the individual twoports are symmetrical. A cascade of n symmetrical sections constitutes a symmetrical twoport. If n is even, the line of symmetry lies between the two center sections; if n is odd, the line of symmetry is coincident with the line of symmetry of the central section. We see, therefore, why $\mathbf{A}_n$ and $\mathbf{D}_n$ are identical in equation (7–218).

Parameters of an n-Section Image Cascade: (n Even)

An image cascade of an even number of sections is illustrated in Fig. 7–31. The sections are identical, but alternate ones are reversed. The total number of sections is even, so that the final one must be oriented as 2–1. We now seek the image parameters of the entire cascade regarded as a single twoport.

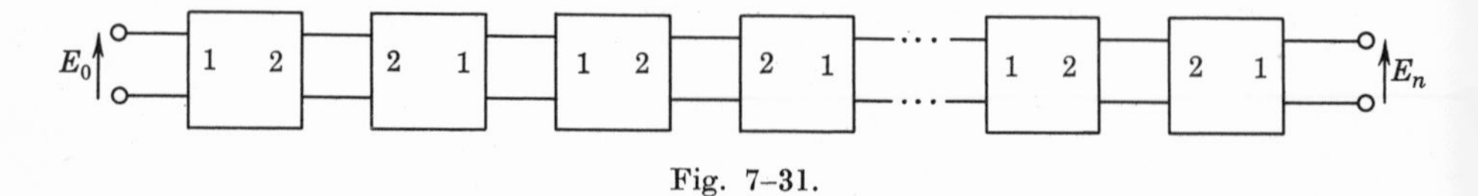

Fig. 7–31.

We first note that an even number of sections forming an image cascade constitute a *symmetrical* twoport. The line of symmetry will be at a junction having an equal number of sections on either side. Now the image impedances and characteristic impedances of a symmetrical twoport are all equal. Hence, we have, in effect, one image impedance, which we may call Z_{I_n}, and this is also the characteristic impedance of the chain when it is regarded as a single twoport. We shall determine this characteristic impedance directly.

For the purpose of calculation, we connect Z_{I_1} to the output terminals of the final twoport (Z_{I_1} being the first image impedance of the individual twoport). The impedance seen at end 2 of this twoport is then Z_{I_2}. The next-to-last twoport is then terminated in Z_{I_2} so that its input impedance must be Z_{I_1}. Proceeding in this way, we find that the input impedance to the entire cascade is Z_{I_1} when the cascade is terminated in Z_{I_1}. Thus an image cascade of an even number of sections constitutes a single symmetrical twoport whose characteristic impedance equals Z_{I_1}, where Z_{I_1} is the first image impedance of the first twoport in the chain. Since the chain constitutes a symmetrical twoport, its image impedance equals its characteristic impedance, and

$$Z_{I_n} = Z_{I_1} \tag{7–219}$$

We now seek θ_n, the image transfer constant of the entire cascade. Since the cascade constitutes a symmetrical twoport, we find from (7–192a) that

$$\frac{E_0}{E_n} = e^{\theta n} \tag{7–220}$$

when Z_{I_1} is used as the terminating impedance. Now using (7–192a) for the individual sections, we have

$$\begin{aligned} \frac{E_0}{E_1} &= \sqrt{\frac{Z_{I_1}}{Z_{I_2}}}e^{\theta} \\ \frac{E_1}{E_2} &= \sqrt{\frac{Z_{I_2}}{Z_{I_1}}}e^{\theta} \\ &\vdots \\ \frac{E_{n-2}}{E_{n-1}} &= \sqrt{\frac{Z_{I_1}}{Z_{I_2}}}e^{\theta} \\ \frac{E_{n-1}}{E_n} &= \sqrt{\frac{Z_{I_2}}{Z_{I_1}}}e^{\theta} \end{aligned} \tag{7–221}$$

In writing (7–221), we have made use of the fact that terminating the entire chain with Z_{I_1} terminates each twoport on the image basis. Now multiplying the n equations of (7–221), we find

$$\frac{E_0}{E_n} = e^{n\theta} \tag{7–222}$$

Comparison of this result with equation (7–220) yields at once

$$\theta_n = n\theta \tag{7–223}$$

The image parameters of the cascade are then Z_{I_1} and $n\theta$, there being but one image impedance for the chain, since it is symmetrical. Applying this result to (7–209, 210, 211, 212) we have, when n is even

$$\begin{Vmatrix} \mathbf{A}_n & \mathbf{B}_n \\ \mathbf{C}_n & \mathbf{D}_n \end{Vmatrix} = \begin{Vmatrix} \cosh n\theta & Z_{I_1} \sinh n\theta \\ \dfrac{1}{Z_{I_1}} \sinh n\theta & \cosh n\theta \end{Vmatrix} \tag{7–224}$$

It is interesting to note that if the individual twoport is symmetrical, i.e., if $Z_{I_1} = Z_{I_2}$, the form of the result (7–224) is unaltered since Z_I does not enter the expression in any case.

Parameters of an Image Cascade of $(n+1)$ *Sections:* $(n+1)$ *Odd*

If a single section, oriented as 1–2, be added to the cascade of Fig. 7–31, we have an image cascade containing an odd number of sections. The **A B C D** coefficients of a single twoport oriented as 1–2 are given by (7–209, 210, 211, 212). The parameters of the cascade containing an odd number of sections can then be obtained directly by a matrix multiplication, thus:

$$\begin{Vmatrix} \mathbf{A}_{n+1} & \mathbf{B}_{n+1} \\ \mathbf{C}_{n+1} & \mathbf{D}_{n+1} \end{Vmatrix}_{\substack{n+1 \\ odd}}$$

$$= \begin{Vmatrix} \cosh n\theta & Z_{I_1} \sinh n\theta \\ \dfrac{1}{Z_{I_1}} \sinh n\theta & \cosh n\theta \end{Vmatrix} \times \begin{Vmatrix} \sqrt{\dfrac{Z_{I_1}}{Z_{I_2}}} \cosh \theta & \sqrt{Z_{I_1} Z_{I_2}} \sinh \theta \\ \dfrac{\sinh \theta}{\sqrt{Z_{I_1} Z_{I_2}}} & \sqrt{\dfrac{Z_{I_2}}{Z_{I_1}}} \cosh \theta \end{Vmatrix} \tag{7–225}$$

Carrying out the indicated matrix multiplication and simplifying the elements of the product matrix, we have

$$\begin{Vmatrix} \mathbf{A}_{n+1} & \mathbf{B}_{n+1} \\ \mathbf{C}_{n+1} & \mathbf{D}_{n+1} \end{Vmatrix} = \begin{Vmatrix} \sqrt{\dfrac{Z_{I_1}}{Z_{I_2}}} \cosh (n+1)\theta & \sqrt{Z_{I_1} Z_{I_2}} \sinh (n+1)\theta \\ \dfrac{1}{\sqrt{Z_{I_1} Z_{I_2}}} \sinh (n+1)\theta & \sqrt{\dfrac{Z_{I_2}}{Z_{I_1}}} \cosh (n+1)\theta \end{Vmatrix} \tag{7–226}$$

If we now compare A_{n+1}, B_{n+1}, C_{n+1}, and D_{n+1} with the corresponding parameters for a single twoport as expressed in (7–209 to 212), we see that the image parameters of an image cascade of an odd number of sections are Z_{I_1}, Z_{I_2}, and $(n+1)\theta$, where $n+1$ is the number of sections.

This conclusion can also be reached by the method of the preceding part of the present subsection: It should be noted that the first twoport in the cascade is taken to be oriented as 1–2. The last twoport in the chain must also be oriented as 1–2, since the cascade contains an odd number of sections. If we terminate this last section with Z_{I_2}, its input impedance will be Z_{I_1}. The next-to-last section is then terminated in Z_{I_1}, so that we shall see Z_{I_2} upon "looking into" its input terminals. Moving back through the cascade in this manner, we shall find Z_{I_1} as the input impedance to the entire chain when the termination is Z_{I_2}. Reversing this procedure and placing Z_{I_1} across the input terminals will lead to Z_{I_2} as the impedance measured at the output terminals. The image impedances of the entire cascade containing an odd number of sections must, then, be Z_{I_1} and Z_{I_2}, as was also indicated by (7–226).

In order to find θ_{n+1} for this cascade, we need merely add one equation to the list (7–221). Thus for the last section

$$\frac{E_n}{E_{n+1}} = \sqrt{\frac{Z_{I_1}}{Z_{I_2}}} e^{\theta} \tag{7–221a}$$

Multiplying the equations (7–221) and (7–221a), we find

$$\frac{E_0}{E_{n+1}} = \sqrt{\frac{Z_{I_1}}{Z_{I_2}}} e^{(n+1)\theta} \tag{7–227}$$

Now since the cascade with an odd number of sections constitutes a single unsymmetrical twoport with image impedances Z_{I_1} and Z_{I_2}, we must have θ_{n+1}, the image transfer constant, given by

$$\frac{E_0}{E_{n+1}} = \sqrt{\frac{Z_{I_1}}{Z_{I_2}}} e^{\theta_{n+1}} \tag{7–228}$$

Comparing (7–228) with (7–227) yields at once

$$\theta_{n+1} = (n+1)\theta \tag{7–229}$$

as was also indicated in the matrix equation (7–226).

7-13 Summary

The subject of the present chapter was the two-port network. The theory was limited to linear twoports (with lumped, constant elements, finite in number), free of applied sources of current or voltage except at the external terminal pairs. For transient analysis, the twoports were assumed to be initially at rest. Each twoport was found to be characterized by no more than four parameters which were functions of either s or $j\omega$ and which were independent of the voltage and current at the external terminal pairs. Special relationships limiting the number of independent parameters were obtained for passive twoports, passive symmetrical twoports, and ideally unilateral twoports.

The basic ideas and procedures of matrix algebra were developed. With this tool at hand, it was possible, in certain cases, to analyze networks as interconnections of twoports. The important cascade connection was easily analyzed with the aid of matrix multiplication. Matrix addition was shown to be applicable to the parallel, series, parallel–series, and series–parallel connections in those cases in which Brune's conditions were satisfied.

The vacuum-tube equivalent circuit, with interelectrode capacitance, in its three main connections (grounded-cathode, grounded-plate, and grounded-grid), was analyzed with the aid of matrices. A low-frequency transistor equivalent circuit was analyzed for its h-parameters.

The Vratsanos theorem was derived in a general form applicable to linear active as well as passive circuits, and to transient as well as sinusoidal steady-state analysis.

Finally, the iterative and image parameters of the passive twoport were defined and used to obtain matrices for cascades of a number of sections connected on either the iterative or image basis.

Problems

7-1. (A) Obtain the y coefficients of a symmetrical Π section and a symmetrical lattice (see figure).

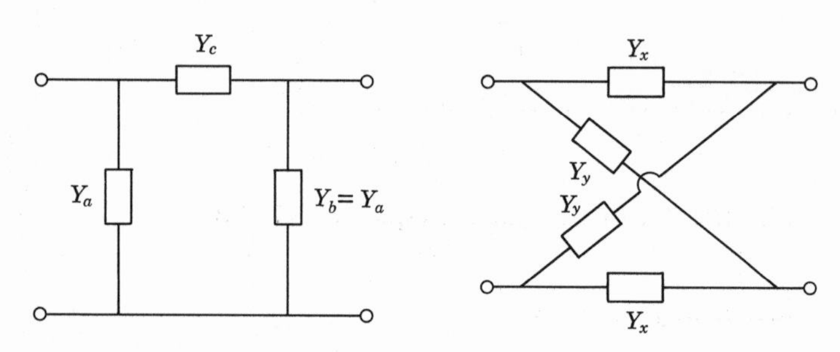

Problem 7-1.

(B) State conditions for which these circuits become equivalent twoports.

(C) If a symmetrical Π section is physically realizable, is the equivalent symmetrical lattice physically realizable in all cases?

(D) If a symmetrical lattice is physically realizable, is the equivalent symmetrical Π section physically realizable in all cases? NOTE: Take "physically realizable" to mean realizable with R's, L's, and C's.

7-2. Obtain the y coefficients of the twoport bounded by broken lines in the figure. Do this by two methods.

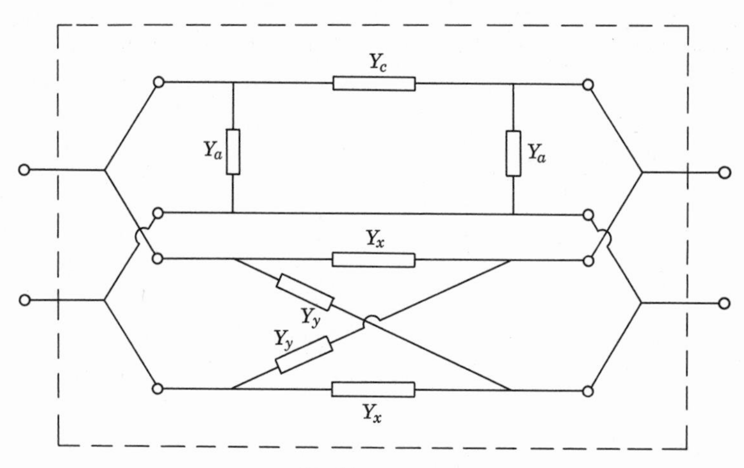

Problem 7–2.

7-3. It was demonstrated in this chapter that a unilateral circuit has the property $y_{12} = 0$. From this we concluded that $\eta = 0$. If $y_{12} = y_{21} = 0$, should the circuit be termed *unilateral*? Justify your conclusion and show an illustrative circuit.

7-4. State which of the circuits in the figure (p. 376) are equivalent twoports. Find the z coefficients of the circuits in (c) and in (d). Comment on the meaning of *equivalent* as used in connection with two-port networks.

7-5. Obtain the **A, B, C, D** coefficients of a bridge circuit. Do these coefficients approach a reasonable limit as the bridge parameters approach the balance condition?

7-6. A passive non-reciprocal twoport, termed a *gyrator*,(11) is defined by the equations

$$E_1 = -aI_2$$

$$E_2 = aI_1$$

where a is a constant having the dimensions of ohms.

(A) Obtain the y coefficients of the gyrator.

(B) Obtain the **A, B, C, D** coefficients of the gyrator.

(C) Evaluate η for the gyrator.

(D) Find the input impedance of the gyrator when it is terminated in an impedance Z.

7-7. Solve Problem 5–4, Chapter 5, with the aid of two-port network analysis.

7-8. A passive, reciprocal, symmetrical ideally reactive twoport is characterzed by an image impedance Z_I and an image transfer function θ.

(A) Show that Z_I is either real, a pure imaginary, or zero, at any one frequency.

(B) Show that when Z_I is real, θ is a pure imaginary. (HINT: Express $\tanh \theta$ in terms of **A**, **B**, **C**, and **D**).

(C) Show that θ has a real component when Z_I is imaginary.

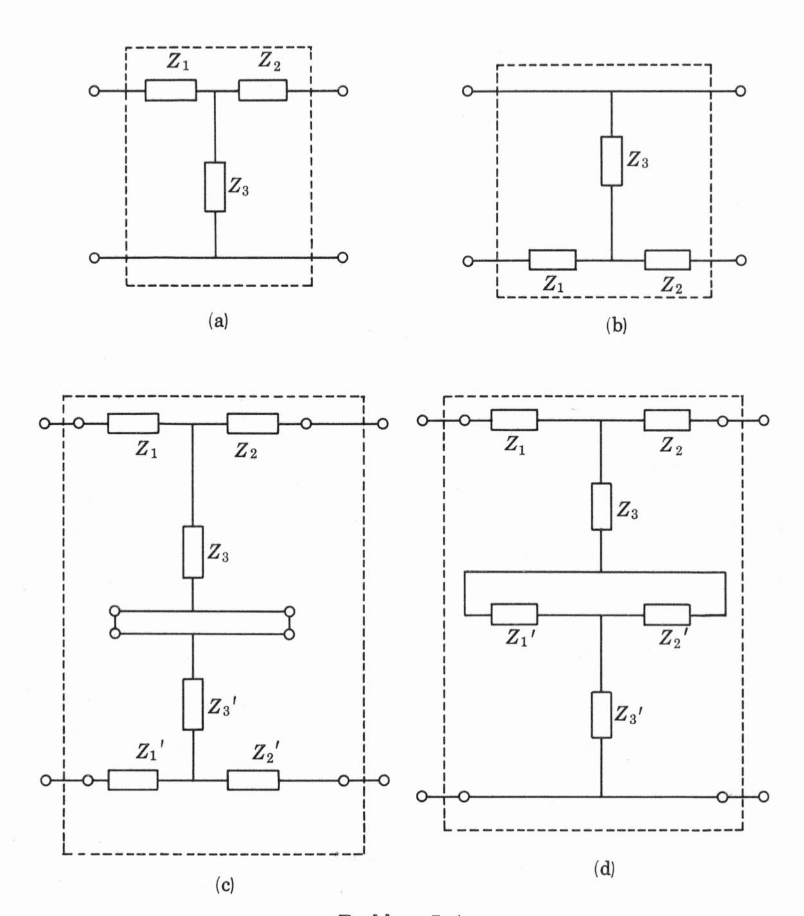

Problem 7–4.

7-9. With the results of Problem 7–8 in mind, explain why the lattice in the figure (p. 377) is known as an "all-pass lattice". Justify your statement.

7-10. A gyrator, defined in the statement of Problem 7–6, is terminated in an impedance Z. Use the generalized Vratsanos theorem derived in this chapter, in order to obtain the ratio $I_b{}^2/I_{IN}{}^2$ where I_b is the Laplace transform of the current in Z and I_{IN} is the Laplace transform of the input current to the gyrator. Confirm your result, using only the defining equations of the gyrator.

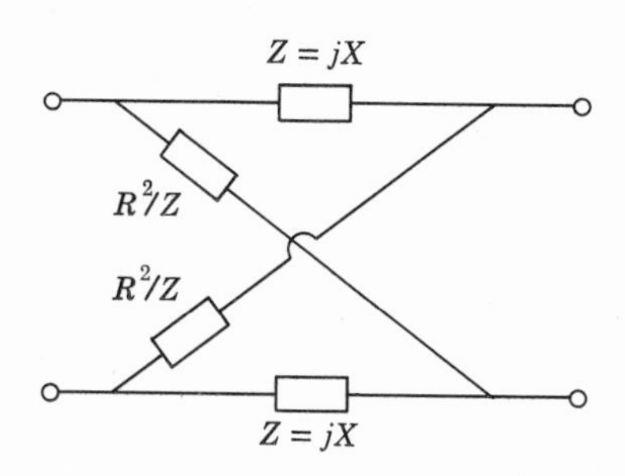

Problem 7–9.

References for Chapter 7

1. Bôcher, M., *Introduction to Higher Algebra*, The Macmillan Co., New York, 1907.
2. Brown, J. S., and Bennett, F. D., "The Application of Matrices to Vacuum-Tube Circuits," *Proc.* IRE, Vol. 36, pp. 844–852 (1948).
3. Brune, O.: "Letter to the Editor. On 'The Conditions for Validity of the Strecker-Feldtkeller Matrix Equations of Four-Pole Systems' (ENT 9: 31, 1932)," *Elek. Nachr. Tech.*, Vol. 9, No. 6, p. 234 (1932).
4. Guillemin, E. A., *Communication Networks*, Vol. II, John Wiley & Sons, Inc., New York, 1935.
5. Guillemin, E. A., *Introductory Circuit Theory*, John Wiley & Sons, Inc., New York, 1953.
6. Le Corbeiller, P., *Matrix Analysis of Electric Networks*, Harvard University Press, Cambridge, 1950.
7. Peterson, L. C., "Equivalent Circuits of Linear Active Four-Terminal Networks," *Bell Telephone System Monograph* B-166, pp. 1–30 (1948).
8. Reich, H. J., *Theory and Application of Electron Tubes*, 2nd ed., McGraw-Hill Book Co., Inc., New York, 1944.
9. Seely, S. *Electron-Tube Circuits*, McGraw-Hill Book Co., Inc., New York, 1950; 2nd ed., 1958.
10. Shea, R. F., Editor, *Principles of Transistor Circuits*, John Wiley & Sons, Inc., New York, 1953; *Transistor Circuit Engineering*, John Wiley & Sons, Inc., New York, 1957.
11. Tellegen, B. D. H., "The Gyrator—A New Electric Network Element," *Philips Research Reports*, Vol. 3, pp. 81–101 (1948).
12. Van Valkenburg, M. E., *Introduction to Modern Network Synthesis*, John Wiley & Sons, Inc., New York, 1960.
13. Vratsanos, J., "Calculation of Current Distribution in a Linear Network," *Arch. elekt. Übertr.*, Vol. 11, pp. 76–80 (Feb. 1957).
14. Weber, E., *Linear Transient Analysis*. Vol. II. *Two-Terminal-Pair Networks. Transmission Lines*, John Wiley & Sons, Inc., New York, 1956.

15. Institute of Radio Engineers, "Standards on Transducers: Definitions of Terms, 1951" *Proc.* IRE, Vol. 39, pp. 897–899 (1951).
16. Institute of Radio Engineers, "Standards on Circuits: Definitions of Terms in Network Topology, 1950," *Proc.* IRE, Vol. 39, pp. 27–29 (1951).
17. Institute of Radio Engineers, "IRE Standards on Methods of Measuring Noise in Linear Twoports, 1959," *Proc.* IRE, Vol. 48, pp. 60–68 (Jan. 1960).
18. Institute of Radio Engineers, "IRE Standards on Electron Tubes: Definitions of Terms, 1957," *Proc.* IRE, Vol. 45, pp. 983–1010 (July 1957).
19. American Standards Association, *American Standard Definitions of Electrical Terms, Group 65 Communication, ASA C42.65 1957*, American Institute of Electrical Engineers, New York, 1957.
20. *International Dictionary of Applied Mathematics*, D. Van Nostrand Company, Inc., Princeton, N.J., 1960.

Chapter 8

SIGNAL FLOW GRAPHS AND FLOW GRAPHS

The *signal flow graph*, originated by Mason,[4,5] is a pictorial representation of equations. Solution of the equations is obtained with the aid of procedures carried out on the graph. While a signal flow graph can be drawn for non-linear systems,[4] the usual application is to linear systems.[4,9] A similar, more recent graphical representation is the *flow graph*, introduced by Coates,[2,3] which leads to a direct evaluation of determinants.*

8-1 Linear Signal Flow Graphs

In order to present signal flow graphs, we consider the set of n simultaneous linear equations:

$$\left.\begin{aligned} a_{11}x_1 + a_{12}x_2 + \cdots + a_{1n}x_n - b_1 &= 0 \\ a_{21}x_1 + a_{22}x_2 + \cdots + a_{2n}x_n - b_2 &= 0 \\ \vdots \qquad \vdots \qquad\quad \vdots \qquad & \vdots \\ a_{n1}x_1 + a_{n2}x_2 + \cdots + a_{nn}x_n - b_n &= 0 \end{aligned}\right\} \tag{8–1}$$

Our presentation will be limited[9] to the case for which we may write $b_r = -g_{0r}x_0$ with $r = 1, 2, \ldots, n$. The minus sign is introduced for convenience (see equations 8–2 below), and, of course, one or more of the quantities g_{0r} may be zero. Thus we assume only one known variable in the set of equations (8–1). (This might represent a known e.m.f.) The limitation is not severe, however, since the principle of superposition may be used in cases in which more than one known variable occurs[4] (see Section 8–5).

* Much of the signal flow graph literature uses the words *flow graph* for brevity when referring to the *signal flow graph*. Since the term *flow graph* has now been used to define a different graph, we shall carefully distinguish between these terms.

Now adding x_1 to the first equation in (8–1), x_2 to the second, and so on, we write

$$\left.\begin{aligned} g_{01}x_0 + g_{11}x_1 + g_{21}x_2 + \cdots + g_{n1}x_n &= x_1 \\ g_{02}x_0 + g_{12}x_1 + g_{22}x_2 + \cdots + g_{n2}x_n &= x_2 \\ \vdots \quad \vdots \quad \vdots \qquad \qquad \vdots \quad & \quad \vdots \\ g_{0n}x_0 + g_{1n}x_1 + g_{2n}x_2 + \cdots + g_{nn}x_n &= x_n \end{aligned}\right\} \tag{8–2}$$

The coefficients in equations (8–2) are related to those in (8–1) as follows. Letting $r = 1, 2, \ldots, n$, and $s = 0, 1, 2, \ldots, n$, we find

$$\left.\begin{aligned} g_{sr} &= a_{rs} && \text{when } r \neq s \text{ and } s \neq 0 \\ g_{0r} &= -b_r/x_0 && \text{when } s = 0 \\ g_{rr} &= a_{rr} + 1 && \text{when } s = r \end{aligned}\right\} \tag{8–2a}$$

A signal flow graph representing any one of the equations (8–2), say the rth one, is drawn (essentially defined) as follows:

(a) Each of the letters $x_0, x_1, \ldots, x_n$ is written on any convenient surface and a small circle placed next to each letter. The small circle next to x_s is called *node* s where s may be any one of the numbers $0, 1, 2, \ldots, n$ as in equations (8–2a).

(b) An arrow (which may be curved) is drawn from each node to the node r, Fig. 8–1(a). One of these arrows is drawn from node r to itself.

(c) The coefficient g_{sr} is written alongside the arrow from s to r as in Fig. 8–1(b). The meaning of this figure is that x_r consists of the sum of terms,*

$$\sum_{s=0}^{n} g_{sr}x_s$$

This sum is the left side of the rth equation of the set (8–2). We observe that when $g_{sr} = 0$ for a particular value of s, the arrow from s to r need not be drawn.

One may think of the point r as receiving signals from the other nodes by way of arrows leading into node r. The signal arriving from a typical node s is then $g_{sr}x_s$. The remaining equations may be added to the diagram by drawing appropriately labeled arrows between the existing nodes, $0, 1, \ldots, n$. However complicated the figure, all the arrows leading into a particular node yield one equation.

* Compare equation 7, in S. J. Mason's article.[5]

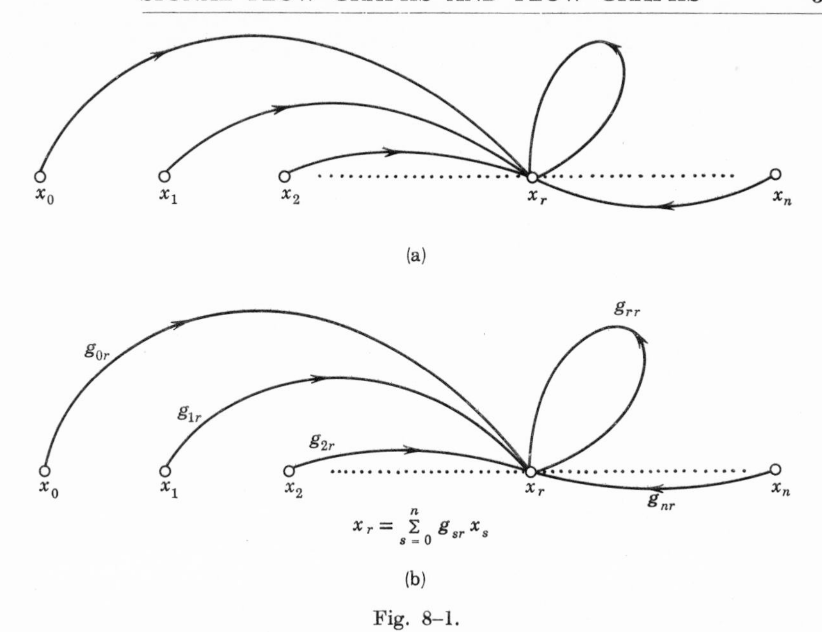

Fig. 8–1.

The graph of Fig. 8–2(a) corresponds to the equations

$$g_{01}x_0 + g_{11}x_1 + g_{21}x_2 = x_1 \tag{8–3}$$

$$g_{12}x_1 + g_{22}x_2 = x_2 \tag{8–4}$$

Equations (8–2) reduce to these equations when $n = 2$ and $g_{02} = 0$.

As seen above, the equations (8–2) are written in a most unusual form. The reasons for this are now apparent:

(a) The variable x_r appears alone on the right-hand side of equation r, so that x_r may be pictured as the total of the contributions arriving from each of the variables.

(b) The order of the subscripts on the coefficients g_{sr} corresponds to the arrow direction s to r.

8-2 Terminology of Signal Flow Graphs[4,11]

A number of special terms are convenient when signal flow graphs are discussed. A *node* has been defined in the previous section. A *branch* is a line segment joining two nodes (or with both ends on a single node). The branches in signal flow graphs are directed branches. A *directed branch* is an arrow joining two nodes (or emanating from and terminating on a single node). The coefficient g_{sr} associated with a branch from s to r is called the *branch gain*, or *branch transmittance*.

A *path* is a sequence of branches traversed in the branch directions. A path along which each node appears only once is an *open path*.

In Figs. 8–1 and 8–2, the number identifying each node appears as a subscript on the variable x; thus x_s identifies node s. (We shall find it convenient later, at times, to refer to a node not by a number, but by the variable associated with it, e.g., node x_0 may be used instead of node 0, or node e_g may be mentioned without an accompanying number.) The subscripts on each branch gain g identify the branch; thus g_{sr} identifies

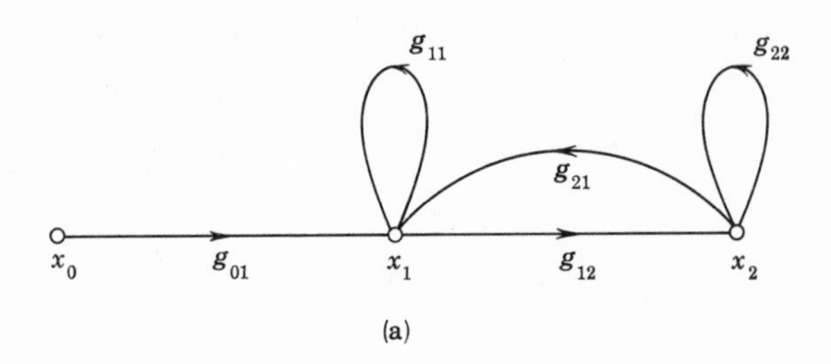

(a)

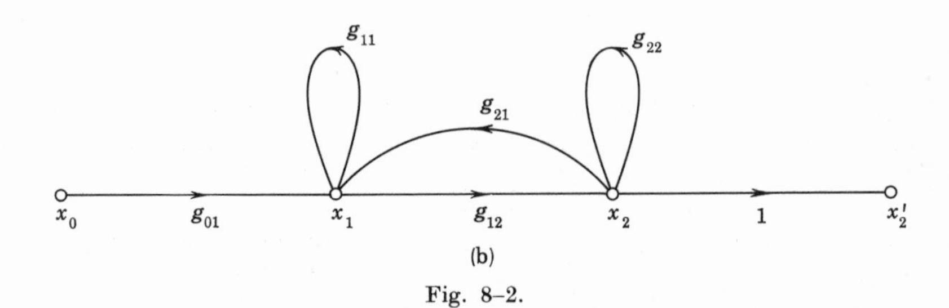

(b)

Fig. 8–2.

the branch from node s to node r. A path is identified by the numbers of the nodes which it touches; thus path 121 in Fig. 8–2(a) starts at node 1, passes through node 2, and returns to node 1.

A *source* is a node from which arrows emanate, but upon which they do not terminate; see node 0, Fig. 8–2(a). As indicated in Section 8–1, we shall develop the theory of signal flow graphs with only a single source, and shall use superposition when more than one source is involved; see problem, Section 8–5. A *sink* is a node upon which arrows terminate, but from which they do not emanate. A sink may be artificially created; see node 2′, Fig. 8–2(b). A set of one or more branches forming a simple closed path which returns to its starting point is called a *loop*, a *feedback loop*, or a *feedback path*; see paths 11, 121, and 22 in Fig. 8–2(b). A feedback loop with only one branch is a *self loop*. Nodes and branches which are not in a feedback loop are called *cascade nodes* and *cascade branches*, respectively; see nodes 0 and 2′ and branches 01 and 22′, Fig. 8–2(b). (If in Fig. 8–2(b), $g_{21} = g_{22} = 0$, the cascade nodes would be 0, 2, and 2′, and the cascade branches would be 01, 12, and 22′.) In a similar manner, nodes and branches which form part of a feedback loop are *feedback nodes* and *feedback branches*: see nodes 1 and 2 and branches 11; 12, 21; and 22 in Fig. 8–2(b). A signal flow graph which contains only cascade branches is a *cascade graph*.

In order to arrive at an important definition which leads to a measure of the complexity of a graph, we consider the procedure of *node splitting*. Let all arrows which terminate on a node, say node r, be redrawn terminating on a new node r'. The new node r' is now a sink and the remaining node r is a source. The node r is said to have been split. The graph with nodes r and r' in place of the single node r cannot represent the original equations on which the graph was based. The procedure of node splitting has a value, however. We note that if a node r was in a feedback loop before splitting, the new graph with r and r' does not contain this feedback path. Now if i is the *minimum* number of nodes which must be split to destroy all feedback paths in the graph, i is the *index* of the graph. The nodes to be split are called *index nodes*. More than one set of index nodes may exist in a particular graph.

When a graph is simplified (see Section 8–4) to the point where its only nodes are sources, sinks, and index nodes, the graph is termed an *index residue*. The signal flow graph of Fig. 8–2(b) is, as it stands, an index residue. The index nodes are 1 and 2. The index of the graph is 2. If we let $g_{22} = 0$, the resulting graph contains two feedback loops. The index of this new graph is 1, for splitting the single index node (node number 1) opens both loops 11 and 121.

For additional information on signal flow graph terminology, the student is referred to the IRE Definitions of Terms for Linear Signal Flow Graphs.[11]

8-3 Rules for Simplifying the Signal Flow Graph[4]

When the equations represented by a signal flow graph can be derived from the equations represented by another signal flow graph, we shall say that the graphs are *equivalent*. We shall now demonstrate that each pair of graphs in Fig. 8–3 are equivalent. These equivalences are useful in solving equations by means of simplifying the signal flow graph. In

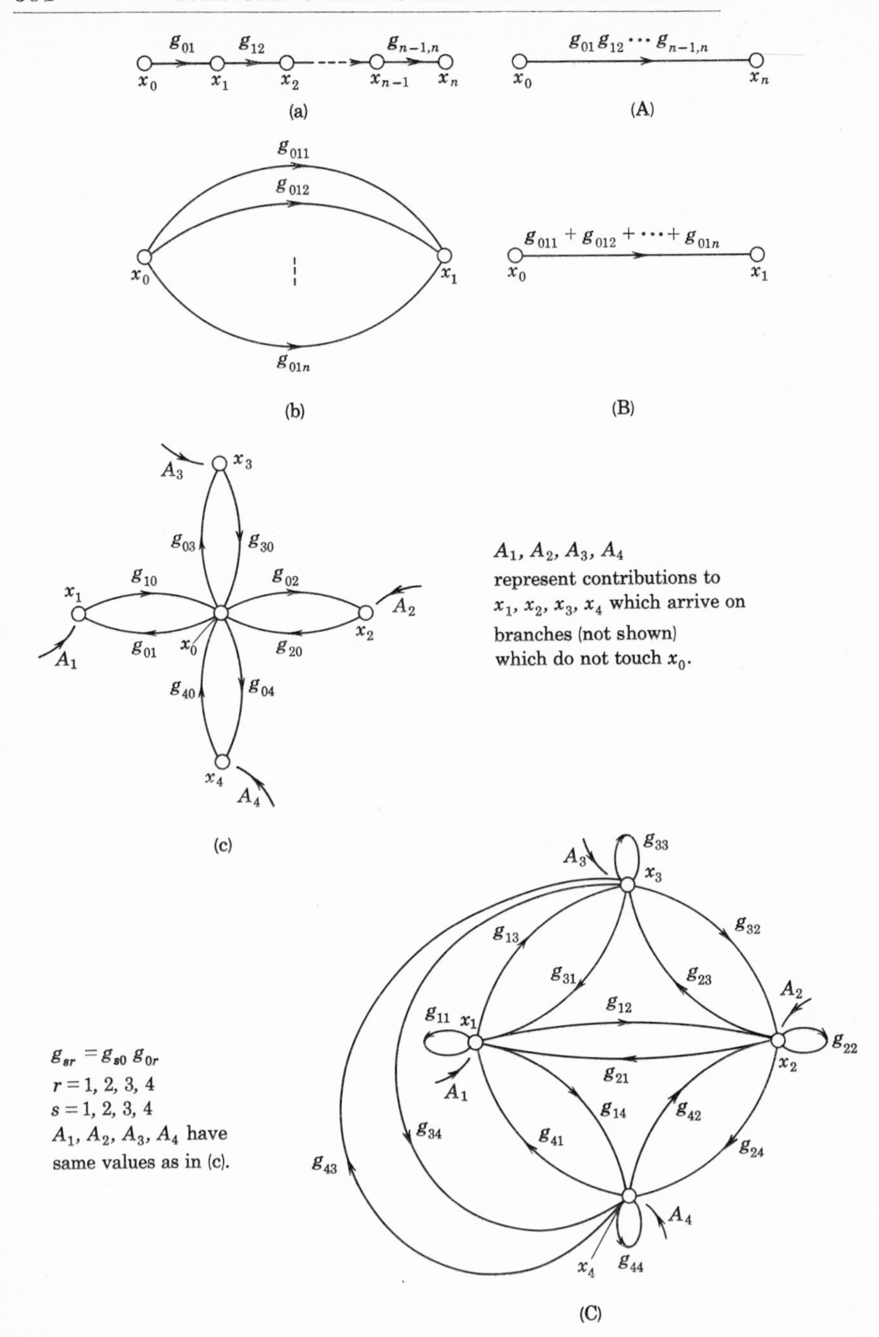

g_{01} g_{12} $g_{n-1,n}$
x_0 x_1 x_2 x_{n-1} x_n
(a)
$g_{01}g_{12}\cdots g_{n-1,n}$
x_0 x_n
(A)
g_{011}
g_{012}
x_0 x_1
g_{01n}
(b)
$g_{011}+g_{012}+\cdots+g_{01n}$
x_0 x_1
(B)
A_3 x_3
g_{03} g_{30}
g_{10} g_{02}
x_1 A_2
g_{01} x_0 g_{20} x_2
A_1
g_{40} g_{04}
x_4 A_4
(c)
A_1, A_2, A_3, A_4
represent contributions to
x_1, x_2, x_3, x_4 which arrive on
branches (not shown)
which do not touch x_0.
g_{33} A_3 x_3
g_{13} g_{32}
g_{31} g_{23}
A_2
g_{11} x_1 g_{12}
g_{22}
x_2
g_{21}
A_1
g_{14} g_{42}
g_{34} g_{41} g_{24}
g_{43}
A_4
x_4 g_{44}
$g_{sr}=g_{s0}\,g_{0r}$
$r=1, 2, 3, 4$
$s=1, 2, 3, 4$
A_1, A_2, A_3, A_4 have
same values as in (c).
(C)

Fig. 8–3.

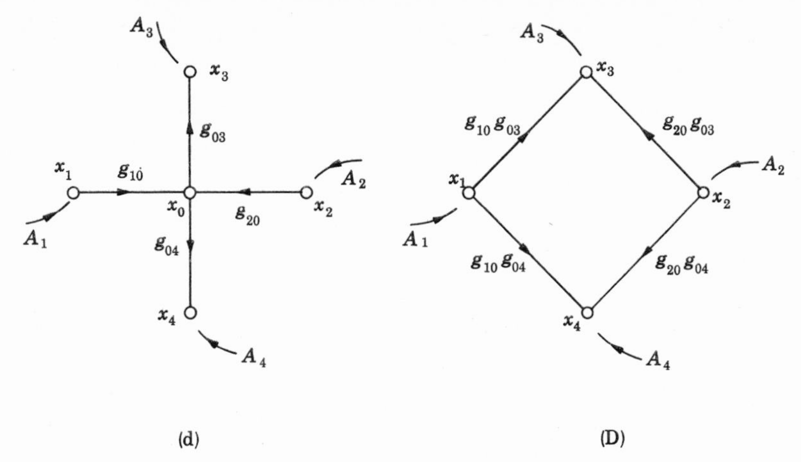

A_1, A_2, A_3, A_4 have same significance in (d) and (D) as in (c) and (C)

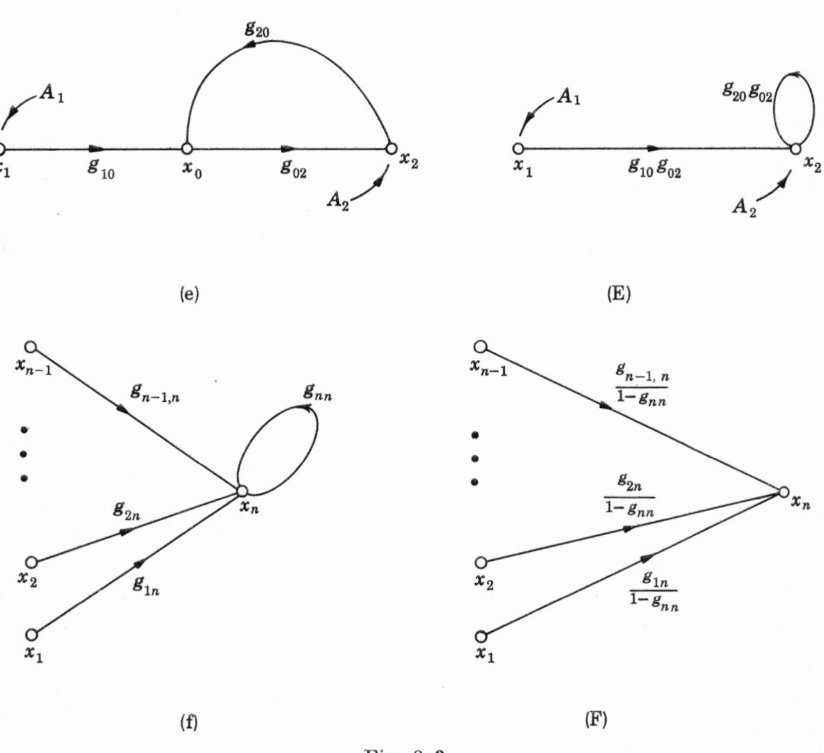

Fig. 8–3.

Fig. 8–3 and in the following discussion, the number 0 is not reserved for a source node, as in the basic equations (8–2).

Pair aA

The graph of Fig. 8–3(a) represents the equations

$$\left.\begin{aligned} x_1 &= g_{01}x_0 \\ x_2 &= g_{12}x_1 \\ \vdots \;&\;\; \vdots \\ x_n &= g_{n-1,n}x_{n-1} \end{aligned}\right\} \tag{8–5}$$

Multiplication of the left and right sides yields at once

$$x_n = (g_{01}g_{12}\cdots g_{n-1,n})x_0 \tag{8–5a}$$

Equation (8–5a) is represented by the graph of Fig. 8–3(A).

Pair bB

The graph of Fig. 8–3(b) represents the equation

$$x_1 = g_{011}x_0 + g_{012}x_0 + \cdots + g_{01n}x_0 \tag{8–6}$$

Factoring yields at once

$$x_1 = (g_{011} + g_{012} + \cdots + g_{01n})x_0 \tag{8–6a}$$

The latter equation is represented by the graph of Fig. 8–3(B).

Pair cC

The third pair of equivalent graphs, Fig. 8–3(c) and 8–3(C), illustrates removal of a node, or *node absorption*. Although only five nodes are shown, the algebraic proof will make it evident that the procedure is general. (A word statement to follow the proof will show that the procedure is not nearly as complicated as a first glance at the figure seems to indicate.) Essential to the conclusion to follow is the fact that the node x_0 is not in a self loop. The symbols A_1, A_2, A_3, and A_4 in the figure and in the equations to follow represent sums of terms which do not include x_0. These terms may each be proportional to any of the variables x_1, x_2, x_3, x_4, or other variables not shown in the figure. In signal flow graph language, we may say that A_1, for example, represents any contributions to x_1 due to a self loop on x_1, due to branches from x_2, x_3, and x_4 directly to x_1, and due to branches arriving from other nodes not shown on the figure. In specific cases, many of these contributions will, of course, be zero.

From the definition of A_1, A_2, A_3, and A_4 just stated, and from the graph, Fig. 8–3(c), we find four equations. These may be expressed compactly as

$$x_r = A_r + g_{0r}x_0 \tag{8–7}$$

where $r = 1, 2, 3$, or 4.

Further,

$$x_0 = \sum_{s=1}^{4} g_{s0}x_s \tag{8–8}$$

Substitution of (8–8) into (8–7) yields

$$x_r = A_r + g_{0r} \sum_{s=1}^{4} g_{s0}x_s \tag{8–9}$$

or

$$x_r = A_r + \sum_{s=1}^{4} g_{s0}g_{0r}x_s \tag{8–10}$$

where $r = 1, 2, 3$, or 4.

We now conclude:

(1) Each two-branch path through x_0 may be replaced by a single branch. This single branch starts on the same node and terminates on the same node as the two-branch path which it replaces. (Expansion of the summation in (8–10) leads, at once, to this conclusion.)

(2) All branches—not shown in Fig. 8–3(c)—which do not touch x_0 remain unaltered. (This follows from the fact that A_r in equation (8–7) is identical with A_r in equation (8–10).)

(3) The principle of node removal described above applies with any number of nodes joined to x_0 by single branches. (This follows because the steps (8–7) to (8–10) can equally well be carried out with $r = 1, 2, \ldots, m$ and

$$x_0 = \sum_{s=1}^{m} g_{s0}x_s$$

where m is the number of nodes connected to 0 by single branches.)

Pair dD

The pair *dD*, referred to as the *star-to-mesh equivalence*, is easily seen to be a special case of pair *cC*. If conclusions (1) and (2) given above are applied to Fig. 8–3(d), we find at once that Fig. 8–3(D) is the equivalent graph. It is also of interest to justify the result algebraically, as a special case of equations (8–7) through (8–10).

Let

$$g_{01} = g_{02} = g_{30} = g_{40} = 0 \tag{8–11}$$

Equation (8–7) then yields

$$x_1 = A_1 \tag{8–12}$$

$$x_2 = A_2 \tag{8–13}$$

$$x_3 = A_3 + g_{03}x_0 \tag{8–14}$$

$$x_4 = A_4 + g_{04}x_0 \tag{8–15}$$

Equation (8–8) yields

$$x_0 = g_{10}x_1 + g_{20}x_2 \tag{8–16}$$

Equations (8–12) through (8–16) correspond to Fig. 8–3(d). The quantities, $A_1, \ldots, A_4$ simply indicate that contributions to nodes $x_1, \ldots, x_4$ may come from variables other than x_0.

From (8–11) and (8–10), when $r = 3$ and 4, we have respectively

$$x_3 = A_3 + g_{10}g_{03}x_1 + g_{20}g_{03}x_2 \tag{8–17}$$

$$x_4 = A_4 + g_{10}g_{04}x_1 + g_{20}g_{04}x_2 \tag{8–18}$$

Note that when $r = 1$ and 2, respectively, (8–10) and (8–11) yield (8–12) and (8–13). Equations (8–17) and (8–18) correspond to the graph Fig. 8–3(D), so that the desired equivalence is established. In this equivalence, x_1, and/or x_2 may, but need not necessarily, be source nodes. Commonly A_3 and A_4 will be zero, i.e., the only contributions to the values of the variables x_3 and x_4 will arrive from x_1 and x_2 through x_0.

Pair eE

A second important special case follows from pair cC. The conclusions following equation (8–10) may be applied to the graph of Fig. 8–3(e). We then find, at once, that the graph of Fig. 8–3(E) is an equivalent one. Again it is of interest to obtain the result through equations (8–7) through (8–10).

Let

$$g_{01} = g_{03} = g_{04} = g_{30} = g_{40} = 0 \tag{8–19}$$

From (8–19) and (8–7), we have

$$x_1 = A_1 \tag{8 20}$$

$$x_2 = A_2 + g_{02}x_0 \tag{8–21}$$

$$x_3 = A_3 \tag{8–22}$$

$$x_4 = A_4 \tag{8–23}$$

Equation (8–8) yields

$$x_0 = g_{10}x_1 + g_{20}x_2 \tag{8–24}$$

Clearly x_3 and x_4 are variables determined in ways which cannot affect the equivalence which we seek to demonstrate. These variables, therefore, are not shown in the figure. Equations (8–20, 21, 24) represent the graph of Fig. 8–3(e). The symbols A_1 and A_2 simply represent additional contributions to x_1 and x_2.

When $r = 2$, we obtain from (8–10) and (8–19)

$$x_2 = A_2 + g_{10}g_{02}x_1 + g_{20}g_{02}x_2 \tag{8–25}$$

When $r = 1$, 3, or 4, we obtain (8–20, 22, and 23).

Pair fF

Pair *fF* is basic to signal flow analysis, for the significance of a self loop must be understood if signal flow graphs are to be reduced to their simplest possible equivalents. Fig. 8–3 (*f*) represents the equation

$$x_n = g_{1n}x_1 + g_{2n}x_2 + \cdots + g_{nn}x_n \tag{8–26}$$

The solution for x_n is

$$x_n = \frac{g_{1n}}{1 - g_{nn}}x_1 + \frac{g_{2n}}{1 - g_{nn}}x_2 + \cdots + \frac{g_{n-1,n}}{1 - g_{nn}}x_{n-1} \tag{8–27}$$

Equation (8–27) represents the graph of Fig. 8–3(F).

The equivalence shown as pair *fF* breaks down when $g_{nn} = 1$. In such a case, x_n need not appear in equation (8–26) as it can be removed simply by its subtraction from both sides. If the signal flow graph is to be drawn, however, each equation must again be written with one unknown on one side as in the equations (8–2).

8-4 A Direct Means of Simplifying a Signal Flow Graph

A signal flow graph may be simplified (i.e., replaced by a simpler equivalent) almost by inspection.(4) This method can be justified with the aid of the conclusions stated after equation (8–10).

We select a set of index nodes, number these 1, 2, . . ., i, and number the source node, 0, and the sink, $i+1$. Let s have any one of the values

0, 1, 2, . . ., i, and let r have any one of the values 1, 2, . . ., i, $i+1$. Let $n_1, n_2, \ldots, n_m$ be numbers identifying nodes other than 0, 1, 2, . . ., i, $i+1$, i.e., other than source, sink, or index nodes. We seek to remove nodes $n_1, \ldots, n_m$. Pair cC, Fig. 8–3, applies to the removal of a node which does not contain a self loop (provided, of course, that it is neither source nor sink). Since a node in a self loop is an index node, none of the nodes $n_1, \ldots, n_m$ is in a self loop. Thus any one of the nodes $n_1, \ldots, n_m$ may be removed by application of pair cC, Fig. 8–3. We can apply pair cC to all the nodes n_1 to n_m in any order, provided that removal of one of these does not result in a self loop on another node to be removed. From Fig. 8–3(c)(C) we see, however, that removal of a node creates a self loop on an adjacent node only if the two nodes are joined to each other by two branches forming a feedback loop. This means that one of them is an index node. Therefore, if the non-index node of the pair is removed, a self loop is added to the index node. Thus we find no obstacle to the removal of all the nodes $n_1, \ldots, n_m$ by pair cC, Fig. 8–3.

Now consider any sequence of branches in the original graph forming a path from node s to node r. (The values of s and r were defined above; if $s = r$, the path terminates at its starting point.) Clearly, the removal of the nodes in this path leaves a single branch whose gain is the product of the gains of the branches in the path. This follows from the fact that one branch of this path terminated on, and one emanated from, each node removed. The same statement may be made about any other path between r and s. Thus, after removal of the nodes $n_1, \ldots, n_m$, we find that each path from s to r in the original graph has been replaced by a single branch with gain equal to the product of the gains of the branches along that path. These parallel branches are now easily combined by pair bB, Fig. 8–3. It is well to note at this point that two paths may have one or more (but, certainly, not all) branches in common.

We now conclude that: A single branch from s to r replaces all paths from s to r which do not pass through an index node. The gain of this single branch is a sum of terms, one term for each path replaced. Each term is the product of the branch gains on the replaced path. All values of s and r as defined above must be used. We note that we can have $s = r$, giving rise to self loops, but that r cannot be zero since we cannot arrive at a source, and s cannot equal $i+1$ since we cannot leave a sink.*

* Only one sink is assumed. In a problem with two sinks, x_a and x_b, we may solve for x_a and x_b separately, since neither can, according to the definition of a sink, affect any of the variables in the problem.

8-5 A Circuit Problem

As an illustration of signal flow graph technique, we consider the difference amplifier, Fig. 6–1, page 268. Since the circuit is free of reactive elements, the equations will be written for instantaneous values. From the equivalent circuit, Fig. 6–1(b), we easily find

$$e_{g1} = e_1 + R_K i_1 + R_K i_2 \tag{8–28}$$

$$e_{g2} = e_2 + R_K i_2 + R_K i_1 \tag{8–29}$$

$$i_1 = -\frac{\mu}{K} e_{g1} - \frac{R_K}{K} i_2 \tag{8–30}$$

$$i_2 = -\frac{\mu}{K} e_{g2} - \frac{R_K}{K} i_1 \tag{8–31}$$

$$e_{p1} = R_L i_1 \tag{8–32}$$

$$e_{p2} = R_L i_2 \tag{8–33}$$

$$e_o = e_{p1} - e_{p2} \tag{8–34}$$

where, in equations (8–30) and (8–31), $K = r_p + R_K + R_L$ and R_K is the same as R_k in Fig. 6–1.

From the resulting signal flow graph, Fig. 8–4(a), we may establish at once that the output voltage e_o is proportional to the difference of the applied voltages. Let e_{p1}' and e_{p2}' be the values of e_{p1} and e_{p2} when $e_1 \neq 0$ and $e_2 = 0$. Then

$$\left.\begin{aligned} e_{p1}' &= Me_1 \\ e_{p2}' &= Ne_1 \end{aligned}\right\} \tag{8–35}$$

M and N are constants because all the branch gains are constants. In view of the symmetry of the portion of the graph to the left of e_{p1} and e_{p2}, we see that if the sources are interchanged, the values of e_{p1} and e_{p2} are interchanged. Now let e_{p1}'' and e_{p2}'' be the values of e_{p1} and e_{p2} when $e_1 = 0$ and $e_2 \neq 0$. Then

$$\left.\begin{aligned} e_{p1}'' &= Ne_2 \\ e_{p2}'' &= Me_2 \end{aligned}\right\} \tag{8–36}$$

We find at once (see equation 8–34) that, with e_o' as the value of e_o when $e_2 = 0$ and $e_1 \neq 0$, and e_o'' as the value of e_o when $e_1 = 0$ and $e_2 \neq 0$,

$$e_o' = (M - N)e_1 \tag{8–37}$$

$$e_o'' = (N - M)e_2 \tag{8–38}$$

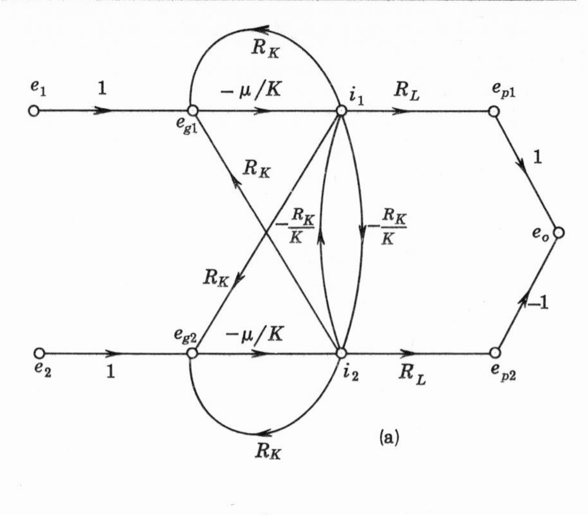
e_1
1
R_K
$-\mu/K$
i_1
R_L
e_{p1}
e_{g1}
R_K
1
$-\frac{R_K}{K}$
$-\frac{R_K}{K}$
e_o
R_K
-1
e_{g2}
$-\mu/K$
e_2
1
i_2
R_L
e_{p2}
R_K
(a)

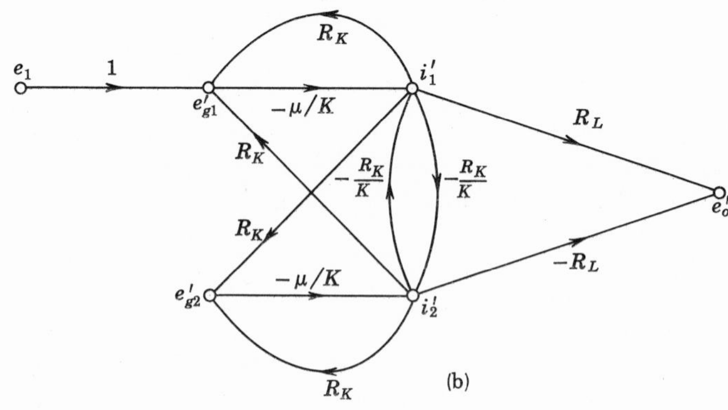
R_K
e_1
1
i_1'
e_{g1}'
$-\mu/K$
R_L
R_K
$-\frac{R_K}{K}$
$-\frac{R_K}{K}$
e_o'
R_K
$-R_L$
$-\mu/K$
e_{g2}'
i_2'
R_K
(b)

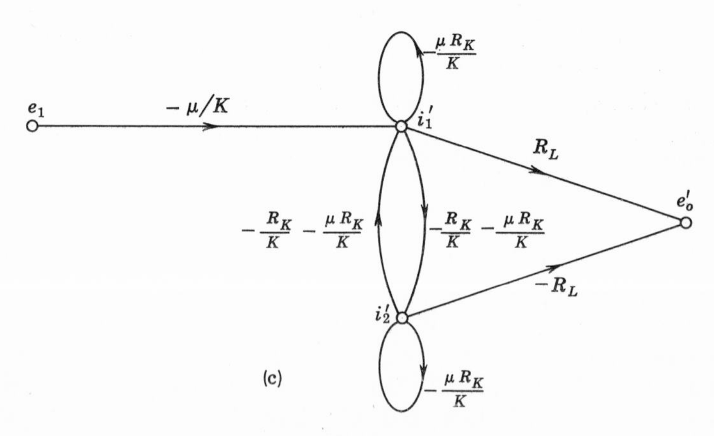
$-\frac{\mu R_K}{K}$
e_1
$-\mu/K$
i_1'
R_L
e_o'
$-\frac{R_K}{K} - \frac{\mu R_K}{K}$
$-\frac{R_K}{K} - \frac{\mu R_K}{K}$
$-R_L$
i_2'
$-\frac{\mu R_K}{K}$
(c)

Fig. 8–4.

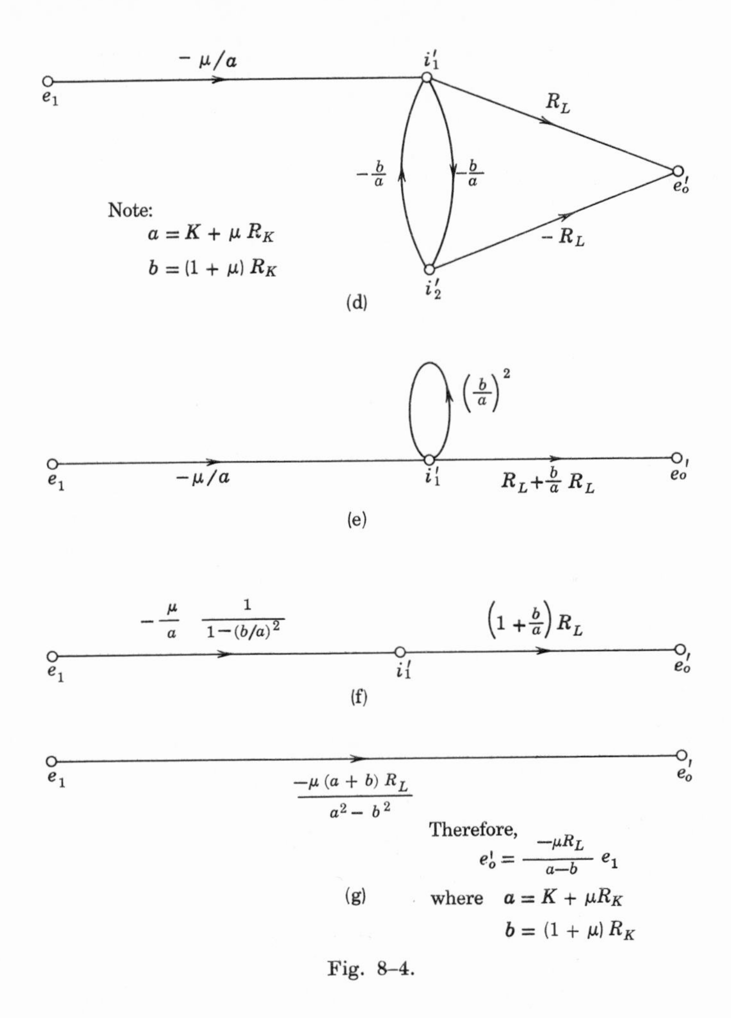

Fig. 8–4.

The superposition principle yields

$$e_o = e_o' + e_o'' = (M - N)(e_1 - e_2) \tag{8-39}$$

Thus, from the symmetry of the graph, the main property of the circuit of Fig. 6–1(b) is established: namely, that the voltage e_o is proportional to the difference of the input signals.

If we seek the actual value of e_o in terms of circuit constants, the signal flow graph must be simplified. Again using (′) to denote the condition $e_1 \neq 0$, $e_2 = 0$, we shall first find e_o'. The path from node i_1 to e_o in Fig. 8–4(a) may be replaced by a single branch according to pair aA,

Fig. 8–3. The same is true of the path from i_2 to e_o, Fig. 8–4(a), so that we begin with the graph, Fig. 8–4(b). We note that if nodes i_1' and i_2' are split, as discussed in Section 8–2, all feedback paths are opened. Since at least two nodes must be so split for all feedback paths to be opened, the graph is of index 2 and, clearly, nodes i_1' and i_2' constitute a possible set of index nodes.

In order to find the index residue, Fig. 8–4(c), we follow the method stated at the end of the preceding section. The result is summarized in Table 8–1.

TABLE 8–1

Nodes joined	Number of Paths	Product of branch gains on each path
$e_1 \to i_1'$	1	$-\mu/K$
$e_1 \to i_2'$	0	0
$e_1 \to e_o'$	0	0
$i_1' \to i_1'$	1	$-\mu R_K/K$
$i_1' \to i_2'$	2	$-R_K/K$ and $-\mu R_K/K$
$i_1' \to e_o'$	1	R_L
$i_2' \to i_1'$	2	$-R_K/K$ and $-\mu R_K/K$
$i_2' \to i_2'$	1	$-\mu R_K/K$
$i_2' \to e_o'$	1	$-R_L$

We note that no path returns to a source or passes through an index node. The table is given as an aid in explanation. We may, with equal ease and greater efficiency, place its data directly on a graph without first tabulating.

The self loops in the index residue, Fig. 8–4(c), are easily removed with the aid of pair fF, Fig. 8–3. The equivalent graph, Fig. 8–4(d), results. The index of this graph is 1. Selecting node i_1 as index node, we obtain a new index residue, Fig. 8–4(e). Again, pair fF of Fig. 8–3 rids us of the self loop and leads to the graph of index zero, Fig. 8–4(f). Then pair aA, Fig. 8–3, yields the final result, Fig. 8–4(g). This result is seen to be consistent with equation (6–14), page 269, when the definitions of K, a, and b used in Fig. 8–4 are introduced. Thus, when $e_2 = 0$, we have

$$e_o' = \frac{-\mu R_L}{a-b} e_1 \tag{8–40}$$

where $a = K+\mu R_K$, $b = (1+\mu)R_K$, and $K = r_p+R_K+R_L$.

With the aid of (8–37) and (8–38), which followed directly from consideration of the symmetry of Fig. 8–4(a), we have

$$e_o'' = \frac{\mu R_L}{a-b} e_2 \tag{8–41}$$

whence, by (8–39)

$$e_o = \frac{-\mu R_L}{a-b}(e_1 - e_2) \tag{8–42}$$

which easily reduces to

$$e_o = \frac{-\mu R_L}{r_p + R_L}(e_1 - e_2) \tag{8–43}$$

(See also Chapter 6, equation 6–18.)

8–6 Inversion

In general, a linear algebraic equation can be rewritten with any one variable expressed in terms of the others. Were we to do this arbitrarily in the set (8–2), we should find more than one equation with the same single variable on the right-hand side. Thus we would have more than one sum of terms equal to, say, x_r, and the signal flow graph would be incorrect or badly complicated. (We might attempt to keep it correct by having more than one node labeled x_r.[4]) In certain cases, however, a correct and simpler graph can be achieved with certain of its equations rewritten. Since the direction of some of the branches is reversed in the process, the procedure is termed *inversion.*

CASE 1. *Inversion of a single branch with source at one end.*

If a single branch from a source node x_0 to a node x_1 exists, we have, included in the list of equations corresponding to the graph, the equation

$$x_1 = g_{01}x_0 + g_{11}x_1 + g_{21}x_2 + \cdots + g_{n1}x_n \tag{8–44}$$

which may be rewritten in the form

$$x_0 = \frac{1}{g_{01}}x_1 - \frac{g_{11}}{g_{01}}x_1 - \frac{g_{21}}{g_{01}}x_2 - \cdots - \frac{g_{n1}}{g_{01}}x_n \tag{8–45}$$

The graphs representing equations (8–44) and (8–45) are shown in Fig. 8–5. Each is a portion of a larger graph. The branch 01 is said to have been *inverted.* We now observe several important facts:

(a) The direction of the branch 01, Fig. 8–5(a), has been reversed, Fig. 8–5(b).

(b) All other branches which terminate on 1, Fig. 8–5(a), terminate on 0, Fig. 8–5(b).

(c) The gain g_{01} of branch 01, Fig. 8–5(a), has been replaced by $1/g_{01}$ as the gain of the lower branch 10, Fig. 8–5(b).

(d) The gain g_{r1} of branch $r1$, Fig. 8–5(a), has been replaced by $-g_{r1}/g_{01}$ as the gain of branch $r0$, Fig. 8–5(b) ($r = 1, 2, \ldots, n$). Here 10 refers to the upper of the two branches 10.

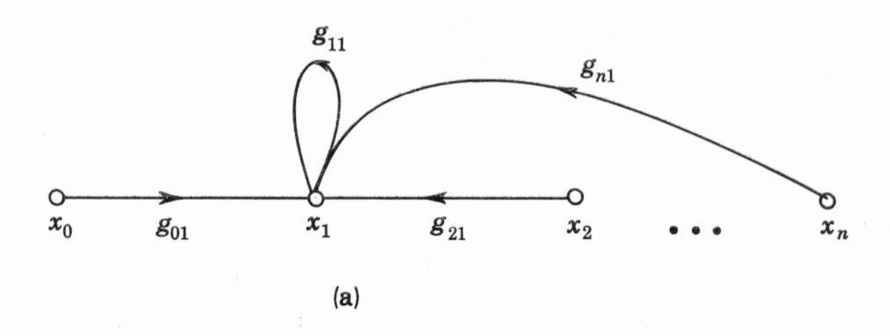

(a)

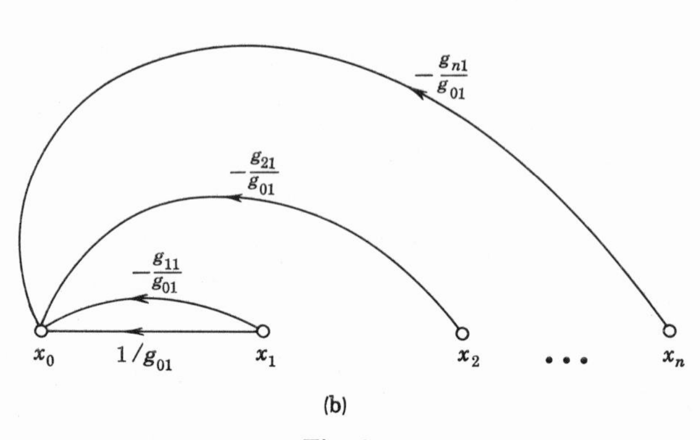

(b)

Fig. 8–5.

(e) *The variable x_0 is a source in the signal flow graph of which Fig. 8–5(a) is a portion.* None of the equations for that graph, then, equates a sum of terms to x_0. Therefore, when equation (8–45) replaces (8–44), the new set of equations contains only one equation (8–45) in which x_0 is equated to a sum of terms. Thus a new signal flow graph, of which Fig. 8–5(b) is a portion, may be drawn.

(*f*) Either from equation (8–45) or from Fig. 8–5(b), we see that there is now no equation which equates terms to x_1; therefore, it is evident that x_1 *is a source in the new graph.*

CASE 2. *An open path*

We now consider an open path starting at a source node x_0, and going to $x_1, x_2, \ldots, x_k$ in order. Let the branch 01 be inverted as discussed under Case 1. According to (f), Case 1, x_1 is now a source node, so that we may invert the branch 12, making 2 a source. The process may be continued until all branches in the path from 0 to k have been inverted. The path is now said to be inverted. We shall see (Section 8–7) that inversion of an open path may simplify a signal flow graph by destroying feedback paths and thereby reducing the graph index.

CASE 3. *A feedback path.*

Inversion may be applied to a feedback path which does not intersect itself, provided that *every branch in the path is inverted.* To demonstrate this, let the nodes in the path be numbered $1, 2, \ldots, p$. The gains $g_{12}, g_{23}, \ldots, g_{p1}$ are not zero. Among the n equations representing the entire graph, we shall find p equations numbered $1, 2, \ldots, p$. The rth equation is

$$\sum_{s=1}^{n} g_{sr}x_s = x_r \tag{8–46}$$

Let us rewrite these equations in accordance with the scheme of Table 8–2.

TABLE 8–2

Equation number	Variable on right side	Variable expressed in terms of all others in rewritten equation	Branch inverted
1	x_1	x_p	$p1$
2	x_2	x_1	12
3	x_3	x_2	23
⋮	⋮	⋮	⋮
p	x_p	x_{p-1}	$(p-1)p$

We see that if every one of the p equations is rewritten as indicated above, we still have a single variable on the right side of each equation, and this variable is not the same for any two of the equations for the n nodes of the entire graph. Thus, as stated above, the feedback loop may be inverted provided that every branch in the loop is inverted. The procedure for inverting individual branches is exactly that shown in Fig. 8–5 and discussed as Case 1. As an illustration, the feedback loop **121** in Fig. 8–2(b) has been inverted, leading to the graph, Fig. 8–6. The equations corresponding to the graph, Fig. 8–6, can easily be shown to be equivalent to equations (8–3) and (8–4), which correspond to the graph, Fig. 8–2(b).

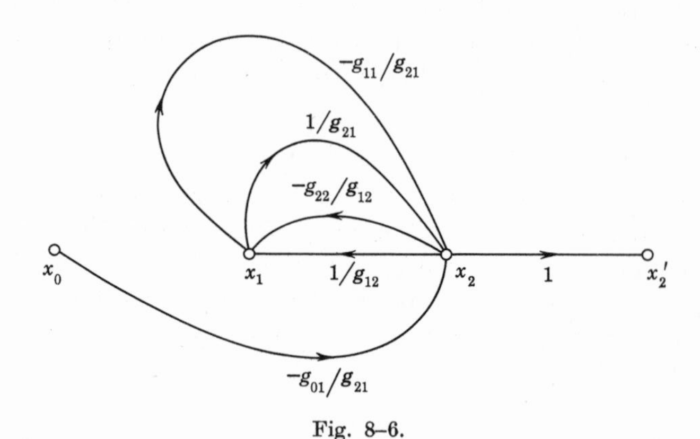

Fig. 8–6.

8-7 An Application of Open Path Inversion

The inversion process may be used to simplify a graph through reduction of index.(4) This technique has been used as an aid in the analysis of ladder networks,(10) and the signal flow graph so obtained has been applied to the finding of ladder networks with equal transfer functions.(8)

As an example, a network with the same ratio of input to output voltage as the one shown in Fig. 8–7(a) will be obtained with the aid of signal flow graphs.* We note that this ratio is unaltered if each R and L is multiplied by, and each C divided by, the same constant. The unit values chosen lead, then, to a result of general significance.

If the circuit of Fig. 8–7(a) is initially at rest, the relations between its voltage and current transforms are:

$$V_1 = E - V_2 \qquad (8\text{–}47)$$

$$I_1 = sV_1 \qquad (8\text{–}48)$$

$$I_2 = I_1 - I_3 \qquad (8\text{–}49)$$

* The circuit of Fig. 8–7(a) is closely related to the one given in reference 8. Replacement of the complex variable s by $1/s$ in each impedance replaces one circuit by the other. The method of analysis closely follows that of the reference.

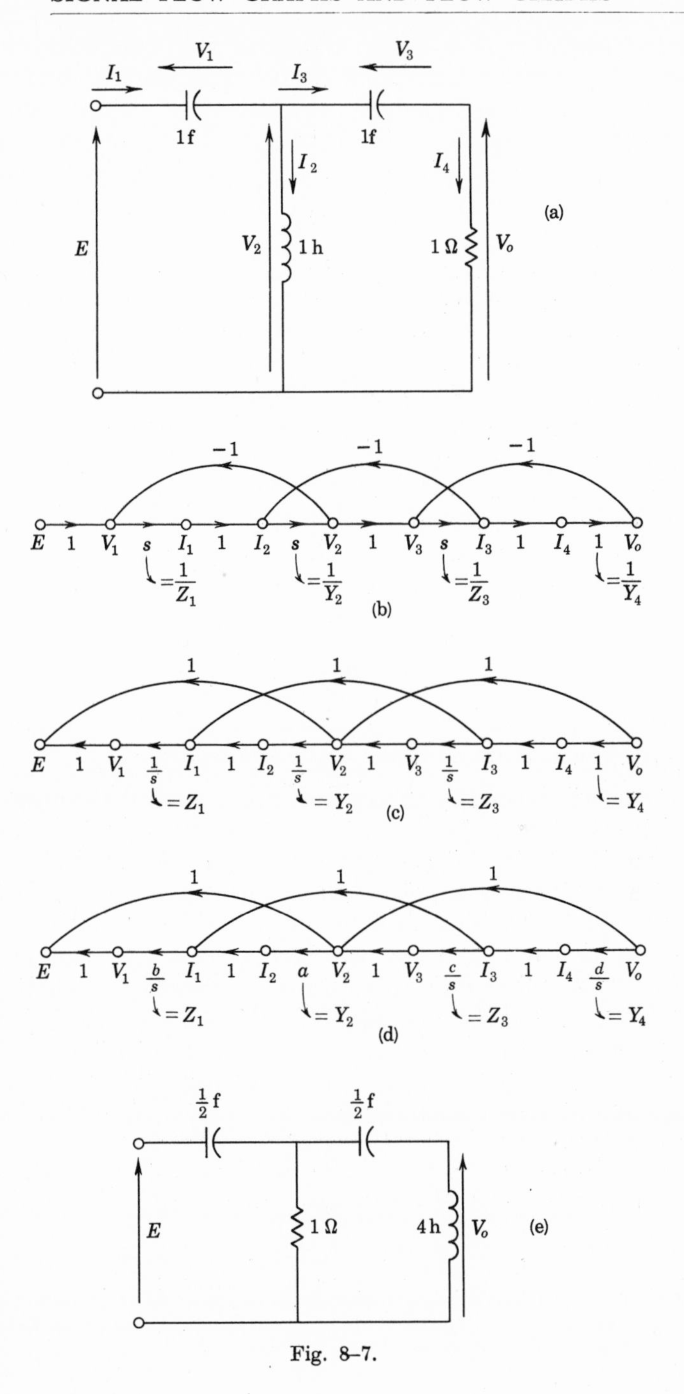

V1
V3
I1
I3
1f
1f
I2
I4
E
V2
1 h
1 Ω
Vo
(a)
−1
−1
−1
E 1 V1 s I1 1 I2 s V2 1 V3 s I3 1 I4 1 Vo
= 1/Z1
= 1/Y2
= 1/Z3
= 1/Y4
(b)
1
1
1
E 1 V1 1/s I1 1 I2 1/s V2 1 V3 1/s I3 1 I4 1 Vo
= Z1
= Y2
= Z3
= Y4
(c)
1
1
1
E 1 V1 b/s I1 1 I2 a V2 1 V3 c/s I3 1 I4 d/s Vo
= Z1
= Y2
= Z3
= Y4
(d)
½ f
½ f
E
1 Ω
4 h
Vo
(e)

Fig. 8–7.

$$V_2 = sI_2 \tag{8–50}$$

$$V_3 = V_2 - V_0 \tag{8–51}$$

$$I_3 = sV_3 \tag{8–52}$$

$$I_4 = I_3 \tag{8–53}$$

$$V_0 = 1I_4 \tag{8–54}$$

The signal flow graph corresponding to these equations is drawn in Fig. 8–7(b). Certain branches are labeled Z or Y so that we may identify the graph with a more general network of the ladder type.

The open path from E to V_0 is next inverted. In accordance with the discussion in the preceding section, we begin with the first branch emanating from the source node and proceed inverting each branch in turn along the path. The result, Fig. 8–7(c), is a signal flow graph of index zero. Thus we can obtain the ratio E/V_0 simply by observing all paths from the new source V_0 to the new sink E, in accordance with the rule stated at the end of Section 8–4. The entire graph is now replaced by a single branch of gain E/V_0, given by

$$\frac{E}{V_0} = 1 + 2\frac{1}{s} + \frac{1}{s^2} + \frac{1}{s^3} \tag{8–55)*}$$

Now the right-hand side of (8–55) is an example of a general cubic polynomial in the complex variable $1/s$. We also note that certain branches of the signal flow graph correspond to specific impedances and admittances in the circuit. With a view to obtaining a new circuit with the same ratio E/V_0, these impedances and admittances are replaced by values other than the ones given, the new values being so chosen that the paths in the signal flow graph yield the same terms that appear on the right-hand side of (8–55).

Fig. 8–7(d) illustrates a possible change in the signal flow graph. Each impedance and admittance has been replaced by a different one. Care has been taken, however, to be certain that the products of the branch gains yield terms proportional to $1/s^3$, $1/s^2$, $1/s$, in addition to the term 1. This is easily accomplished if one notes that, if the straight path yields a term proportional to $1/s^3$, the other paths, which essentially "skip" parts or all of the horizontal path, will yield terms with lower powers of s. For the signal flow graph Fig. 8–7(d) we now find

$$\frac{E}{V_0} = 1 + ab\frac{1}{s} + d(b+c)\frac{1}{s^2} + abcd\frac{1}{s^3} \tag{8–56}$$

* Compare equation 7, reference 8.

If we let

$$\left.\begin{aligned} abcd &= 1 \\ d(b+c) &= 1 \\ ab &= 2 \end{aligned}\right\} \qquad (8\text{–}57)$$

equation (8–56) reduces to equation (8–55). With the coefficients a, b, c, d satisfying (8–57), a network whose equations are represented by the signal flow graph Fig. 8–7(d), then, has a transfer function, V_0/E, identical with the transfer function of the network Fig. 8–7(a). Such a network is easily found. With a equated to 1, the values $b = 2$, $c = 2$, and $d = 1/4$ clearly satisfy (8–57). (Other values can, of course, be used.) Noting the labels Z_1, Y_2, Z_3, and Y_4 on the signal flow graph, Fig. 8–7(d), we obtain the network, Fig. 8–7(e). It is easy to verify that the ratio V_0/E is the same for this network and for the network Fig. 8–7(a). A number of other networks may be obtained in the same manner.

8-8 The Flow Graph*

The *flow graph*, introduced by Coates,[2] differs from the signal flow graph, but is also a representation of linear algebraic equations.[2,3]† The flow graph corresponds exactly to the basic form of the linear equations (8–1). It has been stated[3] to yield the most effective topological means of evaluating the determinants in the ratio Δ_N/Δ occurring in the solution of (8–1) for one of its variables.

When the flow graph is drawn, we number $n+1$ nodes as $0, 1, 2, \ldots, n$. The variables corresponding to the nodes are $x_0, x_1, x_2, \ldots, x_n$, where, by definition, $x_0 = 1$. The variables $x_1, x_2, \ldots, x_n$ are the unknowns in equations (8–1). The node 0 is called a source. When b_r (in those equations) is not zero, a branch of gain $-b_r$ is drawn from node 0 to node r (the words *branch* and *gain* have the same meaning as in the signal flow graph). When a coefficient a_{rs} is not zero, a branch of gain a_{rs} is drawn from node s to node r, the subscript order here being opposite to the branch direction. In this way a graphical representation of a set of n linear equations is obtained.

The flow graph corresponding to equations (8–3) and (8–4) is easily obtained, provided that we rewrite these equations in the basic form indicated by (8–1), thus

$$(g_{11}-1)x_1+g_{21}x_2-b_1 = 0 \qquad (8\text{–}58)$$

$$g_{12}x_1+(g_{22}-1)x_2 = 0 \qquad (8\text{–}59)$$

* See footnote, p. 379.

† The treatment in this section is based on that in Reference 3.

where $b_1 = -g_{01}x_0$. With the obvious substitutions:

$$\begin{aligned} a_{11} &= g_{11} - 1 \\ a_{12} &= g_{21} \\ a_{21} &= g_{12} \\ a_{22} &= g_{22} - 1 \end{aligned}$$

we have the flow graph of Fig. 8–8.(3) If the left-hand side of equation (8–59) contained the unknown quantity, $-b_2$, a branch of gain $-b_2$ would be drawn from node 0 to node 2 in Fig. 8–8.

The flow graph represents equations in the following way: Each branch directed from node s to node r represents a term. The sum of these

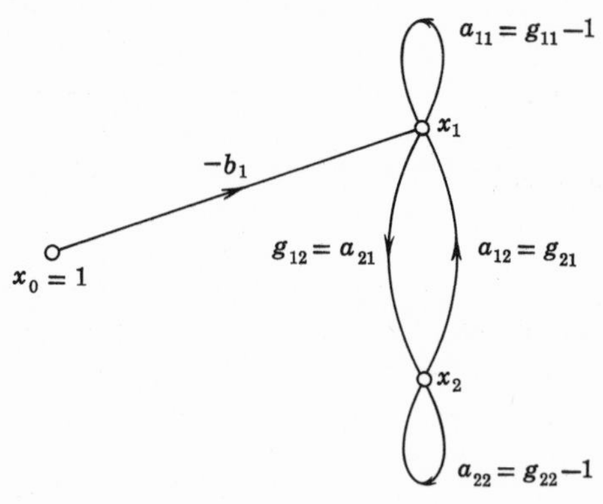

Fig. 8–8.

terms equated to zero constitutes the rth equation. The typical term represented by the branch from node s to node r is $a_{rs}x_s$ where a_{rs} is the branch gain and x_s is the variable associated with node s. By definition, $x_0 = 1$, so that if the branch from 0 to r has a branch gain $-b_r$, the rth equation becomes

$$-b_r + \sum_{s=1}^{n} a_{rs}x_s = 0 \qquad (8\text{–}60)$$

8-9 Comparison of the Signal Flow Graph and the Flow Graph

(1) *Subscript order*. The gain of a branch emanating from s and terminating on r is g_{sr} in signal flow graph notation. It is a_{rs} in flow graph notation. The subscript order is, clearly, arbitrary. (Signal flow graphs can equally well be presented with subscripts in the opposite order, although this is not ordinarily done.)

(2) *Source representation.* No distinction need be made. A signal flow graph can be drawn with a single node labeled x_0, with $x_0 = 1$, for the purpose of source representation. For example, Fig. 8–9 might replace nodes e_1 and e_2 and the branches leaving them in Fig. 8–4(a), thus representing both physical sources e_1 and e_2 as obtained from a single source node.

(3) *Meaning of the graph.* Here a basic distinction is encountered. In the signal flow graph, the sum of terms represented by the branches terminating on a node r is the value of the variable x_r. In the flow graph, the corresponding sum of terms is zero.

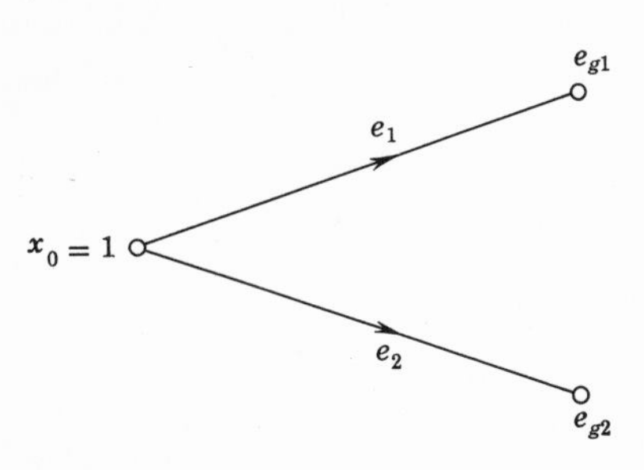

Fig. 8–9. Modification of part of signal flow graph Fig. 8–4(a) to show single source node replacing two physical sources.

(4) *Obtaining a flow graph from a signal flow graph.* The flow graph source representation should be introduced if not already used. Unequal subscripts should be reversed if the usual signal flow graph notation has been used. The gain of each self loop must be reduced by 1. To each node free of a self loop (equivalent to a self loop of gain zero), a self loop with gain -1 must be added.

(5) *Obtaining a signal flow graph from a flow graph.* The flow graph source representation may be retained. Unequal subscripts should be reversed if the usual signal flow graph notation is desired. The gain of each existing self loop must be increased by 1. If a node in the flow graph does not contain a self loop, we are required to add a self loop of gain 1. Unfortunately, when this occurs the signal flow graph is not usable, for elimination of a self loop of unity gain requires division by zero. In such a case, the equations are put in another form in order to have a signal flow graph free of self loops with gain 1.

8-10 Evaluation of Determinants by Flow Graphs[3]

If the source node and branches radiating from it are omitted from a graph G, the remainder of the graph, G_0, constitutes a representation of the determinant of the flow graph equations. Since each node number labels an unknown variable, it is also the number of a column in the determinant. To each non-zero element, a_{rs}, in the rth row of the determinant, there corresponds a branch of gain a_{rs} which enters node r in the graph G_0. To each non-zero element, a_{sr}, in the rth column of the determinant, there corresponds a branch of gain a_{sr} which leaves node r.

Thus the graph G_0 may be drawn from the determinant of the flow graph equations, or (if missing branches are represented by zeros) the determinant may be written from the graph G_0.

This correspondence between a determinant and graph G_0 is illustrated in Fig. 8–10. Δ is the determinant of the equations of the flow graph,

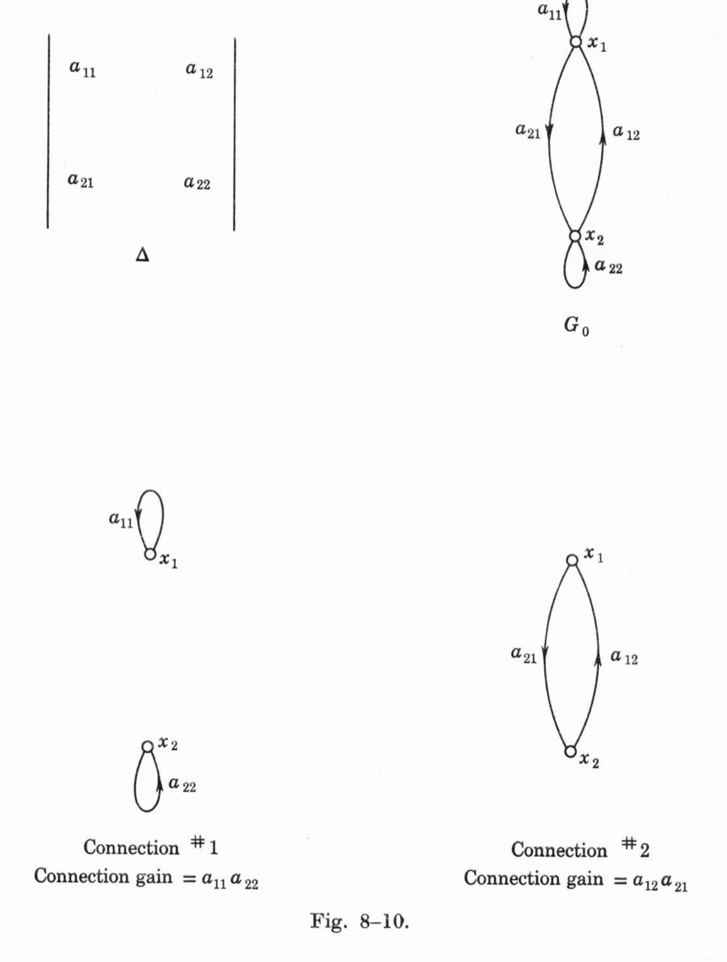

Fig. 8–10.

Fig. 8–8. G_0 is obtained by the deletion of the source node. See also Fig. 8–11(a) and equation (8–62).

We now further consider a graph G_0 (with n nodes) which corresponds to an nth-order determinant, Δ. A number of branches are chosen for special attention in accordance with the following rule: *one selected branch terminates on each node of* G_0, *and one emanates from each node of* G_0. The graph of these branches drawn separately from G_0 is called a *connection* of G_0. Fig. 8–10 shows the two connections of G_0 as obtained from the flow graph, Fig. 8–8. The product of the branch gains of the branches in a connection is called the *connection gain.* Now since one branch of a connection terminates on each of the n nodes of G_0, one of the n factors in the connection gain appears in each row of Δ. Since one branch of the connection emanates from each node of G_0, one of the factors in the connection gain appears in each column of Δ. (Thus no two factors are found in the same row or column of Δ.) Each connection gain, therefore, is the product of the factors in a term in the expansion of Δ. Further, every non-zero term in the expansion of Δ is represented by a connection of G_0. To see this, we note that one of the n factors in such a term appears in each row of Δ. Therefore, each node of G_0 is the termination of a branch representing one of these factors. Since one of the n factors of the term of interest appears in each column of Δ, a branch representing this factor points away from each node of G_0. These n branches (with one emanating from, and one terminating on, each node of G_0) constitute a connection of G_0.

We therefore conclude that in order to obtain the product of the factors in each term in the expansion of Δ, we may compute the connection gain of each connection of G_0.

The signs of the terms may also be topologically determined. We first consider the geometric nature of a connection. To justify each of the statements (a), (b), or (c) below, we observe that contradiction of any of these statements violates the requirement that one branch terminate on, and one emanate from, each node of G_0.

(a) A connection cannot contain a source or a sink. Therefore it consists of a loop or several loops.

(b) The arrow directions in any one loop are all the same. Each loop is then called a *directed loop*.

(c) No two loops can touch.

We now consider the sign preceding the product of factors in any term in a determinant expansion.[1,6] For simplicity, we shall write 6, rather than n, factors. The typical product in the expansion of a determinant may be put in the form $a_{1u}a_{2v}a_{3w}a_{4x}a_{5y}a_{6z}$ where u, v, w, x, y, and z are numbers from 1 to 6, but not necessarily in increasing order. The number of interchanges in order of the integers 1, 2, 3, 4, 5, 6 needed to bring them to the same order as the subscripts u, v, w, x, y, z determines the sign preceding the product of factors. This sign is positive or negative depending on whether the number of interchanges is even or odd.

Now the product of the branch gains of a single directed loop (with, say, four branches) is of the form $a_{ba}a_{cb}a_{dc}a_{ad}$ provided that the nodes appear in the order a, b, c, d, which, of course, need not be an increasing numerical order (e.g., we might have $a = 3$, $b = 2$, $c = 7$, $d = 4$). It is clear, however, that three interchanges of first subscripts bring the subscripts to position aa, bb, cc, dd (the last a is simply moved to the left). Evidently if there are n_1 branches in a loop, $n_1 - 1$ interchanges of order are required to put the first subscripts in the same order as the second ones. Now if there are L such loops, the total number of interchanges needed to obtain the arrangement aa, bb, cc, . . . is $n_1 + n_2 + \cdots + n_L - L$, or $n - L$, where n is the number of nodes in G_0 and, therefore, in the connection.

If b, c, d, a were 1, 2, 3, 4, etc., we would conclude at once that the sign preceding the product of factors in a term of Δ represented by the connection of G_0 would be given by $(-1)^{n-L}$. Now if two rows, say r and s, of a determinant are interchanged and if this interchange is followed by an interchange of columns r and s, the determinant is unaltered. However, this process puts the subscript r in the position of s, and s in the position of r. Thus any subscript may be made to appear as first, second, third, and so on, e.g., 3 could label the first row and column, and 1 could label the third row and column. Therefore, we make no error in interpreting the result obtained with b, c, d, a treated as if they were 1, 2, 3, 4 in determining the sign of each term.

To evaluate the determinant of the flow graph equations, then, we proceed as follows:

(1) Draw the graph G_0.

(2) Draw each connection of G_0.

(3) Evaluate the connection gain of each connection of G_0.

(4) Precede each connection gain by the factor $(-1)^{n-L}$ which equals $(-1)^{n+L}$, where n is the number of nodes in G_0 and L is the number of directed loops in the connection.

(5) Sum the terms found in (3) and (4).

If now we wish to solve for x_r in the set of equations (8–1), we require the determinant Δ_N, which appears in the equation

$$x_r = \frac{\Delta_N}{\Delta} \tag{8–61}$$

The determinant Δ_N is, of course, identical with Δ except that $b_1, b_2, \ldots, b_n$ of equation (8–1) respectively replace the elements $a_{1r}, a_{2r}, \ldots, a_{nr}$ of column r. We therefore define a graph G_{0N} in terms of G_0 as follows:

(a) All branches of G_0 which do not emanate from node r remain.

(b) All branches of G_0 which emanate from node r are removed.

(c) Branches of gain b_s are connected from node r to node s where $s = 1, 2, \ldots, n$. (Naturally, a branch of zero gain need not be drawn.)

We may now evaluate the determinant Δ_N, using the connections of the graph G_{0N}, in exactly the same way in which we evaluated Δ, using the connections of the graph G_0.

A topological method of evaluating Δ_N in terms of its minors may be found in Reference 3.

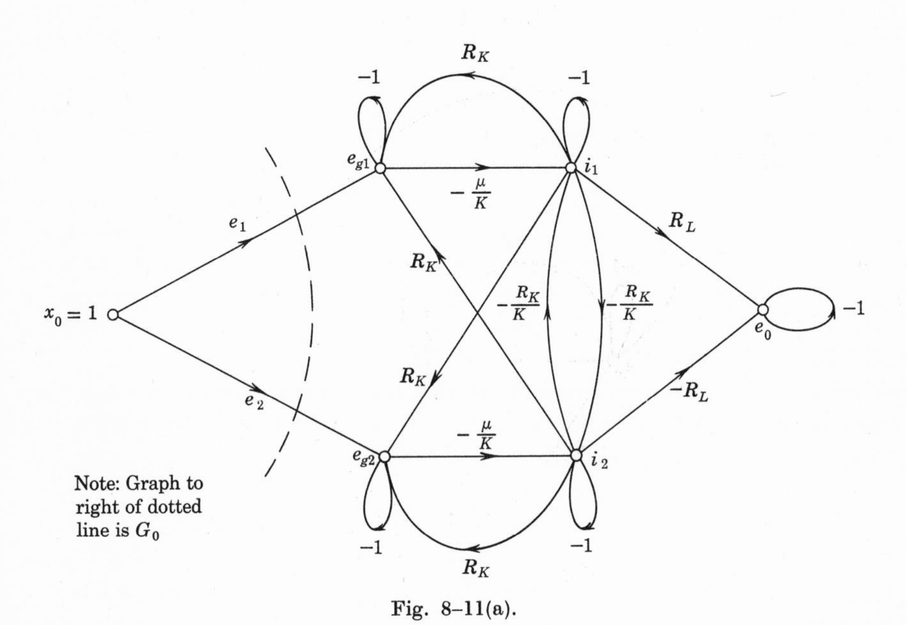

Fig. 8–11(a).

An Illustration

We consider once more the difference amplifier equivalent circuit solved in Chapter 6 and again, by means of signal flow graphs, in this chapter. The flow graph of Fig. 8–11(a) corresponds to equations which follow from (8–28) through (8–34) after the variables e_{p1} and e_{p2} are eliminated, and after the resulting equations are rewritten with zero on one side of each. If nodes e_{p1} and e_{p2} are eliminated from the signal flow graph, Fig. 8–4(a), we may again obtain the flow graph, Fig. 8–11(a), directly with the aid of subsection (4) of Section 8–9.

The determinant of the equations corresponding to Fig. 8–11(a) is

$$\Delta = \begin{vmatrix} -1 & 0 & R_K & R_K & 0 \\ 0 & -1 & R_K & R_K & 0 \\ \dfrac{-\mu}{K} & 0 & -1 & \dfrac{-R_K}{K} & 0 \\ 0 & \dfrac{-\mu}{K} & \dfrac{-R_K}{K} & -1 & 0 \\ 0 & 0 & R_L & -R_L & -1 \end{vmatrix} \tag{8–62}$$

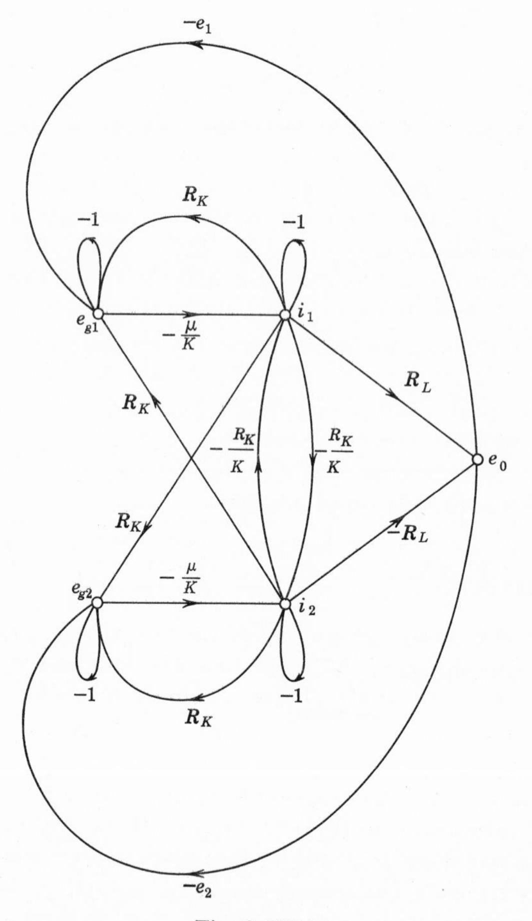

Fig. 8–11(b).

The graph G_0, which remains after deletion of the source node in 8–11(a), has eight connections. As an aid to the student seeking these, we list the corresponding connection gains (each multiplied by $(-1)^{n+L}$):

$$-1,\ -\mu^2x^2,\ \mu x^2,\ \mu x^2,\ \mu^2x^2,\ -\mu x,\ -\mu x,\ x^2$$

where $x = R_K/K$ and $K = r_p+R_K+R_L$ as in the signal flow graph of Fig. 8–4. The sum of these connection gains is equal to Δ.

The numerator determinant in the solution for e_0 is

$$\Delta_N = \begin{vmatrix} -1 & 0 & R_K & R_K & -e_1 \\ 0 & -1 & R_K & R_K & -e_2 \\ \dfrac{-\mu}{K} & 0 & -1 & \dfrac{-R_K}{K} & 0 \\ 0 & \dfrac{-\mu}{K} & \dfrac{-R_K}{K} & -1 & 0 \\ 0 & 0 & R_L & -R_L & 0 \end{vmatrix} \tag{8–63}$$

The graph G_{0N} corresponding to this determinant is shown in Fig. 8–11(b). It is interesting to note that each connection of G_{0N} passes through the branches of gain $-e_1$ and R_L or $-e_2$ and $-R_L$, for there are no paths touching e_0 which do not include these branches. Because of the symmetry of the figure, we find four pairs of symmetrically placed connections. Combining the gains of each such pair, and introducing the proper sign, we have four terms: $(\mu R_L/K)(e_1-e_2)$, $(\mu R_KR_L/K^2)(e_1-e_2)$, $(\mu^2R_KR_L/K^2)(e_1-e_2)$, and $(\mu^2R_KR_L/K^2)(e_1-e_2)$. The sum of these terms is equal to Δ_N.

The ratio of determinants Δ_N/Δ reduces to equation (8–43) obtained through signal flow graph simplification.

8-11 Summary

The major topic of this chapter was the signal flow graph.[4,5] In the latter part of the chapter, the more recently announced flow graph[2,3] and its application to determinant evaluation were presented. The relation between the two types of graph was discussed.

The signal flow graph was set up in terms of basic linear equations, signal flow graph terms were defined, equivalent graphs were defined, and basic equivalences were derived from their corresponding equations. The method of replacing a graph by its index residue was justified. The equivalent circuit of a difference amplifier, solved in Chapter 6, was again solved by signal flow graph methods. The method of inversion was presented, and a recent application[8] of this technique to the design of networks with equal transfer functions was illustrated.

The flow graph was defined and related to the signal flow graph. The representation of determinants and their evaluation by flow graphs were presented and illustrated. The equations of the difference amplifier equivalent circuit were again solved, this time by use of the flow graph technique of determinant evaluation.

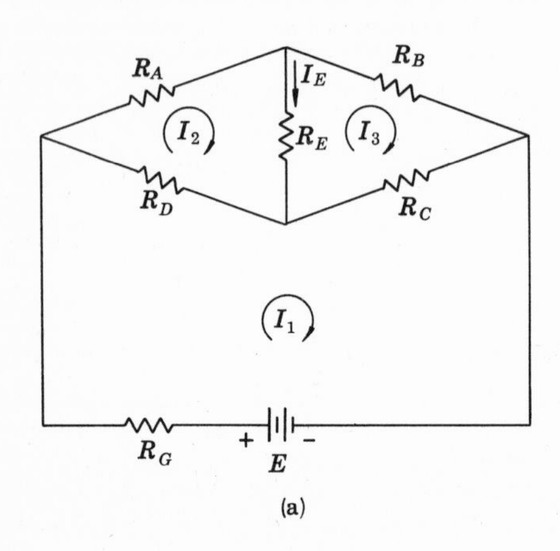

(a)

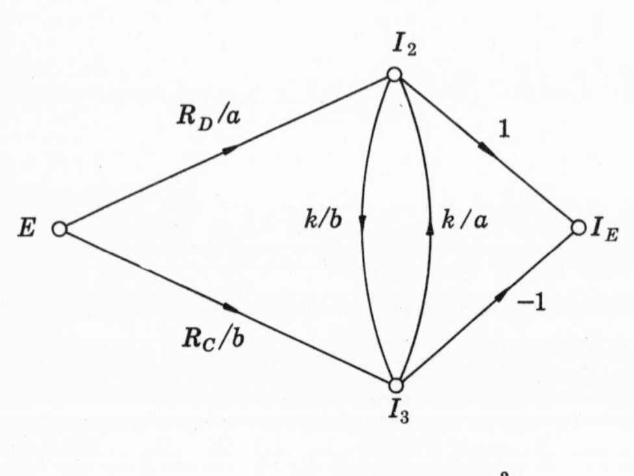

$$a = R_{11}R_{22} - R_D{}^2$$
$$b = R_{11}R_{33} - R_C{}^2$$
$$k = R_E R_{11} + R_D R_C$$
$$R_{11} = R_G + R_D + R_C$$
$$R_{22} = R_A + R_E + R_D$$
$$R_{33} = R_B + R_C + R_E$$

(b)

Problem 8–1.

Problems

NOTE: In these problems, the term *flow graph* is to be distinguished from *signal flow graph*, as discussed in the text of the present chapter.

8-1. (A) Draw the signal flow graph for the currents I_1, I_2, I_3, and I_E shown in the figure.

(B) Reduce this signal flow graph to the form shown in (b) of the figure.

(C) Obtain an expression for I_E and show that it reduces to zero when $R_AR_C = R_BR_D$.

(D) If $R_A = R_B = R_C = R_D$, can you conclude directly from figure (b) that $I_E = 0$?

8-2. Solve Problem 5–4 (Chapter 5) by means of a signal flow graph. Simplify the graph by replacing it by its index residue.

8-3. Solve Problem 8–2, but simplify the graph by means of open-path inversion.

8-4. Express the solution to Problem 8–2 as a ratio of determinants and solve, using the flow graph technique.

8-5. With the aid of a signal flow graph, obtain the gain E_L/E_s of the transistor equivalent circuit used in the figure of Problem 6–6 (Chapter 6).

8-6. Solve for E_L/E_s in Problem 8–5 with the aid of the flow graph technique for determinant evaluation.

8-7. Find a new circuit for which the ratio V_0/E is the same as for the circuits in Figs. 8–7 (a) and 8–7 (e) in the text of this chapter. Use the same method as that with which Fig. 8–7 (e) was determined.

8-8. Solve for the node variable labeled E_g in the figure. (NOTE: With appropriate choice of loops, I_1 and I_2 represent loop currents in the circuit of Problem 8–2 provided that $a = r_p+R_K+R_1+R_2$, $b = R_1+R_2$, $c = R_1+R_2+Z$, $d = R_K+R_2$.)

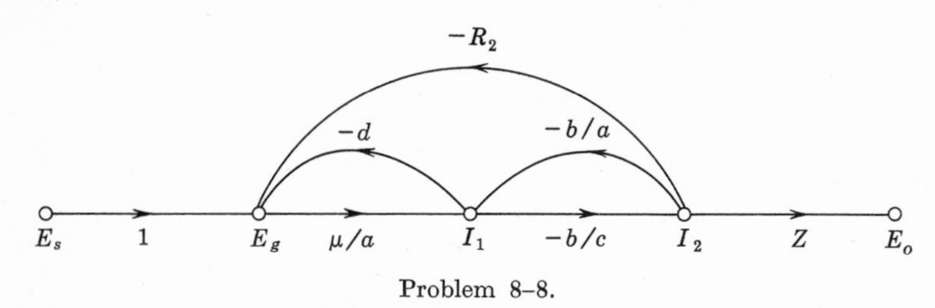

Problem 8–8.

8-9. Convert the signal flow graph in the figure for Problem 8–8 to a flow graph. Evaluate E_g/E_s as a ratio of determinants, each determinant being evaluated with the aid of the flow graph.

8-10. Evaluate Δ and Δ_N given in equations (8–62) and (8–63) of this chapter. Use the flow graph method.

References for Chapter 8

1. Bôcher, M., *Introduction to Higher Algebra*, The Macmillan Co., New York, 1907.
2. Coates, C. S., "Flow-Graph Solutions of Linear Algebraic Equations," IRE *Trans. Circuit Theory*, Vol. CT-6, pp. 170–87 (1959).
3. Desoer, C. A., "The Optimum Formula for the Gain of a Flow Graph or a Simple Derivation of Coates' Formula," *Proc.* IRE, Vol. 48, pp. 883–9 (1960).
4. Mason, S. J., "Feedback Theory—Some Properties of Signal Flow Graphs," *Proc.* IRE, Vol. 41, pp. 1144–56 (1953).
5. Mason, S. J., "Feedback Theory—Further Properties of Signal Flow Graphs," *Proc.* IRE, Vol. 44, pp. 920–926 (1956).
6. Reza, F. M., and Seely, S., *Modern Network Analysis*, McGraw-Hill Book Co., Inc., New York, 1959.
7. Seshu, S., and Balabanian, N., *Linear Network Analysis*, John Wiley & Sons, Inc., New York, 1959.
8. Simone, C. F., "Equivalent Ladder Networks by the Use of Signal Flow Graphs," IRE *Trans. Circuit Theory*, Vol. CT-6, pp. 75–81 (March 1959); Bell Telephone System Monograph 3438.

9. Truxal, J. G., *Automatic Feedback Control System Synthesis*, McGraw-Hill Book Co., Inc., New York, 1955.
10. Wing, O., "Ladder Network Analysis by Signal-Flow Graph—Application to Analog Computer Programming," IRE *Trans. Circuit Theory*, Vol. CT-3, pp. 289–94 (Dec. 1956).
11. Institute of Radio Engineers, "IRE Standards on Circuits: Definitions of Terms for Linear Signal Flow Graphs, 1960," *Proc.* IRE, Vol. 48, pp. 1611–1612 (Sept. 1960).
12. Cheng, D. K., *Analysis of Linear Systems*, Addison-Wesley Publishing Company Inc., Reading, Mass., 1959.

INDEX OF SUBJECTS AND AUTHORS